FLORA OF THE CRETAN AREA

THE NATURAL HISTORY MUSEUM

FLORA OF THE CRETAN AREA

ANNOTATED CHECKLIST & ATLAS

N.J. Turland, L. Chilton & J.R. Press

LONDON : HMSO

A catalogue record for this book is available from the British Library

ISBN 0 11 310043 4

Cover designed by Michael Morey

Printed by St Edmundsbury Press, Bury St Edmunds, Suffolk, England

HMSO publications are available from:

HMSO Publications Centre
(Mail fax and telephone orders only)
PO Box 276, London, SW8 5DT
Telephone orders 071-873 9090
General enquiries 071-873 0011
(queuing system in operation for both numbers)
Fax orders 071-873 8200

HMSO Bookshops
49 High Holborn, London, WC1V 6HB
(counter service only)
071-873 0011 Fax 071-873 8200
258 Broad Street, Birmingham, B1 2HE
021-643 3740 Fax 021-643 6510
Southey House, 33 Wine Street, Bristol, BS1 2BQ
0272 264306 Fax 0272 294515
9-21 Princess Street, Manchester, M60 8AS
061-834 7201 Fax 061-833 0634
16 Arthur Street, Belfast, BT1 4GD
0232 238451 Fax 0232 235401
71 Lothian Road, Edinburgh, EH3 9AZ
031-228 4181 Fax 031-229 2734

HMSO's Accredited Agents
(see Yellow Pages)

and through good booksellers

CONTENTS

FOREWORD

Botanists from Theophrastus, in the 4th Century BC, to many in our own time have mentioned the plants of Crete in their writings, but none, with the possible exception of Gandoger early this century, had felt impelled to distil the accumulated knowledge into a book devoted solely to the island's flora. It is easy to forget that Crete has suffered a great many alien occupations in its very long history; indeed the Turks only finally left the island at the very end of the 19th Century. Crete must often have seemed a remote, harsh and dangerous place in which to travel.

Since the last war, however, communications have improved beyond recognition and it is now possible to cover much of the island by car instead of on foot. As a result, an ever increasing number of botanists and plant-lovers have discovered the beauty and variety of Crete and its plants. They have taken notes, collected herbarium specimens and written articles about their experiences and finds. Prominent among these has been Professor Werner Greuter who, over the last 25 years or so, has published numbers of articles about the flora which are invaluable but scattered in publications which have a limited circulation and are generally inaccessible to amateur botanists. It gradually became clear from the interest aroused by the various works which were appearing that a checklist of Cretan vascular plants would be welcome. In 1979, Desmond Meikle, who was then at the Royal Botanic Gardens, Kew, suggested I compile such a list. For a number of reasons this took longer than expected and it was finally published in December 1986, as *Englera* **6**, by the Botanischer Garten und Botanisches Museum, Berlin-Dahlem.

In August 1987, at the suggestion of Mary Briggs, the Honorary General Secretary of the Botanical Society of the British Isles, I sent a copy of the checklist to Nicholas Turland, because he was particularly interested in the flora. He was able, on the firm basis of the list, to begin a detailed study of the vascular plants. His friend Lance Chilton, for his part, was not only recording plants, but was also engaged in preparing distribution maps; most of the information for these was collected during the years 1989-1991, when he covered much of the island in his researches. All the new and important records made by these two field botanists have been published in two recent papers.

In February 1991, Mr J.R. Press, of the Botany Department of The Natural History Museum, thought that the time had come when an annotated checklist of the Cretan flora could be compiled, and he suggested Turland might like to undertake this as an official, collaborative project and a first publication of the Museum's European Plant Information Centre (EPIC). It was to be aimed at professional and well-informed amateur botanists, and would cover the Cretan area as defined in *Flora Europaea*, by including the Karpathos island group.

The present volume is the result of the close collaboration of these three botanists and is a splendid tribute to their teamwork. Although checklists inevitably get out of date, I would guess that it will be some time before this welcome volume will need to be revised. It is an exemplary first volume in the projected EPIC series, and has set a standard which it will be hard to equal.

Colville Barclay
15th January 1993

PREFACE

This checklist is the first work to cover exclusively, in detail, and in a single volume, the vascular flora of the Cretan area (Crete, Karpathos and nearby islands). *Flora Aegaea* (Rechinger, 1943a) provided a firm foundation for subsequent floristic investigation, but is only partially concerned with the Cretan area. *Flora Europaea* (Tutin et al., 1964-1980) gives a more up-to-date account, and arguably remains the standard work. In general terms, it covers in greater detail more of the taxa in our area than do other recent works, such as *Atlas Florae Europaeae* (Jalas & Suominen, 1972-1991), the *Med-Checklist* (Greuter, Burdet & Long, 1984; 1986; 1989) and *Mountain Flora of Greece* (Strid, 1986; Strid & Tan, 1991). For this reason, this checklist is written in such a format that it may, if required, be used in conjunction with *Flora Europaea*, thereby enabling identifications to be made with the keys and descriptions given in that work, wherever possible.

Preliminary checklists, together covering the flora of Crete and the Karpathos island group have been published within the last decade (Barclay, 1986; Greuter et al., 1983a). These two thorough works have been of foremost importance in compiling the present checklist, since they have condensed into convenient single volumes data which had been widely dispersed in botanical literature, including many floristic corrections and additions post-dating *Flora Aegaea* and *Flora Europaea*.

Since these initial lists appeared, a surprisingly large amount of new work has been published. Furthermore, two of us (Turland and Chilton) have carried out extensive field work in Crete and Karpathos from 1982 onwards, resulting in a significant body of new data, most of which were hitherto unpublished. The present checklist provides copious annotations concerning ecology, distribution (both within and outside the Cretan area), taxonomy and deviations from *Flora Europaea*. Detailed maps clearly show the distributions of most taxa. Diagnostic keys, plant descriptions and full citation of synonymy and type specimens are considered beyond the scope of this checklist, but these would hopefully be included in a future flora, should such a work ever be produced.

The text of this checklist has been primarily the responsibility of Turland, while the distribution maps have been compiled primarily by Chilton.

ACKNOWLEDGEMENTS

We would like to express our thanks to Sir Colville Barclay, for lengthy correspondence, providing copies of relevant books and papers, and generously financing the illustrations. We are also greatly endebted to Dr John Akeroyd, for advice on taxonomic and nomenclatural matters and for various plant records and ethnobotanical data; Malcolm Penn (The Natural History Museum) for technical advice and assistance in producing the maps, and Margaret Tebbs for drawing the illustrations. We are also grateful to Clive Jermy (The Natural History Museum) for checking the *Pteridophyta* account; Peter Boyce (Kew) for checking the *Araceae*, and Michael Foley (University of Lancaster) for communicating his Cretan record of *Orobanche canescens*. We would also like to thank the various botanists who have kindly provided plant records and helpful discussions. The field trip to Karpathos in April 1992 was supported in full by the Park Fund (The Natural History Museum).

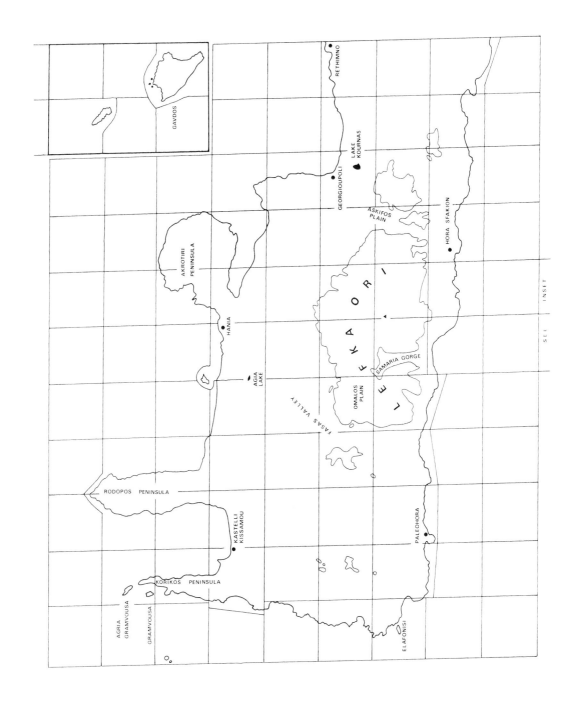

Fig. 1. Western Crete
Grid squares are 8.25km x 8.25km
1000m contour shown

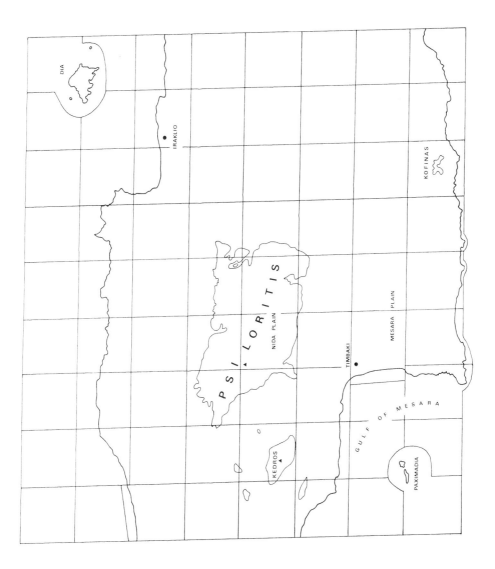

Fig. 2. Central Crete
Grid squares are 8.25km x 8.25km
1000m contour shown

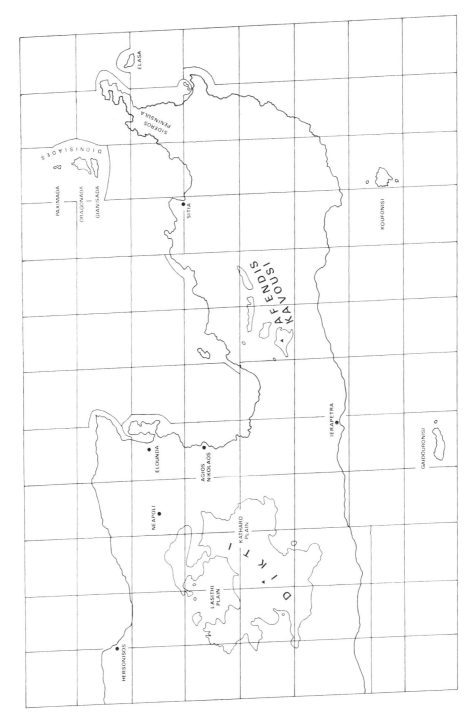

Fig. 3.   Eastern Crete
Grid squares are 8.25km x 8.25km
1000m contour shown

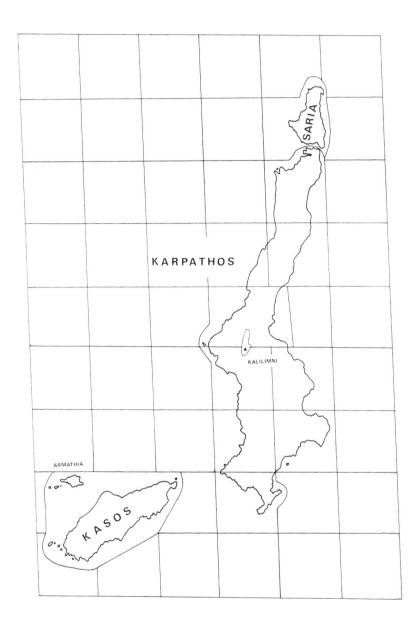

Fig. 4. The Karpathos island group
Grid squares are 8.25km x 8.25km
1000m contour shown

	FAMILIES[1]			GENERA[1]			SPECIES[2]			SPECIES INTRODUCED[3]			SPECIES DOUBTFULLY PRESENT[4]		
	area	Cr	Kp	area	Cr	Kp	area	Cr	Kp	area	Cr	Kp	area	Cr	Kp
PTERIDOPHYTA	16	16	8	22	22	10	34	33	12	0	0	0	3	3	0
GYMNOSPERMAE	3	3	3	4	4	3	5	5	4	0	0	0	0	0	0
DICOTYLEDONES	85	85	68	462	456	319	1286	1219	702	62	63	23	52	57	2
MONOCOTYLEDONES	18	18	12	141	140	92	381	367	187	14	13	3	23	24	2
TOTALS	122	122	91	629	622	425	1706	1624	905	76	76	26	75	81	4

Fig. 5. Basic analysis of the flora

[1] Containing at least one native or doubtfully native species
[2] Native species, including those doubtfully native
[3] Only species numbered in the text
[4] Species preceded by '?' in the text
Cr = Crete
Kp = the Karpathos island group

	No. of spp.	Endemic		Endemic to Cretan area	
		No.	%	No.	%
CRETAN AREA	1706	171	10.02	171	10.02
CRETE	1624	139	8.56	161	9.91
KARPATHOS GROUP	905	10	1.11	32	3.54

Fig. 6. Analysis of the endemic element within the flora

Endemic species include those given as '?Endemic' in the text — such plants are assumed endemic until their occurrence elsewhere can be confirmed.

INTRODUCTION

GEOGRAPHY

The 'Cretan area' is the most south-easterly of the 39 floristic territories defined by *Flora Europaea*. It is situated in the South Aegean region, roughly equidistant from Europe, Asia and Africa, and is politically part of Greece. The island of Crete is the largest in the Aegean and fifth largest in the Mediterranean, with an area of approximately 8700km^2. It is 256km long from west to east and varies between 11km and 56km in width. The Cretan area includes not only Crete, but the Karpathos island group 50km to the north-east, within which Karpathos itself is the largest island at 48km long and up to 12km wide (305km^2). It lies on a north-south axis in complete contrast to Crete. Nearby Kasos (18km x 6km) lies 6km to the south-west, while Saria (9km x 6km) is separated from the northern tip of Karpathos by only a narrow channel. Crete is divided into four prefectures (*nomi*), which are, from west to east: Hania, Rethimno, Iraklio and Lasithi. These are themselves divided into a total of 20 administrative districts (*eparhies*). The Karpathos island group forms a single district within the prefecture of Dodekanissa, the remaining islands of which are treated as part of the Asiatic floristic region, even though they are politically Greek.

The land surface of all these islands is mountainous, with the highest summits of Crete similar in altitude to the majority of those on the Greek mainland. In western Crete, the Lefka Ori or White Mountains rise to 2452m, while the centre of the island includes Kedros (1777m), Psiloritis (2456m) and the Asterousia Ori, which rise to 1231m on Mount Kofinas. The east includes Dikti (2148m) and Afendis Kavousi (1476m). All these massifs are separated by lowlands, which are sometimes flat plains, such as the plain of Mesara north of the Asterousia Ori. Karpathos reaches 1215m on Mount Kalilimni, while Kasos and Saria are lower, at 601m and 630m respectively. Crete has four peninsulas on the northern coast, with those of Korikos and Rodopos at the western end, extending northwards parallel to each other. Some 25km further east is the rounded peninsula of Akrotiri, while the Sideros peninsula forms the north-eastern extremity of Crete. There are also numerous smaller offshore islands, ranging in size from Gavdos, south of western Crete and roughly the same size as Saria, at 10km x 5km, to tiny islets of only a few hundred square metres. Figures 1-4 (pp. vi-ix) show all these features, as well as the delimitation of the three floristic divisions of Crete (western, central and eastern) referred to throughout this checklist.

Another important aspect of our area is the karstic terrain, formed by water solution in the areas of limestone and dolomite. Typical features are deep gorges, extensive cave systems and flat, internally drained upland plains encircled by mountains (poljes, or *oropedia*), all of which can be seen elsewhere in the Balkans. Perennial rivers and streams are more or less restricted to the areas without these porous rocks and consequent underground drainage systems. The only permanent natural lake is that of Kournas in western Crete.

HISTORICAL GEOGRAPHY

An Aegean landmass, of which Crete is a remnant, emerged from the sea during the Oligocene, and was subsequently broken up by tectonic movements. Crete became isolated during the Tortonian period, but was reintegrated with the continents in the Messinian period. During this time the Mediterranean Sea dried up repeatedly, allowing flora and fauna to migrate under a hot dry climate. Then came the Pliocene (5.2 million years ago) and the return of the seas, when Crete was isolated for the last time, initially as a group of islands corresponding to the present high mountain areas described above. These joined during the Pleistocene (starting 1.64 million years ago) to form the single island of today.

GEOLOGY AND SOILS

Palaeozoic rocks in Crete comprise metamorphic calcareous slabs, dolomites and non-calcareous schists (phyllites), the last being at their most extensive south of Hania and in the adjacent westernmost part of Crete. Of Upper Jurassic, Cretaceous and Eocene origin are compact dolomites and limestones, with flyschs from the Eocene. More recent rocks include thin-bedded limestones and flyschs. The calcareous rocks among these dominate the mountain terrain throughout our area, while Neogene sediments, including limestones, sandstones and marls cover large areas of lowland Crete. These are mostly marine deposits, although some originated in fresh water or lagoons; others are continental (breccias and red clays). There are also Quaternary screes and alluvial deposits, such as the coastal conglomerates of compressed pebbles which resemble coarse concrete. Figure 7 (p. 13) shows a simplified distribution of phyllites, limestones/dolomites and Neogene sediments (after Brownsey & Jermy, 1973).

The fertile soils of Crete are rendzinas, most often found on the Neogene sediments. Complete soil profiles are lacking on the island, but a well-developed humus horizon sometimes occurs in woodland. Soil destruction resulting from deforestation is widespread. The decomposition of compact dolomitic and limestone rocks results in red clays (terra rossa) below 1000m and yellow clays above. Most Cretan soils are neutral to alkaline, although acidic soils occur on the phyllites. Organic peaty deposits are very rare, existing here and there in a few small marshes.

CLIMATE

The climate is typically Mediterranean. The winters are cool, extending from November to March, during which the prevailing westerly winds bring rain from the Atlantic. The summers, from June to August, are hot, with prevailing northerly winds which pick up moisture from the Aegean and may cause summer storms in the mountains, although the lowlands remain in almost total drought. The weather is variable during the spring and autumn. Rainfall on the island decreases from west to east and from north to south, and increases with altitude, the rate of increase diminishing from west to east. In addition, fog occurs on the northern mountain slopes, even in summer. The north-western flanks of the Lefka Ori and, in particular, the Fasas valley are probably the wettest part of Crete, while the lowlands around Ierapetra and the islands opposite are probably the driest. There is also an increase in mean temperature from north-west to south-east. The contrast in climate between these two regions is reflected in their respective vegetation. The Fasas valley contains a number of hygrophilous species not found elsewhere in the Cretan area, while the south-east is refuge to a relict North African desert-like floristic element. Karpathos is not, as one might expect, drier than eastern Crete; the north-south axis, already mentioned, exposes the island to the prevailing westerlies during winter, while the mountain summits are prone to mists during the summer months.

Snowfall is a regular winter phenomenon in the high mountains, starting from about late October. Ground above 1600m is snow-covered for most of the winter and often remains so until May. Patches may persist into July at high altitude on the north-facing slopes, and may even be permanent in a few special places, such as the bottoms of deep pot-holes. Avalanches during severe winters can produce heaps of snow which fail to melt completely before the onset of the following winter.

FLORISTIC ELEMENTS

The vascular flora of the Cretan area comprises 1706 native species (see figure 5: p. x). Many of these are widespread Mediterranean and Euro-Siberian plants, but there also exist some special elements resulting from the historical geography of the area. To this total can be added 76 species obviously introduced by man, although it is possible that a much higher proportion of the flora was originally introduced, most of it now completely naturalized and indistinguishable from the truly native plants.

The Cretan area is the central remnant of the arc of mountains which once bounded the southern edge of the former Aegean landmass. These mountains connected those of the Peloponnisos, in southern Greece, with the Taurus mountains of south-western Turkey. The chain is completed by the islands of Kithira and Andikithira, to the north-west of Crete, and Rodos, to the north-east of Karpathos. This former linkage enabled extensive plant migrations, so that today both Balkan and Asiatic elements exist side by side in our area. *Datisca cannabina* and *Lecokia cretica* have their only European localities in Crete, otherwise being entirely Asiatic, while *Ebenus cretica*, *Ricotia cretica*, *R. isatoides* and *Zelkova abelicea* are examples of endemic species belonging to genera whose centres of distribution lie within Asia.

Another element suggests a former link with the flora of North Africa. Species such as *Arum cyrenaicum*, *Phlomis floccosa* and *Stachys tournefortii* are all otherwise from this area, while *Androcymbium rechingeri*, probably endemic, belongs to a genus widespread in North Africa but represented in Europe only in westernmost Crete and south-eastern Spain. A relict North African desert-like element survives in the hot dry area around Ierapetra. It is more prominent on the nearby islands of Gaidouronisi and Koufonisi, probably having been depleted on the main island of Crete during the damp periods of the Pleistocene (Greuter, 1975a). On these small islands, *Astragalus peregrinus*, *Helianthemum stipulatum* and *Periploca angustifolia* have their only known populations in our area.

The relict Aegean endemic element is excellently represented, with a large number of species confined to our area alone, amounting to 10% of the native vascular flora (see figure 6: p. x). There are also many bi-regional endemics, for example those restricted to Crete and the islands of the Kiklades to the north (further vestiges of the ancient Aegean landmass). This combination of island groups, together with Andikithira, has been treated as a separate phytogeographical region, the 'Cardaegean' (Greuter, 1971b), one of the main characteristics of which is the absence of species which have spread during the Pleistocene. The Cardaegean has, therefore, acted as a refuge in which certain plants have survived as relics of an ancient, weakly competitive flora, while being extirpated elsewhere. However, not all of these relics are endemic to the Cardaegean; some have wider distributions within the Aegean and adjacent parts of the continents.

Certain habitats, particularly calcareous cliffs and naturally treeless mountain summits, are very rich in relict endemic species. Being too extreme for the majority of plants, they have provided refuges for adequately specialized species which have lacked the relative competitiveness to survive in habitats affected by migrations of more aggressive plants.

Some endemic species in our area lack close affinites. Others, however, are vicariously represented by relatives in different parts of the Cretan area or elsewhere in the wider Aegean region. This can be explained by considering an original species, which became restricted to a number of isolated population groups, each of which then differentiated by the process of genetic drift into new, allopatric species or subspecies (cf. Snogerup, 1971). This may have occurred even within the main island of Crete, where population groups were separated by natural barriers, such as lowlands between mountains (which would have been sea between islands before the present single island formed in the Pleistocene).

Certain families in the Cretan area are very poor in endemic taxa while others are very rich: *Gramineae* and *Campanulaceae* are respective examples. The relict element in the flora of Crete is discussed in detail by Greuter (1972b).

VEGETATION

The first human visitors to the Cretan area, at the beginning of the Neolithic or possibly earlier, would have encountered aboriginal vegetation, much of which would have been woodland. This has since undergone profound changes brought about partly by the climate having become more arid, but mainly by the activities of man and his grazing animals. The only communities which remain in a natural condition today are those of the calcareous cliffs, along with some maritime areas and offshore islets and, probably, the high mountains above the timberline. Perhaps a few tiny scraps of woodland have never been directly modified by man or his animals, but even in these places it is likely that changes to the surrounding vegetation have had some indirect effects.

Much of the vegetation shows obvious adaptations to the Mediterranean climate. Many plants have leaves with a thick surface (sclerophylls), or are small-leaved or densely covered with hairs — all features that reduce transpiration during the hot dry summers. Some species are geophytes, dying back to subterranean storage organs for the summer, while others are annuals, surviving as seeds. The rains and falling temperatures of autumn initiate growth, which then continues throughout the cool damp winters, leading up to a spring flowering period for most species. A climatic regime more analogous to northern Europe exists in the high mountains, where plants are snow-covered in winter, and grow and flower during spring and summer.

Another feature common to many plants in our area is the presence of spines or a pungent taste, making them resistant to browsing. Such adaptations obviously assist survival today, but would also have been important before the arrival of man and his animals, since a number of now extinct herbivores existed, including elephant, hippopotamus and deer (Rackham, 1990*b*). Since no predator larger than a badger is known to have existed, it seems likely that the chief factor limiting population sizes among these herbivores would have been the availability of food, implying a significant browsing pressure upon the vegetation. The history of browsing in Crete probably has very early beginnings indeed — observe the phenomenon of spininess among relict endemic plants, such as *Verbascum spinosum*. It is likely that the high mountain flora, which contains several spiny elements, is still in a more or less natural condition, the native herbivores having been replaced by sheep (or almost entirely so: the wild goat *Capra aegagrus* lingers in small numbers in the Lefka Ori, and is perhaps native). Land in our area which is potentially accessible to herbivores cannot be regarded as being in a natural condition if it is subject to little or no browsing.

The phytosociology of vegetation in Crete has been studied intensively by Zaffran (1990), particularly in the high mountain areas.

Woodlands

The aboriginal woodlands of the Cretan area would have covered much of the land surface, apart from the high mountains and certain other places, but the canopy would have been continuous only where water availability and root space permitted sufficient tree growth. The concept of certain areas having a mosaic of woodland and open ground is supported by pollen analysis, which has revealed that, as well as trees, there existed plants characteristic of dry open conditions, for example members of the *Caryophyllaceae*, yellow-flowered *Compositae* and *Centaurea*-like species. Their presence in the pollen record is very significant, even though the quantitites are not usually large, because they shed much less pollen than do most trees (being pollinated by insects rather than the wind), so presumably must have occurred in moderate numbers. Moreover, they fail to flower and produce pollen at all when growing in shade (Rackham, 1990*b*). Pollen analysis has also shown that the aboriginal woodland was dominated by evergreen and deciduous *Quercus* species, while

Cupressus and *Pinus*, although present, were not particularly abundant. There also existed certain northern European trees, such as *Betula* and *Tilia*, which are now extinct in Crete (Rackham, 1990*c*).

This woodland was degraded and reduced in extent by woodcutting, burning and browsing, and the constituency of the woods which exist today depends on the biology of individual species and how they are affected by these factors as well as by changes in climate. For example, *Pinus brutia* is disliked by goats because of its pungent taste, but is killed by fire or felling; *Quercus coccifera*, although prickly, is still eaten by goats, but will sprout from the stump if burnt or cut down. Nowadays, Cretan woods are mainly composed of Mediterranean sclerophylls, such as *Acer sempervirens, Cupressus sempervirens, Phillyrea latifolia, Pistacia terebinthus, Quercus coccifera* and *Q. ilex*, while the richer soils on softer rocks may support non-sclerophyllous species, such as the deciduous oak *Quercus pubescens*. In some areas, *Pinus brutia* has greatly increased.

It is important to mention that most tree species in Crete have actually become more numerous over the last 200 years. This phenomenon is largely the result of a reduction in sheep and goat numbers coupled with a retreat in agriculture (Rackham, 1990*b*), which has allowed not only new trees to grow from seed, but also the recovery of existing, mutilated bush-like individuals. Indeed, it is quite likely that trees have increased similarly during episodes in the past, making the notion of a relentless and cumulative destruction of woodland, from the aboriginal forest to the present day, a fallacy.

The evergreen oak *Quercus ilex* is rather uncommon in Crete and very rare in Karpathos, although in a few places, such as the Sfakoriako valley south-east of Rethimno, it forms patches of woodland on non-calcareous soils with the evergreen *Arbutus unedo* and deciduous *Pistacia terebinthus*. The trees are often draped with evergreen climbers, such as *Rosa sempervirens* and *Smilax aspera*, so that very little sunlight reaches the woodland floor and the ground flora is consequently depauperate to barely existent.

Quercus ilex also occurs in woodland on calcareous soils, a fine example existing on a west-facing slope at about 600m in the mountains south-west of Rethimno. Here it grows with *Acer sempervirens, Crataegus monogyna* subsp. *azarella, Olea europaea, Phillyrea latifolia, Pistacia terebinthus, Pyrus spinosa* and *Quercus pubescens*, on extremely rocky ground. The canopy here is more open than in the example described above, permitting the development of a richer ground flora. In some areas, *Quercus ilex* is restricted to crevices of calcareous cliffs, where limiting factors such as browsing, woodcutting and burning are absent.

Calcareous woodland is quite extensive in the Lefka Ori and Psiloritis massifs. The evergreen *Cupressus sempervirens* can be observed covering the eastern slopes of the Lefka Ori above the Askifos plain, as well as above the Imbros gorge to the south, but is not restricted to the mountains, often occurring in ravines down to sea level. It is native in Crete but not or doubtfully so elsewhere in Europe. In other parts of the Lefka Ori, it grows together with *Acer sempervirens* (which is normally deciduous in spite of its name) and the other evergreen oak in the Cretan area *Quercus coccifera*, which is the dominant tree in the montane woods of the eastern and southern slopes of Psiloritis. On mountainsides with a northerly aspect, the endemic *Zelkova abelicea* may be present as well. On Mount Kalilimni, in Karpathos, relics of calcareous woodland exist: on the eastern flanks are a few very small low stands of *Crataegus monogyna* subsp. *aegeica*, which is probably endemic, while on the western side, just below the summit, is a low scrub of *Acer sempervirens*.

In the mountains of Crete, restricted to a few calcareous cliffs, grow arborescent species such as *Amelanchier ovalis* subsp. *cretica, Rhus coriaria, Sorbus aria* subsp. *cretica* and *S. umbellata*, while at lower altitudes, in gorges, *Celtis tournefortii* occurs in the same habitat. These are better regarded as part of the specialized cliff flora, rather than essentially woodland species confined to cliffs by browsing.

The deciduous oak *Quercus pubescens* forms a forest belt above the sclerophylls in many other parts of the Mediterranean region, although this appears not to be the case in our area, where it usually occurs as scattered trees around villages or in cultivated or formerly cultivated areas. The other deciduous oak in Crete, *Quercus ithaburensis* subsp. *macrolepis*, behaves similarly but is doubtfully native, having been extensively cultivated in Europe for tanning. It forms a large area of woodland around Armeni, south of Rethimno.

Castanea sativa is found in the northern foothills of the Lefka Ori and the westernmost part of Crete, in the areas of highest rainfall and usually on acidic soils, where it sometimes forms groves. The trees are valued for their edible fruits (sweet chestnuts), and their native status is doubtful.

Pinus brutia occurs on drier substrata, especially those with a sunny aspect. Extensive pure stands exist in eastern Crete, in the southern and eastern foothills of the Dikti massif and on the western lower slopes of Mount Afendis Kavousi, as well as in Karpathos. These woodlands are doubtfully natural, however, the pines probably having replaced the original trees. The canopy casts only moderate shade, and the understorey is often poorly developed, allowing ground flora to exist. Orchids of several genera may be frequent and, in a few places, the tufted *Carex illegitima* is found. Such pinewoods are highly flammable, and a number of large fires have occurred in recent years, as for example on Afendis Kavousi and in Karpathos. Fire is a natural and inevitable part of the biology of pine and, in the absence of other ignition, can be started by lightning. The trees are usually killed by the flames, but new plants will grow from seed to replace them. Pines invading sclerophyllous woodland may, therefore, eventually cause the land to enter an indefinite pine-fire-pine cycle. This fate may await the southern slopes of the Lefka Ori, where *Pinus brutia* often occurs together with *Cupressus sempervirens* and *Quercus coccifera*, reaching altitudes of about 1200m.

Platanus orientalis forms narrow gallery woods and small groves along watercourses and by springs from sea level up to 1200m, frequently with an undergrowth of the exotic-looking shrub *Nerium oleander*. Both *Salix alba* and *Tamarix parviflora* are similarly hygrophilous, occurring along the banks of streams and rivers, usually close to the sea, often with the shrubby *Vitex agnus-castus*. At Georgioupoli, in western Crete, *Ulmus minor* subsp. *canescens* grows along river-banks and, nearby, on the shore of Lake Kournas.

Juniperus oxycedrus subsp. *macrocarpa* is found on maritime sands and other dry rocky and sandy places by the sea. It mostly forms rather open scrub, but low woodlands occur locally on the southern coast of Crete and on some of the islands opposite, as for example on Gaidouronisi south of Ierapetra.

Phoenix theophrasti is known from at least ten localities around the coast of Crete, lining watercourses, surrounding springs and, at the eastern end of Crete, forming an extensive grove on a damp valley-floor leading to the sea. It is one of the only two palms native in Europe, occurring outside Crete locally in south-western Turkey. It belongs to the desert-like floristic element already mentioned.

The endemic element within the woodland flora, apart from the only endemic tree, *Zelkova abelicea*, includes a number of geophytes, such as *Cephalanthera cucullata*, *Cyclamen creticum*, *Epipactis cretica*, *Orchis prisca* and *Paeonia clusii* subsp. *clusii*. Presumably *Chaerophyllum creticum*, endemic to the Omalos plain in the Lefka Ori (1050m), is another example, although its woodland habitat has been reduced to clumps of bushes. *Viola cretica* is also an endemic species typical of woodland, though not a geophyte.

As a final note, it is worth mentioning that Mediterranean mountain conifers such as *Abies*, *Cedrus*, *Pinus nigra* and certain arborescent *Juniperus* species, although present under analogous ecological conditions on the adjacent continents, do not grow in our area, having spread in post-isolation times.

Maquis

The term *maquis* is often employed in a broad sense to cover Mediterranean scrub communities in general, although throughout this checklist it is used to describe *Quercus ilex* woodland of non-calcareous soils in areas of relatively high rainfall, which has been degraded by woodcutting and burning. Typical Cretan maquis is an often impenetrable, rather uniform and species-poor scrub, usually 1-3m high, dominated by *Arbutus unedo* and *Erica arborea*. Other shrubby species may also be present, such as *Calicotome villosa*, *Chamaecytisus creticus*, *Cistus salviifolius*, *Genista acanthoclada* and *G. monspessulana*, the last having been discovered in several places in western and central Crete since 1989. Another feature of maquis is the presence of occasional trees. The vegetation is richer along streams, with *Laurus nobilis*, *Myrtus communis*, *Cyclamen creticum* and, in western Crete, *Osmunda regalis* and the endemic *Lathyrus neurolobus*. Two distinctive orchids are *Dactylorhiza romana* and *Orchis provincialis*, the latter only in westernmost Crete and Karpathos.

Scrub communities

Within this category are included all the taller scrub communities (1m or more) other than maquis. These too may represent anthropogenic degradation of woodland, although an important and probably more or less natural type of evergreen sclerophyllous scrub is found in the coastal areas and peninsulas, where it extends down to the seashore. This scrub tends to be impenetrable, usually dominated by *Pistacia lentiscus*, often with *Ceratonia siliqua*, *Juniperus phoenicea*, *Olea europaea* and, in some areas, *Phillyrea latifolia*. A good example exists at the northern end of the Rodopos peninsula. It is likely that exposure to high winds and even salt spray are at least partly responsible for preventing the formation of woodland in these areas, by limiting the development of those tree species which are able to survive. At one locality near the village of Rodakino on the southern coast of western Crete, *Daphne gnidioides*, a principally East Aegean and Turkish species discovered in Crete as recently as 1984, forms scrub with *Pistacia lentiscus*.

Garigue

This is a further stage in the degradation of woodland, created and maintained by a combination of woodcutting, browsing and burning. Large shrubs and trees are absent, replaced by mutilated individuals of potentially arborescent species, usually around 1m high. Numerous spiny undershrubs resistant to browsing are also present, especially *Calicotome villosa*, *Genista acanthoclada* and *Sarcopoterium spinosum*, as well as various geophytes. *Quercus coccifera* is often seen in garigue communities, nibbled into prickly, mounded living sculptures. Surprisingly, it can flower and fruit even in this damaged state. If such a bitten-down tree escapes woodcutting and fires, and if growth exceeds browsing, as it might in a series of wet years, the uppermost twigs will eventually reach the critical height at which they are out of reach of sheep and goats. They will then accelerate upwards and begin to form a proper tree.

Phrygana

Where browsing and burning are severe, or where conditions are very dry or exposed, the vegetation may be reduced to *phrygana*, which is a Greek word meaning dry firewood or twigs. It is defined here as an assemblage of hemispherical, usually spiny, often aromatic dwarf shrubs, all resistant to drought and grazing and rarely growing above 50cm high.

Typical species include *Cichorium spinosum*, *Coridothymus capitatus*, *Euphorbia acanthothamnos*, *Genista acanthoclada*, *Sarcopoterium spinosum*, *Stachys spinosa* and, in the Karpathos island group, *Carlina tragacanthifolia*. The same shrubby mode of growth is possessed by *Verbascum spinosum*, which adds an endemic element to phrygana communities in western Crete, although it is essentially a mountain plant of the Lefka Ori. Among these shrubs may be small patches of bare ground, in which numerous geophytes find a niche, including several orchids.

Steppe

Steppe vegetation, in which grasses, annuals, herbaceous plants and geophytes predominate, may occur where the land is too dry for the development of woodland or other communities, or where the ground is so compacted that roots cannot readily penetrate to reach water. Steppe may be observed along the narrow coastal band either side of Ierapetra, in south-eastern Crete, where the climate is hotter and drier than most other parts of the island, and where the substrata are massive compacted marls. Here, the North African desert-like floristic element persists. The tufted, drought-resistant perennial grass *Lygeum spartum* occurs in this type of community, as well as *Erodium crassifolium*, which is otherwise found only in similarly dry parts of North Africa and south-western Asia.

   Lygeum also occurs in the driest phrygana formations in both this region and other parts of easternmost Crete, as well as in the dry headland area south of Timbaki, in central Crete, and at the south-western corner, near Elafonisi island.

Above the timberline

The natural limit of woodland in Crete extends from about 1450m on the northern mountain slopes to 1700-1800m in sheltered south-facing situations. Northerly gales during the growing season probably prevent trees from reaching higher altitudes on the northern side. The Lefka Ori, Psiloritis, Dikti and, to a limited extent, Kedros massifs all have naturally treeless slopes. The highest point of the Asterousia Ori, Mount Kofinas, consists mostly of vertical cliffs and has probably always lacked tree cover, despite rising to only 1231m. Neither Afendis Kavousi nor Kalilimni rise above the potential timberline.

   The vegetation of these areas is extremely interesting, with an important relict endemic element, as has been discussed earlier. The alpine and arctic-alpine elements of the central and northern European mountains are virtually absent, replaced by a mixture of Balkan and Asiatic orophytic elements. The terrain is invariably of limestone or dolomite, with steep rocky slopes often covered with loose shattered rubble. Mobile and stabilized screes exist and, in heavily karstic areas, there are flat expanses of rock and gravel, with deep craters, pot-holes or flat clayey areas in depressions (dolines). There are also calcareous cliffs, especially in the western portion of the Lefka Ori. Alpine grassland, such as is found further north in Europe, is absent, although some areas have sparse rocky grasslands, which may include *Festuca* and *Poa* species, the endemic *Brachypodium sylvaticum* subsp. *creticum* and the otherwise Asiatic *Bromus tomentellus*. Surface water, except during unusually rapid snow-melt or torrential rain, is restricted to a few tiny springs, owing to the highly porous nature of the ground. Rock is the predominant feature, and the landscape above 1800m often appears completely grey or white and devoid of vegetation until examined more carefully.

   On stony slopes, where at least some soil is present, there occur low prickly scrub formations of *Berberis cretica* and *Euphorbia acanthothamnos*, with *Juniperus oxycedrus* subsp. *oxycedrus* near the timberline. Communities of spiny, cushion-shaped dwarf shrubs, such as *Acantholimon ulicinum*, *Astracantha cretica*, *Astragalus angustifolius* and *Satureja spinosa* grow at higher altitudes. These species are restricted to the high mountains, while

Coridothymus capitatus, *Euphorbia acanthothamnos* and *Verbascum spinosum* are equally at home here or in the similar phrygana communities at lower altitudes. These communities support several geophytes, many of which shoot up and flower as soon as the snow has melted, for example *Corydalis uniflora*, *Crocus sieberi* subsp. *sieberi* and *Scilla nana* — all endemic to Crete.

The mobile screes have their own specialized plants, a characteristic feature of which is long flexuous stems growing up through the rocks which have fallen and covered them. The endemic *Silene variegata* is a good example.

The flat clayey areas occupying the bottoms of dolines also have distinctive vegetation, which may need to tolerate periodic waterlogging, severe soil compression and resultant lack of air circulation, followed by drying, shrinkage and cracking. There may also be soil disturbance caused by inundations of water and trampling from sheep. The plants of such places are mostly annuals, some of them rare in Crete though widespread in Europe, such as *Elatine alsinastrum*, *Myosurus minimus* and *Trifolium ornithopodioides*. Some dolines are drier, with a more friable soil, and support grazed carpets of the endemic creeping perennials *Hypericum kelleri*, which is almost restricted to the Lefka Ori, and *Polygonum idaeum*, which is found in the Dikti and Psiloritis masifs (in the latter area, it is dominant over much of the the Nida plain, which is in effect a vast doline). It is well worth mentioning the recently described genus and species *Horstrissea dolinicola*, a geophyte ideally suited to the drier type of doline, and currently known only from a small area in the Psiloritis massif. The ecology of these communities has been studied by Egli (1989; 1991).

The endemic element in the mountain flora contains some very rare and localized species, such as *Centaurea baldaccii*, *Centranthus sieberi*, *Myosotis solange*, *Nepeta sphaciotica* and *Ranunculus radinotrichus*, all of which are restricted to the Lefka Ori above 1800m.

Cliffs

Chasmophytes are plants which have become specialized to tolerate the harsh conditions of cliffs, namely vertical surfaces, lack of well-developed soil layer, severe drought effects and extreme diurnal temperatures. As these conditions become more extreme, fewer species are able to tolerate them, so the degree of interspecific competition falls. There is, therefore, a selective pressure on chasmophytes to become more and more specialized in order to benefit from less competition. This specialization does not, however, appear to have resulted in increased relative competitiveness, and is disadvantageous in other habitats densely populated with aggressive species. Chasmophytes also tend to lack deterrents to browsing, presumably because the selective pressure to evolve such features is absent on cliffs inaccessible to herbivorous fauna. For these reasons they are effectively restricted to their present habitat in our area. Such plants are termed obligate chasmophytes, as for example *Centaurea argentea*.

It is interesting that a number of normally obligate chasmophytes are quite at home growing in the pine woodland of Afendis Kavousi in eastern Crete. The shade cast by the trees here is only moderate and the ground flora is sparse, so the chasmophytes are presumably able to compete. There is also an unusually low number of sheep and goats in this region.

Facultative chasmophytes are able to tolerate the difficult conditions of cliffs to a certain extent, while remaining adequately competitive in more favourable habitats. Those which are also resistant to browsing, as for example *Lithodora hispidula*, may occur in the garigue and phrygana communities.

Some cliffs have only a sparse covering of chasmophytes. These may nevertheless be considered closed communities, even if not spatially so, in that all possible situations are occupied as far as is permitted by the degree of specialization of the species present. The bare patches comprise smooth rock, or are too dry (usually the case beneath overhangs), or contain crevices too fine for colonization. Oblique cliffs which are merely very steep slopes of rock tend to have a stepped surface with crevices in the intervening angles. Such 'step-crevice' communities are usually spatially closed, and contain a higher proportion of facultative chasmophytes than vertical cliffs.

The refuge status of cliffs and the high level of relict endemism among chasmophytes has already been discussed. *Petromarula pinnata* is a good example of a Cretan endemic chasmophyte without close affinities (it is a monospecific genus). *Hypericum jovis* and *H. amblycalyx* are closely related vicariants, endemic to central and eastern Crete respectively. *Dianthus fruticosus* also occurs vicariously, as eight allopatric subspecies endemic to various parts of southern Greece and the Aegean region, five of them occurring in the Cretan area. Some chasmophytes, however, are extremely localized endemics: *Hypericum aciferum* is known only from three stations, all within about 4km of each other on the southern coast of western Crete; *Thymbra calostachya* is known only from two gorges in south-eastern Crete, and *Bupleurum kakiskalae* is known only from its type locality in the Lefka Ori.

Maritime communities

It has already been suggested that some maritime areas support only scrub communities because storms and salt spray have prevented the formation of woodland. Where these limiting factors are severe, such as on exposed headlands, then only dwarf shrub communities may be able to survive in the open rocky terrain. These may represent the origin of many of the phrygana plants (Greuter, 1975a).

Maritime rocks and cliffs actually within the splash zone have a limited but distinctive flora, of which *Crithmum maritimum*, *Lotus cytisoides* and various *Limonium* species are characteristic. Some members of the last genus are endemic, such as *L. carpathum*, in Karpathos, and *L. sitiacum*, which is known only from north-eastern Crete and one small islet north of Kasos.

The mobile maritime communities of sandy beaches and dunes share many species in common with the coasts of the rest of Europe. Examples include *Calystegia soldanella*, *Eryngium maritimum* and *Euphorbia paralias*. Some species, however, are strictly eastern Mediterranean, such as *Centaurea aegialophila*, which is confined in our area to eastern Crete, Kasos and Karpathos. There is even a tropical and subtropical element in *Ipomoea imperati*, which occurs on two sandy beaches in westernmost Crete. It is restricted in Europe to a few southerly stations such as these, the outposts of a much wider distribution further south.

Well-developed saltmarshes, such as exist on the Atlantic coasts of Europe, are of course absent from the almost tideless Cretan area, although coastal freshwater marshes are often brackish or saline in places. Species found in such areas include *Apium graveolens*, *Aster tripolium* and *Juncus subulatus*. There are also flat expanses of bare mud or silt, flooded by the sea during storms, on which saltmarsh-like communities exist. Where riparian *Tamarix* groves occur on saline ground close to the sea, *Cynanchum acutum* may be present, twining up into the trees.

Offshore islets

The numerous small islets which surround the coasts of the Cretan area often have a very distinctive flora. The prevailing dry rocky conditions limit the species which are able to grow, thus reducing interspecific competition. This is not, however, a situation exclusive to islets, whose special feature is *unusually* low numbers of species, for reasons which are not yet fully understood. Moreover, sheep and goats are only occasionally present, or absent altogether. Certain species with a very low level of relative competitiveness and a strong intolerance of grazing are, therefore, better able to survive on small islets than under similar ecological conditions on the main islands. These plants have been termed 'islet specialists', examples of which in our area include *Anthemis scopulorum*, *Asparagus stipularis*, *Lavatera arborea*, *Orobanche sanguinea*, *Silene holzmannii* and *Trigonella rechingeri*.

It is possible to recognize similarities between the ecology of these islets and the cliff communities already described, so it is not entirely anomalous that a number of normally obligate chasmophytes also occur. Such 'islet chasmophytes' include *Achillea cretica*, *Allium bourgaei*, *Helichrysum orientale*, *Matthiola sinuata* and *Medicago arborea*. Islets do not have the long-term stability of many cliffs, however, since tectonic movements and fluctuations in sea level can fuse them to the main islands or submerge them altogether.

The special vegetation of small islets in the Karpathos island group has been studied by Höner & Greuter (1988) and Raus (1990).

Marine communities

The marine algae occurring around the coasts of the Cretan area are beyond the scope of this account. However, four vascular plants are also restricted to the sea, all of them monocotyledons. The most obvious is *Posidonia oceanica*, which forms underwater 'meadows' in areas with a rocky compressed sea-bed. The dead leaves can often be observed piled up along beaches, together with spongy balls of leaf tissue — the result of wave action. *Zostera marina* occurs in areas where the water is shallow and the sea-bed sandy or silty. The two other marine species are *Cymodocea nodosa* and *Halophila stipulacea*, the latter having entered the Mediterranean from the Red Sea, soon after the opening of the Suez Canal in 1869.

Wetlands

Coastal marshes, usually at the mouths of streams or rivers, have vegetation which largely comprises widespread European hygrophilous species, such as *Iris pseudacorus* and *Phragmites australis*. The natural lake of Kournas has a rather poor flora, with most of its shore dominated by a dense scrub of *Vitex agnus-castus* whereas, somewhat ironically, the artificial lake at Agia, south-west of Hania, has probably the most varied selection of wetland communities anywhere in the Cretan area. Rivers and streams provide linear wetland habitats, particularly well-developed in the Fasas valley, where the endemic *Lathyrus neurolobus* occurs. Small marshes sometimes exist near springs and, in the Psiloritis massif, a few such areas support the only known populations of the endemic *Carex idaea*. Another marsh, in the Dikti massif, is the only known locality for the endemic *Cirsium creticum* subsp. *dictaeum*, while subsp. *creticum* is a frequent hygrophilous plant of the lowlands. In some places water seeps to the surface creating an area of damp ground, but without obvious run-off. To this list of wetland habitats can be added artificial ponds and cisterns, which may support aquatics such as *Myriophyllum spicatum*, *Potamogeton nodosus* and *Ranunculus trichophyllus*. The hygrophilous vegetation of western Crete has been intensively studied by Gradstein & Smittenberg (1968; 1977).

Human settlements and cultivated areas

Weed communities in and around villages often indicate high nutrient levels, resulting from the presence of domestic livestock. *Ecballium elaterium*, *Hyoscyamus albus* and *Urtica* species are characteristic. Old walls in villages and towns, especially those with deteriorating mortar, support plants which would normally inhabit rock-crevices, including endemic chasmophytes such as *Petromarula pinnata* and *Verbascum arcturus*.

The olive, *Olea europaea*, has been grown in our area since Minoan times and is still extensively planted and grafted onto wild stock. Olive cultivation has greatly increased in Crete since agricultural statistics were published by Raulin in the mid-19th century and, today, groves are a widespread and distinctive feature of the lowlands up to about 600m. There are also citrus groves, orchards and vineyards. All of these are very often infested with the introduced South African geophyte *Oxalis pes-caprae*, which forms drifts of glaring yellow when in flower during the spring. In groves less severely affected, there is often a rich weed flora, limited to annuals and geophytes by regular tilling of the soil, although this is now being disrupted by the increasing use of chemical herbicides.

Cereal cultivation for grain production, which had been important since Neolithic times, has now greatly declined in the Cretan area. Abandoned terraces, reverted to garigue or even woodland, are a common feature on hillsides. Many of these would once have been used for cereals, with adjacent threshing floors and ruined, water-driven chimney mills surviving as evidence. Aerial photographs of Crete taken during World War II show that most of the abandoned terraces of today were already out of use even then. Some former cereal terraces, often as little as 2m wide, were probably converted to olive cultivation: in parts of Crete, ruined watermills, once used for grinding corn, are now surrounded by terraced olive groves.

Labour-intensive crop production on small terraces, once so important to the survival of village communities with only steep land, is nowadays no longer necessary, as grain can be imported from mechanized farms elsewhere, and there are plenty of easier ways in which to earn a living. Cereal cultivation on the plains and mountain plateaux, still potentially economical because of the suitability of the terrain for tractors, may have been abandoned more recently. It is also likely that traditional farming methods were irrevocably disrupted by the effects of World War II upon the rural population. Much of the agriculture in Crete today, apart from olives, citrus fruits and vines, consists of market gardening inside polythene greenhouses (*thermokipia*), which are particularly abundant on the Mesara plain and on the coastal belt west of Ierapetra.

There is a notable exception to the general abandonment of old cereal terraces. This is in northern Karpathos, around the villages of Olimbos and Avlona, to which there was no vehicular access until 1975, and in which a traditional way of life has survived. This ancient method of cultivation, without the use of herbicides or deep mechanical ploughing, favours rich weed communities with annuals and geophytes prevailing. A typical example of the latter is *Leontice leontopetalum*, which is now rare in Crete but conspicuous in the terraces at Avlona. Among the annuals here are *Adonis annua* subsp. *cupaniana* and *Isatis lusitanica*, both of which are known nowhere else in the Cretan area (and the latter nowhere else in Europe). These plants, which rely on old systems of cultivation for their survival, were presumably anciently introduced by man, and are termed *archaeophytes*. They are often restricted to particular areas by the strong isolation under which the traditional rural economy developed.

Another old agricultural system survives in eastern Crete, on the Katharo plain in the Dikti massif, where vehicular access is again only comparatively recent. Special archaeophytes occurring here include *Asperula arvensis*, *Cerastium dichotomum*, *Taeniatherum caput-medusae* subsp. *crinitum* and *Ventenata subenervis*. The fertile Anopoli plateau, on the southern side of the Lefka Ori, is a further area of former difficult access. The deep red-flowered form of *Ranunculus asiaticus* is probably an archaeophyte in the fields here, replacing the normal white, pink or yellow variants which predominate elsewhere in Crete. Cultivated fields in central Crete, particularly on the upland plain of Gious Kambos, north-west of Kedros, have the red-flowered *Tulipa doerfleri*, which is endemic to this region except for two tiny, outlying and possibly introduced populations in the adjacent part of western Crete. The tulips are sterile, propagating entirely vegetatively by offsets and stolons, thereby infesting the fields, to which they are ecologically confined. This species presumably could not have survived before agriculture was brought to Crete, and it is interesting to speculate that the tulips might have been deliberately introduced, perhaps in Neolithic times, as an undercrop, so that if the cereals failed there would be a supply of bulbs, which are edible. *T. saxatilis* (including the variant known as *T. bakeri*) also grows in arable fields in various parts of Crete, notably the Omalos plain in the Lefka Ori. Other tulips are weeds of cultivation elsewhere in Greece and Turkey, for example *T. hageri* Heldr. and *T. undulatifolia* Boiss.

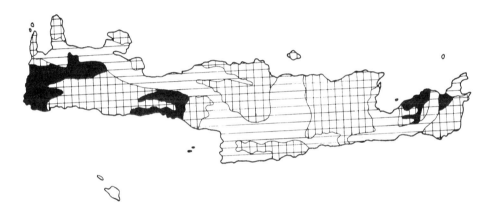

Fig. 7.   Geology of Crete (simplified)

■ = phyllites

⊞ = limestones and dolomites

▭ = Neogene sediments

(after Brownsey & Jermy, 1973)

ILLUSTRATIONS

The following ten plates were generously financed by Sir Colville Barclay, and drawn by Margaret Tebbs. Most of the taxa depicted are endemic to the Cretan area, often with very localized distributions. Several are legally protected and included on revised appendix 1 of the Berne Convention.

Plate 1.

1. **Campanula carpatha** Halácsy
2. **Campanula hierapetrae** Rech.f.
3. **Dianthus xylorrhizus** Boiss. & Heldr.
4. **Silene ammophila** Boiss. & Heldr.
   subsp. **ammophila**
5. **Silene holzmannii** Heldr. ex Boiss.
6. **Silene thessalonica**
   subsp. **dictaea** (Rech.f.) Melzh.
7. **Ricotia isatoides** (Barbey) B.L.Burtt

Plate 2.

1. **Anthemis glaberrima** (Rech.f.) Greuter
2. **Carlina diae** (Rech.f.) Meusel & Kästner
3. **Carlina sitiensis** Rech.f.

Plate 3.

1. **Centaurea baldaccii** Degen ex Halácsy
2. **Centaurea lancifolia** Sieber ex Spreng.
3. **Centaurea poculatoris** Greuter
4. **Helichrysum heldreichii** Boiss.

Plate 4.

1. **Euphorbia sultan-hassei** Strid, Bentzer, Bothmer, Engstrand & M.A.Gust.
2. **Hypericum aciferum** (Greuter) N.Robson
3. **Nepeta sphaciotica** P.H.Davis
4. **Origanum vetteri** Briq. & Barbey
   a. habit, b. inflorescence

Plate 5.

1. **Thymbra calostachya** (Rech.f.) Rech.f.
2. **Lathyrus neurolobus** Boiss. & Heldr.
3. **Medicago strasseri** Greuter, Matthäs & Risse
4. **Ononis verae** Sirj.

Plate 6.

1. **Limonium carpathum** (Rech.f.) Rech.f.
2. **Limonium hierapetrae** Rech.f.
3. **Clematis elisabethae-carolae** Greuter
4. **Ranunculus radinotrichus** Greuter & Strid

Plate 7.

1. **Daphne jasminea** Sm.
2. **Zelkova abelicea** (Lam.) Boiss.
   a. habit, b. flowering twig
3. **Bupleurum kakiskalae** Greuter
4. **Chaerophyllum creticum** Boiss. & Heldr.
   a. flowering plant, b. ripe fruit
5. **Horstrissea dolinicola** Greuter, Gerstb. & Egli

Plate 8.

1. **Centranthus sieberi** Heldr.
2. **Arum purpureospathum** P.C.Boyce
3. **Carex idaea** Greuter, Matthäs & Risse

Plate 9.

1. **Sesleria doerfleri** Hayek
2. **Phoenix theophrasti** Greuter
   a. female inflorescence,
   b. infructescence,
   c. ripe fruit, d. seed

Plate 10.

1. **Allium dilatatum** Zahar.
2. **Tulipa goulimyi** Sealy & Turrill
3. **Cephalanthera cucullata** Boiss. & Heldr.
4. **Ophrys aegaea** Kalteisen & H.R.Reinhard subsp. **aegaea**

PLATE 1

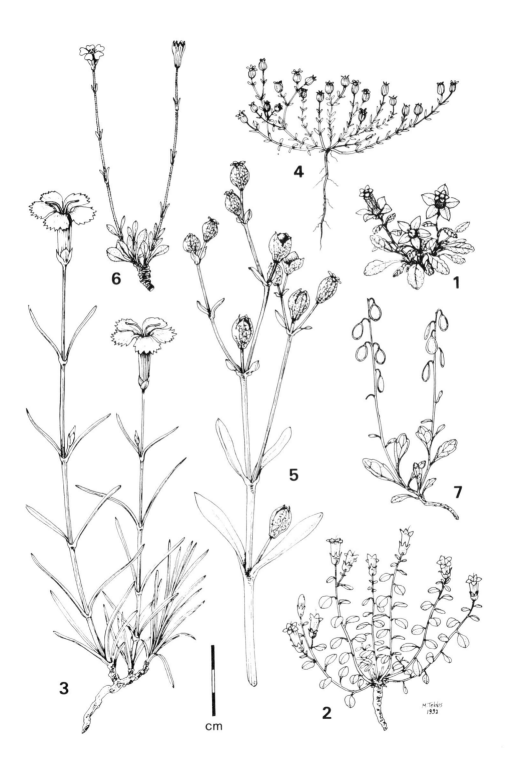

M. Tebbs
1992

PLATE 2

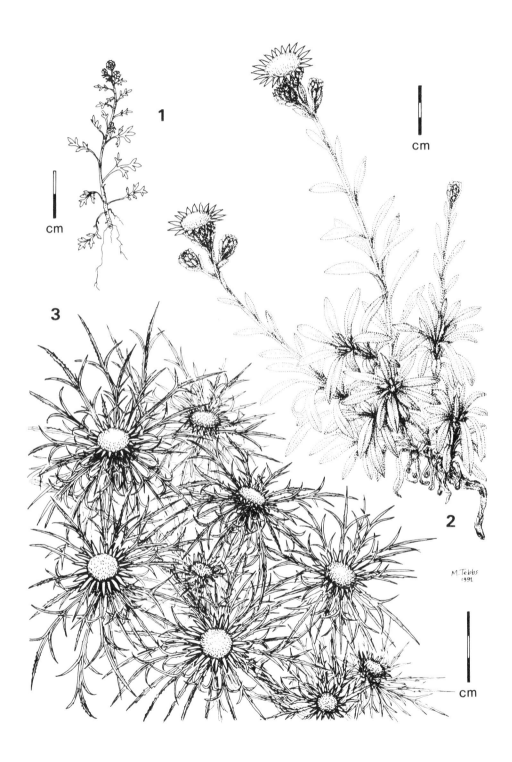

M.Tebbs
1991

PLATE 3

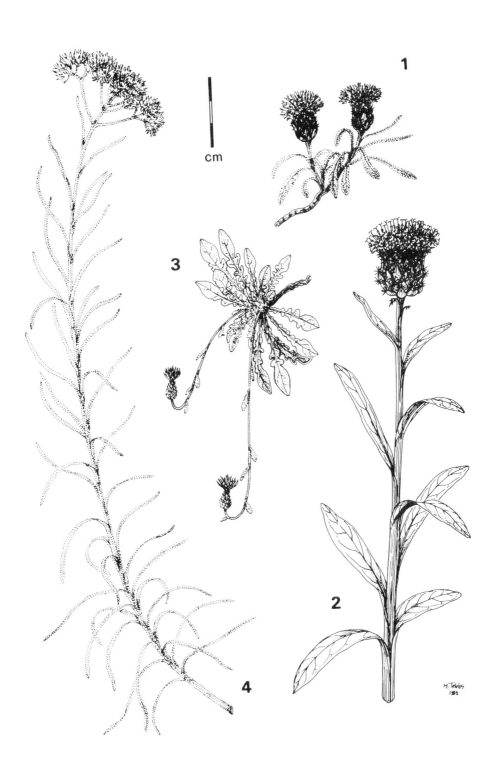

M. Tebbs
1982

PLATE 4

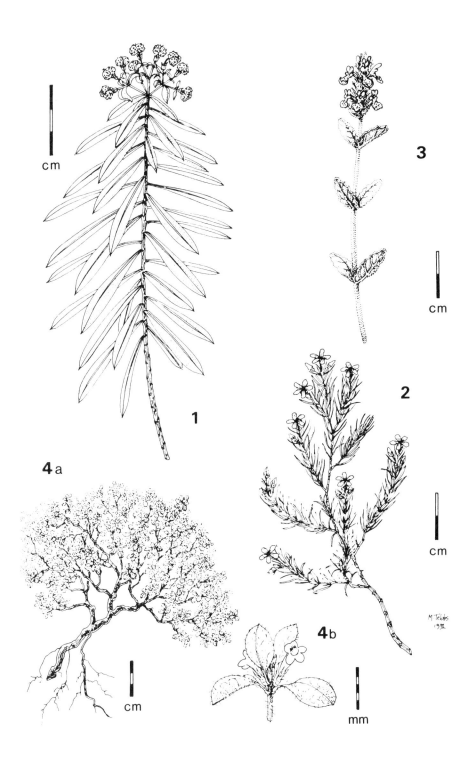

1

4a

3

2

4b

cm

cm

cm

cm

mm

M. Telles
1992

PLATE 5

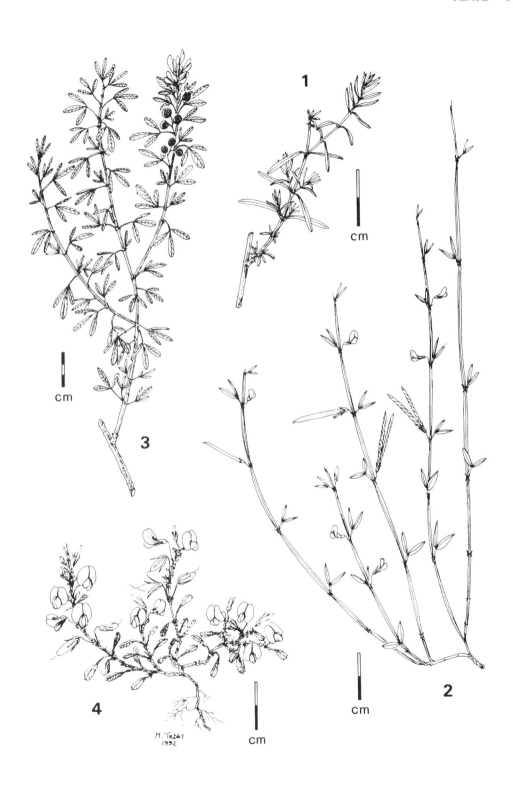

M. Tebbs
1992

PLATE   6

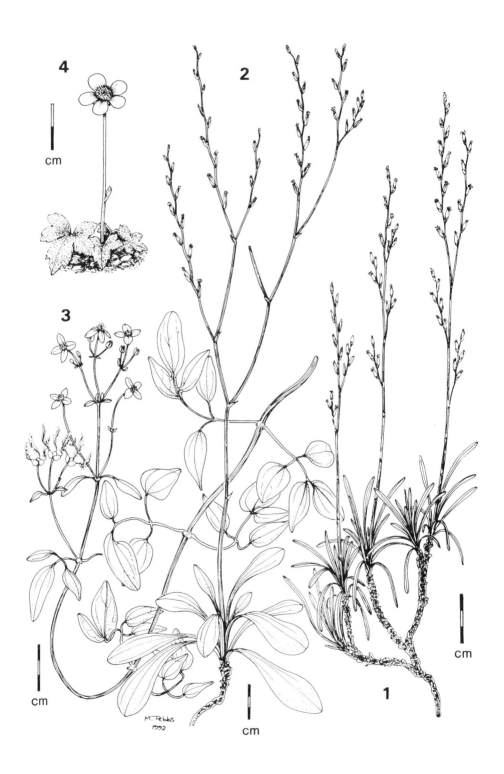

4

cm

2

3

1

cm

cm

cm

cm

M. Tebbs
1992

PLATE   7

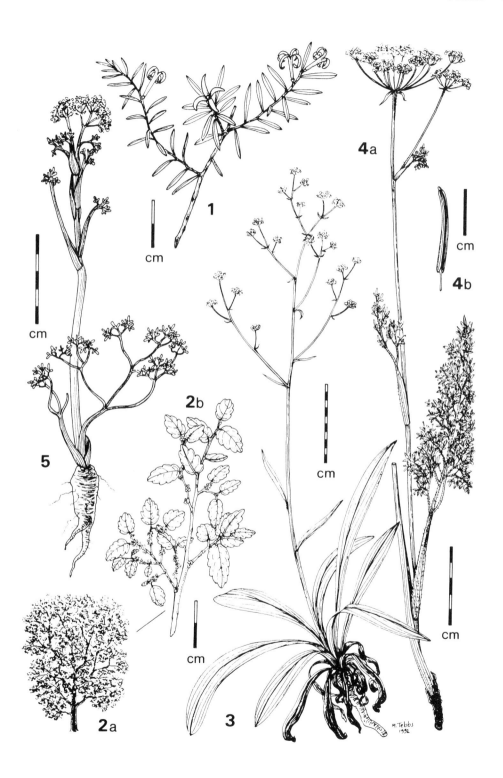

M. Tebbs
1992

PLATE 8

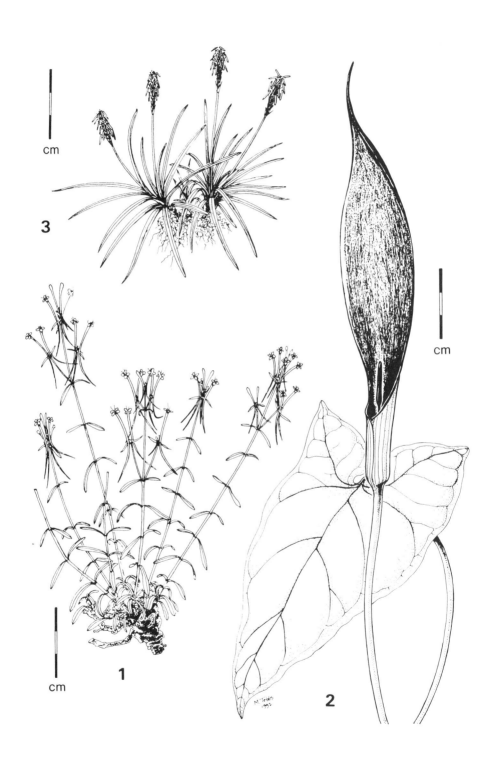

PLATE   9

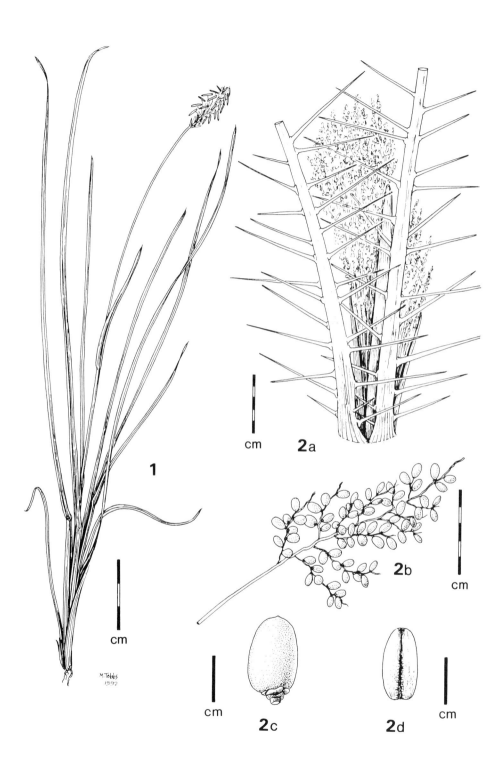

1

2a

cm

2b

cm

2c

2d

cm

cm

cm

M.Tebbs
1992

PLATE 10

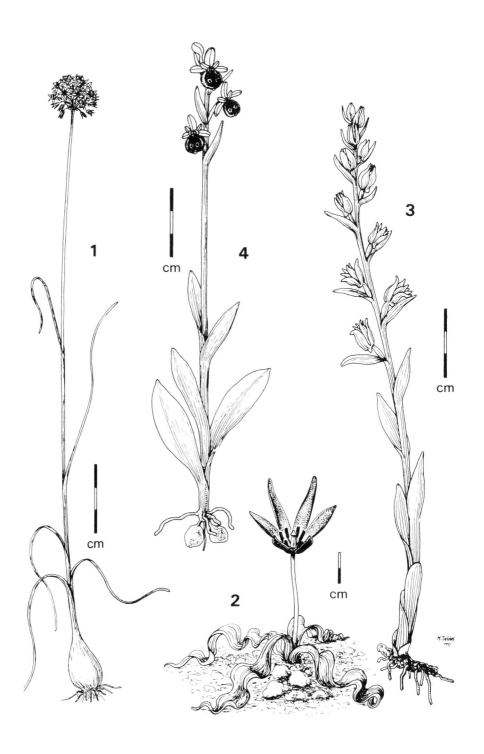

ORGANIZATION OF THE CHECKLIST

SCOPE

This checklist includes all vascular plants known to occur in the Cretan area, except those which are purely cultivated, planted or casual. All taxa down to the rank of subspecies are dealt with, as well as hybrids. Varieties and forms are cited only when of particular interest (e.g. if they are endemic). Taxa only doubtfully recorded as present are included as such.

FORMAT

The order of taxa is alphabetical by families, genera, species, and then subspecies, although the four main groups are arranged thus: *Pteridophyta, Gymnospermae, Dicotyledones* and *Monocotyledones*. Family names such as *Compositae* and *Gramineae* are preferred to *Asteraceae* and *Poaceae*, although the latter are included in parentheses. Genera are numbered, and cited together with their authority. Species are numbered and subspecies lettered, cited with both their authority and place of publication:

>**14. Paracaryum** (DC.) Boiss.
>
>**1. P. lithospermifolium** (Lam.) Grande in *Boll. Orto bot., Napoli* **4**: 183 (1914).
>**a.** subsp. **cariense** (Boiss.) R.R.Mill in *Notes R. bot. Gdn Edinb.* **35**: 307 (1977).

The names of introduced taxa are enclosed in square brackets:

>**[1. O. ficus-barbarica]** A.Berger, *Monatsschr. Kakteenk.* **22**: 181 (1912).

The names of endemic taxa are preceded by an solid circle:

>●**1. V. creticum** Browicz in *Fragm. flor. geobot.* **21**: 263 (1975).

Taxa doubtfully recorded as present are not numbered or lettered but preceded by a question-mark:

>**? A. adiantum-nigrum** L., *Sp. pl.*: 1081 (1753).

Hybrids are included at the end of a genus, arranged in alphabetical order of the parents, with hybrid names cited, if known, together with their authority and place of publication:

>**A. lepidum** subsp. **lepidum** x **A. ruta-muraria**
>= **A. x javorkae** Kümmerle in *Magy. bot. Lap.* **21**: 1 (1923).

The names of all taxa accepted as present or doubtfully present in the Cretan area are given in bold type, whereas all others, including synonyms, taxa erroneously recorded, or merely cultivated or casual, are given in italics.

Authorities and places of publication largely follow *Flora Europaea* (Tutin et al., 1964-1980), but are often factually different in the following works: *Med-Checklist* (Greuter,

Burdet & Long, 1984; 1986; 1989), *Flora of Turkey* (Davis, 1965-1985; Davis et al., 1988), and *Mountain Flora of Greece* (Strid, 1986; Strid & Tan, 1991). In such cases, the citation given in the most recent publication is taken as correct, unless it has been checked at source. Unfortunately, it has not been possible to check at source each and every authority and place of publication cited in this checklist, and it is realised that some errors will remain uncorrected.

Abbreviations of authors' names follow Brummitt & Powell, *Authors of plant names*, Royal Botanic Gardens, Kew, 1992; titles of journals follow *Serial publications in the British Museum (Natural History) library* ed.3, 1980, and titles of books follow Stafleu & Cowan, *Taxonomic literature* ed.2, 1976-1992.

Place-names outside Greece are in English, while all those within Greece are in Greek (except the words 'Crete', 'Aegean' and 'Ionian'). Transliteration follows Turland (1992*b*), which in turn follows official Greek usage. The aim is to provide the closest possible phonetic equivalent of the Greek pronunciation, without resorting to unwieldy letter combinations.

ANNOTATIONS

Flora Europaea references & synonyms

The appropriate volume and page reference to *Flora Europaea* is included immediately after place of publication for all taxa mentioned in that work, for which the acronym *FE* is used throughout this checklist. Synonymy follows if a taxon is named differently in *Flora Europaea*, and is also included, with a cross reference, at the appropriate alphabetical position in the text (but only if the taxon is given for the Cretan area in *Flora Europaea*).

> **3. O. collina** Banks & Sol. in Russell, *Nat. hist.*
> *Aleppo* ed.2, **2**: 264 (1794) - *FE* **5**: 340 as *O.*
> *saccata* Ten.
>
> *O. saccata* Ten. (*FE* **5**: 340) = **3**.

Ecological data

Habitats, altitudinal ranges and flowering times are given in a composite statement, in italic type, based on the collections and field observations of Chilton and Turland, literature sources (see references: p. 424) and, in some cases, unpublished records by other botanists, which include collections at The Natural History Museum (BM). Most taxa are reasonably well-annotated, although it must be stressed that these data are seldom fully comprehensive. They may refer to a species in the broad sense (sensu lato), if there is insufficient information available for individual subspecies. The status of introduced plants is indicated, if known, and flowering times are given as months, numerically (i.e. 1 = January, etc.)

> *Woodland, scrub, garigue; 0-1200m; fl. 3-5.*

Distribution within the Cretan area

The basic information provided is presence or absence within six main divisions arranged thus: Crete (western, central, eastern); Kasos, Karpathos, Saria. This is given firstly in acronyms, to facilitate quick reference, and then in words (see below), usually in more detail, with information on plants which are localized or show apparent trends in their distribution. The term 'Karpathos group' is used to indicate presence on all three islands of that archipelago. Endemic taxa are indicated as such.

Crete (widespread); Karpathos group
Crete (sporadic); Karpathos
Crete (Lefka Ori, Psiloritis & Dikti); Karpathos
(Kalilimni)
Mainly W. & C. Crete; Karpathos
C. & E. Crete (N. coast); Kasos, Karpathos
W. Crete (Lefka Ori) - Endemic.
?Crete; Kasos, Karpathos

Taxa 'widespread' in Crete are present in all three divisions, are usually more or less evenly distributed, and occur in about 20 or more grid squares on their respective distribution maps. Taxa 'sporadic' in Crete are still present in the three divisions, but are often erratically distributed; they occur in fewer than 20 grid squares, down to a minimum of three.

It must be stressed that this distribution is usually based only on records which satisfy the criteria for inclusion on the distribution maps and may, therefore, be narrower than that given in *Mountain Flora of Greece*, which hardly ever cites its records with an indication of date, thereby preventing mapping (see pp. 196-198). Any apparent discrepancies resulting from this situation are explained by means of textual notes.

Where a taxon is recorded merely from Crete or the Cretan area, without further details, the distribution is given thus:

Crete
Cretan area

Distributions that might mislead are also omitted, e.g. subspecies which appear to be very rare, but are thought to be under-recorded because the species is frequent and widespread. In cases such as this, or where the records of individual subspecies are otherwise inadequate, distribution within the Cretan area may be confined to the species sensu lato.

Distributional acronyms and map references

These are included on a single line, in bold type. The first eight examples given above would appear thus:

Cr (W, C, E) Ks Kp Sa - *MAP 1*
Cr (W, C, E) Kp - *MAP 2*
Cr (W, C, E) Kp - *MAP 3*
Cr (W, C, E) Kp - *MAP 4*
Cr (C, E) Ks Kp - *MAP 5*
Cr (W) - *MAP 6*
?Cr Ks Kp - *MAP 7*
Cr - *NOT MAPPED*

Distribution outside the Cretan area

This immediately follows the Cretan area distribution, and is enclosed in square brackets. Only the range within Europe is given, using the territories and regions defined in *Flora Europaea*. If, however, this is of a localized nature, or nil, then the remainder of the full distribution is given. A question-mark is placed immediately before a territory in which a taxon is doubtfully present. Introduced taxa which are not native in Europe are annotated with their native range.

> [S. Europe].
> [?Spain, Italy].
> [Sicily & S. Greece; otherwise N. Africa &
> S.W. Asia]
> [E. Aegean Islands (Rodos) & S.W. Turkey].
> [S. Europe; from S. Africa]

Notes enabling compatibility with *Flora Europaea*

As explained above, a page reference and, if necessary, synonyms are included for all taxa mentioned in *Flora Europaea*; otherwise 'not cited in *FE*' is given, unless a plant has been described as new to science or recorded as new to Europe since the publication of *Flora Europaea*.

Taxa recorded from the Cretan area since *Flora Europaea* are annotated accordingly. Usually only the first record is cited, although separate references may be given for Crete and the Karpathos island group. A similar approach is adopted for taxa given as doubtfully present in the Cretan area in *Flora Europaea*, but since confirmed. A note is included, with a reference, if a taxon is erroneously regarded as absent from the Cretan area in *Flora Europaea* (i.e. it was previously and correctly recorded).

Notes are also included, with references, if taxa are incorrectly given as present in the Cretan area in *Flora Europaea*. There may be no records as a basis for their inclusion, or, if these do exist, they may be erroneous or almost certainly so. The names used for such taxa are those cited in *Flora Europaea*, even if different names are now in use.

If a plant is given for the Cretan area in *Flora Europaea* under a misapplied name, this is cited in double quotation marks, without authority, and is referred to the correct taxon. The source of the correction is given as a reference. The name is also cited in the synonymy of the correct taxon if it has been generally misapplied throughout the European range of the plant.

> **[1. O. ficus-barbarica]** A.Berger, *Monatsschr.*
> *Kakteenk.* **22**: 181 (1912) - *FE* **2**: 300 as "*O.*
> *ficus-indica*"
>
> "*O. ficus-indica*" (*FE* **2**: 300) = **1** (Greuter in
> Greuter & Rechinger, 1967: 37-38).

A reference is provided if a taxon is given as doubtfully present in the Cretan area in this checklist, but not in *Flora Europaea* (i.e. it is regarded there as either definitely present or absent).

In fact, every effort has been made to ensure that all discrepancies, apparent and real, between the checklist and *Flora Europaea* are explained, so that the former provides a revision of the latter as far as the Cretan area is concerned.

Notes enabling compatibility with other major works wholly or partly concerning the Cretan area

Major discrepancies between the checklist and the works listed below are explained. However, citation of page numbers is limited to these explanatory notes only, while synonyms are given only in cases where not to do so would cause confusion. In common with *Flora Europaea*, the most important works are abbreviated to acronyms:

Atlas FE = *Atlas Florae Europaeae* **1-9** (Jalas & Suominen, 1972-1991).
M-Ch = *Med-Checklist* **1; 3; 4** (Greuter, Burdet & Long, 1984; 1986; 1989).
MFG = *Mountain Flora of Greece* **1-2** (Strid, 1986; Strid & Tan, 1991).

The remaining works are cited in the same way as other references:

Barclay, 1986 = Crete. Checklist of the vascular plants.
Greuter, 1973*a* = Additions to the flora of Crete, 1938-1972.
Greuter, 1974 = Floristic report on the Cretan area.
Greuter et al., 1983*a* = The vascular flora of the Karpathos island group (Dodecanesos, Greece).
Greuter et al., 1984*a* = Additions to the flora of Crete 1973-1983 - I.
Greuter et al., 1984*b* = Additions to the flora of Crete 1973-1983 (1984) - II.
Greuter et al., 1985 = Additions to the flora of Crete 1973-1983 (1984) - III.
Zaffran, 1990 = *Contributions à la flore et à la végétation de la Crète.*

The last of these is partly a revision of an earlier work by the same author (1976), and the two are often cited together. See references (p. 424) for full citations of all the works listed above.

General notes

These include other important and useful data, such as the affinities of recently described taxa, ethnobotanical data, and plate references for those plants which are illustrated. Brief notes on legally protected species are given, citing IUCN categories for Europe (endangered, vulnerable or rare), based on Revised Appendix 1 of the Berne Convention (strictly protected flora species), 1990.

CHECKLIST

PTERIDOPHYTA

ADIANTACEAE

1. Adiantum L.

1. A. capillus-veneris L., *Sp. pl.*: 1096 (1753) - *FE* **1**: 10.
Cr (W, C, E) Ks Kp - *MAP 1*
Damp rock-crevices, springs, other moist places; 0-800m.
Mainly W. & C. Crete; Kasos, Karpathos [W. & S. Europe].

ASPIDIACEAE

1. Dryopteris Adans.

"D. filix-mas" (*FE* **1**: 21) ?= **1** (Brownsey & Jermy, 1973: 346).

1. D. pallida (Bory) Maire & Petitm. in *Bull. Séanc. Soc. Sci. Nancy* ser.3, **9**: 480 (1908) - *FE* **1**: 21 as *D. villarii* subsp. *pallida* (Bory) Heywood.
a. subsp. **pallida**
Cr (W, C, E) Kp - *MAP 2*
Shady rocks, cliffs, Platanus and Castanea woodland; 200-1950m.
Mainly W. Crete; Karpathos [Mediterranean region].

D. villarii subsp. *pallida* (Bory) Heywood (*FE* **1**: 21) = **1**.

Gymnocarpium dryopteris (L.) Newman (*FE* **1**: 22) was almost certainly recorded in error (Greuter, 1974: 154).

2. Polystichum Roth

1. P. lonchitis (L.) Roth, *Tent. fl. Germ.* **3**: 71 (1799) - *FE* **1**: 20.
Cr (W) - *MAP 3*
Calcareous rock-crevices; 1500-2200m.
W. Crete (Lefka Ori) [most of Europe].

2. P. setiferum (Forssk.) Woyn. in *Mitt. naturw. Ver. Steierm.* **49**: 181 (1913) - *FE* **1**: 20.
Cr (W) - *MAP 4*
450-2100m.
W. Crete [W., C. & S. Europe].
Recorded since *FE* (*Atlas FE* **1**: 98).

ASPLENIACEAE

1. Asplenium L.

? A. adiantum-nigrum L., *Sp. pl.*: 1081 (1753) - *FE* **1**: 16.
Doubtfully present in Crete (Greuter, 1974: 154) [most of Europe].
Records are possibly referable to **6** (Brownsey & Jermy, 1973: 338).

1. A. aegaeum Lovis, Reichst. & Greuter in *Annls Mus. Goulandris* **1**: 141 (1973).
Cr (W, C, E) - *MAP 5*
Calcareous rock-crevices; 1700-2200m.
Crete (Lefka Ori, Psiloritis & Dikti) [C. Greece; otherwise S.W. Turkey].

2. A. bourgaei Milde in *Bot. Ztg* **24**: 384 (1866).
Kp - *MAP 6*
Karpathos [S.W. Asia].
Shady clefts beneath large calcareous boulders; 250m.
Recorded since *FE* (Greuter et al., 1983a: 47, b).

●**3. A. creticum** Lovis, Reichst. & Zaffran in *Annls Mus. Goulandris* **1**: 145 (1973).
Cr (W, E) - *MAP 7*
Calcareous rock-crevices; 1700-2200m.
W. & E. Crete (Lefka Ori & Dikti) - ?Endemic. Two collections from S. Turkey may be referable to this species but confirmation is required (Davis et al., 1988: 4). Probably an alloploid based on the two diploids **1** & **9** (Brownsey & Jermy, 1973: 339).

A. fontanum (L.) Bernh. (*FE* **1**: 15) was almost certainly recorded in error (Greuter, 1974: 154).

4. A. lepidum C.Presl in *Verh. Ges. vaterl. Mus. Prag* **14**: 63 (1836) - *FE* **1**: 16.
a. subsp. **haussknechtii** (Godet & Reut.) Brownsey in *Bot. J. Linn. Soc.* **72**: 261 (1976).
Cr (C, E) - *MAP 8*
Calcareous rock-crevices; 1700-2150m.
C. & E. Crete (Psiloritis & Dikti) [S.W. Asia]. Recorded since *FE* (Zaffran, 1970: 241).
b. subsp. **lepidum**
Cr (W) - *MAP 9*
Calcareous rock-crevices; 1800-2100m.
W. Crete (Lefka Ori) [S.E. & S. Europe]. Recorded since *FE* (Zaffran, 1970: 240). An earlier record is referable to subsp. **a** (Greuter, 1973a: 25).

5. A. obovatum Viv., *Fl. Libyc. spec.*: 68 (1824) - *FE* **1**: 16.
a. subsp. obovatum
Cr (W) - *MAP 10*
W. Crete (S. of Kastelli Kissamou) [Mediterranean region].
Recorded since *FE* (*Atlas FE* **1**: 73).

6. A. onopteris L., *Sp. pl.*: 1081 (1753) - *FE* **1**: 16.
Cr (W, C) - *MAP 11*
Woodland, maquis, shady banks & rocks; 350-1850m.
W. & C. Crete [W. Europe & Mediterranean region].

7. A. ruta-muraria L., *Sp. pl.*: 1081 (1753) - *FE* **1**: 16.
a. subsp. ruta-muraria
Cr (W, C, E) Kp - *MAP 12*
Calcareous rock-crevices; 1150-2200m.
Crete (Lefka Ori, Psiloritis & Dikti); Karpathos (Kalilimni) [almost throughout Europe].
Recorded since *FE* (Zaffran, 1970: 241).

8. A. trichomanes L., *Sp. pl.*: 1080 (1753) - *FE* **1**: 15.
Cr (W, C, E) Kp - *MAP 13*.
a. subsp. inexpectans Lovis in *Brit. Fern Gaz.* **9**: 155 (1964) - *FE* **1**: 15 cited without name in a note following subsp. **c**.
Cr (W) - *MAP 14*
Calcareous rock-crevices; 1200-1400m.
W. Crete (Lefka Ori) [mainly C. & S.E. Europe].
Recorded since *FE* (Brownsey & Jermy, 1973: 338). Additionally recorded from Psiloritis in C. Crete in *MFG* **1**: 18.
b. subsp. pachyrachis (H.Christ) Lovis & Reichst. in *Willdenowia* **10**: 18 (1980) - not cited in *FE*.
Cr (W) - *MAP 15*
Moist shady calcareous rock-crevices; 1850m.
W. Crete (Lefka Ori) [C. & S. Europe].
Recorded by Reichstein et al. (1973: 149).
c. subsp. quadrivalens D.E.Mey. in *Ber. dt. bot. Ges.* **74**: 456 (1962) - *FE* **1**: 15.
Cr - *NOT MAPPED*
Calcareous rock-crevices; 0-2100m.
Crete [most of Europe].
The species sensu lato is widespread in Crete (mainly in the mountains) and occurs also in Karpathos; most records are probably referable to subsp. **c**.

9. A. trichomanes-ramosum L., *Sp. pl.*: 1082 (1753) - *FE* **1**: 15 as *A. viride* Hudson.
Cr (W) - *MAP 16*
N.-facing calcareous rock-crevices; 1850-2000m.
W. Crete (Lefka Ori) [most of Europe].

Recorded since *FE* (Zaffran, 1970: 241).

Hybrids:

A. creticum x **A. trichomanes** subsp. **quadrivalens**
Shady rock-crevice; 1950m.
W. Crete (Lefka Ori).
Recorded by Brownsey & Jermy (1973: 339).

A. lepidum subsp. **haussknechtii** x **A. ruta-muraria**
1900m.
E. Crete (Dikti).
Recorded by Reichstein et al. (1973: 151).

A. lepidum subsp. **lepidum** x **A. ruta-muraria** = **A.** x **javorkae** Kümmerle in *Magy. bot. Lap.* **21**: 1 (1923).
1850m.
W. Crete (Lefka Ori).
Recorded by Zaffran (1970: 242).

A. lepidum subsp. **lepidum** x **A. trichomanes** subsp. **quadrivalens** = **A.** x **aprutianum** Lovis, H.Melzer & Reichst. in *Bauhinia* **3**: 89 (1966).
2050m.
W. Crete (Lefka Ori).
Recorded by Reichstein et al. (1973: 151).

Barclay (1986: 2) lists the above hybrids for Crete except *A. lepidum* subsp. *haussknechtii* x *A. ruta-muraria*, giving instead *A. creticum* x *A. ruta-muraria*. There are no records as a basis for this and it should be regarded as a printing error. Zaffran (1976: 12; 1990: 66), presumably because of a similar error, gives the parents of *A.* x *javorkae* as *A. aegaeum* and *A. ruta-muraria*.

Biropteris antri-jovis Kümmerle (*FE* **1**: 17) is included in synonymy of **Phyllitis 1a**.

2. Ceterach Willd.

1. C. officinarum Willd., *Anleit. Selbststud. Bot.*: 578 (1804) - *FE* **1**: 17.
a. subsp. officinarum
Cr (W, C, E) Ks Kp - *MAP 17*
Cliffs, rocks & crevices, old walls; 0-2000m.
Crete (widespread, rarer towards E.); Kasos, Karpathos [W., C. & S. Europe].

3. Phyllitis Hill

"*P. sagittata*" (*FE* **1**: 17) was referred by Brownsey & Jermy (1973: 340-346) to *Asplenium scolopendrium* subsp. *antri-jovis* (Kümmerle) Brownsey & Jermy (= *Biropteris antri-jovis* Kümmerle - *FE* **1**: 17), which is included here in synonymy of **1a**.

1. P. scolopendrium (L.) Newman, *Hist. brit. ferns* ed.2: 10 (1844) - *FE* **1**: 17.
a. subsp. **scolopendrium** (including *Biropteris antri-jovis* Kümmerle - *FE* **1**: 17).
Cr (W, C, E) - *MAP 18*
Calcareous cliffs & rock-crevices, walls of caves; 1200-1900m.
Crete (Lefka Ori, Psiloritis & Dikti) [mainly W., C. & S. Europe].

ATHYRIACEAE

1. Athyrium Roth

1. A. filix-femina (L.) Roth, *Tent. fl. Germ.* **3**: 65 (1799) - *FE* **1**: 18.
Cr (W, C) - *MAP 19*
Damp stream-banks in maquis, marshy ground, irrigation channels.
W. & C. Crete [almost throughout Europe].

2. Cystopteris Bernh.

1. C. fragilis (L.) Bernh. in *Neues J. Bot.* **1**(2): 27 (1805) - *FE* **1**: 18.
Cr (W, C, E) - *MAP 20*
Calcareous rocks, cliffs; (160-)1450-2200m.
Crete (Korikos peninsula, Lefka Ori, Psiloritis & Dikti) [almost throughout Europe].

BLECHNACEAE

1. Blechnum L.

1. B. spicant (L.) Roth in *Annln Bot.* **10**: 56 (1794) - *FE* **1**: 23.
Cr (W) - *MAP 21*
Shady non-calcareous rocks; 300m.
W. Crete [most of Europe].

2. Woodwardia Sm.

1. W. radicans (L.) Sm. in *Memorie Accad. Sci. Torino* **5**: 412 (1793) - *FE* **1**: 23.
Cr (W) - *MAP 22*
Humid open deciduous woodland, tall maquis.
W. Crete (Fasas valley) [mainly S.W. Europe].
Recorded since *FE* (Gradstein & Smittenberg, 1968). Vulnerable species, legally protected.

EQUISETACEAE

1. Equisetum L.

1. E. arvense L., *Sp. pl.*: 1061 (1753) - *FE* **1**: 8.
Cr (W, E) - *NOT MAPPED*
W. & E. Crete [almost throughout Europe].

"*E. hyemale*" (*FE* **1**: 7) = **2** (*Atlas FE* **1**: 32).

"*E. palustre*" (*FE* **1**: 7) ? = **2** (*Atlas FE* **1**: 37).

2. E. ramosissimum Desf., *Fl. atlant.* **2**: 398 (1799) - *FE* **1**: 7.
Cr (W, C, E) Kp - *MAP 23*
Damp olive groves, vineyards, thickets by watercourses, stream-sides, marshes, damp maritime sands.
Mainly W. & C. Crete; Karpathos [mostly C. & S. Europe].

E. sylvaticum L. (*FE* **1**: 7) was almost certainly recorded in error (Greuter, 1974: 154).

3. E. telmateia Ehrh. in *Hannover. Mag.* **21**: 287 (1783) - *FE* **1**: 8.
Cr (W, C) - *MAP 24*
River-banks, streams, springs, ditches, marshy lake-margin, often in shade; 0-300m.
Mainly W. Crete [most of Europe].

GYMNOGRAMMACEAE

1. Anogramma Link

1. A. leptophylla (L.) Link, *Fil. spec.*: 137 (1841) - *FE* **1**: 11.
Cr (W, C, E) Ks Kp Sa - *MAP 25*
Seasonally damp rocks & vertical exposures of bare earth; 100-550m.
Mainly W. Crete; Karpathos group [W. Europe & Mediterranean region].

HYPOLEPIDACEAE

1. Pteridium Scop.

1. P. aquilinum (L.) Kuhn in Kerst., *Reis. Ost-Afr.* **3**(3): 11 (1879) - *FE* **1**: 12.
Cr (W, C, E) - *MAP 26*
Woodland, olive groves, maquis, scrub, open hillsides, beneath cliffs, flat clayey areas, preferring deeper soils; 0-1500m.
W. & C. Crete, one record from E. Crete [almost throughout Europe].
The population in E. Crete (Dikti) has been referred to *P. tauricum* Gross. (Brownsey & Jermy, 1973: 337 as *P. aquilinum* subsp. *brevipes* (Tausch) Wulf), which is otherwise known from Crimea and the Caucasus, but is treated as doubtfully distinct from *P. aquilinum* in *M-Ch* **1**: 21, and is not separated here.

ISOËTACEAE

1. Isoëtes L.

1. I. histrix Bory in *C. r. hebd. Séanc. Acad. Sci., Paris* **18**: 1167 (1844) - *FE* **1**: 6.

Cr (W) - *MAP 27*
Damp ground; 50-1050m.
W. Crete [W. Europe & Mediterranean region].

OPHIOGLOSSACEAE

Botrychium Sw.

? B. lunaria (L.) Sw. in *J. Bot. Göttingen*
1800(2): 110 (1802) - *FE* **1**: 9.
Doubtfully present in Crete [almost throughout
Europe].

1. Ophioglossum L.

1. O. lusitanicum L., *Sp. pl.*: 1063 (1753) - *FE*
1: 8.
Cr (W, E) - *MAP 28*
Sparse phrygana, flat ledges on cliffs; 0-300m.
W. & E. ends of Crete [W. Europe &
Mediterranean region].
Additionally recorded from W./C. Crete in *Atlas
FE* **1**: 42.

O. vulgatum L. is given for the Cretan area in
FE **1**: 8, although there are no records as a basis
for this (Greuter, 1974: 139).

OSMUNDACEAE

1. Osmunda L.

1. O. regalis L., *Sp. pl.*: 1065 (1753) - *FE* **1**: 9.
Cr (W, C) - *MAP 29*
*Platanus woodland, stream-banks in maquis,
moist shady rocks, irrigation channels,
preferring non-calcareous substrata; 50-300m.*
W. & C. Crete [mostly W. & S. Europe].

POLYPODIACEAE

1. Polypodium L.

P. australe Fée (*FE* **1**: 23) = **1a**.

1. P. cambricum L., *Sp. pl.*: 1086 (1753) - not
cited in *FE*.
a. subsp. **australe** (Fée) Greuter & Burdet in
Willdenowia **11**: 24 (1981) - *FE* **1**: 23 as *P.
australe* Fée.
Cr (W, C, E) Ks Kp - *MAP 30*
Calcareous cliffs & rock-crevices; 0-800m.
Crete (sporadic); Kasos, Karpathos [W. & S.
Europe].

? P. vulgare L., *Sp. pl.*: 1085 (1753) - *FE* **1**:
23.
Doubtfully present in Crete (Greuter, 1974: 154)
[most of Europe].

PTERIDACEAE

1. Pteris L.

P. cretica L. (*FE* **1**: 11) was recorded in error
(Greuter, 1974: 154).

1. P. vittata L., *Sp. pl.*: 1074 (1753) - *FE* **1**:
11.
Cr (W, C) - *MAP 31*
*Moist banks, shady places by streams &
irrigation channels; 0-150m.*
W. & C. Crete [Mediterranean region].

SELAGINELLACEAE

1. Selaginella P.Beauv.

1. S. denticulata (L.) Spring in *Flora, Jena* **21**:
149 (1838) - *FE* **1**: 5.
Cr (W, C, E) Ks Kp - *MAP 32*
*Rocks, cliffs, vertical exposures of bare earth; 0-
1650m.*
Mainly W. & C. Crete; Kasos, Karpathos [S.
Europe].

SINOPTERIDACEAE

1. Cheilanthes Sw.

C. catanensis (Cosent.) H.P.Fuchs (*FE* **1**: 10) =
Cosentinia 1.

C. fragrans Sw. (*FE* **1**: 10) = **1**.

1. C. maderensis Lowe in *Trans. Camb. phil.
Soc.* **6**: 528 (1838) - *FE* **1**: 10 as *C. fragrans*
Sw.
Cr (W, C, E) Ks Kp Sa - *MAP 33*
Cliffs, rock-crevices, old walls; 0-450m.
Crete (widespread); Karpathos group [S.
Europe].

2. C. persica (Bory) Mett. ex Kuhn, *Bot. Ztg*
26: 234 (1868) - *FE* **1**: 10.
Cr (W, C, E) - *MAP 34*
N.-facing calcareous rock-crevices; 1650m.
Crete (sporadic) [Balkan peninsula & Crimea,
probably extinct in Italy].

C. pteridioides (Reichard) C.Chr. (Barclay,
1986: 4; and others) = **1**.

2. Cosentinia Tod.

1. C. vellea (Aiton) Tod. in *G. Sci. nat. econ.
Palermo* **1**: 220 (1866) - *FE* **1**: 10 as *Cheilanthes
catanensis* (Cosent.) H.P.Fuchs.
Cr (W, C, E) Kp - *MAP 35*
Cliffs, rock-crevices, old walls; 0-300m.

Mainly W. & E. Crete (mainly coastal);
Karpathos [Mediterranean region].

THELYPTERIDACEAE

1. Christella Lév.

1. C. dentata (Forssk.) Brownsey & Jermy in
Brit. Fern Gaz. **10**: 338 (1973) - *FE* **1**: 14 as
Cyclosurus dentatus (Forssk.) Ching.
Cr (W) - *MAP 36*
*By streams & irrigation channels in orange
groves; -275m.*
W. Crete (Fasas valley) [Azores, S. Spain &
Italy; otherwise Macaronesia, Africa & Arabia].
Recorded since *FE* (*Atlas FE* **1**: 66).

SPERMATOPHYTA
GYMNOSPERMAE

CUPRESSACEAE

1. Cupressus L.

1. C. sempervirens L., *Sp. pl.*: 1002 (1753) -
FE **1**: 37.
Cr (W, C, E) - *MAP 37*
*Rocky areas in mountains & ravines, on hillsides
& cliffs, forming woodland with other trees or as
pure stands, also frequently planted on
roadsides, around villages & in cemeteries; 0-
1800m.*
Crete (widespread, rarer towards E.) [mainly E.
Mediterranean region].
Within Europe native only in Crete, as forma
horizontalis (Mill.) Voss, characterized by
spreading branches.

2. Juniperus L.

J. excelsa M.Bieb. (*FE* **1**: 39) was recorded in
error (Greuter, 1974: 154).

1. J. oxycedrus L., *Sp. pl.*: 1038 (1753) - *FE* **1**:
38.
a. subsp. **macrocarpa** (Sm.) Ball in *J. Linn.
Soc. (Bot.)* **16**: 670 (1878) - *FE* **1**: 38.
Cr (W, C, E) Kp - *MAP 38*
*Maritime sands & rocky ground by sea,
sometimes forming low woodland.*
Crete (mainly S. coast & islands opposite);
Karpathos [S. Europe].
Erroneously regarded as absent from the Cretan
area in *FE* (Greuter, 1974: 140).
b. subsp. **oxycedrus**
Cr (W, C, E) - *MAP 39*
Calcareous cliffs & rocky ground, usually near

timberline; 900-1800m.
Crete (in mountains) [S. Europe].
Erroneously regarded as absent from the Cretan
area in *FE* (Greuter, 1974: 140).

2. J. phoenicea L., *Sp. pl.*: 1040 (1753) - *FE* **1**:
39.
Cr (W, E) Ks Kp Sa - *MAP 40*
*Rocky or sandy places, scrub, phrygana, usually
near sea; 0-750m.*
W. & E. Crete; Karpathos group
[Mediterranean region].
Additionally recorded from W./C. Crete in *Atlas
FE* **2**: 34.
Subsp. *mediterranea* Lebreton & Thirend is
given for the Cretan area in *M-Ch* **1**: 27, but as
doubtfully distinct from subsp. *phoenicea*; it is
not separated here.

EPHEDRACEAE

1. Ephedra L.

1. E. campylopoda C.A.Mey. in *Mém. Acad.
Sci. St. Petersb.* sér.6, *Sci. Math., Seconde Pt.
Sci. Nat.* 7(2): 263 (1846) - *FE* **1**: 40 as *E.
fragilis* subsp. *campylopoda* (C.A.Mey.)
K.Richt.
Cr (W, C, E) Ks Kp Sa - *MAP 41*
*Calcareous cliffs, walls, or sometimes growing
through shrubs; 0-900m; fl. 8-10.*
Crete (widespread); Karpathos group [E.
Mediterranean region].

E. fragilis subsp. *campylopoda* (C.A.Mey.)
K.Richt. (*FE* **1**: 40) = **1**.

PINACEAE

1. Pinus L.

1. P. brutia Ten., *Fl. napol.* **1**: lxxii (1811-
1815) - *FE* **1**: 35.
Cr (W, C, E) Kp - *MAP 42*
*Calcareous screes, banked rubble in gorges,
rocky slopes, usually S.-facing, often forming
extensive woodland; 0-1200m.*
Crete (widespread); Karpathos [N. Aegean
region; otherwise S.W. Asia; extinct in S.
Italy].

P. halepensis Mill. (*FE* **1**: 35) was recorded in
error (Greuter, 1975a: 19).

P. nigra Arnold (*FE* **1**: 33) was recorded in
error (Greuter, 1975a: 19).

P. pinea L. (*FE* **1**: 35) is erroneously given as
native to the Cretan area in *FE* (Greuter, 1974:
154); it is probably only planted.

ANGIOSPERMAE

DICOTYLEDONES

ACANTHACEAE

1. Acanthus L.

1. A. spinosus L., *Sp. pl.*: 639 (1753) - *FE* 3: 284.
Cr (W, C, E) Ks Kp - *MAP 43*
Olive groves, roadsides, rocky places, waste areas; 0-800m; fl. 4-6.
Crete (widespread); Kasos, Karpathos [mainly E. Mediterranean region].

ACERACEAE

1. Acer L.

1. A. sempervirens L., *Mant. pl.*: 128 (1767) - *FE* 2: 239.
Cr (W, C, E) Kp - *MAP 44*
Calcareous woodland, rocky slopes, dolines, ravines; 200-1700m; fl. 4-5.
Crete (widespread, mainly in mountains); Karpathos (Kalilimni) [Greece & Aegean region].

AIZOACEAE

1. Aizoon L.

1. A. hispanicum L., *Sp. pl.*: 488 (1753) - *FE* 1: 112.
Cr - *NOT MAPPED*
Crete [W. & C. Mediterranean region].
Recorded from W./C. Crete in *Atlas FE* 5: 102.

2. Aptenia N.E.Br.

[1. A. cordifolia] (L.f.) Schwantes in *Gartenflora* 77: 69 (1928) - *FE* 1: 113.
Cr (E) - *MAP 45*
Cultivated for ornament and naturalized on rocky coast.
E. Crete (Agios Nikolaos) [mainly S.W. Europe; from S. Africa].
Recorded since *FE* (Greuter, 1974: 146).

3. Carpobrotus N.E.Br.

C. acinaciformis (L.) L.Bolus (*FE* 1: 112) is given for Crete - as an introduction - by Barclay (1986: 6), and for Karpathos by Greuter et al. (1983a: 48). However, Akeroyd & Preston (1987: 352-353) suggest that at least some Greek records are probably referable to **1** var. **rubescens**, which also has purple petals, but differs in having yellow, rather than purple, stamens.

[1. C. edulis] (L.) N.E.Br. in Phillips, *Gen. S. Afr. fl. pl.*: 249 (1926) - *FE* 1: 113.
Cr - *NOT MAPPED*
Cultivated for ornament and planted for binding loose earth, possibly naturalized on roadsides, seashores; 0-200m; fl. 3-6(-8).
Crete [coasts of W. & S. Europe; from S. Africa].
Recorded since *FE* by Akeroyd & Preston (1987: 352), as both var. **edulis** (yellow petals) and var. **rubescens** Druce (purple). The authors have observed only *C. edulis* in Crete, never *C. acinaciformis*.

4. Mesembryanthemum L.

1. M. crystallinum L., *Sp. pl.*: 480 (1753) - *FE* 1: 113.
Cr (W, C, E) - *MAP 46*
Calcareous screes, walls, dry waste areas; near s.l.; fl. 4-6.
Crete (N. coast, mainly Iraklio area) [Mediterranean region].
Doubtfully native (*Atlas FE* 5: 104).

2. M. nodiflorum L., *Sp. pl.*: 480 (1753) - *FE* 1: 113.
Cr (W, C, E) Ks Kp Sa - *MAP 47*
Open ground in hot dry places, maritime rocks, walls; near s.l.; fl. 4-6.
Mainly C. & E. Crete; Karpathos group [Mediterranean region].

AMARANTHACEAE

1. Amaranthus L.

[1. A. albus] L., *Syst. nat.* ed.10, 2: 1268 (1759) - *FE* 1: 110.
Cr (E) Kp - *MAP 48*
Naturalized as a weed.
E. Crete; Karpathos [most of Europe; from N. America].
Recorded since *FE* (Greuter, 1973a: 30).

[2. A. blitoides] S.Watson in *Proc. Am. Acad. Arts Sci.* 12: 273 (1877) - *FE* 1: 110.
Cr (W, C, E) Kp - *MAP 49*
Cultivated as a vegetable and naturalized in weed communities, wet places, river-banks, cultivated fields, waste areas; 0-100m.
Crete (sporadic); Karpathos [mainly C. & S. Europe; from N. America].
Recorded since *FE* (*Atlas FE* 5: 94).

A. caudatus L. (*FE* **1**: 109) has been recorded from Karpathos as a casual escape from cultivation (Greuter et al., 1983*a*: 48).

A. cruentus L. (*FE* **1**: 109) is included in synonymy of **5**.

3. A. graecizans L., *Sp. pl.*: 990 (1753) - *FE* **1**: 110.
Cr (W, C, E) Kp - *MAP 50*
Weed communities, fields, also cultivated as a vegetable.
Crete (sporadic); Karpathos [C. & S. Europe].
Not native in Karpathos (Greuter et al., 1983*a*: 48).

"*A. hybridus*" (*FE* **1**: 109) = **4** (*Atlas FE* **5**: 92).

[4. A. hypochondriacus] L., *Sp. pl.*: 991 (1753) - *FE* **1**: 109, included in synonymy of *A. hybridus* L.
Cr (W) - *MAP 51*
Naturalized.
W. Crete [C. & S.E. Europe; from America].

A. lividus L. is given for the Cretan area in *FE* **1**: 110, although there are no records as a basis for this (Greuter, 1974: 139).

[5. A. paniculatus] L., *Sp. pl.* ed.2: 1406 (1763) - *FE* **1**: 109. (Including *A. cruentus* L. - *FE* **1**: 109.)
Cr (C) - *MAP 52*
Naturalized; 400m.
C. Crete [C. & S. Europe; from tropical & subtropical America].

[6. A. retroflexus] L., *Sp. pl.*: 991 (1753) - *FE* **1**: 109.
Cr (W) Kp - *MAP 53*
Naturalized as a weed in fallow fields.
W. Crete; Karpathos [most of Europe; from N. America].
Additionally recorded from W./C. Crete in *Atlas FE* **5**: 93.

[7. A. viridis] L., *Sp. pl.* ed.2: 1405 (1763).
Cr (W, E) Kp - *MAP 54*
Cultivated as a vegetable, occurring as a weed and possibly naturalized in damp places.
W. & E. Crete; Karpathos [Mediterranean region; ?from S. America].
Erroneously omitted from *FE* (Greuter, 1974: 140). Additionally recorded from W./C. Crete in *Atlas FE* **5**: 98.

ANACARDIACEAE

1. Cotinus Mill.

1. C. coggygria Scop., *Fl. carniol.* ed.2, **1**: 220 (1772) - *FE* **2**: 237.

Cr (W) - *MAP 55*
W. Crete (Samaria gorge) [S. Europe].

2. Pistacia L.

1. P. lentiscus L., *Sp. pl.*: 1026 (1753) - *FE* **2**: 237.
Cr (W, C, E) Ks Kp Sa - *MAP 56*
Pinus brutia woodland, scrub, garigue, steep rocky banks, gorge-beds, maritime sands, often forming impenetrable thickets; 0-500m; fl. 3-5.
Crete (widespread, mainly coastal); Karpathos group [Mediterranean region].

2. P. terebinthus L., *Sp. pl.*: 1025 (1753) - *FE* **2**: 237.
a. subsp. **terebinthus**
Cr (W, C, E) Kp - *MAP 57*
Rocky woodland, maquis, calcareous cliffs; 100-700m; fl. 4-5.
Mainly W. & C. Crete; Karpathos [Mediterranean region].

3. Rhus L.

1. R. coriaria L., *Sp. pl.*: 265 (1753) - *FE* **2**: 236.
Cr (C) - *MAP 58*
Calcareous rock-crevices; 1450m.
C. Crete (Psiloritis) [S. Europe].

APOCYNACEAE

1. Nerium L.

1. N. oleander L., *Sp. pl.*: 209 (1753) - *FE* **3**: 68.
a. subsp. **oleander**
Cr (W, C, E) Kp - *MAP 59*
Watercourses, springs, damp places, maritime sands, widely planted for roadside landscaping; 0-500m; fl. 4-8.
Crete (widespread); Karpathos [Mediterranean region].

2. Vinca L.

[1. V. major] L., *Sp. pl.*: 209 (1753) - *FE* **3**: 69.
[a. subsp. **major]**
Cr (W) Kp - *MAP 60*
Cultivated for ornament and naturalized on abandoned terraces, roadsides.
W. Crete; Karpathos [mainly Mediterranean region].

ARALIACEAE

1. Hedera L.

1. H. helix L., *Sp. pl.*: 202 (1753) - *FE* 2: 314.
a. subsp. helix
Cr (W, C, E) Kp - *MAP 61*
Woodland, trees, cliffs, walls; 0-1200m; fl. 10-11.
Crete (widespread); Karpathos [most of Europe].
Doubtfully native in Karpathos.
Subsp. *poetarum* Nyman (*FE* 2: 314) occurs occasionally in town and village habitats in Crete, presumably planted there for its ornamental orange-yellow fruits.

ARISTOLOCHIACEAE

1. Aristolochia L.

A. clematitis L. is given for the Cretan area in *FE* 1: 74, although there are no records as a basis for this (Greuter, 1974: 139).
●**1. A. cretica** Lam., *Encycl.* 1: 255 (1783) - *FE* 1: 74.
Cr (W, C, E) Ks Kp Sa - *MAP 62*
Woodland, olive groves, scrub, phrygana, calcareous rocky places, bases of dry-stone walls; 0-800m; fl. 3-5.
Crete (widespread, rarer in W. & C.); Karpathos group - Endemic.
Records from the E. Aegean island of Rodos are referable to *A. guichardii* P.H.Davis & M.S.Khan (Davis in Greuter, 1981: 30).

A. longa L. is given for the Cretan area in *FE* 1: 74, although there are no records as a basis for this (Greuter, 1974: 139).

A. pallida Willd. is given for the Cretan area in *FE* 1: 74, although there are no records as a basis for this (Greuter, 1974: 139).

2. A. parvifolia Sm., *Fl. Graec. prodr.* 2: 222 (1816).
Cr (E) Ks ?Kp Sa - *MAP 63*
Among calcareous rocks, bases of dry-stone walls; fl. 3-4.
E. Crete (near Elounda); Kasos, ?Karpathos, Saria [S. Peloponnisos & Kiklades; otherwise S.W. Asia].
Recorded since *FE* (Greuter, 1974: 147; Greuter et al., 1984a: 29; Nardi, 1991: 51). Given for Karpathos in *Atlas FE* 3: 120, although its occurrence there is doubted by Greuter et al. (1983a: 49), and no such records are cited by Nardi (loc. cit.)

A. rotunda L. is given for the Cretan area in *FE* 1: 74, although there are no records as a basis for this (Greuter, 1974: 139).

3. A. sempervirens L., *Sp. pl.*: 961 (1753) - *FE* 1: 74.
Cr (W, C, E) - *MAP 64*
Woodland, hedges, scrub, rocky places; 0-2000m; fl. 3-5.
Crete (widespread) [Mediterranean region].

ASCLEPIADACEAE

1. Asclepias L.

[1. A. fruticosa] L., *Sp. pl.*: 216 (1753) - *FE* 3: 70 as *Gomphocarpus fruticosus* (L.) W.T.Aiton.
Cr (W, C) - *MAP 65*
Naturalized on alluvial deposits of rivers, other damp places; 0-350m.
W. & C. Crete [S. Europe; from S. Africa].

2. Cionura Griseb.

1. C. erecta (L.) Griseb., *Spic. fl. rumel.* 2: 69 (1844) - *FE* 3: 73.
Cr (W, C) - *MAP 66*
Calcareous rubble in gorge-beds; 500-600m.
W. & C. Crete [Balkan peninsula & Aegean region].

3. Cynanchum L.

1. C. acutum L., *Sp. pl.*: 212 (1753) - *FE* 3: 71.
a. subsp. acutum
Cr (W, C, E) - *MAP 67*
Tamarix scrub, marshes & damp ground near sea; fl. 6-10.
Crete (sporadic) [S. Europe].

Gomphocarpus fruticosus (L.) W.T.Aiton (*FE* 3: 70) = **Asclepias 1**.

4. Periploca L.

1. P. angustifolia Labill., *Icon. pl. Syr.* 2: 13 (1791) - *FE* 3: 70 as *P. laevigata* subsp. *angustifolia* (Labill.) Markgr.
Cr (W, E) - *MAP 68*
Sandy soil among Juniperus phoenicea bushes, bare rocky places.
W. & E. Crete (Gavdos & Gaidouronisi islands) [Spain, Sicily & Malta; otherwise N. Africa].

P. graeca L. is given as doubtfully present in the Cretan area in *FE* 3: 70, presumably based on an old record from Crete cited by Rechinger

(1943*a*: 559), referring to cultivated plants.

P. laevigata subsp. *angustifolia* (Labill.) Markgr. (*FE* 3: 70) = 1.

5. Vincetoxicum Wolf

"*V. canescens*" (*FE* 3: 71) = 1 (Browicz, 1975).

●1. V. creticum Browicz in *Fragm. flor. geobot.* 21: 263 (1975).
Cr (E) - *MAP 69*
Calcareous open rocky slopes, stony pastures, rubble, screes, flat clayey areas; 1200-2100m; fl. 6-7.
E. Crete (Dikti) - Endemic.

BERBERIDACEAE

1. Berberis L.

1. B. cretica L., *Sp. pl.*: 331 (1753) - *FE* 1: 245.
Cr (W, C, E) - *MAP 70*
Calcareous rocky places in mountains, along field-margins on mountain plain, forming low scrub in dolines & flat clayey areas; 900-2200m; fl. 5-6.
Crete (mainly Lefka Ori, Kedros, Psiloritis, Dikti & Afendis Kavousi) [Greece & Aegean region].

2. Leontice L.

1. L. leontopetalum L., *Sp. pl.*: 312 (1753) - *FE* 1: 244.
a. subsp. leontopetalum
Cr (W, C, E) Ks Kp Sa - *MAP 71*
Cultivated, fallow & abandoned land; 0-500m; fl. 3.
Crete (sporadic); Karpathos group [S.E. Balkan peninsula & Aegean region].

BETULACEAE

1. Corylus L.

1. C. avellana L., *Sp. pl.*: 998 (1753) - *FE* 1: 60.
Cr (W, C) - *MAP 72*
Scrub, field-margins, possibly merely persisting after having been planted for its edible nuts; 200-550m.
W. & C. Crete [almost throughout Europe]. Doubtful occurrence confirmed since *FE*, although considered doubtfully native (*Atlas FE* 3: 64).

BORAGINACEAE

1. Alkanna Tausch

●1. A. sieberi DC., *Prodr.* 10: 99 (1846) - *FE* 3: 97.
Cr (W, C, E) - *MAP 73*
Stony Pinus brutia woodland, sparse calcareous phrygana, maritime sands, abandoned cultivated land; 0-330m; fl. 3-4.
Crete (sporadic) - Endemic.

2. A. tinctoria (L.) Tausch in *Flora, Jena* 7: 234 (1824) - *FE* 3: 96.
Cr (W, C, E) Kp - *MAP 74*
Garigue, dry calcareous rocky places, cliff; 0-500m; fl. 3-4.
Crete (sporadic); Karpathos [S. Europe].
Subsp. *anatolica* Hub.-Mor. has been recorded from Karpathos (Huber-Morath, 1971: 207), and is otherwise known from the E. Aegean island of Rodos and W. Turkey, although the distinctions between it and subsp. *tinctoria* are unsatisfactory according to Carlström (1987: 103). It is not separated here.

2. Anchusa L.

1. A. aegyptiaca (L.) DC., *Prodr.* 10: 48 (1846) - *FE* 3: 108.
Cr (W, C, E) Ks Kp Sa - *MAP 75*
Dry rocky places, sandy ground near sea; 0-100m; fl. 3-4.
Crete (S. coast, Sideros peninsula & Dionisiades islands); Karpathos group [?Sicily, S. Aegean region].
"*A. azurea*" (*FE* 3: 108) = 4 (*M-Ch* 1: 70).

●2. A. cespitosa Lam., *Encycl.* 1: 504 (1785) - *FE* 3: 107.
Cr (W) - *MAP 76*
Calcareous rocky slopes, soil-pockets among rocks, flat clayey areas; 1200-2200m; fl. 4-7.
W. Crete (Lefka Ori) - Endemic.
An old record from S.W. Turkey has never been confirmed (Chamberlain in Davis, 1978: 402).

3. A. hybrida Ten., *Fl. napol.* 1: 45 (1811-1815) - *FE* 3: 107 as *A. undulata* subsp. *hybrida* (Ten.) Cout.
Cr (W, C, E) Ks Kp - *MAP 77*
Vineyards, dry rocky areas, disturbed ground, waste areas; 0-1050m; fl. 4.
Crete (sporadic); Kasos, Karpathos [Mediterranean region].

4. A. italica Retz., *Observ. bot.* 1: 12 (1779) - *FE* 3: 108 as "*A. azurea*".
Cr (W, C, E) Ks Kp Sa - *MAP 78*
Abandoned cultivated land, disturbed ground,

rocky places, roadside banks, waste areas; 0-730m; fl. 4-5.
Crete (widespread); Karpathos group [S.C. & S. Europe].

A. undulata subsp. hybrida (Ten.) Cout. (FE 3: 107) = 3.

5. A. variegata (L.) Lehm., Pl. Asperif. nucif.: 223 (1818) - FE 3: 109.
Cr (W, C) - MAP 79
Calcareous rocky & gravelly places, screes; 0-1000m; fl. 4-5.
Mainly W. Crete [S. Greece & S. Aegean region].

3. Asperugo L.

1. A. procumbens L., Sp. pl.: 138 (1753) - FE 3: 110.
Ks - MAP 80
Grazed area; 400m.
Kasos [mainly N., E.C. & E. Europe].
Recorded since FE (Raus in Greuter & Raus, 1983: 278).

4. Borago L.

1. B. officinalis L., Sp. pl.: 137 (1753) - FE 3: 109.
Cr (W, C, E) - MAP 81
Weed communities, roadsides, also occasionally cultivated by bee keepers; 0-350m; fl. 3-5.
Mainly W. & C. Crete [most of Europe].

Buglossoides arvensis (L.) I.M.Johnst. subsp. arvensis (FE 3: 87) = **Lithospermum 1**.

B. arvensis subsp. gasparrinii (Heldr. ex Guss.) R.Fern. (FE 3: 87) = **Lithospermum 2**.

B. arvensis subsp. sibthorpiana (Griseb.) R.Fern. (FE 3: 87) = **Lithospermum 3**.

5. Cerinthe L.

1. C. major L., Sp. pl.: 136 (1753) - FE 3: 95.
a. subsp. **major**
Cr (W, C) - MAP 82
Cultivated & abandoned land, disturbed ground, waste areas; 0-450m; fl. 4-5.
W. & C. Crete [Mediterranean region].

? **C. minor** L., Sp. pl.: 137 (1753) - FE 3: 94.
Doubtfully present in Crete [C., E. & S. Europe].

2. C. retorta Sm., Fl. Graec. prodr. 1: 120 (1806) - FE 3: 95.

Cr (W, E) - MAP 83
Ledges of calcareous cliffs & debris below; 150-700m; fl. 3-5.
W. & E. Crete [W. & S. Balkan peninsula].
Doubtful occurrence confirmed since FE (Greuter, 1974: 140).

6. Cynoglossum L.

1. C. columnae Ten., Fl. napol. 1: xiv (1811-1815) - FE 3: 120.
Cr (W, C, E) Kp - MAP 84
Olive groves, disturbed ground; 0-450m; fl. 4-5.
Mainly W. & C. Crete; Karpathos [C. & E. Mediterranean region].

2. C. creticum Mill., Gard. Dict. ed.8: no.3 (1768) - FE 3: 120.
Cr (W, C, E) Ks Kp - MAP 85
Olive groves, disturbed ground; 0-450m; fl. 3-5.
Mainly W. & C. Crete; Kasos, Karpathos [S. Europe].

●**3. C. sphacioticum** Boiss. & Heldr. in Boiss, Diagn. pl. orient. ser.1, 11: 125 (1849) - FE 3: 120.
Cr (W) - MAP 86
Calcareous rocky slopes, crevices & screes; 1700-2400m.
W. Crete (Lefka Ori) - Endemic.

7. Echium L.

1. E. angustifolium Mill., Gard. Dict. ed.8: no.6 (1768) - FE 3: 98.
a. subsp. **angustifolium**
Cr (W, C, E) Ks Kp - MAP 87
Rocky places, rubble, maritime sands, Lygeum steppe, roadsides; 0-200m; fl. 4-5.
Crete (widespread, mainly coastal); Kasos, Karpathos [Aegean region].

2. E. arenarium Guss., Index sem. hort. boccad. 1825: 5 (1825) - FE 3: 100.
Cr (W, E) Ks Kp - MAP 88
Maritime sands, rocky places; 0-250m; fl. 3-4.
W. & E. Crete (coastal); Kasos, Karpathos [Mediterranean region].

3. E. italicum L., Sp. pl.: 139 (1753) - FE 3: 98.
a. subsp. **biebersteinii** (Lacaita) Greuter & Burdet in Willdenowia 11: 37 (1981) - not cited in FE.
Cr (W, C, E) - MAP 89
Rocky places, abandoned cultivated land, disturbed ground, waste areas; 0-500m; fl. 4-5.
Crete (widespread) [mainly C. & E. Mediterranean region].

4. E. parviflorum Moench, *Methodus*: 423
(1794) - *FE* 3: 100.
Cr (W, C, E) Ks Kp Sa - *MAP 90*
*Among calcareous rocks in low phrygana,
maritime sands; 0-400m; fl. 3-4.*
Crete (sporadic, coastal); Karpathos group
[Mediterranean region].

5. E. plantagineum L., *Mant. pl. alt.*: 202
(1771) - *FE* 3: 99.
Cr (W, C, E) Kp - *MAP 91*
*Rocky places, abandoned cultivated land,
disturbed ground, waste areas; 0-450m; fl. 4-5.*
Mainly W. & C. Crete; Karpathos [W. & S.
Europe].

E. vulgare L., given for the Cretan area in *FE*
3: 99, is considered doubtfully present by
Greuter (1974: 159), is omitted by Barclay
(1986: 10) and has never been recorded by the
authors.

8. Heliotropium L.

1. H. dolosum De Not., *Repert. fl. ligust.*: 284
(1844) - *FE* 3: 85.
Cr (W, C) Kp - *MAP 92*
*Calcareous screes, maritime shingle, fallow
fields.*
W. & C. Crete; Karpathos [C. & E.
Mediterranean region].

2. H. europaeum L., *Sp. pl.*: 130 (1753) - *FE*
3: 85.
Cr (W, C) Kp - *MAP 93*
*Maritime pebbles, bare ground, fields, tracks,
roadsides, waste areas; 0-150m; fl. 5-9.*
W. & C. Crete; Karpathos [W., C. & S.
Europe].

3. H. hirsutissimum Grauer, *Pl. min. cogn.
Dec.*: 1 (1784) - *FE* 3: 85.
Cr (W, C, E) Kp - *MAP 94*
*Sandy & rocky places near coast, fallow fields,
waste areas; 0-800m.*
Mainly C. Crete; Karpathos [Greece & Aegean
region].

H. suaveolens subsp. *bocconei* (Guss.) Brummitt
(*FE* 3: 85) was almost certainly recorded in
error (Greuter, 1974: 158).

H. suaveolens M.Bieb. subsp. *suaveolens* (*FE* 3:
85) was recorded in error (Greuter, 1974: 158).

4. H. supinum L., *Sp. pl.*: 130 (1753) - *FE* 3:
86.
Cr (C) Kp - *MAP 95*
Sandy ground by sea.
C. Crete; Karpathos [S. Europe].

9. Lithodora Griseb.

1. L. hispidula (Sm.) Griseb., *Spic. fl. rumel.*
2: 531 (1846) - *FE* 3: 88.
a. subsp. **hispidula**
Cr (W, C) Ks Kp Sa - *MAP 96*
*Calcareous cliffs, garigue, phrygana; 0-1200m;
fl. 3-4.*
W. & C. Crete (S. coast); Karpathos group [E.
Aegean Islands & W. Turkey].
Much more frequent and widespread in
Karpathos than in Crete.

10. Lithospermum L.

1. L. arvense L., *Sp. pl.*: 132 (1753) - *FE* 3: 87
as *Buglossoides arvensis* (L.) I.M.Johnst. susbp.
arvensis.
Cr (W) - *MAP 97*
Olive groves, pathsides; 0-800m; fl. 4-5.
W. Crete [most of Europe].

2. L. incrassatum Guss., *Fl. sicul. prodr.* 1:
211 (1827) - *FE* 3: 87 as *Buglossoides arvensis*
subsp. *gasparrinii* (Heldr. ex Guss.) R.Fern.
Cr (W, C) - *MAP 98*
*Soil-pockets in open calcareous woodland, rocky
places, bare stony ground; 1200-1900m; fl. 4-5.*
Crete (Lefka Ori, Kedros & Psiloritis)
[Mediterranean region].

3. L. sibthorpianum Griseb., *Spic. fl. rumel.* 2:
86 (1844) - *FE* 3: 87 as *Buglossoides arvensis*
subsp. *sibthorpiana* (Griseb.) R.Fern.
Cr Kp - *NOT MAPPED*
*Soil-pockets in calcareous phrygana, bare
ground, cultivated terraces; 200-1150m; fl. 3-4.*
Crete; Karpathos [S.E. Europe].

Mattiastrum lithospermifolium (Lam.) Brand (*FE*
3: 121) = **Paracaryum 1.**

11. Myosotis L.

1. M. congesta Shuttlew. ex Albert & Reyn. in
Bull. Soc. Etud. sci. & arch. Draguignan **1891**:
16 (1891) - *FE* 3: 113.
Cr (W, C) - *MAP 99*
Open ground; 50-500m.
Mainly W. Crete [Mediterranean region].

2. M. incrassata Guss., *Fl. sicul. syn.* **1**: 214
(1843) - *FE* 3: 112.
Cr (W, C, E) Kp - *MAP 100*
Calcareous rocky places; 500-2100m.
Mainly W. & C. Crete; Karpathos [mainly S.E
Europe].

3. M. ramosissima Rochel in Schult., *Oestr. Fl.*
ed.2, 1: 366 (1814) - *FE* 3: 112.
Cr (W, C) ?Ks Kp - *MAP 101*

Calcareous rocky places & screes, flat clayey areas; 200-1050m.
W. & C. Crete; ?Kasos, Karpathos [most of Europe].
Both subsp. *ramosissima* and subsp. *gracillima* (Loscos & Pardo) Greuter & Burdet have been recorded from Crete (Barclay, 1986: 11), although the latter is treated as doubtfully distinct in *M-Ch* 1: 98, and is not separated here.

4. M. refracta Boiss., *Voy. bot. Espagne* 2: 433 (1841) - *FE* 3: 113.
Subsp. *aegagrophila* Greuter & Grau (*FE* 3: 113) is included in synonymy of subsp. **b**, after *MFG* 2: 51.
a. subsp. **paucipilosa** Grau in *Mitt. bot. StSamml. Münch.* 7: 90 (1968) - *FE* 3: 113.
Cr (W) - *MAP 102*
1250-1350m.
W. Crete (Lefka Ori) [Greece; otherwise E. Aegean Islands (Samos) & S. Turkey].
b. subsp. **refracta** (including subsp. *aegagrophila* Greuter & Grau - *FE* 3: 113).
Cr (W, C, E) - *MAP 103*
Calcareous rocky places, wet ground in cave; 1400-2100m.
Crete (Lefka Ori, Psiloritis & Dikti) [mainly S. Spain & E. Mediterranean region].

●**5. M. solange** Greuter & Zaffran in *Willdenowia* 11: 38 (1981).
Cr (W) - *MAP 104*
N.-facing mountain slope; 2100m; fl. 7.
W. Crete (Lefka Ori) - Endemic.
Known only from a few square metres at the type locality. Related to *M. alpestris* F.W.Schmidt, from the mountains of C. Europe.

M. stricta Link ex Roem. & Schult. (*FE* 3: 113) was almost certainly recorded in error (Greuter, 1974: 159).

12. Neatostema I.M.Johnst.

1. N. apulum (L.) I.M.Johnst. in *J. Arnold Arbor.* 34: 6 (1953) - *FE* 3: 86.
Cr (W, C, E) Kp - *MAP 105*
Open phrygana, sandy & rocky places, screes, bare ground; 0-550m; fl. 4-5.
Crete (sporadic, coastal); Karpathos [S. Europe].

13. Onosma L.

1. O. erectum Sm., *Fl. Graec. prodr.* 1: 121 (1806) - *FE* 3: 94.
a. subsp. **erectum**
Cr (W, C, E) - *MAP 106*

Calcareous cliffs, ledges, rocky places, stony *Cupressus* woodland; 200-1800m; fl. 4-5.
Mainly W. Crete [S. Greece; otherwise E. Aegean Islands (Samos)].

O. frutescens Lam. (*FE* 3: 91) was almost certainly recorded in error (Greuter, 1974: 159).

2. O. graecum Boiss., *Diagn. pl. orient.* ser.1, **11**: 106 (1849) - *FE* 3: 91.
Cr (W, C, E) - *MAP 107*
Soil-pockets in calcareous rocks, fine rocky debris; 0-850m; fl. 4-5.
Mainly W. & E. Crete [S. Greece & S. Aegean region; otherwise E. Aegean Islands & W. Turkey].

14. Paracaryum (DC.) Boiss.

1. P. lithospermifolium (Lam.) Grande in *Boll. Orto bot., Napoli* 4: 183 (1914) - *FE* 3: 121 as *Mattiastrum lithospermifolium* (Lam.) Brand.
a. subsp. **cariense** (Boiss.) R.R.Mill in *Notes R. bot. Gdn Edinb.* 35: 307 (1977) - not cited in *FE*.
Cr (W) - *MAP 108*
Calcareous rocky slopes, crevices, screes & rubble; 1550-2350m; fl. 6-7.
W. Crete (Lefka Ori) [Turkey].

Procopiania cretica (Willd.) Guşul. (*FE* 3: 105) = **Symphytum 1**.

P. insulare Pawł. (*FE* 3: 106) = **Symphytum 2**.

15. Symphytum L.

1. S. creticum (Willd.) Runemark ex Greuter & Rech.f. in *Boissiera* 13: 100 (1967) - *FE* 3: 105 as *Procopiania cretica* (Willd.) Guşul.
Cr (W, C, E) - *MAP 109*
Calcareous cliffs, ledges & fine debris below, shady rocky places; 0-800m; fl. 3-5.
Mainly W. & E. Crete [Ionian Islands (Zakinthos), S. Peloponnisos & Kithira].

2. S. insulare (Pawł.) Greuter & Burdet in *Willdenowia* 11: 39 (1981) - *FE* 3: 106 as *Procopiania insulare* Pawł.
Ks Kp Sa - *MAP 110*
Calcareous cliffs & ledges, shady places among boulders; 50-450m; fl. 4.
Karpathos group [Kiklades].

CACTACEAE

1. Opuntia Mill.

[1. O. ficus-barbarica] A.Berger, *Monatsschr. Kakteenk.* 22: 181 (1912) - *FE* 2: 300 as "*O.*

ficus-indica".
Cr (W, C) Kp - *MAP 111*
Naturalized in waste areas, field-margins,
usually near buildings; 100-350m.
W. & C. Crete; Karpathos [Mediterranean
region; from tropical America].

"*O. ficus-indica*" (*FE* **2**: 300) = **1** (Greuter in
Greuter & Rechinger, 1967: 37-38).

[**2. O. vulgaris**] Mill., *Gard. Dict.* ed.8: no.1
(1768) - *FE* **2**: 299.
Cr - *NOT MAPPED*
Naturalized.
Crete [S.C. & S. Europe; from N. America].

CALLITRICHACEAE

1. Callitriche L.

1. C. cophocarpa Sendtn., *Veg.-Verh. Südbay.*:
773 (1854) - *FE* **3**: 125.
Cr (W) - *MAP 112*
Fresh water.
W. Crete (Agia lake) [most of Europe].
Recorded since *FE* (Greuter, 1973a: 45).

2. C. pulchra Schotsman in Jovet, *Fl. France* **1**:
40 (1967) - *FE* **3**: 124.
Cr (W) - *MAP 113*
Marshy pools.
W. Crete (Gavdos island) [N.E. Libya].

C. truncata subsp. *occidentalis* (Rouy)
Schotsman (*FE* **3**: 124) is given for the Cretan
area in *M-Ch* **1**: 119, based on a distribution
map by Cook (1983: 551), on which the two
Cretan localities appear to correspond to those
of species **1** & **2** above. The possibility of an
error cannot be ruled out, especially since **2** is
given by Cook from Gavdos island in his text,
but wrongly mapped from a different part of
Crete (op. cit.: 550, 568).

CAMPANULACEAE

1. Asyneuma Griseb. & Schenk

1. A. giganteum (Boiss.) Bornm., *Beih. bot.
Zbl.* **38**(2): 341 (1921).
Kp - *MAP 114*
Crevices of W.-facing calcareous cliff; 1150m.
Karpathos (Kalilimni) [E. Aegean Islands (Halki
& Rodos)].
Recorded here as new to Karpathos, the Cretan
area, and Europe.

2. Campanula L.

1. C. aizoides Zaffran ex Greuter, *Fl. Rep.
Cretan Area*: 15 (1972) - *FE* **4**: 79 as *C. aizoon*

subsp. *aizoides* Fed.
Cr (W) - *MAP 115*
Calcareous cliffs & rock-crevices; 1800-2300m;
fl. 6-8.
W. Crete (Lefka Ori) [N. Peloponnisos
(Helmos)].

C. aizoon subsp. *aizoides* Fed. (*FE* **4**: 79) = **1**.

●**2. C. carpatha** Halácsy, *Consp. fl. graec.* **2**:
252 (1902) - *FE* **4**: 82.
?Ks Kp Sa - *MAP 116*
Shady cliffs & rock-crevices; 0-1200m; fl. 3-5.
?Kasos, Karpathos, Saria - Endemic.
[Plate 1.] Related to **10** & **15**.

●**3. C. cretica** (A.DC.) D.Dietr., *Syn. pl.* **1**:
758 (1839) - *FE* **4**: 93 as *Symphyandra cretica*
A.DC. subsp. *cretica*.
Cr (W) - *MAP 117*
Shady cliffs & steep rocky banks; 50-1700m; fl.
7-9.
W. Crete - Endemic.

●**4. C. creutzburgii** Greuter in *Boissiera* **13**:
133 (1967) - *FE* **4**: 88 as *C. drabifolia* subsp.
creutzburgii (Greuter) Fed.
Cr (W, C, E) - *MAP 118*
Calcareous rock-crevices in cliffs & phrygana;
0-100m; fl. 4.
Crete (sporadic, coastal) - Endemic.

5. C. delicatula Boiss., *Diagn. pl. orient.* ser.1,
11: 67 (1849) - *FE* **4**: 88.
Ks Kp Sa - *MAP 119*
Calcareous rocky places & crevices; fl. 3-4.
Karpathos group [E. Kiklades; otherwise S.W.
Asia].

C. drabifolia subsp. *creutzburgii* (Greuter) Fed.
(*FE* **4**: 88) = **4**.

C. drabifolia subsp. *pinatzii* (Greuter & Phitos)
Fed. (*FE* **4**: 88) = **11**.

6. C. erinus L., *Sp. pl.*: 169 (1753) - *FE* **4**: 88.
Cr (W, C, E) Ks Kp - *MAP 120*
Calcareous rocky places, old walls, fallow
fields; 0-600m; fl. 3-5.
Mainly W. Crete; Kasos, Karpathos [S.
Europe].

●**7. C. hierapetrae** Rech.f. in *Öst. bot. Z.* **84**:
170 (1935) - *FE* **4**: 84.
Cr (E) - *MAP 121*
Crevices of calcareous rock-faces; 1000-1450m;
fl. 7-8.
E. Crete (Afendis Kavousi) - Endemic.
[Plate 1.]

●**8. C. jacquinii** (Sieber) A.DC., *Monogr.
Campan.*: 251 (1830) - *FE* **4**: 95 as *Trachelium
jacquinii* (Sieber) Boiss. subsp. *jacquinii*.
Cr (W, C, E) - *MAP 122*

Calcareous cliffs; 1100-2200m; fl. 7-8.
Crete (Lefka Ori, Psiloritis, Kofinas & Dikti) -
Endemic.
Given in *FE* as occurring outside the Cretan area
(Athos, in N.E. Greece). However, these plants
belong to *C. chalcidica* (Buser) Phitos & Kamari
(Phitos & Kamari, 1988).

9. C. laciniata L., *Sp. pl.*: 165 (1753) - *FE* **4**:
82.
Cr (W, E) Kp - *MAP 123*
Calcareous cliffs; 0-550m; fl. 5.
W. & E. Crete (W. of Hora Sfakion & W. of
Sitia); Karpathos [Kiklades].

●**10. C. pelviformis** Lam., *Encycl.* **1**: 586
(1785) - *FE* **4**: 82.
Cr (E) - *MAP 124*
*Calcareous cliffs & stony slopes, thickets, steep
roadside banks; 0-950m; fl. 4-5.*
E. Crete - Endemic.

●**11. C. pinatzii** Greuter & Phitos in *Boissiera*
13: 134 (1967) - *FE* **4**: 88 as *C. drabifolia*
subsp. *pinatzii* (Greuter & Phitos) Fed.
Ks Kp Sa - *MAP 125*
Calcareous cliffs; 0-800m.
Karpathos group - Endemic.

12. C. saxatilis L., *Sp. pl.*: 167 (1753) - *FE* **4**:
82.
●**a.** subsp. **saxatilis**
Cr (W) - *MAP 126*
*Calcareous rock-crevices, cliffs & old walls; 0-
300m; fl. 4-5.*
W. Crete - Endemic.
C. saxatilis occurs outside the Cretan area only
in Kithira & Andikithira, as subsp. *cytherea*
Rech.f. & Phitos (*FE* **4**: 82).

13. C. spatulata Sm., *Fl. Graec. prodr.* **1**: 137
(1806) - *FE* **4**: 79.
●**a.** subsp. **filicaulis** (Halácsy) Phitos in *Verh.
zool.-bot. Ges. Wien.* **103-104**: 228 (1964) - *FE*
4: 80.
Cr (C, E) - *MAP 127*
*Phrygana, rocky places, screes, often growing
through dwarf spiny shrubs; 150-1600m; fl. 4-6.*
Mainly E. Crete - Endemic.
Much more widespread in Crete than stated by
Hartvig (in *MFG* **2**: 374). The same author also
erroneously records subsp. *spatulata* from
Crete, citing as a reference Greuter (1974: 141),
but the latter mentions only subsp. **a**. An
unconfirmed record from the E. Aegean Island
of Rodos (Damboldt in Davis, 1978: 64) is
referable to *Legousia pentagonia* (L.) Druce
(Carlström, 1987: 97).

14. C. trichocalycina Ten., *Cat. hort. neapol.,
App. prima*: 35 (1815) - *FE* **4**: 89.
Cr (W) - *MAP 128*

Calcareous cliffs; 1800-1850m.
W. Crete (Lefka Ori) [Italy, Sicily & Balkan
peninsula].

●**15. C. tubulosa** Lam., *Encycl.* **1**: 586 (1785)
- *FE* **4**: 82.
Cr (W, C) - *MAP 129*
*Crevices of rock-faces & cliffs, shady banks;
100-800m; fl. 4-5.* W. & C. Crete - Endemic.

"Laurentia gasparrinii" (*FE* **4**: 102) =
Solenopsis 1 (cf. Meikle, 1979).

3. Legousia Durande

1. L. falcata (Ten.) Janch. in *Mitt. naturw. Ver.
Univ. Wien* **5**: 100 (1907) - *FE* **4**: 94.
Cr Kp - *NOT MAPPED*
Crete; Karpathos [Mediterranean region].

2. L. hybrida (L.) Delarbre, *Fl. Auvergne* ed.2:
47 (1800) - *FE* **4**: 94.
Cr (W, C) Kp - *MAP 130*
*Fallow, cultivated & abandoned land; 200-
1400m; fl. 3-4.*
W. & C. Crete; Karpathos [mainly W. & S.
Europe].

3. L. pentagonia (L.) Druce, *List Brit. pl.*: 46
(1908) - *FE* **4**: 94.
Cr (W, C, E) Kp - *MAP 131*
*Calcareous rocky places, stony ground beneath
cliffs, olive terraces; 50-600m; fl. 4-5.*
Crete (sporadic); Karpathos [mainly E. Balkan
peninsula & Aegean region].

4. L. speculum-veneris (L.) Chaix, *Pl. Vap.*:
34 (1785) - *FE* **4**: 94.
Cr (W) Kp - *MAP 132*
*Calcareous open stony ground, screes; 1300m;
fl. 5.*
W. Crete; Karpathos [mainly S.C. & S.
Europe].

4. Petromarula Vent. ex R.Hedwig

●**1. P. pinnata** (L.) A.DC., *Monogr.
Campan.*: 209 (1830) - *FE* **4**: 95.
Cr (W, C, E) - *MAP 133*
*Calcareous cliffs & crevices, steep banks, rocky
& shady places, old stone walls; 0-1200m; fl. 4-
5.*
Crete (widespread) - Endemic.
The genus is monospecific.

5. Solenopsis C.Presl

1. S. minuta (L.) C.Presl, *Prodr. monogr.
Lobel.*: 32 (1836) - not cited in *FE*.

●**a.** subsp. **annua** Greuter, Matthäs & Risse in *Willdenowia* **14**: 30 (1984).
Cr (W, C) - *MAP 134*
Seasonally moist bare earth, shady ledges, rocks; 0-900m; fl. 4-5.
Mainly W. Crete - Endemic.
b. subsp. **minuta**
Cr (W, E) - *MAP 135*
450-1300m.
W. & E. Crete (S. of Rethimno, Dikti & Afendis Kavousi area) [?Spain, Sardinia].

Symphyandra cretica A.DC. subsp. *cretica* (*FE* **4**: 93) = **Campanula 3**.

Trachelium jacquinii (Sieber) Boiss. subsp. *jacquinii* (*FE* **4**: 95) = **Campanula 8**.

CAPPARACEAE

1. Capparis L.

C. orientalis Veill. (*M-Ch* **1**: 155; Barclay, 1986: 13) = **1a**.

C. ovata var. *canescens* (Coss.) Heywood (*FE* **1**: 259) = **1b** var **canescens**.

1. C. spinosa L., *Sp. pl.*: 503 (1753) - *FE* **1**: 259.
a. subsp. **rupestris** (Sm.) Nyman, *Consp. fl. eur.*: 68 (1878) - *FE* **1**: 259 as var. *inermis* (Turra) Zohary.
Cr (W, C, E) Ks Kp Sa - *MAP 136*
Calcareous cliffs, coastal rocks; 0-200m; fl. 4-5.
Crete (widespread, mainly coastal); Karpathos group [mainly Mediterranean region].
Subsp. *sicula* (Veill.) Holmboe (Barclay, 1986: 13) = subsp. **b** var. **canescens**.
b. subsp. **spinosa** var. **canescens** Coss., *Notes pl. crit.*: 28 (1849) - *FE* **1**: 259 as *C. ovata* var. *canescens* (Coss.) Heywood.
Cr (W, C, E) - *MAP 137*
Cultivated & disturbed ground, waste areas, among ancient ruins; 0-400m; fl. 6-9.
Crete (widespread) [Mediterranean region].

CAPRIFOLIACEAE

1. Lonicera L.

1. L. etrusca Santi, *Viagg. Montamiata*: 113 (1795) - *FE* **4**: 47.
Cr (W, C, E) Kp Sa - *MAP 138*
Woodland, scrub, cliffs, stone walls of terraces, rocky places; 300-1000m; fl. 5.
Mainly W. & E. Crete; Karpathos, Saria [S. Europe].

2. L. nummulariifolia Jaub. & Spach, *Ill. pl. orient.* **1**: 133 (1843) - *FE* **4**: 47.
a. subsp. **nummulariifolia**
Cr (W) - *MAP 139*
Calcareous rocky garigue, ravines, gorge-bed; 300-1200m; fl. 5.
W. Crete [S. Greece; otherwise S.W. Asia].

2. Sambucus L.

1. S. ebulus L., *Sp. pl.*: 269 (1753) - *FE* **4**: 44.
Cr (W) - *MAP 140*
Roadsides, scrub; 0-100m; fl. 7.
W. Crete [most of Europe].

S. nigra L. (*FE* **4**: 44) occurs in Crete as a casual (Rechinger, 1943a: 583; *M-Ch* **1**: 159); it is found near human habitation, as isolated bushes, and is perhaps a relic of cultivation.

3. Viburnum L.

1. V. lantana L., *Sp. pl.*: 268 (1753) - *FE* **4**: 45.
Cr - *NOT MAPPED*
Crete [mainly C. & S. Europe].

2. V. tinus L., *Sp. pl.*: 267 (1753) - *FE* **4**: 45.
Cr (E) - *MAP 141*
Roadside scrub; 30m.
E. Crete [S. Europe].
Regarded as absent from the Cretan area in *FE*, although previously recorded by Rechinger (1943a: 583). Considered doubtfully native in *M-Ch* **1**: 159, where it is given as the species sensu lato, although only subsp. *tinus* is shown to occur in the Mediterranean region.

CARYOPHYLLACEAE

1. Agrostemma L.

1. A. githago L., *Sp. pl.*: 435 (1753) - *FE* **1**: 157.
Cr (W, C) - *MAP 142*
Cultivated & fallow fields; 0-500m; fl. 4-5.
W. & C. Crete [almost throughout Europe].

2. Arenaria L.

1. A. cretica Spreng., *Syst. veg.* **2**: 396 (1825) - *FE* **1**: 121.
Cr (W) - *MAP 143*
Calcareous rocks & screes; 1700-2200m; fl. 6.
W. Crete (Lefka Ori) [Albania, S. Bulgaria & Greece].

"*A. deflexa*" (*FE* **1**: 121) = **3** (*Atlas FE* **6**: 24).

2. A. filicaulis Fenzl in Griseb., *Spic. fl. rumel.*
1: 203 (1843) - *FE* 1: 120.
a. subsp. **graeca** (Boiss.) McNeill in *Notes R.*
bot. Gdn Edinb. **24**: 270 (1963) - *FE* 1: 120.
Cr (W) - *MAP 144*
Calcareous cliffs; 1700-1850m.
W. Crete (Lefka Ori) [?S. Bulgaria, Greece;
otherwise W. Turkey].
Recorded since *FE* (Zaffran, 1976: 22).

●**3. A. fragillima** Rech.f. in *Reprium Spec.*
nov. Regni veg. **47**: 49 (1939) - *FE* 1: 121.
Cr (W, C, E) Ks Kp - *MAP 145*
Calcareous cliffs & rock-crevices; 200-2000m;
fl. 5-7.
Crete (Lefka Ori, Psiloritis, Kofinas, Dikti &
Afendis Kavousi); Kasos, Karpathos - Endemic.
A record from the S.E. Kikladean island of
Sirna (*Atlas FE* **6**: 24) is erroneous according to
Carlström (1986a: 369).

4. A. guicciardii Boiss., *Diagn. pl. orient.*
ser.2, **5**: 60 (1856) - *FE* 1: 122.
Cr (W, C, E) - *MAP 146*
Rocky slopes, flat areas in calcareous screes;
600-1700m.
Crete (Lefka Ori, Kofinas & Afendis Kavousi
area) [S. Greece; otherwise E. Aegean Islands
(Samos & Rodos)].
Recorded since *FE* (Greuter, 1973a: 31).

A. leptoclados (Rchb.) Guss. (*FE* 1: 121) = **7b**.

5. A. muralis (Link) Sieber ex Spreng., *Syst.*
veg. **2**: 397 (1825) - *FE* 1: 122.
Cr (W, C, E) Kp - *MAP 147*
Calcareous cliffs, shady rocks, stony Cupressus
woodland; 50-1150m.
Crete (widespread); Karpathos [Aegean region].

6. A. saponarioides Boiss. & Balansa in Boiss.,
Diagn. pl. orient. ser.2, **6**: 35 (1859) - *FE* 1:
122.
Cr (W, C, E) - *MAP 148*
Calcareous rocky slopes, screes, dry stream-
beds; 1500-2200m; fl. 5-7.
Crete (Lefka Ori, Psiloritis & Dikti) [S.W.
Turkey & Cyprus].
The distinctions between subsp. *saponarioides*
(from Turkey) and subsp. *boissieri* (Pax)
McNeill (from Crete & Cyprus; *FE* 1: 122) are
considered obscure and are not recognized here
(cf. Meikle, 1977: 265).

7. A. serpyllifolia L., *Sp. pl.*: 423 (1753) - *FE*
1: 121.
a. subsp. **aegaea** (Rech.f.) Akeroyd in *Bot. J.*
Linn. Soc. **97**: 337 (1988) - *FE* 1: 121, included
in synonymy of *A. leptoclados* (Rchb.) Guss.
Cr (E) Ks Kp - *MAP 149*
Rocky & stony places near sea, usually on
offshore islets.

E. Crete; Kasos, Karpathos [Kiklades; otherwise
E. Aegean Islands (Halki)].
b. subsp. **leptoclados** (Rchb.) Nyman, *Consp.*
fl. eur.: 115 (1878) - *FE* 1: 121 as *A.*
leptoclados (Rchb.) Guss.
Cr (W, C, E) Ks Kp - *MAP 150*
Calcareous rocky places & screes, sandy places,
waste areas; 0-1400m; fl. 4.
Mainly W. & E. Crete; Kasos, Karpathos [W.,
C. & S. Europe].
c. subsp. **serpyllifolia**
Cr (W, C, E) - *MAP 151*
Calcareous rocky places & screes, mountain
pastures; 600-2200m.
Crete (Lefka Ori, Psiloritis & Dikti) [almost
throughout Europe].

3. Bolanthus (Ser.) Rchb.

●**1. B. creutzburgii** Greuter in *Candollea* **20**:
210 (1965).
Cr (W, C) - *MAP 152*
Calcareous screes, rocky places; 1700-2000m.
W. & C. Crete (Lefka Ori & Psiloritis) -
Endemic.
A record from maritime sands E. of Paleohora
in W. Crete (Zaffran, 1976: 40; 1990: 105)
seems unlikely because of its low altitude; it
requires confirmation.

4. Bufonia L.

1. B. stricta (Sm.) Gürke in K.Richt., *Pl. eur.*
2: 247 (1899) - *FE* 1: 133.
●**a.** subsp. **cecconiana** (Bald.) Rech.f. in *Öst.*
bot. Z. **94**: 159 (1947) - not cited in *FE*.
Cr (C, E) - *MAP 153*
Rocky places, crevices & screes; 1700-2450m;
fl. 6-7.
C. & E. Crete (Psiloritis & Dikti) - Endemic.
b. subsp. **stricta**
Cr (W, E) - *MAP 154*
Stony Cupressus woodland, rocky places,
crevices & screes; 600-2350m; fl. 6-7.
W. & E. Crete (Lefka Ori, Dikti & Afendis
Kavousi area) [S. Greece].

5. Cerastium L.

1. C. brachypetalum Pers., *Syn. pl.* 1: 520
(1805) - *FE* 1: 143.
Cr (W, C, E) Kp - *MAP 155*
●**a.** subsp. **doerfleri** (Halácsy ex Hayek)
P.D.Sell & Whitehead in *Feddes Reprium Spec.*
nov. veg. **69**: 18 (1964) - *FE* 1: 143.
Cr (C) - *MAP 156*

Summit area of mountain; 1700m.
C. Crete (Kedros) - Endemic.
b. subsp. **roeseri** (Boiss. & Heldr.) Nyman,
Consp. fl. eur.: 109 (1878) - *FE* **1**: 144.
Cr (W, C, E) - *MAP 157*
*Calcareous rocky places, flat clayey areas,
mountain pastures; 1050-2100m.*
Crete (Lefka Ori, Psiloritis & Dikti) [S.
Europe].
The species sensu lato occurs also in Karpathos
(Lastos plain E. of Kalilimni).

2. C. comatum Desv. in *J. Bot. Agric. Pharm.
Med. Arts Paris* **3**: 228 (1816) - *FE* **1**: 142 as *C.
illyricum* subsp. *comatum* (Desv.) P.D.Sell &
Whitehead.
Cr (W, C, E) Kp - *MAP 158*
*Calcareous open rocky slopes, soil-patches
among rocks; 0-1700m; fl. 3-5.*
Mainly W. & C. Crete; Karpathos [?Spain,
Corsica & Aegean region].

3. C. dichotomum L., *Sp. pl.*: 438 (1753) - *FE*
1: 138.
Cr (E) - *MAP 159*
Cultivated ground; 1100m.
E. Crete (Katharo plain in Dikti) [Spain & S.
Greece].
Recorded since *FE* (Greuter et al., 1984a: 31).

C. fontanum Baumg. (*FE* **1**: 142) is not known
to occur (*Atlas FE* **6**: 104).

4. C. glomeratum Thuill., *Fl. env. Paris* ed.2:
226 (1800) - *FE* **1**: 144.
Cr (W, C) Kp - *MAP 160*
*Flat clayey areas, fallow fields, bare &
disturbed ground; 0-1050m; fl. 3-4.*
W. & C. Crete; Karpathos [almost throughout
Europe].

C. illyricum subsp. *comatum* (Desv.) P.D.Sell &
Whitehead (*FE* **1**: 142) = **2**.

C. ligusticum Viv. (*FE* **1**: 144) was recorded in
error (Greuter, 1974: 155).

C. pumilum subsp. *litigiosum* (Lens) P.D.Sell &
Whitehead (*FE* **1**: 145) was recorded in error
(Greuter, 1974: 155).

●**5. C. scaposum** Boiss. & Heldr. in Boiss.,
Diagn. pl. orient. ser.1, **8**: 104 (1849) - *FE* **1**:
143.
Cr (W, C, E) - *MAP 161*
*Open calcareous woodland, soil-patches in
garigue, rocky places, screes; 200-1900m; fl. 3-
5.*
Crete (Rodopos & Akrotiri peninsulas, Lefka
Ori, Psiloritis & Afendis Kavousi) - Endemic.

6. C. semidecandrum L., *Sp. pl.*: 438 (1753) -
FE **1**: 144.
Cr (W, E) Kp - *NOT MAPPED*
W. & E. Crete; Karpathos [almost throughout
Europe].
The species is divided in *M-Ch* **1**: 183, with *C.
balearicum* F.Herm. and *C. pentandrum* L.
given for the Cretan area, but not *C.
semidecandrum* sensu stricto.

6. Corrigiola L.

1. C. litoralis L., *Sp. pl.*: 271 (1753) - *FE* **1**:
149.
a. subsp. **litoralis**
Cr (W) - *MAP 162*
*Flat clayey areas in dolines, periodically
waterlogged; 700-1050m; fl. -10.*
W. Crete (Omalos & Askifos plains in Lefka
Ori) [W., C. & S. Europe].

7. Dianthus L.

"*D. arboreus*" (*FE* **1**: 201) = **2** (Runemark,
1980).

1. D. cinnamomeus Sm., *Fl. Graec. prodr.* **1**:
287 (1809) - *FE* **1**: 199.
Ks Kp - *MAP 163*
Calcareous rocks & screes.
Kasos, Karpathos [Kiklades; otherwise S.
Turkey].
Recorded since *FE* (Greuter, 1971c: 53; *Atlas
FE* **7**: 187).

2. D. fruticosus L., *Sp. pl.*: 413 (1753) - *FE* **1**:
201.
a. subsp. **amorginus** Runemark in *Bot. Notiser*
133: 485 (1980).
Cr (E) - *MAP 164*
Calcareous cliffs.
E. Crete (Dionisiades islands) [Kiklades].
●**b.** subsp. **carpathus** Runemark in *Bot.
Notiser* **133**: 487 (1980).
Ks Kp Sa - *MAP 165*
Calcareous cliffs; 0-800m.
Karpathos group - Endemic.
●**c.** subsp. **creticus** (Tausch.) Runemark in *Bot.
Notiser* **133**: 488 (1980) - not cited in *FE*.
Cr (W, C, E) - *MAP 166*
Calcareous cliffs; 0-400m; fl. 6-11.
Crete (sporadic) - Endemic.
d. subsp. **occidentalis** Runemark in *Bot. Notiser*
133: 483 (1980).
Cr (W, C) - *MAP 167*
Calcareous cliffs; -175m; fl. -10.
W. & C. Crete (near Kastelli Kissamou &
Paximadia islands) [Ionian Islands (Kefallinia),
S. Peloponnisos, Idra & Kithira].

●e. subsp. **sitiacus** Runemark in *Bot. Notiser* **133**: 488 (1980).
Cr (E) - *MAP 168*
Calcareous cliffs; 0-300m.
E. Crete - Endemic.
All five subspecies occur mainly on coastal cliffs.

●**3. D. juniperinus** Sm. in *Trans. Linn. Soc. Lond.* **2**: 303 (1794) - *FE* **1**: 201.
a. subsp. **aciphyllus** (Sieber ex Ser.) Turland in *Bull. Br. Mus. nat. Hist. (Bot.)* **22**: 168 (1992) - *FE* **1**: 201, included in synonymy of **3**.
Cr (E) - *MAP 169*
Calcareous cliffs; 800-1700m; fl. 6-7.
E. Crete (Dikti) - Endemic.
b. subsp. **bauhinorum** (Greuter) Turland in *Bull. Br. Mus. nat. Hist. (Bot.)* **22**: 168 (1992).
Cr (C) - *MAP 170*
Calcareous cliffs; 600-800m, fl. 6-8.
C. Crete - Endemic.
Described since *FE*, as *D. aciphyllus* var. *bauhinorum* Greuter (Greuter, 1965: 190).
c. subsp. **heldreichii** Greuter in *Candollea* **20**: 187 (1965).
Cr (W) - *MAP 171*
Calcareous cliffs; 600-650m; fl. 6-7.
W. Crete - Endemic.
Additionally recorded from W./C. Crete in *Atlas FE* **7**: 199.
d. subsp. **idaeus** Turland in *Bull. Br. Mus. nat. Hist. (Bot.)* **22**: 168 (1992).
Cr (C) - *MAP 172*
Calcareous cliffs; 600m; fl. 6-7.
C. Crete (S. edge of Psiloritis) - Endemic.
e. subsp. **juniperinus**
Cr (W) - *MAP 173*
Calcareous cliffs; 1100-1750m; fl. 6-8.
W. Crete (Lefka Ori) - Endemic.
f. subsp. **kavusicus** Turland in *Bull. Br. Mus. nat. Hist. (Bot.)* **22**: 168 (1992).
Cr (E) - *MAP 174*
Calcareous cliffs; 900m; fl. -9.
E. Crete (Afendis Kavousi area) - Endemic.
g. subsp. **pulviniformis** (Greuter) Turland in *Bull. Br. Mus. nat. Hist. (Bot.)* **22**: 166 (1992).
Cr (C) - *MAP 175*
Calcareous cliffs; 600-1300m; fl. 7-8.
C. Crete (Kedros) - Endemic.
Described since *FE*, as *D. pulviniformis* Greuter (Greuter, 1965: 189).

D. monadelphus Vent. is given for the Cretan area in *M-Ch* **1**: 198, although there appear to be no records as a basis for its inclusion.

●**4. D. sphacioticus** Boiss. & Heldr. in Boiss., *Diagn. pl. orient.* ser.1, **8**: 70 (1849) - *FE* **1**: 199.
Cr (W) - *MAP 176*

Calcareous rock-crevices, screes & gravel; 1700-2400m; fl. 7-8.
W. Crete (Lefka Ori) - Endemic.

5. D. strictus Banks & Sol. in Russell, *Nat. hist. Aleppo* ed.2, **2**: 252 (1794) - *FE* **1**: 200.
a. subsp. **multipunctatus** (Ser.) Greuter & Burdet in *Willdenowia* **12**: 187 (1982) - *FE* **1**: 200, included in synonymy of **5**.
Cr (W) - *NOT MAPPED*
W. Crete [S.W. Asia].

6. D. tripunctatus Sm., *Fl. Graec. prodr.* **1**: 286 (1809) - *FE* **1**: 200.
Cr (W, C, E) Kp - *MAP 177*
Sandy cultivated ground.
Crete (sporadic); Karpathos [Mediterranean region].

●**7. D. xylorrhizus** Boiss. & Heldr. in Boiss., *Diagn. pl. orient.* ser.1, **8**: 67 (1849) - *FE* **1**: 195.
Cr (W) - *MAP 178*
Calcareous cliffs & rock-crevices; 300-700m; fl. 4-5.
W. Crete (near Kastelli Kissamou) - Endemic.
[Plate 1.] Records from Kasos are referable to **1** (Greuter, 1971c: 53).

8. Gypsophila L.

1. G. nana Bory & Chaub., *Nouv. fl. Pélop.*: 26 (1838) - *FE* **1**: 182.
Cr (W, C) - *MAP 179*
Calcareous rock-crevices, rubble, screes; 1500-2300m; fl. 6-8.
W. & C. Crete (Lefka Ori & Kedros) [S. Greece].

9. Herniaria L.

1. H. cinerea DC. in Lam. & DC., *Fl. franç.* ed.3, **5**: 375 (1815) - *FE* **1**: 152.
Cr (W, C, E) Ks Kp Sa - *MAP 180*
Seashores, abandoned terraces; 0-600m.
Crete (sporadic); Karpathos group [Mediterranean region].

2. H. hirsuta L., *Sp. pl.*: 218 (1753) - *FE* **1**: 152.
Cr (W, C, E) - *MAP 181*
Bare sandy ground near sea; fl. 3-5.
Crete (sporadic) [mainly C. & S. Europe].

3. H. parnassica Heldr. & Sart. ex Boiss., *Diagn. pl. orient.* ser.2, **1**: 95 (1854) - *FE* **1**: 151.
●**a.** subsp. **cretica** Chaudhri in *Meded. bot.*

Mus. Rijks-Univ. Utrecht **285**: 333 (1968).
Cr (W, C, E) - *MAP 182*
Calcareous rocky places, screes, flat clayey areas, fallow fields; 500-2300m.
Crete (Lefka Ori, Psiloritis, Kofinas, Dikti & Afendis Kavousi) - Endemic.

10. Holosteum L.

1. H. umbellatum L., *Sp. pl.*: 88 (1753) - *FE* **1**: 136.
a. subsp. **umbellatum**
Cr (W, C, E) Kp - *MAP 183*
Calcareous rocky places; 1200-2100m.
C. Crete (Lefka Ori, Kedros, Psiloritis & Dikti); Karpathos (Kalilimni) [mainly C., E. & S. Europe].

Lychnis flos-cuculi L. is given for the Cretan area in *FE* **1**: 156, although there are no records as a basis for this (Greuter, 1974: 139).

11. Minuartia L.

1. M. globulosa (Labill.) Schinz & Thell. in *Bull. Herb. Boissier* ser.2, **7**: 403 (1907) - *FE* **1**: 128.
Cr (E) - *MAP 184*
Sandy coastal areas.
E. Crete (W. of Ierapetra) [W. & S. Balkan peninsula].

2. M. hybrida (Vill.) Schischk. in Kom., *Fl. URSS* **6**: 488 (1936) - *FE* **1**: 127.
a. subsp. **hybrida**
Cr (W, C, E) Ks Kp - *MAP 185*
Calcareous rocky places; 0-1900m.
Crete (sporadic); Kasos, Karpathos [mainly W. & S. Europe].
"Subsp. *lydia*" (*FE* **1**: 127) = **4a** (Greuter, 1973a: 31; *Atlas FE* **6**: 40).

3. M. mediterranea (Link) K.Malý in *Glasn. zemalj. Mus. Bosni Herceg.* **20**: 363 (1908) - *FE* **1**: 127.
Cr (W, E) Kp - *MAP 186*
Calcareous rocky places, screes.
W. & E. Crete; Karpathos [mainly Mediterranean region].

4. M. mesogitana (Boiss.) Hand.-Mazz. in *Annln naturh. Mus. Wien* **26**: 148 (1912) - *FE* **1**: 127.
a. subsp. **kotschyana** (Boiss.) McNeill in *Notes R. bot. Gdn Edinb.* **28**: 19 (1967) - not cited in *FE*.
Cr (W, C, E) - *MAP 187*
Calcareous screes; 1000-1200m.
Crete (sporadic) [?Ukraine, ?Bulgaria, S.

Greece & Kiklades; otherwise E. Aegean Islands & Turkey].
Recorded by Greuter (1973a: 31).

M. thymifolia (Sm.) Bornm. (*FE* **1**: 127) was almost certainly recorded in error (Greuter, 1974: 155).

5. M. verna (L.) Hiern in *J. Bot., Lond.* **37**: 320 (1899) - *FE* **1**: 130.
a. subsp. **attica** (Boiss. & Spruner) Graebn. in Asch. & Graebn., *Syn. mitteleur. Fl.* **5(1)**: 745 (1918) - *FE* **1**: 131. (Including subsp. *idaea* (Halácsy) Hayek - *FE* **1**: 131.)
Cr (W, C, E) - *MAP 188*
Open rocky areas, rubble, screes; 1700-2400m; fl. 6.
Crete (Lefka Ori, Psiloritis & Dikti) [Italy, Balkan peninsula & Aegean region].
"Subsp. *verna*" (*FE* **1**: 131) = subsp. **a** (Greuter, 1974: 155).

●**6. M. wettsteinii** Mattf. in *Bot. Jb.* **57** *Beibl.* 127: 62 (1922) - *FE* **1**: 131.
Cr (E) - *MAP 189*
Crevices of calcareous rock-faces; 1100-1400m; fl. 5.
E. Crete (Afendis Kavousi) - Endemic.

Moehringia trinervia (L.) Clairv. is given for the Cretan area in *FE* **1**: 124, although there are no records as a basis for this (Greuter, 1974: 139).

12. Moenchia Ehrh.

1. M. graeca Boiss. & Heldr. in Boiss., *Diagn. pl. orient.* ser.2, **1**: 91 (1854) - *FE* **1**: 145.
Cr (W, C) Kp - *MAP 190*
Flat clayey areas, fallow fields; 700-1700m; fl. 3-4.
W. & C. Crete (Lefka Ori & Kedros); Karpathos [W. & S. Balkan peninsula & Aegean region].

M. mantica (L.) Bartl. (*FE* **1**: 146) was almost certainly recorded in error (Greuter, 1974: 155).

Myosoton aquaticum (L.) Moench (*FE* **1**: 146) was almost certainly recorded in error (Greuter, 1974: 155).

13. Paronychia Mill.

1. P. argentea Lam., *Fl. franç.* **3**: 230 (1779) - *FE* **1**: 150.
Kp - *MAP 191*
Open ground near sea.
Karpathos [S. Europe].

"*P. capitata*" (*FE* **1**: 150) = **3** (Greuter, 1965: 176).

2. P. echinulata Chater in *Feddes Reprium Spec. nov. veg.* **69**: 52 (1964) - *FE* **1**: 150.
Cr (W) - *MAP 192*
Coastal rocks.
W. Crete (Korikos & Akrotiri peninsulas) [S. Europe].

"*P. kapela* subsp. *chionaea*" (*FE* **1**: 150) = **3** (Greuter, 1965: 176).

3. P. macrosepala Boiss., *Diagn. pl. orient.* ser.1, **3**: 11 (1843) - *FE* **1**: 150.
Cr (W, C, E) Ks Kp Sa - *MAP 193*
Rocky places, screes, maritime sands & rocks, flat clayey areas; 0-2400m.
Crete (widespread); Karpathos group [Greece & Aegean region].

14. Petrorhagia (Ser. ex DC.) Link

●**1. P. candica** P.W.Ball & Heywood in *Bull. Br. Mus. nat. Hist. (Bot.)* **3**: 141 (1964) - *FE* **1**: 187.
Cr (W, C, E) - *MAP 194*
Phrygana, among stones; 200-1150m.
Crete (sporadic) - Endemic.

●**2. P. dianthoides** (Sm.) P.W.Ball & Heywood in *Bull. Br. Mus. nat. Hist. (Bot.)* **3**: 158 (1964) - *FE* **1**: 187.
Cr (W) - *MAP 195*
Cliffs.
W. Crete - Endemic.

P. glumacea (Chaub. & Bory) P.W.Ball & Heywood (*FE* **1**: 188) was recorded in error (Greuter, 1974: 155).

3. P. illyrica (Ard.) P.W.Ball & Heywood in *Bull. Br. Mus. nat. Hist. (Bot.)* **3**: 133 (1964) - *FE* **1**: 186.
a. subsp. **taygetea** (Boiss.) P.W.Ball & Heywood in *Bull. Br. Mus. nat. Hist. (Bot.)* **3**: 137 (1964) - *FE* **1**: 186.
Cr (W, E) - *MAP 196*
Stony Pinus brutia woodland, among calcareous rocks, crevices, screes, flat clayey areas; 300-1900m.
Crete (Lefka Ori, Dikti & Afendis Kavousi area) [Peloponnisos].
Additionally recorded from W./C. Crete in *Atlas FE* 7: 141. The species is erroneously given as doubtfully present in the Cretan area in *FE*, as "subsp. *illyrica*" (cf. Greuter, 1973a: 32-33).

4. P. velutina (Guss.) P.W.Ball & Heywood in *Bull. Br. Mus. nat. Hist. (Bot.)* **3**: 166 (1964) - *FE* **1**: 188.
Cr (W, C, E) Ks Kp - *MAP 197*

Olive groves, sandy & rocky places, fallow fields, disturbed ground; 0-1700m; fl. 3-5.
Mainly W. & C. Crete; Kasos, Karpathos [S. Europe].

15. Polycarpon Loefl. ex L.

P. alsinifolium (Biv.) DC. (*FE* **1**: 153) is included in synonymy of **1**.

P. diphyllum Cav. (*FE* **1**: 153) is included in synonymy of **1**.

1. P. tetraphyllum (L.) L., *Syst. nat.* ed.10, **2**: 881 (1759) - *FE* **1**: 153. (Including *P. alsinifolium* (Biv.) DC. and *P. diphyllum* Cav. - both *FE* **1**: 153.)
Cr (W, C, E) Ks Kp Sa - *MAP 198*
Seashores & sandy places, bare ground, fallow fields; 0-300m; fl. 3-4.
Crete (widespread, coastal); Karpathos group [mainly S. Europe].

16. Sagina L.

1. S. apetala Ard., *Animadv. bot. spec. Alt.* **2**: 22 (1764) - *FE* **1**: 147.
Cr (W, E) Ks Kp - *MAP 199*
Bare damp ground, flat clayey areas, vineyards; 0-1050m; fl. 3-4.
W. & E. Crete; Kasos, Karpathos [most of Europe].
Additionally recorded from W./C. Crete in *Atlas FE* 6: 128.

2. S. maritima Don, *Herb. Brit.* fasc.7: 155 (1810) - *FE* **1**: 148.
Cr (W, C, E) Ks Kp - *MAP 200*
Damp bare & saline ground, maritime rocky places, pavements and wall-tops near sea; fl. 3-4.
Crete (sporadic, coastal); Kasos, Karpathos [coasts of most of Europe].

? **S. procumbens** L., *Sp. pl.*: 128 (1753) - *FE* **1**: 147.
Doubtfully present in Crete (Greuter, 1974: 155) [throughout Europe].

17. Saponaria L.

1. S. calabrica Guss., *Index sem. hort. boccad.* **1825**: 10 (1825) - *FE* **1**: 185.
Cr (W) - *NOT MAPPED*
W. Crete [C. & E. Mediterranean region].
Additionally recorded from W./C. Crete in *Atlas FE* 7: 138.

2. S. glutinosa M.Bieb., *Fl. taur.-caucas* **1**: 322 (1808) - *FE* **1**: 185.
Cr (E) - *MAP 201*

Calcareous rocky places, phrygana; (900-)1200-2000m; fl. 5.
E. Crete (Dikti) [E. Spain & S.E. Europe].

S. officinalis L. is given for the Cretan area in *FE* 1: 185, although there are no records as a basis for this (Greuter, 1974: 139).

18. Scleranthus L.

"*S. annuus* subsp. *annuus*" (*FE* 1: 149) ?= **1** (Greuter, 1973a: 31).

S. annuus subsp. *verticillatus* (Tausch) Arcang. (*FE* 1: 149) = **1**.

1. S. verticillatus Tausch in *Flora, Jena* **12(1)** Ergänz.: 50 (1829) - *FE* 1: 149 as *S. annuus* subsp. *verticillatus* (Tausch) Arcang.
Cr (C) - *MAP 202*
Flat clayey areas in dolines; 1500m.
C. Crete (Psiloritis) [S.C. & S. Europe].

19. Silene L.

S. alba L. is given for the Cretan area in *FE* 1: 174, although there are no records as a basis for this (Greuter, 1974: 139).

●**1. S. ammophila** Boiss. & Heldr. in Boiss., *Diagn. pl. orient.* ser.1, **8**: 82 (1849) - *FE* 1: 180.
a. subsp. **ammophila**
Cr (E) - *MAP 203*
Maritime sands; fl. 3-5.
E. Crete (Gaidouronisi island & coast E. of Ierapetra) - Endemic.
[Plate 1.]
b. subsp. **carpathae** Chowdhuri in *Notes R. bot. Gdn Edinb.* **22**: 278 (1957) - *FE* 1: 180.
Ks Kp - *MAP 204*
Maritime sands; fl. 3-5.
Kasos (Armathia island), Karpathos - Endemic.
Recorded from Kasos since *FE* (*Atlas FE* **7**: 118; Raus, 1990: 25).

●**2. S. antri-jovis** Greuter & Burdet in *Willdenowia* **16**: 440 (1987).
Cr (C, E) - *MAP 205*
Calcareous cliffs, rock-crevices, rocky slopes, flat clayey areas; 950-2200m; fl. 6-7.
C. & E. Crete (Kedros, Psiloritis, Dikti & Afendis Kavousi area) - Endemic.
Formerly *S. fruticulosa* Sieber ex Otth, which is included in synonymy of *S. saxifraga* L. in *FE* 1: 171.

3. S. apetala Willd., *Sp. pl.*: **2(1)**: 703 (1799) - *FE* 1: 180.
Cr Kp - *NOT MAPPED*
Crete; Karpathos [S. Europe].
Recorded from W./C. Crete in *Atlas FE* **7**: 117.

4. S. behen L., *Sp. pl.*: 418 (1753) - *FE* 1: 177.
Cr (W, C, E) Ks Kp Sa - *MAP 206*
Olive groves, calcareous rocky places, maritime sands, bare & disturbed ground; 0-300m; fl. 4.
Crete (sporadic); Karpathos group [C. & E. Mediterranean region].

5. S. bellidifolia Juss. ex Jacq., *Hort. bot. vindob.* **2**: 44 (1777) - *FE* 1: 179.
Cr (W, C) - *MAP 207*
Olive groves, disturbed ground, waste areas; fl. 3-5.
W. & C. Crete [Mediterranean region].

6. S. cerastoides L., *Sp. pl.*: 417 (1753) - *FE* 1: 179.
Cr (W, E) Kp - *MAP 208*
Open rocky & sandy ground near sea; fl. 4.
W. & E. Crete; Karpathos [mainly W. Mediterranean region].
Recorded since *FE* (Greuter, 1973a: 33; Greuter et al., 1983a: 50).

7. S. colorata Poir., *Voy. Barbarie* **2**: 163 (1789) - *FE* 1: 180.
a. subsp. **colorata**
Cr (W, C, E) - *MAP 209*
Maritime sands, other sandy & disturbed ground, often in abundance; fl. 3-5.
Mainly W. Crete [S. Europe].

8. S. conica L., *Sp. pl.*: 418 (1753) - *FE* 1: 180 as *S. conica* L. subsp. *conica*.
Cr (E) - *NOT MAPPED*
E. Crete [mainly C. & S. Europe].

9. S. cretica L., *Sp. pl.*: 420 (1753) - *FE* 1: 176.
Cr (W, C, E) Kp - *MAP 210*
Olive groves, rocky & sandy places, disturbed ground; 0-1500m; fl. 4-5.
Mainly W. & C. Crete; Karpathos [mainly S. Europe].

10. S. dichotoma Ehrh., *Beitr. Naturk.* **7**: 143 (1792) - *FE* 1: 178.
a. subsp. **racemosa** (Otth) Graebn. & P.Graebn. in Asch. & Graebn., *Syn. mitteleur. Fl.* **5(2)**: 93 (1920) - *FE* 1: 178.
Cr (W, C, E) - *MAP 211*
Step-crevices of cliffs & steep banks, roadside gravel; 400-900m; fl. 4-5.
Mainly C. Crete [mainly N. Balkan peninsula & Kiklades].

S. dictaea Rech.f. (*FE* 1: 164) = **27a**.

11. S. discolor Sm., *Fl. Graec. prodr.* **1**: 292 (1809) - *FE* 1: 179.
Kp - *MAP 212*
Maritime sands; fl. 4.
Karpathos [Kiklades (Milos); otherwise S.W. Asia].

Recorded since *FE* (Greuter, 1974: 147).

12. S. fabaria (L.) Sm., *Fl. Graec. prodr.* **1**: 293 (1809) - *FE* **1**: 169.
Kp Sa - *MAP 213*
Calcareous coastal cliffs and rocks; 0-180m; fl. 5.
Karpathos (N. end), Saria [Aegean region].
Recorded since *FE* (Greuter & Raus, 1984: 46).

13. S. fruticosa L., *Sp. pl.*: 417 (1753) - *FE* **1**: 164.
Cr (W, C, E) Ks Kp Sa - *MAP 214*
Calcareous cliffs, steep rocky banks, often on coast; 0-300m; fl. 4-6.
Crete (sporadic); Karpathos group [C. & E. Mediterranean region].

S. fruticulosa Sieber ex Otth (Barclay, 1986: 18; and others) = **2**.

14. S. fuscata Link in Brot., *Fl. lusit.* **2**: 187 (1804) - *FE* **1**: 175.
Cr (C) - *MAP 215*
C. Crete (E. of Iraklio) [Mediterranean region].
Recorded since *FE* (Greuter, 1974: 147).

15. S. gallica L., *Sp. pl.*: 417 (1753) - *FE* **1**: 179.
Cr (W, C, E) Ks Kp - *MAP 216*
Olive groves, sandy & rocky places, disturbed ground, waste areas; 0-450m; fl. 3-5.
Mainly W. & C. Crete; Kasos, Karpathos [C. & S. Europe].

16. S. gigantea L., *Sp. pl.*: 418 (1753) - *FE* **1**: 164.
Cr (W, C, E) Kp - *MAP 217*
Cliffs, steep rocky & gravelly banks; 0-1050m; fl. 4-5.
Crete (widespread); Karpathos [Balkan peninsula & Aegean region].

17. S. holzmannii Heldr. ex Boiss., *Fl. orient., Suppl.*: 91 (1888) - *FE* **1**: 177.
Cr (E) Ks Kp - *MAP 218*
Restricted to offshore islets.
E. Crete (off E. coast of Sideros peninsula); Kasos, Karpathos [S. Aegean region].
[Plate 1.] Recorded since *FE* (Damboldt & Phitos, 1970; Greuter et al., 1983a: 51).
Vulnerable species, legally protected. For detailed ecological studies concerning *S. holzmannii* in the Cretan area see Greuter (1972a) and Höner & Greuter (1988).

●**18. S. insularis** Barbey in *Bull. Soc. vaud. Sci. nat.* ser.3, **21**: 220 (1886) - *FE* **1**: 176.
Kp - *MAP 219*
Calcareous rubble, clayey soil-patches in low sparse rocky phrygana; 800-1150m; fl. 4.
Karpathos (Kalilimni area) - Endemic.

19. S. integripetala Bory & Chaub. in Bory, *Exp. sci. Morée, Bot.*: 123 (1832) - *FE* **1**: 176.
●**a.** subsp. **greuteri** (Phitos) Akeroyd in *Bot. J. Linn. Soc.* **97**: 341 (1988).
Cr (W) - *MAP 220*
Calcareous gravel in ravines & below cliffs; 50-300m; fl. 3-5.
W. Crete - Endemic.
Described since *FE*, as *S. greuteri* Phitos (Phitos, 1982).

"*S. italica*" (*FE* **1**: 163) = **25** (Greuter, 1976: 206).

20. S. macrodonta Boiss., *Diagn. pl. orient.* ser.1, **1**: 37 (1843).
Kp - *MAP 221*
Karpathos [S.W. Asia].
Recorded since *FE* (Greuter, 1974: 147).

21. S. multicaulis Guss., *Pl. rar.*: 172, tab.35 (1826) - *FE* **1**: 171.
●**a.** subsp. **cretica** Melzh. in *Phyton, Horn* **21**: 132 (1981).
Cr (E) - *MAP 222*
Calcareous rocky slopes, crevices & screes in degraded woodland & mountain pastures, often sheltered by spiny plants; 1400-2150m; fl. 6-8.
E. Crete (Dikti) - Endemic.
Considered doubtfully distinct from **2** by Greuter et al. (1984a: 33).

S. noctiflora L. (*FE* **1**: 174) was almost certainly recorded in error (Greuter, 1974: 155).

22. S. nocturna L., *Sp. pl.*: 416 (1753) - *FE* **1**: 179 as *S. nocturna* L. subsp. *nocturna*.
Cr (W, C, E) Ks Kp Sa - *MAP 223*
Rocky places, disturbed ground; 0-350m; fl. 3-5.
Crete (sporadic); Karpathos group [Mediterranean region].

S. pendula L. (*FE* **1**: 177) was almost certainly recorded in error (Greuter, 1974: 155).

●**23. S. pinetorum** Boiss. & Heldr. in Boiss., *Diagn. pl. orient.* ser.1, **8**: 75 (1849) - *FE* **1**: 175.
Cr (W, E) - *MAP 224*
Stony Pinus brutia woodland, calcareous rubble, sandy places near coast; 0-800m.
W. & E. Crete (S. side) - Endemic.

S. rigidula Sm., non L. (*FE* **1**: 175) is not known to occur (Greuter & Raus, 1984: 49).

"*S. saxifraga*" (*FE* **1**: 171) = **2** (*Atlas FE* **7**: 73).

24. S. sedoides Poir., *Voy. Barbarie* **2**: 164 (1789) - *FE* **1**: 176.
Cr (W, C, E) Ks Kp Sa - *MAP 225*
Maritime sands & rocks; 0-50m; fl. 3-5.
Crete (widespread, coastal); Karpathos group

[Mediterranean region].

● **25. S. sieberi** Fenzl, *Pug. pl. nov. Syr.*: 8 (1842) - *FE* 1: 163.
Cr (W, C, E) - *MAP 226*
Rock-crevices & ledges, stony ground; 50-1900m; fl. 5-8.
Crete (widespread) - Endemic.

26. S. succulenta Forssk., *Fl. aegypt.-arab.*: lxvi & 89 (1775) - *FE* 1: 170.
a. subsp. **succulenta**
Cr (W, E) - *MAP 227*
Maritime sands on offshore islands; fl. 3-5.
W. & E. Crete (Elafonisi, Gavdos, Gaidouronisi & Koufonisi islands) [N. Africa & adjacent S.W. Asia].

27. S. thessalonica Boiss. & Heldr. in Boiss., *Diagn. pl. orient.* ser.2, 1: 74 (1854) - *FE* 1: 170.
● **a.** subsp. **dictaea** (Rech.f.) Melzh. in *Bot. Jb.* 98: 45 (1977) - *FE* 1: 164 as *S. dictaea* Rech.f.
Cr (E) - *MAP 228*
Among calcareous rocks & in crevices; 1700-2050m; fl. 7-8.
E. Crete (Dikti) - Endemic.
[Plate 1.]

S. trinervia Sebast. & Mauri (*FE* 1: 177) was almost certainly recorded in error (Greuter, 1974: 155), possibly for **6** (Greuter, 1973a: 33).

● **28. S. variegata** (Desf.) Boiss. & Heldr. in Boiss., *Diagn. pl. orient.* ser.1, 8: 82 (1849) - *FE* 1: 169.
Cr (W, C, E) - *MAP 229*
Calcareous mobile screes, sometimes on rocky slopes & ledges; 1400-2400m; fl. 6-8.
Crete (Lefka Ori, Psiloritis & Dikti) - Endemic. Given in *FE* as occurring outside the Cretan area, on the N. Aegean island of Samothraki. These plants have been called *S. caesia* subsp. *samothracica* (Rech.f.) Melzh. (= *S. variegata* var. *samothracica* Rech.f.), which occurs also on the E. Aegean island of Hios (*MFG* 1: 150).

29. S. vulgaris (Moench) Garcke, *Fl. N. Mitt.-Deutschland* ed.9: 64 (1869) - *FE* 1: 168.
a. subsp. **macrocarpa** Turrill in *Hooker's Icon. Pl.* 36: t.3551 (1956) - *FE* 1: 169.
Cr (W, C, E) Ks Kp Sa - *MAP 230*
Olive groves, phrygana, rocky places, cultivated and abandoned terraces, waste areas; 0-1800m; fl. 3-5.
Crete (widespread); Karpathos group [Mediterranean region].
Recorded since *FE* (Greuter et al., 1984a: 33)
b. subsp. **suffrutescens** Greuter, Matthäs & Risse in *Willdenowia* 14: 34 (1984).
Cr (W, C, E) - *MAP 231*
Calcareous cliffs; 50-1450m; fl. 4-5.

Crete (sporadic) [Peloponnisos].
Records of other subspecies are considered erroneous by Greuter et al. (1984a: 33).

20. Spergula L.

1. S. arvensis L., *Sp. pl.*: 440 (1753) - *FE* 1: 154.
Cr (W) - *MAP 232*
Flat clayey areas, fallow fields; 1050m.
W. Crete (Omalos plain in Lefka Ori) [throughout Europe].

21. Spergularia (Pers.) J. & C.Presl

1. S. bocconei (Scheele) Graebn. in Asch. & Graebn., *Syn. mitteleur. Fl.* 5(1): 849 (1919) - *FE* 1: 156.
Cr (W, C, E) Ks Kp - *MAP 233*
Maritime sands & rocks, saline ground; fl. 3-5.
Crete (sporadic); Kasos, Karpathos [S.W Europe & Mediterranean region].

2. S. diandra (Guss.) Boiss., *Fl. orient.* 1: 733 (1867) - *FE* 1: 155.
Cr (W, C, E) - *MAP 234*
Sandy places.
Crete (sporadic, coastal) [S. Europe].

3. S. lycia Monnier & Quézel in *Candollea* 25: 359 (1970).
Cr (W) - *MAP 235*
Flat clayey areas in dolines; 1500-1700m; fl. 8.
W. Crete (Lefka Ori) [S.W. Turkey].
Described from S.W. Turkey; recorded from Crete by Greuter (1973a: 30).

S. marina (L.) Griseb. (*FE* 1: 155) = **4**.

S. media (L.) C.Presl (*FE* 1: 155) was almost certainly recorded in error (Greuter, 1974: 155).

"*S. rubra*" (*FE* 1: 155) = **1** (Greuter, 1973a: 30; Barclay, 1986: 19).

4. S. salina J. & C.Presl, *Fl. cech.*: 95 (1819) - *FE* 1: 155 as *S. marina* (L.) Griseb.
Cr (W, C, E) Kp - *MAP 236*
Brackish coastal marshes, saline & sandy places.
Crete (sporadic); Karpathos [most of Europe].

22. Stellaria L.

1. S. cupaniana (Jord. & Fourr.) Bég. in *Nuovo G. Bot. ital.* ser.2, 15: 552 (1909) - *FE* 1: 134 as *S. media* subsp. *cupaniana* (Jord. & Fourr.) Nyman. (Including *S. media* subsp. *postii* Holmboe - *FE* 1: 134.)
Cr (W, C, E) - *MAP 237*

Olive groves, calcareous screes, mountain pastures, weed communities, disturbed ground; 0-1200m; fl. 3-5.
Mainly W. Crete [Mediterranean region].

2. S. media (L.) Vill., *Hist. pl. Dauphiné* **3**: 415 (1789) - *FE* **1**: 134 as *S. media* (L.) Vill. subsp. *media*.
Cr (W, C) Kp - *MAP 238*
Stony ground beneath cliffs, flat clayey areas, disturbed ground; 0-1050m; fl. 3-4.
Mainly W. Crete; Karpathos [throughout Europe].
Subsp. *cupaniana* (Jord. & Fourr.) Nyman (*FE* **1**: 134) = **1**.
Subsp. *postii* Holmboe (*FE* **1**: 134) is included in synonymy of **1**.

"*S. neglecta*" (Greuter, 1974: 140) = **1** (Barclay, 1986: 19).

3. S. pallida (Dumort) Piré in *Bull. Soc. r. Bot. Belg.* **2**: 49 (1863) - *FE* **1**: 134.
Cr (W, C, E) - *MAP 239*
Olive groves.
Crete (sporadic) [W., C. & S. Europe].
Additionally recorded from N. Karpathos or Saria in *Atlas FE* **6**: 74.

23. Telephium L.

1. T. imperati L., *Sp. pl.*: 271 (1753) - *FE* **1**: 156.
"Subsp. *orientale*" (*FE* **1**: 156) = subsp. **a** (Greuter, 1965: 179).
● **a.** subsp. **pauciflorum** (Greuter) Greuter & Burdet in *Willdenowia* **12**: 191 (1982).
Cr (W, C, E) - *MAP 240*
Calcareous rocky slopes, rubble, screes; 1200-2400m; fl. 5-7.
Crete (Lefka Ori, Kedros, Psiloritis, Dikti & Afendis Kavousi) - Endemic.
Described since *FE*, as *T. imperati* subsp. *orientale* var. *pauciflorum* Greuter (Greuter, 1965: 179).

24. Vaccaria Wolf

1. V. hispanica (Mill.) Rauschert in *Wiss. Z. Martin-Luther-Univ. Halle-Wittenb.* **14**: 496 (1965) - *FE* **1**: 186 as *V. pyramidata* Medik.
Cr (W, C, E) Kp - *NOT MAPPED*
a. subsp. **grandiflora** (Ser.) Holub in *Folia geobot. phytotax. bohemoslovaca* **11**: 83 (1976) - *FE* **1**: 186, included in synonymy of *V. pyramidata* Medik.
Crete; Karpathos.
b. subsp. **hispanica**
Crete.

The species sensu lato is distributed mainly in C. & S. Europe.

V. pyramidata Medik. (*FE* **1**: 186) = **1**.

25. Velezia L.

1. V. rigida L., *Sp. pl.*: 332 (1753) - *FE* **1**: 204.
Cr (W, C, E) Ks Kp Sa - *MAP 241*
Calcareous rocky places; 200-1500m; fl. 5-7.
Crete (sporadic); Karpathos group [S. Europe].

CERATOPHYLLACEAE

1. Ceratophyllum L.

1. C. demersum L., *Sp. pl.*: 992 (1753) - *FE* **1**: 206.
a. subsp. **demersum**
Cr (W) - *MAP 242*
Fresh water; 0-50m.
W. Crete [most of Europe].
Recorded since *FE* (Gradstein & Smittenberg, 1968).

CHENOPODIACEAE

1. Arthrocnemum Moq.

A. fruticosum (L.) Moq. (*FE* **1**: 101) = **Sarcocornia fruticosa**.

A. glaucum Ung.-Sternb. (*FE* **1**: 101) = **1**.

1. A. macrostachyum (Moric.) Moris, *Enum. sem. hort. taur.* **1854**: 35 (1854) - *FE* **1**: 101 as *A. glaucum* Ung.-Sternb.
Cr (W, C, E) Ks Kp - *MAP 243*
Maritime sands & rocks, mainly on offshore islets.
Crete (sporadic); Kasos, Karpathos [coasts of S. Europe].

A. perenne (Mill.) Moss (*FE* **1**: 101) = **Sarcocornia 1**.

2. Atriplex L.

1. A. halimus L., *Sp. pl.*: 1052 (1753) - *FE* **1**: 95.
Cr (W, C, E) Ks Kp - *MAP 244*
Maritime sands & rocky places, offshore islets, also planted for ornament.
Crete (sporadic); Kasos, Karpathos [S. Europe].

A. hortensis L. (*FE* **1**: 96) occurs in Crete as a casual.

2. A. patula L., *Sp. pl.*: 1053 (1753) - *FE* 1: 96.
Cr (W, C, E) - *MAP 245*
Coastal Juncus stands, damp sands & fields near sea, flat clayey areas, waste areas; 0-1750m.
Crete (sporadic) [almost throughout Europe].
Recorded since *FE* (*Atlas FE* 5: 42).

3. A. portulacoides L., *Sp. pl.*: 1053 (1753) - *FE* 1: 97 as *Halimione portulacoides* (L.) Aellen.
Cr (W, C, E) Ks Kp - *MAP 246*
Sandy saltmarshes, coastal saline ground.
Crete (sporadic); Kasos, Karpathos [mainly coasts of W. & S. Europe].
Regarded as absent from the Cretan area in *FE*, although old records existed; occurrence since confirmed (Greuter, 1973a: 29).

? A. prostrata Boucher ex DC. in Lam. & DC., *Fl. franç.* ed.3, 3: 387 (1805) - *FE* 1: 97 as "*A. hastata*".
Doubtfully present in Crete [almost throughout Europe].
Known only from a field observation made at Georgioupoli in W. Crete (Gradstein & Smittenberg, 1968, as "*A.* cf. *hastata*"), and requiring confirmation (Greuter et al., 1984a: 34).

4. A. recurva d'Urv. in *Mém. Soc. linn. Paris* 1: 284 (1822) - *FE* 1: 96, included in synonymy of *A. tatarica* L.
Cr (C, E) - *MAP 247*
Calcareous maritime rocks on offshore islets.
C. & E. Crete [Aegean region].
Erroneously regarded as absent from the Cretan area in *FE* (Greuter, 1974: 140). Additionally recorded from W./C. Crete in *Atlas FE* 5: 41.

5. A. rosea L., *Sp. pl.* ed.2: 1493 (1763) - *FE* 1: 96.
Cr (W, C, E) - *MAP 248*
Maritime rocks, vineyards, waste areas.
Crete (sporadic) [C. & S. Europe].

3. Bassia All.

[1. B. scoparia] (L.) A.J.Scott in *Feddes Reprium* 89: 108 (1978) - *FE* 1: 99 as *Kochia scoparia* (L.) Schrad.
Cr (W, C, E) - *MAP 249*
Cultivated for ornament and becoming naturalized on paths, roadsides, stream gravel, waste areas; 0-850m.
Mainly W. & C. Crete [C., E. & S. Europe; from temperate Asia].
Recorded since *FE* (Turland, 1992b: 160).

4. Beta L.

1. B. adanensis Aellen in *Notes R. bot. Gdn Edinb.* 28: 29 (1967).
Cr (E) Kp - *MAP 250*
Fallow fields near sea.
E. Crete (near Elounda); Karpathos [N.E. Greece (Tnraki); otherwise S.W. Asia].
Described from S. Turkey; recorded from the Cretan area in *Atlas FE* 5: 13, and by Greuter et al. (1984a: 34). Vulnerable species, legally protected.

2. B. macrocarpa Guss., *Fl. sicul. prodr.* 1: 302 (1827) - *FE* 1: 92.
Cr (E) Kp - *MAP 251*
Dry eroded slopes with loose soil; 50m.
E. Crete (Hersonisos); Karpathos [Mediterranean region].
Recorded since *FE* (Greuter, 1974: 146; Greuter et al., 1984a: 35).

3. B. vulgaris L., *Sp. pl.*: 222 (1753) - *FE* 1: 91.
a. subsp. **maritima** (L.) Arcang., *Comp. fl. ital.*: 593 (1882) - *FE* 1: 92.
Cr (W, C, E) Kp - *MAP 252*
Maritime sands & cliffs, disturbed ground on coast; fl. 3-4.
Crete (sporadic); Karpathos [coasts of W. & S. Europe].
Subsp. *vulgaris* is cultivated as a vegetable in both Crete and Karpathos and also occurs as a casual escape (Rechinger, 1943a: 119, b: 67; Greuter et al., 1983a: 51).

5. Chenopodium L.

1. C. album L., *Sp. pl.*: 219 (1753) - *FE* 1: 94 as *C. album* L. subsp. *album*.
Cr (W, C, E) Kp - *MAP 253*
Cultivated & disturbed ground, villages, animal enclosures, waste areas; 0-500m; fl. 4-6.
Crete (sporadic); Karpathos [almost throughout Europe].

[2. C. ambrosioides] L., *Sp. pl.*: 219 (1753) - *FE* 1: 93.
Cr (W) - *MAP 254*
Naturalized on roadsides & by streams.
W. Crete [C. & S. Europe; from tropical America].

[3. C. giganteum] D.Don, *Prodr. fl. nepal.*: 75 (1825) - *FE* 1: 95.
Cr (C, E) Kp - *MAP 255*
Cultivated as a vegetable and naturalized in fields, gardens, waste areas; 40-350m.
C. & E. Crete; Karpathos [Mediterranean region; from N. India].

Recorded since *FE* (*Atlas FE* **5**: 33; Greuter et al., 1983*a*: 51).

4. C. murale L., *Sp. pl.*: 219 (1753) - *FE* **1**: 94.
Cr (W, C, E) Ks Kp Sa - *MAP 256*
Ledges and caverns of cliffs, cultivated & disturbed ground, waste areas, villages, animal enclosures; 0-300m; fl. 4-6.
Crete (sporadic, coastal); Karpathos group [most of Europe].

5. C. opulifolium Schrad. in W.D.J.Koch & Ziz, *Cat. pl.*: 6 (1814) - *FE* **1**: 94.
Cr (W, C, E) - *MAP 257*
Fallow fields, waste areas.
Crete (sporadic) [most of Europe].

C. polyspermum L. (*FE* **1**: 94) was recorded in error (*Atlas FE* **5**: 24).

6. C. vulvaria L., *Sp. pl.*: 220 (1753) - *FE* **1**: 94.
Cr (W, C, E) - *MAP 258*
Cultivated & disturbed ground; 0-1050m.
Crete (sporadic) [most of Europe].

6. Noaea Moq.

1. N. mucronata (Forssk.) Asch. & Schweinf. in *Mém. Inst. égypt.* **2**: 131 (1887) - *FE* **1**: 107.
a. subsp. **mucronata**
Cr (W) Ks - *NOT MAPPED*
Maritime rocks.
W. Crete (Akrotiri peninsula); Kasos [Aegean region].
Regarded as absent from the Cretan area in *FE*, although collected from the Akrotiri peninsula nearly a century ago (Turland, 1992*b*: 160). Recorded from Kasos by Greuter (1974: 146).

7. Salicornia L.

1. S. europaea L., *Sp. pl.*: 3 (1753) - *FE* **1**: 102.
Cr (E) - *MAP 259*
Saltmarshes.
E. Crete [most of Europe].

8. Salsola L.

1. S. aegaea Rech.f. in *Denkschr. Akad. Wiss. Wien* **105(2,1)**: 67 (1943) - *FE* **1**: 106.
Cr (C, E) Ks Kp - *MAP 260*
Rock-crevices, offshore islets; 0-300m.
Mainly E. Crete; Kasos, Karpathos [Kiklades; otherwise E. Aegean Islands (Rodos & Halki)].

2. S. carpatha P.H.Davis in *Notes R. bot. Gdn Edinb.* **21**: 139 (1953) - *FE* **1**: 106.
Cr (E) Kp Sa - *MAP 261*

Calcareous cliffs, coastal rocks; 0-400m.
E. Crete; Karpathos, Saria [S.E. Kiklades].
Recorded from Crete since *FE* (Greuter, 1972*a*: 160; 1973*a*: 29). Given for Kasos & Karpathos, rather than Karpathos & Saria, by Greuter et al. (1983*a*: 51); this contradicts other records and is presumably a printing error.

3. S. kali L., *Sp. pl.*: 222 (1753) - *FE* **1**: 105.
a. subsp. **kali**
Cr (W, C, E) Ks Kp Sa - *MAP 262*
Maritime sands.
Crete (widespread); Karpathos group [coasts of most of Europe].

9. Sarcocornia A.J.Scott

? S. fruticosa (L.) A.J.Scott in *Bot. J. Linn. Soc.* **75**: 367 (1977) - *FE* **1**: 101 as *Arthrocnemum fruticosum* (L.) Moq.
Doubtfully present in Crete (Greuter, 1974: 155) [coasts of S. Europe].

1. S. perennis (Mill.) A.J.Scott in *Bot. J. Linn. Soc.* **75**: 367 (1977) - *FE* **1**: 101 as *Arthrocnemum perenne* (Mill.) Moss.
Cr (W, C, E) Kp - *MAP 263*
Saltmarshes & damp sand, saline ground.
Crete (sporadic); Karpathos [coasts of W. & S. Europe].

Spinacia oleracea L. (*FE* **1**: 95) has been recorded from Crete as a casual (Rechinger, 1943*a*: 120).

10. Suaeda Scop.

? S. maritima (L.) Dumort., *Fl. belg.*: 22 (1827) - *FE* **1**: 103.
Doubtfully present in Crete (Greuter, 1974: 155) [most of Europe].

1. S. vera J.F.Gmel., *Syst. nat.* ed.13, 2(1): 503 (1791) - *FE* **1**: 103.
Cr (W, C, E) Ks Kp - *MAP 264*
Maritime rocks, offshore islets, old walls, waste areas; 0-50m.
Crete (sporadic); Kasos, Karpathos [W. & S. Europe].

CISTACEAE

1. Cistus L.

1. C. creticus L., *Syst. nat.* ed.10: 1077 (1759) - *FE* **2**: 283 as *C. incanus* subsp. *creticus* (L.) Heywood.
Cr (W, C, E) Ks Kp - *MAP 265*
Light woodland, maquis, garigue, phrygana; 0-

1200m; fl. 3-5..
a. subsp. **creticus**
Crete [Mediterranean region].
b. subsp. **eriocephalus** (Viv.) Greuter & Burdet
in *Willdenowia* **11**: 275 (1981) - not cited in *FE*.
Crete [Mediterranean region].
The species sensu lato is widespread in Crete
and occurs also in Kasos & Karpathos.

C. incanus subsp. *creticus* (L.) Heywood (*FE* **2**:
283) = **1**.

2. C. monspeliensis L., *Sp. pl.*: 524 (1753) -
FE **2**: 283.
Cr (W, C, E) - *MAP 266*
Garigue; 0-100m; fl. 3-5.
Crete (sporadic) [S. Europe].

3. C. parviflorus Lam., *Encycl.* **2**: 14 (1786) -
FE **2**: 283.
Cr (W, C, E) Ks Kp - *MAP 267*
*Pinus brutia woodland, garigue, phrygana; 0-
400m; fl. 3-5.*
Mainly W. & E. Crete; Kasos, Karpathos
[Turkey-in-Europe; otherwise Libya, E. Aegean
Islands & Turkey; extinct in Sicily
(Lampedusa)].

4. C. salviifolius L., *Sp. pl.*: 524 (1753) - *FE* **2**:
284.
Cr (W, C, E) Kp - *MAP 268*
*Woodland, maquis, garigue, phrygana; 0-900m;
fl. 4-5.*
Crete (widespread); Karpathos [S. Europe].

2. Fumana (Dunal) Spach

1. F. arabica (L.) Spach in *Annls Sci. nat.* ser.2
(Bot.), **6**: 359 (1836) - *FE* **2**: 291.
Cr (W, C, E) Ks Kp - *MAP 269*
Maquis, garigue, phrygana; 0-600m; fl. 3-5.
Mainly W. & E. Crete; Kasos, Karpathos [S.
Europe].

"F. ericoides" (*FE* **2**: 291) = **3a** (Greuter,
1973a: 39).

2. F. laevipes (L.) Spach in *Annls Sci. nat.*
ser.2 (Bot.), **6**: 359 (1836) - *FE* **2**: 292.
Cr Kp - *NOT MAPPED*
Pinus brutia woodland; 50m; fl. 3-4.
Crete; Karpathos [Mediterranean region].

3. F. paphlagonica Bornm. & Janch. in *Öst.
bot. Z.* **58**: 439 (1908) - not cited in *FE*.
a. subsp. **alpina** (Janch.) Greuter, *Fl. Rep.
Cretan Area*: 26 (1972) - not cited in *FE*.
Cr (W) - *MAP 270*
Rock-hollows & crevices, screes; 1400-2100m.
W. Crete (Lefka Ori) [Greece].

"F. procumbens" (*FE* **2**: 291) = **3a** (Greuter,
1973a: 39).

? F. scoparia Pomel, *Mat. fl. atl.*: 10 (1860) -
FE **2**: 291.
Doubtfully present in Crete [Mediterranean
region].

4. F. thymifolia (L.) Spach ex Webb, *Iter
hispan.*: 69 (1838) - *FE* **2**: 292.
Cr (W, C, E) Ks Kp - *MAP 271*
*Garigue, phrygana, Lygeum steppe, rocky
places, gorge-beds, maritime sands & gravel; 0-
400m; fl. 3-5.*
Crete (widespread); Kasos, Karpathos
[Mediterranean region].

3. Helianthemum Mill.

1. H. aegyptiacum (L.) Mill., *Gard. Dict.*
ed.8: no.23 (1768) - *FE* **2**: 289.
Cr Kp - *NOT MAPPED*
Crete; Karpathos [Mediterranean region].

2. H. apenninum (L.) Mill., *Gard. Dict.* ed.8:
no.4 (1768) - *FE* **2**: 288.
?Cr Ks - *MAP 272*
Calcareous rocks, gorge.
?Crete; Kasos [W. & S. Europe].

3. H. hymettium Boiss. & Heldr. in Boiss.,
Diagn. pl. orient. ser.2, **1**: 52 (1854) - *FE* **2**:
290.
Cr (W, E) - *MAP 273*
Dry rocky places; -2000m.
W. & E. Crete (Lefka Ori & Afendis Kavousi)
[S. Greece].

"H. lavandulifoium" (*FE* **2**: 287) = **8** (*M-Ch* **1**:
328).

? H. ledifolium (L.) Mill., *Gard. Dict.* ed.8:
no.20 (1768) - *FE* **2**: 289.
Doubtfully present in Crete (Greuter, 1974: 156)
[S. Europe].

4. H. lippii (L.) Dum.Cours., *Bot. cult.* **3**: 130
(1802) - *FE* **2**: 289.
Cr (C) - *MAP 274*
C. Crete (S. of Timbaki) [S. Italy & Sicily;
otherwise N. Africa & adjacent S.W. Asia].
Recorded since *FE* (Greuter & Raus, 1981:
275).

"H. nummularium subsp. *tomentosum"* (*FE* **2**:
288) = **7** (Rechinger, 1943b: 80; Greuter,
1973a: 38).

5. H. salicifolium (L.) Mill., *Gard. Dict.* ed.8:
no.21 (1768) - *FE* **2**: 289.
Cr (W, C, E) Ks Kp - *MAP 275*
*Garigue, phrygana, rocky places; 0-1350m; fl.
3-4.*

Crete (sporadic); Kasos, Karpathos [S. Europe].

6. H. sanguineum (Lag.) Lag. ex Dunal in DC., *Prodr.* **1**: 273 (1824) - *FE* **2**: 289.
Cr - *NOT MAPPED*
Crete [Portugal & Spain; otherwise Morocco & Algeria; extinct in Italy].

7. H. stipulatum (Forssk.) C.Chr. in *Dansk bot. Ark.* **4(3)**: 20 (1922) - *FE* **2**: 289.
Cr (E) - *MAP 276*
Maritime sands.
E. Crete (Gaidouronisi & Koufonisi islands) [N.W. Peloponnisos; otherwise N. Africa & S.W. Asia].
Regarded as absent from the Cretan area in *FE*, although previously recorded by Rechinger (1943*b*: 80 as *H. ellipticum* (Desf.) Pers.); cf. Greuter (1973*a*: 38).

8. H. syriacum (Jacq.) Dum.Cours., *Bot. cult.* **3**: 129 (1802) - *FE* **2**: 287 as "*H. lavandulifolium*".
a. subsp. syriacum
Cr - *NOT MAPPED*
Crete [Greece; otherwise S.W. Asia].

4. Tuberaria (Dunal) Spach

1. T. guttata (L.) Fourr. in *Annls Soc. linn. Lyon* nov. ser., **16**: 340 (1868) - *FE* **2**: 286.
Cr (W, E) Ks Kp - *MAP 277*
Bare soil-patches in sparse phrygana, open rocky places; 0-600m; fl. 3-4.
Mainly W. Crete; Kasos, Karpathos [W. & S. Europe].
Most Cretan material belongs to *T. lipopetala* (Murb.) Greuter & Burdet, which includes cleistogamous plants lacking petals (Greuter et al., 1984*a*: 35). However, this taxon is treated as doubtfully distinct from *T. guttata* in *M-Ch* **1**: 330, and is not separated here.

COMPOSITAE
(ASTERACEAE)

1. Achillea L.

1. A. cretica L., *Sp. pl.*: 899 (1753) - *FE* **4**: 165.
Cr (W, C) Kp Sa - *MAP 278*
Calcareous cliffs, rarely phrygana & offshore islets; 0-550m; fl. 4-5.
W. & C. Crete; Karpathos, Saria [Aegean region; otherwise S.W. Asia].

2. A. ligustica All., *Auct. syn. stirp. horti taur.*: 17 (1773) - *FE* **4**: 164.
Cr - *NOT MAPPED*
Crete [Mediterranean region].

2. Aetheorhiza Cass.

1. A. bulbosa (L.) Cass. in *Dict. Sci. nat.* **48**: 426 (1827) - *FE* **4**: 326.
a. subsp. microcephala Rech.f. in *Phyton, Horn* **16**: 217 (1974) - *FE* **4**: 327.
Cr (W, C, E) Ks Kp Sa - *MAP 279*
Rock-crevices, screes, phrygana, earthy banks, coastal saline ground; 0-700m; fl. 3-5.
Crete (widespread); Karpathos group [Aegean region; otherwise S.W. Asia].

3. Ambrosia L.

1. A. maritima L., *Sp. pl.*: 988 (1753) - *FE* **4**: 142.
Cr - *NOT MAPPED*
Crete [Mediterranean region].

4. Anthemis L.

●**1. A. abrotanifolia** (Willd.) Guss., *Fl. sicul. syn.* **2**: 490 (1844) - *FE* **4**: 150.
Cr (C, E) - *MAP 280*
Calcareous rocks & screes, open stony ground, flat clayey areas; 500-2300m; fl. 6-7.
C. & E. Crete (Psiloritis, Dikti & Afendis Kavousi area) - Endemic.
Additionally recorded from the Lefka Ori in W. Crete in *MFG* **2**: 427.

2. A. altissima L., *Sp. pl.*: 893 (1753) - *FE* **4**: 157.
Cr (E) Kp - *MAP 281*
Vineyards; 800m.
E. Crete; Karpathos [S. Europe].

3. A. ammanthus Greuter in *Candollea* **23**: 145 (1968) - *FE* **4**: 158.
a. subsp. ammanthus
Cr (E) Ks Kp Sa - *MAP 282*
Open rocky ground near sea, offshore islets.
E. Crete (Sideros peninsula, Dionisiades & Elasa islands); Karpathos group [S.E. Kiklades].
●**b. subsp. paleacea** Greuter in *Candollea* **23**: 146 (1968) - *FE* **4**: 158.
Cr (E) Kp - *MAP 283*
Open rocky ground near sea, offshore islets; 0-200m.
E. Crete; Karpathos - Endemic.

4. A. arvensis L., *Sp. pl.*: 894 (1753) - *FE* **4**: 153.
Cr (W) Ks Kp - *MAP 284*
Fallow fields; -1050m.
W. Crete (Omalos plain in Lefka Ori); Kasos, Karpathos [almost throughout Europe].
Subsp. *incrassata* (Loisel.) Nyman (*FE* **4**: 153) was recorded from the Omalos plain by

Rechinger (1943*b*: 142); other records cannot be referred to a particular subspecies with any certainty, however, and the species is not divided here.

5. A. chia L., *Sp. pl.*: 894 (1753) - *FE* **4**: 155.
Cr (W, C, E) Kp Sa - *MAP 285*
Cupressus woodland, rocky places & ledges, screes, phrygana, fallow fields, gardens; 0-1200m; fl. 3-5.
Mainly W. Crete; Karpathos, Saria [C. & E. Mediterranean region].

6. A. cotula L., *Sp. pl.*: 894 (1753) - *FE* **4**: 155.
Cr (W) - *MAP 286*
Fallow fields.
W. Crete (W. of Hania) [almost throughout Europe].

●**7. A. filicaulis** (Boiss. & Heldr.) Greuter in *Candollea* **23**: 148 (1968) - *FE* **4**: 158.
Cr (E) - *MAP 287*
Calcareous rocky places near sea; 0-100m.
E. Crete (Sideros peninsula) - Endemic.

●**8. A. glaberrima** (Rech.f.) Greuter in *Candollea* **23**: 148 (1968) - *FE* **4**: 159.
Cr (W) - *MAP 288*
Maritime rocks; fl. 4-5.
W. Crete (Agria Gramvousa island) - Endemic. [Plate 2.] Described from Agria Gramvousa island, not the nearby Gramvousa island as given in *FE*. Endangered species, legally protected.

9. A. melanolepis Boiss., *Fl. orient., Suppl.*: 297 (1888) - *FE* **4**: 158 as *A. syriaca* Bornm.
Cr (W) - *MAP 289*
W. Crete [?Greece; otherwise S.W. Asia].

10. A. pseudocotula Boiss., *Diagn. pl. orient.* ser.1, **6**: 86 (1845) - *FE* **4**: 155.
Kp - *MAP 290*
Karpathos [Turkey-in-Europe; otherwise Libya, Sinai & S.W. Asia].
Doubtful occurrence confirmed since *FE* (Greuter et al., 1983*a*: 52).

11. A. rigida (Sm.) Boiss. ex Heldr. in *Herb. graec. norm.* no.503 (1856) [?*c*. 1857] - *FE* **4**: 154.
a. subsp. liguliflora (Halácsy) Greuter in *Candollea* **23**: 263 (1968) - *FE* **4**: 154, included in synonymy of **11**.
Kp - *MAP 291*
Bare ground in abandoned field near sea; fl. 3-4.
Karpathos [also recorded from Kithira].
b. subsp. rigida
Cr (W, C, E) Ks Kp - *MAP 292*

Open rocky & sandy places, screes, flat clayey areas, maritime sands, fallow fields; 0-2200m; fl. 4-5.
Crete (widespread); Kasos, Karpathos [Greece & Aegean region; otherwise S.W. Asia].

12. A. scopulorum Rech.f. in *Öst. bot. Z.* **85**: 61 (1936) - *FE* **4**: 154.
Kp - *MAP 293*
Karpathos (offshore islets) [Kiklades; otherwise E. Aegean Islands].
Given as absent from the Cretan area in *FE*, although previously recorded by Greuter (1974: 150).

A. syriaca Bornm. (*FE* **4**: 158) = **9**.

●**13. A. tomentella** Greuter in *Candollea* **23**: 148 (1968) - *FE* **4**: 158.
Cr (E) - *MAP 294*
Calcareous rocky places & screes; 50-1200m.
E. Crete - Endemic.

Arctium L.

? A. lappa L., *Sp. pl.*: 816 (1753) - *FE* **4**: 215.
Doubtfully present in Crete [almost throughout Europe].

Arctotheca calendula (L.) Levyns (*FE* **4**: 208) has been recorded as a casual from near Kastelli Kissamou in W. Crete (Greuter & Raus, 1989: 28).

5. Artemisia L.

1. A. arborescens L., *Sp. pl.* ed.2: 1188 (1763) - *FE* **4**: 180.
Cr (W, C) Kp - *MAP 295*
Dry garigue, grassy banks, often near villages; 0-350m.
W. & C. Crete; Karpathos [Mediterranean region].

2. A. herba-alba Asso, *Syn. Stirp. Aragon.*: 117 (1779) - *FE* **4**: 185.
Cr (W) - *MAP 296*
Soft limestone in clearing of Pinus brutia woodland.
W. Crete (Gavdos island) [Spain & S.W. France; otherwise N. Africa & S.W. Asia].
Recorded since *FE* (Greuter et al., 1984*b*: 271).

6. Aster L.

1. A. creticus (Gand.) Rech.f. in *Phyton, Horn* **1**: 211 (1949) - *FE* **4**: 116.
Cr (E) Kp Sa - *MAP 297*
Calcareous cliffs; 0-800m; fl. -10.
E. Crete; Karpathos, Saria [E. Aegean Islands

(Rodos) & S.W. Turkey (Marmaris peninsula)].
Not endemic to the Cretan area as given in *FE*
(cf. Carlström, 1987: 88, 208).

[2. A. squamatus] (Spreng.) Hieron. in *Bot. Jb.*
29: 19 (1900) - *FE* **4**: 115.
Cr (W, C) - *MAP 298*
*Naturalized in roadside weed communities; fl.
10-11.*
W. & C. Crete [Mediterranean region; from C.
& S. America].

3. A. tripolium L., *Sp. pl.*: 872 (1753) - *FE* **4**:
115.
Cr (W) - *MAP 299*
Brackish marshes near sea; fl. 4, 11.
W. Crete (Georgioupoli) [most of Europe].

7. Asteriscus Tourn. ex Mill.

A. aquaticus (L.) Less. (*FE* **4**: 139) =
Bubonium 1.

1. A. spinosus (L.) Sch.Bip. in Webb &
Berthel., *Hist. nat. Iles Canaries* **2**: 230 (1844) -
FE **4**: 139 as *Pallenis spinosa* (L.) Cass.
(Including subsp. *microcephala* (Halácsy)
Rech.f. - *FE* **4**: 139.)
Cr (W, C, E) Ks Kp Sa - *MAP 300*
*Olive groves, open phrygana, rocky & sandy
places; 0-700m; fl. 4-5.*
Crete (widespread); Karpathos group [Aegean
region].

8. Atractylis L.

1. A. cancellata L., *Sp. pl.*: 830 (1753) - *FE* **4**:
211.
a. subsp. cancellata
Cr (W, C, E) Ks Kp Sa - *MAP 301*
*Calcareous rocky places, phrygana, seashores,
abandoned terraces; 0-350m; fl. 5.*
Crete (widespread, mainly coastal); Karpathos
group [Mediterranean region].

2. A. gummifera L., *Sp. pl.*: 829 (1753) - *FE*
4: 211.
Cr (W, C, E) Kp - *MAP 302*
*Phrygana, fallow & abandoned land; 0-600m;
fl. 9-11.*
Crete (sporadic); Karpathos [Mediterranean
region].

9. Bellis L.

1. B. annua L., *Sp. pl.*: 887 (1753) - *FE* **4**:
111.
a. subsp. annua
Cr (W, C) Ks Kp - *MAP 303*
Flat clayey areas in dolines, bare soil, coastal

*saline ground, often if damp or periodically
waterlogged; 0-1050m; fl. 2-4.*
Mainly W. Crete; Kasos, Karpathos
[Mediterranean region].

●**2. B. longifolia** Boiss. & Heldr. in Boiss.,
Diagn. pl. orient. ser.1, **11**: 1 (1849) - *FE* **4**:
112.
Cr (W, C, E) Kp - *MAP 304*
*Sheltered soil-pockets in calcareous rock, damp
places by springs, flat clayey areas in dolines;
1300-1900m; fl. 4-7.*
Crete (Lefka Ori, Psiloritis & Dikti); Karpathos
- Endemic.
Recorded from Karpathos since *FE* (Greuter et
al., 1983*a*: 52).

3. B. perennis L., *Sp. pl.*: 886 (1753) - *FE* **4**:
111.
Cr (W, C) - *MAP 305*
*Bare or sparsely vegetated ground; -1400m; fl.
3-4.*
W. & C. Crete [almost throughout Europe].

4. B. sylvestris Cirillo, *Pl. rar. neapol.* **2**: 22
(1792) - *FE* **4**: 112.
Cr (W, C, E) Kp - *MAP 306*
Scrub, phrygana; 0-700m; fl. 10, 3-4.
Mainly W. Crete; Karpathos [S. Europe].

10. Bellium L.

1. B. minutum (L.) L., *Mant. pl. alt.*: 286
(1771) - *FE* **4**: 112.
Cr (W, C, E) Ks Kp Sa - *MAP 307*
*Crevices & hollows in calcareous rock, usually
on coast; 0-100m; fl. 3-4.*
Mainly W. & E. Crete; Karpathos group [C. &
E. Mediterranean region].

Bombycilaena (DC.) Smoljan.

? **B. erecta** (L.) Smoljan. in *Bot. Mater. Gerb.
glavn. bot. Sada* **17**: 450 (1955) - *FE* **4**: 125.
Doubtfully present in Crete [C. & S. Europe].

11. Bubonium Hill

1. B. aquaticum (L.) Hill, *Veg. syst.* **2**: 147
(1761) - *FE* **4**: 139 as *Asteriscus aquaticus* (L.)
Less.
Cr (W, C, E) Ks Kp - *MAP 308*
*Calcareous rocky places, maritime sands; 0-
450m; fl. 5-6.*
Crete (sporadic, coastal); Kasos, Karpathos
[Mediterranean region].

12. Calendula L.

1. C. arvensis L., *Sp. pl.* ed.2: 1303 (1763) - *FE* **4**: 207.
Cr (W, C, E) Ks Kp - *MAP 309*
Open stony ground, screes, maritime sands; 0-700m; fl. 2-5, 9-11.
Crete (widespread); Kasos, Karpathos [S.C. & S. Europe].

13. Cardopatium Juss.

1. C. corymbosum (L.) Pers., *Syn. pl.* **2**: 500 (1807) - *FE* **4**: 212.
Cr (C) - *MAP 310*
C. Crete [E. Mediterranean region].

14. Carduncellus Adans.

1. C. caeruleus (L.) C.Presl, *Fl. sicul.*: xxx (1826) - *FE* **4**: 304.
Cr (W, C, E) Ks Kp - *MAP 311*
Calcareous rocky places, fallow fields; 0-550m; fl. 3-5.
Crete (sporadic); Kasos, Karpathos [Mediterranean region].

15. Carduus L.

1. C. argentatus L., *Mant. pl. alt.*: 280 (1771) - *FE* **4**: 230.
Cr (W, C, E) Ks Kp Sa - *MAP 312*
Step-crevices of rocks, beneath cliffs, gorge-beds; 0-750m; fl. 3-5.
Crete (sporadic); Karpathos group [N. Aegean region (Samothraki); otherwise S.W. Asia].

2. C. pycnocephalus L., *Sp. pl.* ed.2: 1151 (1763) - *FE* **4**: 231.
Cr (W, C, E) Ks Kp - *MAP 313*
Olive groves, fallow fields, rocky places, disturbed ground, roadsides, waste areas; 0-750m; fl. 3-5.
Mainly W. & C. Crete; Kasos, Karpathos [S.E. & S. Europe].

16. Carlina L.

●**1. C. barnebiana** B.L.Burtt & P.H.Davis in *Kew Bull.* **4**: 103 (1949) - *FE* **4**: 210.
Cr (E) Kp - *MAP 314*
Schistose rocks near sea.
E. Crete (E. of Sitia); Karpathos - Endemic.
Recorded from Karpathos since *FE* (Greuter et al., 1983a: 52).

2. C. corymbosa L., *Sp. pl.*: 828 [1231] (1753) - *FE* **4**: 209.

●**a.** subsp. **curetum** (Heldr. ex Halácsy) Rech.f. in *Denkschr. Akad. Wiss. Wien* **105(1)**: 644 (1943) - *FE* **4**: 209.
Cr (W, C, E) - *MAP 315*
Calcareous garigue, phrygana & rocky places, flat clayey areas; 300-2000m; fl. 8.
Crete (Lefka Ori, Psiloritis, Dikti & Afendis Kavousi) - Endemic.
Records from Karpathos are referable to subsp. **b** (Greuter et al., 1983a: 52).

b. subsp. **graeca** (Boiss.) Nyman, *Consp. fl. eur.*: 400 (1879) - *FE* **4**: 209.
Cr (W, C, E) Ks Kp Sa - *MAP 316*
Calcareous phrygana & rocky places; 0-1200m; fl. 8-10.
Crete (widespread); Karpathos group [Balkan peninsula & Aegean region].

●**3. C. diae** (Rech.f.) Meusel & Kästner in *Feddes Reprium* **83**: 228 (1972) - *FE* **4**: 209.
Cr (C, E) - *MAP 317*
Calcareous cliffs near sea; 0-150m; fl. 6-7.
C. & E. Crete (Dia island, Sideros peninsula & Dionisiades islands) - Endemic.
[Plate 2.] Vulnerable species, legally protected.

4. C. lanata L., *Sp. pl.*: 828 (1753) - *FE* **4**: 211.
Cr (W, C, E) Kp - *MAP 318*
Gorges, open rocky ground, fallow fields.
Crete (sporadic); Karpathos [Mediterranean region].

●**5. C. sitiensis** Rech.f. in *Reprium Spec. nov. Regni veg.* **43**: 147 (1938) - *FE* **4**: 209.
Cr (E) Ks - *MAP 319*
Calcareous open stony ground near sea; fl. 8.
E. Crete (Sideros peninsula); Kasos (offshore islets) - Endemic.
[Plate 2.] Recorded from Kasos since *FE* (Raus, 1990: 26). Related and similar to **2**.

6. C. tragacanthifolia Klatt in *Leopoldina* **20**: 94 (1884) - *FE* **4**: 209.
Ks Kp Sa - *MAP 320*
Phrygana, coastal rocks; 0-1200m; fl. 7.
Karpathos group [S.E. Kiklades (Sirna); otherwise E. Aegean Islands & S.W. Turkey (Marmaris peninsula)].

17. Carthamus L.

1. C. boissieri Halácsy in *Verh. zool.-bot. Ges. Wien* **49**: 186 (1899) - *FE* **4**: 302.
Cr (W) Kp - *MAP 321*
W. Crete; Karpathos [S. Aegean region; otherwise E. Aegean Islands (Simi & Rodos) & Cyprus].

2. C. dentatus (Forssk.) Vahl, *Symb. bot.* **1**: 69 (1790) - *FE* **4**: 302.

a. subsp. **ruber** (Link) Hanelt in *Feddes Reprium Spec. nov. veg.* **67**: 98 (1963) - *FE* **4**: 302.
Cr (W, C, E) - *MAP 322*
Calcareous rocky places, fallow fields; 0-900m.
Crete (sporadic) [S. Greece & Aegean region].

3. C. lanatus L., *Sp. pl.*: 830 (1753) - *FE* **4**: 303.
a. subsp. **baeticus** (Boiss. & Reut.) Nyman, *Consp.*: 419 (1879) - *FE* **4**: 303.
Cr (W, C, E) Kp - *MAP 323*
Calcareous rocky places; 0-700m; fl. 5-6.
Crete (sporadic); Karpathos [Mediterranean region].

4. C. leucocaulos Sm., *Fl. Graec. prodr.* **2**: 160 (1813) - *FE* **4**: 302.
Cr (C, E) Kp Sa - *MAP 324*
Field-margins, rubble; -700m.
C. & E. Crete; Karpathos, Saria [S. Greece & Aegean region].

●**5. C. rechingeri** P.H.Davis in *Notes R. bot. Gdn Edinb.* **21**: 128 (1953) - *FE* **4**: 303.
Kp - *MAP 325*
Calcareous rocks, phrygana; fl. 7.
Karpathos - Endemic.
Perhaps the hybrid **1** x **4** (Greuter, 1974: 150).

18. Catananche L.

1. C. lutea L., *Sp. pl.*: 812 (1753) - *FE* **4**: 305.
a. subsp. **lutea**
Cr Kp - *NOT MAPPED*
Crete; Karpathos [Mediterranean region].

19. Centaurea L.

1. C. aegialophila Wagenitz in *Notes R. bot. Gdn Edinb.* **33**: 230 (1974) - *FE* **4**: 269.
Cr (E) Ks Kp - *MAP 326*
Maritime sands; fl. 3-5.
E. Crete; Kasos, Karpathos [S. Turkey & Cyprus].

2. C. argentea L., *Sp. pl.*: 912 (1753) - *FE* **4**: 271.
Cr (W, C, E) - *MAP 327*
Calcareous cliffs; 0-1800m; fl. 4-5.
Crete (sporadic) [S. Peloponnisos & Kithira].
Very variable in habit, leaf shape and phyllary appendages. Part of this polymorphism was recognized by Rechinger, who described two varieties (1943*b*: 151), but further study is required.

●**3. C. baldaccii** Degen ex Halácsy in *Bull. Herb. Boissier* **6**: 582 (1898) - *FE* **4**: 298.
Cr (W) - *MAP 328*

Calcareous mountain pastures & rocky outcrops; 1900-2100m; fl. 7.
W. Crete (Lefka Ori) - Endemic.
[Plate 3.]

4. C. calcitrapa L., *Sp. pl.*: 917 (1753) - *FE* **4**: 282.
a. subsp. **calcitrapa**
Cr (W, C, E) Kp - *MAP 329*
Waste places, disturbed ground; 50-400m; fl. 5-6.
Mainly W. & C. Crete; Karpathos [W., C. & S. Europe].

C. crocodylium L. was probably recorded in error (*FE* **4**: 263).

5. C. hyalolepis Boiss., *Diagn. pl. orient.* ser.1, **6**: 133 (1845) - *FE* **4**: 282.
Cr - *NOT MAPPED*
Crete [S.E. Greece; otherwise S.W. Asia].

●**6. C. idaea** Boiss. & Heldr. in Boiss., *Diagn. pl. orient.* ser.1, **10**: 119 (1849) - *FE* **4**: 284.
Cr (W, C, E) - *MAP 330*
Rock-crevices, phrygana, stony ground, flat clayey areas; 100-2200m; fl. 4-8.
Crete (widespread) - Endemic.

●**7. C. lancifolia** Sieber ex Spreng., *Syst. veg.* ed.16, **3**: 406 (1826) - *FE* **4**: 301 as *Wagenitzia lancifolia* (Sieber ex Spreng.) Dostál.
Cr (W) - *MAP 331*
Calcareous cliffs; 1800-1850m.
W. Crete (Lefka Ori) - Endemic.
[Plate 3.] Vulnerable species, legally protected.

8. C. melitensis L., *Sp. pl.*: 917 (1753) - *FE* **4**: 285.
Cr (E) Kp - *MAP 332*
Lygeum steppe.
E. Crete (near Ierapetra); Karpathos [S. Europe].
Given as doubtfully present in Crete by Barclay (1986: 27), but occurrence confirmed by Zaffran (1976: 183; 1990: 329).

C. napifolia L. (*FE* **4**: 284) was probably recorded in error (Rechinger, 1943*a*: 669).

●**9. C. poculatoris** Greuter in *Bauhinia* **3**: 252 (1967) - *FE* **4**: 275.
Cr (W) - *MAP 333*
Calcareous cliffs & rock-crevices; 50-300m; fl. 4-5.
W. Crete (E. of Hora Sfakion) - Endemic.
[Plate 3.]

10. C. pumilio L., *Cent. pl.* **1**: 30 (1755) - *FE* **4**: 269.
Cr (W) - *MAP 334*
Maritime sands; fl. 4-5.
W. Crete [S. Peloponnisos (Elafonisi island);

otherwise N.E. Africa & Syria].

11. C. raphanina Sm., *Fl. Graec. prodr.* 2: 205 (1813) - *FE* 4: 268.
●**a.** subsp. **raphanina**
Cr (W, C, E) Ks Kp - *MAP 335*
Cliffs, rock-crevices, old walls, rocky phrygana, bare stony ground, flat clayey areas; 0-2300m; fl. 4-7.
Crete (widespread); Kasos, Karpathos - Endemic.
C. raphanina occurs outside the Cretan area in S. & E. Greece, the Kiklades and the E. Aegean islands of Psara & Ikaria, as subsp. *mixta* (DC.) Runemark (*FE* 4: 269). Numerous forms intermediate between the two subspecies exist in the Kiklades (cf. Runemark, 1967c).

●**12. C. redempta** Heldr. in *Bull. Soc. bot. Fr.* 37: 243 (1890) - *FE* 4: 267.
Cr (W, C) - *MAP 336*
Calcareous cliffs; 30-1200m; fl. 4-5.
Mainly W. Crete - Endemic.

? *C. salonitana* Vis. in *Flora, Jena* 12 (Ergänz. 1): 23 (1829) - *FE* 4: 264.
Doubtfully present in Crete [E.C. & S.E. Europe].

C. saxatilis K.Koch was described from Crete in 1851 but has never been refound; its status is uncertain (*FE* 4: 297).

13. C. solstitialis L., *Sp. pl.*: 917 (1753) - *FE* 4: 284.
Cr (W, C, E) - *MAP 337*
Olive groves, rocky places, dry hills; 0-400m; fl. 6.
Crete (sporadic) [mainly C. & S. Europe].

C. sonchifolia L. (*FE* 4: 283) was probably recorded in error (Rechinger, 1943a: 669).

C. sphaerocephala L. (*FE* 4: 283) was probably recorded in error (Rechinger, loc. cit.)

14. C. spinosa L., *Sp. pl.*: 912 (1753) - *FE* 4: 282.
a. subsp. **spinosa**
Cr (W, C, E) - *MAP 338*
Maritime sands; fl. 6-7.
Crete (N. coast) [Greece & Aegean region].

15. C. spruneri Boiss. & Heldr. in Boiss., *Diagn. pl. orient.* ser.1, 6: 132 (1845) - *FE* 4: 267.
●**a.** subsp. **minoa** (Heldr. ex Boiss.) Dostál in *Bot. J. Linn. Soc.* 71: 195 (1976) - *FE* 4: 267.
Cr (C) - *MAP 339*
Fallow fields, margins of fields & vineyards, grassy roadsides; 200-500m; fl. 6-7.
C. Crete - Endemic.

20. Chamaemelum Mill.

1. C. mixtum (L.) All., *Fl. pedem.* 1: 185 (1785) - *FE* 4: 165.
Cr - *NOT MAPPED*
Crete [mainly Mediterranean region].

Chamomilla recutita (L.) Rauschert (*FE* 4: 167) = **Matricaria 2.**

21. Chlamydophora Ehrenb. ex Less.

1. C. tridentata (Delile) Ehrenb. ex Less., *Syn. gen. Compos.*: 266 (1832) - *FE* 4: 178.
Cr (W) - *MAP 340*
Karstic rocks & coast.
W. Crete (Gavdos island) [Tunisia, Egypt, E. Aegean Islands (Rodos) & Cyprus].

22. Chondrilla L.

1. C. juncea L., *Sp. pl.*: 796 (1753) - *FE* 4: 343.
Cr (W, C, E) Kp - *MAP 341*
Maritime sands, dry waste areas; 0-50m; fl. 9-10.
Crete (sporadic); Karpathos [mainly C. & S. Europe].

2. C. ramosissima Sm., *Fl. Graec. prodr.* 2: 128 (1813) - *FE* 4: 343.
Cr (W) - *MAP 342*
Coastal grassland; fl. 7.
W. Crete [Greece & S. Aegean region].

23. Chrysanthemum L.

1. C. coronarium L., *Sp. pl.*: 890 (1753) - *FE* 4: 169.
Cr (W, C, E) Ks Kp - *MAP 343*
Disturbed ground, roadsides, waste areas, maritime sands; 0-500m; fl. 3-5.
Crete (widespread); Kasos, Karpathos [mainly Mediterranean region].
Both var. **coronarium**, with entirely yellow ligules, and var. **discolor** d'Urv., with ligules yellow at the base and white distally, occur in the Cretan area.

2. C. segetum L., *Sp. pl.*: 889 (1753) - *FE* 4: 168.
Cr (W, C, E) Ks Kp Sa - *MAP 344*
Cultivated & fallow land, rocky places, disturbed ground, waste areas; 0-450m; fl. 3-5.
Mainly W. & C. Crete; Karpathos group [most of Europe].

24. Cichorium L.

C. endivia subsp. *divaricatum* (Schousb.)
P.D.Sell (*FE* 4: 305) = 2.

1. **C. intybus** L., *Sp. pl.*: 813 (1753) - *FE* 4:
304.
Cr (W, C, E) Kp - *MAP 345*
Dry slopes, open stony ground; fl. 4-5, 9-10.
Mainly W. & C. Crete; Karpathos [most of
Europe].

2. **C. pumilum** Jacq., *Observ. bot.* 4: 3, t.80
(1771) - *FE* 4: 305 as *C. endivia* subsp.
divaricatum (Schousb.) P.D.Sell.
Cr (W, C, E) Ks Kp Sa - *MAP 346*
*Calcareous rocky places, rubble, seashores,
fallow fields; fl. 7.*
Crete (sporadic); Karpathos group [S. Europe].

3. **C. spinosum** L., *Sp. pl.*: 813 (1753) - *FE* 4:
305.
Cr (W, C, E) Ks Kp Sa - *MAP 347*
*Phrygana, flat clayey areas, maritime sands &
rocks; 0-1500m; fl. 7-10.*
Crete (widespread); Karpathos group
[Mediterranean region].
Known as *stamnangathia* to the local people,
who collect the leaf rosettes as a wild salad
vegetable.

Hybrid:

C. pumilum x **C. spinosum**
Maritime sand.
Crete (sporadic).
Recorded by Rechinger (1943*b*: 153).

25. Cirsium Mill.

1. **C. creticum** (Lam.) d'Urv. in *Mém. Soc.
linn. Paris* 1: 363 (1822) - *FE* 4: 242.
a. subsp. **creticum**
Cr (W, C, E) - *MAP 348*
*Woodland, stream-banks, springs, marshes &
other damp places; 0-800m.*
Mainly W. & C. Crete [S. Italy, Sicily &
Balkan peninsula].
●**b.** subsp. **dictaeum** Greuter, Matthäs & Risse
in *Willdenowia* 14: 271 (1984).
Cr (E) - *MAP 349*
Marshy place; 1000m.
E. Crete (Dikti) - Endemic.

●2. **C. morinifolium** Boiss. & Heldr. in
Boiss., *Fl. orient.* 3: 530 (1875) - *FE* 4: 235.
Cr (W, C, E) - *MAP 350*
*Calcareous open rocky garigue & phrygana, flat
clayey areas; 1200-2100m; fl. 7-8.*
Crete (Lefka Ori, Psiloritis & Dikti) - Endemic.

3. **C. vulgare** (Savi) Ten., *Fl. napol.* 5: 209
(1835-1838) - *FE* 4: 237.
Cr (W) - *MAP 351*
*Weed communities & sandy alluvial soil at river-
mouths.*
W. Crete [almost throughout Europe].
Recorded since *FE* (Greuter et al., 1984*b*: 272).

26. Cnicus L.

1. **C. benedictus** L., *Sp. pl.*: 826 (1753) - *FE* 4:
301.
Cr - *NOT MAPPED*
Crete [mainly Mediterranean region].

Coleostephus myconis (L.) Rchb.f. (*FE* 4: 174)
= **Leucanthemum 1**.

27. Conyza Less.

[1. **C. albida**] Willd. ex Spreng., *Syst. veg.* 3:
514 (1826).
Cr (W) - *MAP 352*
Naturalized along ditches & roadsides; 0-400m.
W. Crete [Mediterranean region; from S.
America].
Recorded since *FE*, apparently invaded since
1975, spreading W. to E. (Danin in Greuter &
Raus, 1983: 283).

[2. **C. bonariensis**] (L.) Cronquist in *Bull.
Torrey bot. Club* 70: 632 (1943) - *FE* 4: 120.
Cr (W) Kp - *NOT MAPPED*
Naturalized in scrub.
W. Crete; Karpathos [Mediterranean region;
from S. America].

[3. **C. canadensis**] (L.) Cronquist in *Bull.
Torrey bot. Club* 70: 632 (1943) - *FE* 4: 120.
Cr (W) - *MAP 353*
Naturalized; 200m.
W. Crete (Fasas valley) [almost throughout
Europe; from N. America].

28. Crepis L.

●1. **C. auriculifolia** Sieber ex Spreng., *Syst.
veg.* 3: 634 (1826) - *FE* 4: 351.
Cr (W, C, E) - *MAP 354*
*Calcareous cliffs, crevices, ledges & rocky
slopes; 200-2200m; fl. 5-7.*
Crete (widespread, mainly in mountains) -
Endemic.

2. **C. commutata** (Spreng.) Greuter, *Colloque
OPTIMA Crète, Guide Excurs.*: 23 (1975) - *FE*
4: 354 as *C. foetida* subsp. *commutata* (Spreng.)
Babc.
Cr (W, C, E) Ks Kp Sa - *MAP 355*

Rocky places & rubble, fallow fields; 0-600m; fl. 3-4.
Crete (sporadic); Karpathos group [S. Balkan peninsula & Aegean region].

●**3. C. cretica** Boiss., *Diagn. pl. orient.* ser.1, **11**: 53 (1849) - *FE* **4**: 356 as *C. neglecta* subsp. *cretica* (Boiss.) Vierh.
Cr (W, C, E) Ks Kp - *MAP 356*
Calcareous rocky places, soil-filled hollows; 0-2000m; fl. 3-5.
Crete (widespread); Kasos, Karpathos - Endemic.

4. C. dioscoridis L., *Sp. pl.* ed.2: 1133 (1763) - *FE* **4**: 355.
Cr (W) - *NOT MAPPED*
W. Crete [mainly Albania, Greece & Aegean region].

5. C. foetida L., *Sp. pl.*: 807 (1753) - *FE* **4**: 354 as *C. foetida* L. subsp. *foetida*.
Cr (W, C, E) - *MAP 357*
Olive groves, rocky & sandy places; fl. 5.
Crete (sporadic) [most of Europe].
Subsp. *commutata* (Spreng.) Babc. (*FE* **4**: 354) = **2**.

6. C. fraasii Sch.Bip. in *Flora, Jena* **25**: 173 (1842) - *FE* **4**: 348.
Cr (W, C, E) Ks Kp - *MAP 358*
Calcareous cliffs & crevices, rocky places, mountain slopes, screes; 100-2300m; fl. 4-8.
Crete (widespread); Kasos, Karpathos [C. & S. Greece; otherwise S.W. Asia].
Both subsp. *fraasii* and subsp. *mungieri* (Boiss. & Heldr.) P.D.Sell are given for the Cretan area in *FE* **4**: 349; the latter is treated at varietal rank under *C. fraasii* in *MFG* **2**: 582, and is not separated here.

7. C. micrantha Czerep. in Bobrov & Tzvelev, *Fl. URSS* **29**: 684 (1964) - *FE* **4**: 355.
Cr Ks Kp Sa - *NOT MAPPED*
Crete; Karpathos group [mainly E. Greece & Aegean region; otherwise Egypt & S.W. Asia].

8. C. multiflora Sm., *Fl. Graec. prodr.* **2**: 138 (1813) - *FE* **4**: 355.
Cr (W, E) Ks Kp Sa - *MAP 359*
Maritime sands & coastal rocky places.
W. & E. Crete; Karpathos group [S.E. Greece & S. Aegean region; otherwise E. Aegean Islands & W. Turkey].

C. neglecta subsp. *cretica* (Boiss.) Vierh. (*FE* **4**: 356) = **3**.

"*C. neglecta* subsp. *neglecta*" (*FE* **4**: 356) = **3** (Barclay, 1986: 29).

9. C. pusilla (Sommier) Merxm. in *Mitt. bot. StSamml. Münch.* **7**: 275 (1968) - *FE* **4**: 355.
Cr (W, C) Kp - *MAP 360*
Flat clayey areas, hard stony ground, abandoned terraces; 200-700m; fl. 3-4.
W. & C. Crete; Karpathos [S. Portugal, Balearic Islands (Mallorca), Malta (including Gozo) & S. Greece; otherwise ?N.E. Libya & S.W. Turkey (Kastellorizo)].

10. C. rubra L., *Sp. pl.*: 806 (1753) - *FE* **4**: 354.
Cr (W, C, E) - *MAP 361*
Calcareous phrygana, maritime sands & rocks; 0-100m; fl. 4.
Crete (sporadic) [S. Italy & Balkan peninsula].

11. C. sancta (L.) Babc. in *Univ. Calif. Publs Bot.* **19**: 403 (1941) - *FE* **4**: 354.
Cr - *NOT MAPPED*
Crete [S. Europe].

●**12. C. sibthorpiana** Boiss. & Heldr. in Boiss., *Diagn. pl. orient.* ser.1, **11**: 56 (1849) - *FE* **4**: 352.
Cr (W, C) - *MAP 362*
Calcareous rocky places, screes, flat clayey areas; 1400-2450m; fl. 6-9.
W. & C. Crete (Lefka Ori & Psiloritis) - Endemic.

●**13. C. tybakiensis** Vierh. in *Öst. bot. Z.* **65**: 73 (1915) - *FE* **4**: 357.
Cr (W, C, E) Ks Kp - *MAP 363*
Calcareous cliffs, ledges, crevices & rubble, rocky scrub, phrygana; 0-1350m; fl. 5.
Crete (widespread); Kasos, Karpathos - Endemic.

14. C. vesicaria L., *Sp. pl.*: 805 (1753) - *FE* **4**: 356.
Cr (W, C, E) - *MAP 364*
Olive groves, rocky places, open stony ground; 0-800m; fl. 3-5.
Crete (sporadic) [W., C. & S. Europe].

15. C. zacintha (L.) Babc. in *Univ. Calif. Publs Bot.* **19**: 404 (1941) - *FE* **4**: 355.
Cr (W, C, E) Kp - *MAP 365*
River-beds, Lygeum steppe, abandoned fields; 0-200m; fl. 4-5.
Crete (sporadic); Karpathos [Mediterranean region].

29. Crupina (Pers.) Cass.

1. C. crupinastrum (Moris) Vis., *Fl. dalmat.* **2**: 42 (1847) - *FE* **4**: 301.
Cr (W, C, E) Ks Kp Sa - *MAP 366*
Calcareous open phrygana & rocky places, roadsides; 0-450m; fl. 4-5.

Crete (widespread); Karpathos group
[Mediterranean region].

30. Cynara L.

1. C. cardunculus L., *Sp. pl.*: 827 (1753) - *FE*
4: 248.
Cr - *NOT MAPPED*
Crete [Mediterranean region].

2. C. cornigera Lindl. in Sm., *Fl. graec.* **9**: 25
(1837) - *FE* **4**: 248.
Cr (W, C, E) Ks Kp Sa - *MAP 367*
Calcareous phrygana, open rocky places; 0-
600m; fl. 4-5.
Mainly W. & E. Crete (coastal); Karpathos
group [S. Greece & Aegean region; otherwise
E. Aegean Islands & Cyprus].

C. scolymus L. (*FE* **4**: 249) is cultivated only.

31. Dittrichia Greuter

1. D. graveolens (L.) Greuter in *Exsicc. genav.*
Conserv. Bot. distrib. **4**: 71 (1973) - *FE* **4**: 137.
Cr (W, C, E) Ks Kp - *MAP 368*
River gravels, fallow fields, waste areas; 0-
150m; fl. 8-10.
Crete (sporadic); Kasos, Karpathos [W. & S.
Europe].

2. D. viscosa (L.) Greuter in *Exsicc. genav.*
Conserv. Bot. distrib. **4**: 71 (1973) - *FE* **4**: 137.
a. subsp. viscosa
Cr (W, C, E) Ks Kp Sa - *MAP 369*
Damp ground on coast, dry stream-beds,
ditches, cliffs, fallow fields, roadsides, waste
areas; 0-800m; fl. 9-11.
Crete (widespread); Karpathos group [S.
Europe].

32. Echinops L.

1. E. spinosissimus Turra, *Farsetia*: 13 (1765) -
FE **4**: 213.
Cr (W, C, E) Ks Kp Sa - *MAP 370*.
Olive groves, rocky places, open stony ground
near sea, maritime sands; 0-550m; fl. 5-7.
a. subsp. bithynicus (Boiss.) Kozuharov in *Bot.*
J. Linn. Soc. **71**: 41 (1975) - *FE* **4**: 213.
Cr (E) - *MAP 371*
E. Crete [S. Aegean region; otherwise S.W.
Asia].
b. subsp. spinosissimum
Cr (W, C, E) Ks Kp Sa - *MAP 372*
Crete; Karpathos group [Sicily & Greece;
otherwise E. Aegean Islands & W. Turkey].
The species sensu lato is widespread in Crete.

33. Erigeron L.

1. E. glabratus Hoppe & Hornsch. ex Bluff &
Fingerh., *Comp. fl. German.* **2**: 364 (1825) - *FE*
4: 119.
Cr (W) - *MAP 373*
Slopes with calcareous cliffs, screes; 2100-
2300m.
W. Crete (Lefka Ori) [mountains of C. & S.
Europe].
Recored since *FE* (Greuter et al., 1984*b*: 273).

34. Eupatorium L.

[1. E. adenophorum] Spreng., *Syst. veg.* **3**:
420 (1826) - *FE* **4**: 109.
Cr (W) Kp - *MAP 374*
Cultivated for ornament and naturalized in
Citrus groves, moist hedges, margins of maquis,
seasonally wet places, ditches; 0-100m; fl. 3-4.
W. Crete (N. side); Karpathos [S. Europe; from
Mexico].

Evax contracta Boiss. (*FE* **4**: 125) = **Filago 3**.

E. pygmaea (L.) Brot. (*FE* **4**: 124) = **Filago 9**.

Filaginella uliginosa (L.) Opiz (*FE* **4**: 127) =
Gnaphalium uliginosum.

35. Filago L.

1. F. aegaea Wagenitz in *Willdenowia* **6**: 126
(1970) - *FE* **4**: 122.
a. subsp. aegaea
Cr (E) Kp - *MAP 375*
Among calcareous rocks, open stony ground,
bare soil in phrygana, maritime sands; 0-
1100m.
E. Crete; Karpathos [S.E. Kiklades].
b. subsp. aristata Wagenitz in *Willdenowia* **6**:
129 (1970) - *FE* **4**: 122.
Cr (W, C, E) Kp - *MAP 376*
Among calcareous rocks, sandy hills, bare soil,
open phrygana; 0-1850m.
Mainly W. & E. Crete; Karpathos [Ionian
Islands (Zakinthos) & S. Aegean region;
otherwise E. Aegean Islands & Cyprus].
A collection from Saria is transitional between
the two subspecies (Wagenitz, 1970: 131).

2. F. arvensis L., *Sp. pl.*: addenda post indicem
(1753) - *FE* **4**: 123 as *Logfia arvensis* (L.)
Holub.
Cr (W, C) - *MAP 377*
Among calcareous rocks; 1500-1900m.
W. & C. Crete (Lefka Ori & Psiloritis) [most of
Europe].

3. F. contracta (Boiss.) Chrtek & Holub in *Preslia* **35**: 3 (1963) - *FE* **4**: 125 as *Evax contracta* Boiss.
Cr (W, C, E) Ks Kp - *MAP 378*
Open rocky places, 200-1150m.
Crete (sporadic); Kasos, Karpathos [S. Aegean region; otherwise N. Africa & S.W. Asia].

4. F. cretensis Gand., *Fl. cret.*: 58 (1916) - *FE* **4**: 122.
a. subsp. **cretensis**
Cr (W, C, E) Ks Kp Sa - *MAP 379*
Among calcareous rocks, soil-filled crevices, open places in maquis, abandoned fields; 0-1150m.
Crete (sporadic); Karpathos group [S. Aegean region].
b. subsp. **cycladum** Wagenitz in *Willldenowia* **6**: 124 (1970) - *FE* **4**: 122.
Ks Kp Sa - *MAP 380*
Cliffs, sandy ground by sea; 0-250m; fl. 4.
Karpathos group [Kiklades; otherwise E. Aegean Islands].

5. F. eriocephala Guss., *Pl. rar.*: 344 (1826) - *FE* **4**: 121.
Cr (W, C, E) Kp Sa - *MAP 381*
Open stony ground; 0-850m.
Crete (sporadic); Karpathos, Saria [Mediterranean region].

6. F. eriosphaera (Boiss. & Heldr.) Chrtek & Holub in *Preslia* **35**: 3 (1963) - *FE* **4**: 123.
Kp - *MAP 382*
Karpathos [S.W. Asia].
Given also for Crete in *FE*, although there are no records as a basis for this (Greuter et al., 1984b: 273).

7. F. gallica L., *Sp. pl.*: addenda post indicem (1753) - *FE* **4**: 124 as *Logfia gallica* (L.) Coss. & Germ.
Cr (W, C) Kp - *MAP 383*
Calcareous rocky places, gorge-beds; 0-300m.
W. & C. Crete; Karpathos [W., W.C. & S. Europe].

8. F. germanica (L.) Huds., *Fl. angl.*: 328 (1762) - *FE* **4**: 121 as *F. vulgaris* Lam.
Cr (W) - *MAP 384*
200-1050m.
W. Crete (Fasas valley & Omalos plain in Lefka Ori) [W., C. & S. Europe].

9. F. pygmaea L., *Sp. pl.*: 927 (1753) - *FE* **4**: 124 as *Evax pygmaea* (L.) Brot.
a. subsp. **pygmaea**
Cr (W, C, E) Ks Kp - *MAP 385*
Soil-pockets among rocks, screes, bare & stony ground, fallow fields; 0-700m.
Crete (widespread); Kasos, Karpathos [Mediterranean region].

10. F. pyramidata L., *Sp. pl.*: 1199, [1230] (1753) - *FE* **4**: 122.
Cr (W, C, E) Ks Kp Sa - *MAP 386*
Calcareous rocky places, maritime sands; 0-600m.
Crete (sporadic); Karpathos group [W. & S. Europe].

F. vulgaris Lam. (*FE* **4**: 121) = **8**.

36. Galactites Moench

1. G. tomentosa Moench, *Methodus*: 558 (1794) - *FE* **4**: 244.
Cr (W, C, E) - *MAP 387*
Olive groves, disturbed ground, roadsides, waste areas; 0-450m; fl. 2-5.
Mainly W. & C. Crete [mainly Mediterranean region].

37. Geropogon L.

1. G. hybridus (L.) Sch.Bip. in Webb. & Berthel., *Hist. nat. Iles Canaries* **2**: 471 (1850) - *FE* **4**: 325 as *Tragopogon hybridus* L.
Cr (W, C, E) Kp - *MAP 388*
Olive groves, roadsides; 0-400m; fl. 3-5.
Crete (sporadic); Karpathos [S. Europe].

Gnaphalium L.

G. luteo-album L. (*FE* **4**: 128) =
Pseudognaphalium 1.

? G. uliginosum L., *Sp. pl.*: 856 (1753) - *FE* **4**: 127 as *Filaginella uliginosa* (L.) Opiz.
Doubtfully present in Crete [most of Europe].

38. Hedypnois Mill.

1. H. cretica (L.) Dum.Cours., *Bot. cult.* **2**: 339 (1802) - *FE* **4**: 307.
Cr (W, C, E) Ks Kp Sa - *MAP 389*
Phrygana, calcareous rocky places, maritime sands, coastal saline ground, vineyards, cultivated terraces; 0-400m; fl. 3-5.
Crete (widespread); Karpathos group [S. Europe].
H. cretica shows great morphological and cytological diversification, especially in the E. Mediterranean region; however, the geographical distributions of the various chromosome numbers are widespread and largely sympatric, and it is difficult to define and circumscribe individual taxa within the species (cf. Nordenstam, 1971).

39. Helichrysum Mill.

1. H. barrelieri (Ten.) Greuter in *Boissiera* **13**: 138 (1967) - *FE* **4**: 129 as *H. stoechas* subsp. *barrelieri* (Ten.) Nyman.
Cr (W, C, E) Ks Kp Sa - *MAP 390*
Phrygana, rocky places, maritime sands; 0-500m; fl. 4-6.
Crete (widespread); Karpathos group [C. & E. Mediterranean region].

●**2. H. doerfleri** Rech.f. in *Magy. bot. Lap.* **33**: 15 (1934) - *FE* **4**: 129.
Cr (E) - *MAP 391*
Calcareous open rocky ground, often beneath spiny dwarf shrubs; 800-1400m; fl. 5-6.
E. Crete (Afendis Kavousi area) - Endemic. The plant does not grow on cliffs as stated in *FE.*

●**3. H. heldreichii** Boiss., *Fl. orient.* **3**: 229 (1875) - *FE* **4**: 130.
Cr (W) - *MAP 392*
Calcareous cliffs in gorges; 0-450m; fl. 5.
W. Crete (W. of Hora Sfakion) - Endemic. [Plate 3.]

H. italicum subsp. *microphyllum* (Willd.) Nyman (*FE* **4**: 130) = **4**.

4. H. microphyllum (Willd.) Cambess., *Mém. Hist. Nat.* **14**: 272 (1827) - *FE* **4**: 130 as *H. italicum* subsp. *microphyllum* (Willd.) Nyman.
Cr (W, C, E) - *MAP 393*
Calcareous open woodland, garigue, phrygana, open rocky places; 300-2100m.
Crete (mainly Lefka Ori, Psiloritis, Kofinas, Dikti & Afendis Kavousi) [Mediterranean region].

5. H. orientale (L.) Gaertn., *Fruct. sem. pl.* **2**: 404 (1791) - *FE* **4**: 130.
Cr (W, C, E) Ks Kp Sa - *MAP 394*
Calcareous cliffs, rarely on offshore islets; 0-1150m; fl. 4-5.
Mainly W. & E. Crete; Karpathos group [Greece & Aegean region; otherwise E. Aegean Islands & W. Turkey].

H. stoechas subsp. *barrelieri* (Ten.) Nyman (*FE* **4**: 129) = **1**.

40. Helminthotheca Vaill. ex Zinn

1. H. echioides (L.) Holub in *Folia geobot. phytotax.* **8**(2): 176 (1973) - *FE* **4**: 316 as *Picris echioides* L.
Cr (W, C, E) Kp - *MAP 395*
Olive groves, cultivated & fallow fields; 0-500m; fl. 6-7.
Crete (sporadic); Karpathos [W., C. & S. Europe].

41. Hieracium L.

FE **4** gives four taxa for Crete: *H. friwaldii* Rchb.f. (p. 389); *H. leithneri* (Heldr. & Sart. ex Boiss.) Zahn (p. 390); *H. pallidum* Biv. (p. 380) and the *H. parnassi* group (p. 392). Records for all of these should be considered erroneous, with the exception of *H. pallidum* (Greuter et al., 1984*b*: 273), which is included in the synonymy of the following species, after *MFG* **2**: 617.

1. H. schmidtii Tausch in *Flora, Jena* **11** (Ergänz. 1): 65 (1828) - *FE* **4**: 380. (Including *H. pallidum* Biv. - *FE* **4**: 380.)
Cr (W) - *MAP 396*
Calcareous cliffs & rocks; 1800-2400m; fl. 7.
W. Crete (Lefka Ori) [most of Europe].

42. Hymenonema Cass.

1. H. graecum (L.) DC., *Prodr.* **7**: 116 (1838) - *FE* **4**: 306.
Cr (W) - *MAP 397*
Margin of coastal saline ground.
W. Crete (E. of Hania) [S. Aegean region].

43. Hyoseris L.

1. H. lucida L., *Mant. pl.*: 103 (1767) - *FE* **4**: 307 as *H. radiata* subsp. *graeca* Halácsy.
Cr (W, C) - *MAP 398*
Maritime sands & compacted soil near sea; fl. 3-4.
Mainly W. Crete [mainly C. Mediterranean region].

H. radiata subsp. *graeca* Halácsy (*FE* **4**: 307) = **1**.

H. radiata L. subsp. *radiata* (*FE* **4**: 307) was almost certainly recorded in error (Greuter, 1974: 161).

2. H. scabra L., *Sp. pl.*: 809 (1753) - *FE* **4**: 307.
Cr (W, C, E) Ks Kp - *MAP 399*
Phrygana, calcareous rocks, bare stony ground; 50-1200m; fl. 3-4.
Crete (sporadic); Kasos, Karpathos [Mediterranean region].

44. Hypochoeris L.

1. H. achyrophorus L., *Sp. pl.*: 810 (1753) - *FE* **4**: 309.
Cr (W, C, E) Ks Kp - *MAP 400*
Olive groves, calcareous rocky places; 0-400m.
Mainly W. & E. Crete; Kasos, Karpathos [Mediterranean region].

2. H. cretensis (L.) Bory & Chaub. in Bory, *Exp. sci. Morée, Bot.*: 237 (1832) - *FE* **4**: 309.
Cr - NOT MAPPED
Crete [C. & E. Mediterranean region].

3. H. glabra L., *Sp. pl.*: 811 (1753) - *FE* **4**: 309.
Cr (W) - MAP 401
Coastal saline & sandy ground.
W. Crete [most of Europe].

4. H. radicata L., *Sp. pl.*: 811 (1753) - *FE* **4**: 309.
Cr (W, E) Kp - MAP 402
Calcareous rocky places, fallow fields; 600-1050m.
W. & E. Crete; Karpathos [most of Europe].

●**5. H. tenuiflora** (Boiss.) Boiss., *Fl. orient.* **3**: 785 (1875) - *FE* **4**: 309.
Cr (W, E) - MAP 403
Calcareous rocky places, crevices & screes, flat clayey areas; 1500-2400m; fl. 6-8.
W. & E. Crete (Lefka Ori & Dikti) - Endemic.

45. Inula L.

1. I. candida (L.) Cass. in *Dict. Sci. nat.* **23**: 554 (1822) - *FE* **4**: 135 as *I. candida* (L.) Cass. subsp. *candida*.
Cr (W, C) - MAP 404
Calcareous cliffs; 0-800m; fl. 5-6.
Mainly W. Crete [Kithira].
Subsp. *decalvans* (Halácsy) P.W. Ball ex Tutin (*FE* **4**: 135) = **4**.

2. I. crithmoides L., *Sp. pl.*: 883 (1753) - *FE* **4**: 136.
Cr (W) Kp - MAP 405
Calcareous maritime cliffs & rocks; fl. 9.
W. Crete; Karpathos [coasts of W. & S. Europe].

3. I. heterolepis Boiss., *Diagn. pl. orient.* ser.2, **3**: 12 (1856) - *FE* **4**: 136 as *I. verbascifolia* subsp. *heterolepis* (Boiss.) Tutin.
Kp - MAP 406
Calcareous cliffs & rocks; 0-1200m.
Karpathos [S.W. Asia].

●**4. I. pseudolimonella** (Rech.f.) Rech.f. in *Denkschr. Akad. Wiss. Wien* **105(2,1)**: 140 (1943) - *FE* **4**: 135 as *I. candida* subsp. *decalvans* (Halácsy) P.W.Ball ex Tutin.
Cr (E) - MAP 407
Calcareous cliffs & rocks; (330-)800-2000m; fl. 8.
E. Crete (Dikti & Afendis Kavousi) - Endemic.

I. verbascifolia subsp. *heterolepis* (Boiss.) Tutin (*FE* **4**: 136) = **3**.

46. Lactuca L.

L. acanthifolia (Willd.) Boiss. (*FE* **4**: 329) = **Scariola 1**.

1. L. saligna L., *Sp. pl.*: 796 (1753) - *FE* **4**: 330.
Cr (W, C, E) - MAP 408
Weed communities near sea.
Crete (sporadic, N. coast) [mainly C. & S. Europe].

L. sativa L. (*FE* **4**: 330) is cultivated in Crete as a salad vegetable and has been recorded as a casual escape (Rechinger, 1943b: 161).

2. L. serriola L., *Cent. pl.* **2**: 29 (1756) - *FE* **4**: 330.
Cr (W, C, E) Kp - MAP 409
Olive groves, stream-banks, dry sandy places, disturbed ground, waste areas; 0-200m; fl. 6-8.
Crete (widespread); Karpathos [most of Europe].

L. viminea subsp. *alpestris* (Gand.) Feráková (*FE* **4**: 329) = **Scariola 2**.

L. viminea (L.) J. & C.Presl subsp. *viminea* (*FE* **4**: 329) = **Scariola 3**.

47. Lamyropsis (Kharadze) Dittrich

1. L. cynaroides (Lam.) Dittrich in *Candollea* **26**: 98 (1971) - *FE* **4**: 244.
Cr (W, C, E) - MAP 410
Calcareous open woodland & rocky places; 100-1050m; fl. 5-6.
Crete (widespread) [S. Greece; otherwise E. Aegean Islands (Samos) & W. Turkey].

48. Leontodon L.

"L. cichoraceus" (*FE* **4**: 312) = **1** (*MFG* **2**: 527).

1. L. tuberosus L., *Sp. pl.*: 799 (1753) - *FE* **4**: 315.
Cr (W, C, E) Ks Kp - MAP 411
Woodland, olive groves, maquis, phrygana, rocky places, marshes, damp ground, fallow & abandoned land; 0-1200m; fl. 3-5.
Crete (widespread); Kasos, Karpathos [Mediterranean region].

49. Leucanthemum Mill.

1. L. myconis (L.) Giraud in *Ann. Univ. Grenoble Sect. Sci.-Med.* **11**: 195-201 (1935) - *FE* **4**: 174 as *Coleostephus myconis* (L.) Rchb.f.
Cr (W) - NOT MAPPED

Waste area.
W. Crete [S. Europe].

Logfia arvensis (L.) Holub (*FE* **4**: 123) =
Filago 2.

L. gallica (L.) Coss. & Germ. (*FE* **4**: 124) =
Filago 7.

50. Matricaria L.

1. M. macrotis Rech.f. in *Denkschr. Akad.
Wiss. Wien* **105(1)**: 634 (1943).
Sa - *MAP 412*
Saria [E. Aegean Islands (Simi & Rodos) &
S.W. Turkey].
Recorded since *FE* (Raus, 1991: 303).

2. M. recutita L., *Sp. pl.*: 891 (1753) - *FE* **4**:
167 as *Chamomilla recutita* (L.) Rauschert.
Cr (W, E) Kp - *MAP 413*
Coastal saline ground, roadsides; 0-100m; fl. 4.
W. & E. Crete; Karpathos [most of Europe].

51. Notobasis Cass.

1. N. syriaca (L.) Cass. in *Dict. Sci. nat.* **35**:
171 (1825) - *FE* **4**: 242.
Cr (W, C, E) Ks Kp - *MAP 414*
*Disturbed ground, roadsides, waste areas; 0-
1050m; fl. 4-6.*
Mainly W. & C. Crete; Kasos, Karpathos
[Mediterranean region].

52. Onopordum L.

1. O. bracteatum Boiss. & Heldr. in Boiss.,
Diagn. pl. orient. ser.1, **10**: 91 (1849) - *FE* **4**:
247.
a. subsp. **bracteatum**
Kp - *MAP 415*
Rocky places; fl. 7.
Karpathos [S.W. Asia].
●**b.** subsp. **creticum** Franco in *Bot. J. Linn.
Soc.* **71**: 46 (1975) - *FE* **4**: 247.
Cr (W, C, E) - *MAP 416*
*Quercus coccifera woodland, calcareous rocky
places, maritime sands; 0-1600m; fl. 5-6.*
Crete (sporadic) - Endemic.
Endemic status not noted in *FE*.

2. O. illyricum L., *Sp. pl.*: 827 (1753) - *FE* **4**:
247.
a. subsp. **cardunculus** (Boiss.) Franco in *Bot.
J. Linn. Soc.* **71**: 46 (1975) - *FE* **4**: 247.
Cr (W) Kp - *MAP 417*
Calcareous rocky places.
W. Crete (Paleohora); Karpathos [E.
Mediterranean region].

3. O. majoris Beauverd in *Bull. Soc. bot.
Genève* ser.2, **6**: 152 (1914) - *FE* **4**: 248.
Cr (E) - *MAP 418*
Calcareous rubble.
E. Crete (E. of Ierapetra); Karpathos [E.
Aegean Islands].

O. myriacanthum Boiss., recorded from
Karpathos by Greuter et al. (1983a: 54), is
probably an error. The taxon is otherwise
endemic to Mt Parnon in E. Peloponnisos.

4. O. tauricum Willd., *Sp. pl.*: **3**: 1687 (1803)
- *FE* **4**: 246.
Cr (W, C) - *MAP 419*
*Calcareous rocky places, open stony ground,
flat clayey areas, roadsides; 200-800m; fl. 5-6.*
W. & C. Crete [S.E. Europe].

53. Otanthus Hoffmanns. & Link

1. O. maritimus (L.) Hoffmanns. & Link, *Fl.
portug.* **2**: 365 (1834) - *FE* **4**: 168.
Cr (W, C, E) Ks Kp - *MAP 420*
Maritime sands; fl. 6-7.
Crete (mainly N. coast); Kasos, Karpathos
[coasts of W. & S. Europe].

Pallenis spinosa (L.) Cass. (*FE* **4**: 139) =
Asteriscus 1.

54. Phagnalon Cass.

1. P. graecum Boiss. & Heldr. in Boiss.,
Diagn. pl. orient. ser.1, **11**: 6 (1849) - *FE* **4**:
133.
Cr (W, C, E) Ks Kp Sa - *MAP 421*
*Cliffs, rocky & sandy places, phrygana; 0-600m;
fl. 4-5.*
Crete (widespread); Karpathos group [S.E.
Europe].

P. pumilum (Sm.) DC. (*FE* **4**: 133) = **2**.

●**2. P. pygmaeum** (Sieber) Greuter, *Colloque
OPTIMA Crète, Guide Excurs.*: 23 (1975) - *FE*
4: 133 as *P. pumilum* (Sm.) DC.
Cr (W, C, E) - *MAP 422*
*Calcareous rock-crevices & screes; 1600-
2150m; fl. 8.*
Crete (Lefka Ori, Psiloritis & Dikti) - Endemic.

55. Picnomon Adans.

1. P. acarna (L.) Cass. in *Dict. Sci. nat.* **40**:
188 (1826) - *FE* **4**: 242.
Cr (W, C, E) Kp Sa - *MAP 423*
*Garigue, phrygana, open stony ground,
roadsides, waste areas; 0-1600m; fl. 5-8.*

Crete (widespread); Karpathos, Saria [S. Europe].

56. Picris L.

1. P. altissima Delile, *Fl. d'Égypte*: 260(116), t. 41 (1813) - *FE* **4**: 317 as "*P. sprengeriana*".
Cr (W, C, E) Kp Sa - *MAP 424*
Calcareous rocky places; 0-600m.
Mainly W. Crete; Karpathos, Saria [Mediterranean region].

P. echioides L. (*FE* **4**: 316) = **Helminthotheca 1**.

2. P. pauciflora Willd., *Sp. pl.*: 3: 1557 (1803) - *FE* **4**: 317.
Cr (W, C, E) Kp Sa - *MAP 425*
Calcareous rocky places; 0-400m.
Crete (sporadic, coastal); Karpathos, Saria [mainly Balkan peninsula].

"*P. sprengeriana*" (*FE* **4**: 317) = **1** (Greuter et al., 1984*b*: 274).

57. Pseudognaphalium Kirp.

1. P. luteo-album (L.) Hilliard & B.L.Burtt. in *Bot. J. Linn. Soc.* **82**: 206 (1981) - *FE* **4**: 128 as *Gnaphalium luteo-album* L.
Cr (W) - *MAP 426*
Damp rocks, bare disturbed ground; 300m; fl. 4.
W. Crete (Fasas valley) [mainly C. & S. Europe].

58. Ptilostemon Cass.

1. P. chamaepeuce (L.) Less., *Gen. Cynaroceph.*: 5 (1832) - *FE* **4**: 243.
Cr (W, C, E) Ks Kp Sa - *MAP 427*
Cliffs & rocks, usually calcareous; 0-600m; fl. 4-6.
Crete (widespread); Karpathos group [Greece & Aegean region; otherwise S.W. Asia].

2. P. gnaphalodes (Cirillo) Soják in *Novit. Bot. Hort. bot. Univ. Carol. Prag.* **1962**: 46 (1962) - *FE* **4**: 243.
a. subsp. pseudofruticosus (Pamp.) Greuter in *Candollea* **24**: 48 (1969) - *FE* **4**: 243.
Cr (W) - *MAP 428*
Rock-crevices; 20-450m.
W. Crete (S. side) [S. Greece; otherwise E. Aegean Islands (Ikaria)].

3. P. stellatus (L.) Greuter in *Boissiera* **13**: 146 (1967) - *FE* **4**: 244.
Cr (C) - *MAP 429*
Calcareous step-crevices, rocky garigue &

phrygana; -800m; fl. 5-6.
C. Crete (Kedros area) [E. Mediterranean region].

59. Pulicaria Gaertn.

P. arabica (L.) Cass. (*FE* **4**: 137) has been recorded historically from Crete but never since confirmed (Rechinger, 1943*a*: 619).

1. P. dysenterica (L.) Bernh., *Syst. Verz.*: 153 (1800) - *FE* **4**: 137.
Cr (W, C, E) - *MAP 430*
Marshes, lake-shore, stream-sides, ditches & other damp ground; 0-150m.
Crete (sporadic) [W., C. & S. Europe].

2. P. odora (L.) Rchb., *Fl. germ. excurs.*: 239 (1831) - *FE* **4**: 137.
Cr (W, C) - *MAP 431*
Woodland, maquis, garigue; 0-700m; fl. 5-6.
Mainly W. Crete [Mediterranean region].

3. P. sicula (L.) Moris, *Fl. sardoa* **2**: 363 (1840-1843) - *FE* **4**: 137.
Cr - *NOT MAPPED*
Crete [Mediterranean region].

? P. vulgaris Gaertn., *Fruct. sem. pl.* **2**: 461 (1791) - *FE* **4**: 137.
Doubtfully present in Crete [most of Europe].

60. Reichardia Roth

1. R. intermedia (Sch.Bip.) Cout., *Fl. Portugal*: 676 (1913) - *FE* **4**: 325.
Cr (E) Ks Kp - *MAP 432*
E. Crete (near Sitia); Kasos, Karpathos [Mediterranean region].

2. R. orientalis (L.) Hochr. in *Annu. Conserv. Jard. bot. Genève* **7-8**: 238 (1904) - *FE* **4**: 325, included in synonymy of *R. tingitana* (L.) Roth.
Cr (E) - *MAP 433*
Maritime sands & rocks.
E. Crete (Gaidouronisi, Koufonisi & Dionisiades islands) [Aegean region; otherwise S.W. Asia to N.E. India].
R. orientalis is the eastern vicariant of *R. tingitana*, which occurs further west in the Mediterranean region.

3. R. picroides (L.) Roth, *Bot. Abh. Beobacht.*: 35 (1787) - *FE* **4**: 325.
Cr (W, C, E) Ks Kp Sa - *MAP 434*
Rocky places & crevices, earthy banks, maritime sands, disturbed ground, old walls; 0-700m; fl. 3-5.
Crete (widespread); Karpathos group [S. Europe].

"*R. tingitana*" (*FE* 4: 325) = **2** (Rechinger, 1949: 218).

61. Rhagadiolus A.Juss.

R. edulis Gaertn. (Barclay, 1986: 35) see **1**.

1. R. stellatus (L.) Gaertn., *Fruct. sem. pl.* 2: 354 (1791) - *FE* 4: 308.
Cr (W, C, E) Ks Kp - *MAPS 435, 436 & 437*
Woodland, olive groves, scrub, garigue, rocky places, cultivated areas; 0-650m; fl. 3-5.
Mainly W. & C. Crete; Kasos, Karpathos [S. Europe].
Plants with lyrately divided leaves and glabrous involucral bracts have been treated as *R. edulis* Gaertn. (or *R. stellatus* var. *edulis* (Gaertn.) DC.), which appears to be almost sympatric with *R. stellatus* in the Cretan area, but with a tendency to grow in more humid habitats. It is not separated here.

Santolina chamaecyparissus L. (*FE* 4: 145) is given for Crete - as an introduction - by Barclay (1986: 35), based on old records cited by Rechinger (1943a: 622). It is possible that some or all of these are referable to *Achillea cretica* L., which has a similar appearance when sterile. Genuine *Santolina* is rarely cultivated for ornament in Crete.

62. Scariola F.W.Schmidt

1. S. acanthifolia (Willd.) Soják in *Novit. Bot. Hort. bot. Univ. Carol. Prag.* 1962: 46 (1962) - *FE* 4: 329 as *Lactuca acanthifolia* (Willd.) Boiss.
Cr (W, C, E) Ks Kp - *MAP 438*
Calcareous cliffs; 0-700m; fl. 8-10.
Crete (widespread); Kasos, Karpathos [E. Peloponnisos (Idra) & Kiklades; otherwise E. Aegean Islands & S.W. Turkey].

●**2. S. alpestris** (Gand.) Greuter, Matthäs & Risse in *Willdenowia* 14: 274 (1984) - *FE* 4: 329 as *Lactuca viminea* subsp. *alpestris* (Gand.) Feráková.
Cr (W, C, E) - *MAP 439*
Calcareous garigue, dwarf shrub communities, rocky slopes, rubble, screes, especially above timberline; (100-)900-2400m; fl. 7-10.
Crete (mainly Lefka Ori, Kedros, Psiloritis, Kofinas, Dikti & Afendis Kavousi) - Endemic.

3. S. viminea (L.) F.W.Schmidt, *Samml. phys.-ökon. Aufs.* 1: 270 (1795) - *FE* 4: 329 as *Lactuca viminea* (L.) J. & C.Presl subsp. *viminea*.
Cr (W) - *MAP 440*

Calcareous rocky places & crevices; 200-600m. W. Crete [C. & S. Europe].

63. Scolymus L.

1. S. hispanicus L., *Sp. pl.*: 813 (1753) - *FE* 4: 304.
Cr (W, C, E) Ks Kp Sa - *MAP 441*
Open rocky places, roadsides, waste areas; 0-500m; fl. 6-9.
Crete (widespread); Karpathos group [S. Europe].

? S. maculatus L., *Sp. pl.*: 813 (1753) - *FE* 4: 304.
Doubtfully present in Crete [S. Europe].

64. Scorzonera L.

1. S. cretica Willd., *Sp. pl.*: 3: 1504 (1803) - *FE* 4: 322. (?Including *S. dependens* Rech.f. - *FE* 4: 322.)
Cr (W, C, E) - *MAP 442*
Calcareous cliffs, rocky phrygana, maritime sands; 0-1400m; fl. 3-5.
Mainly C. & E. Crete [Andikithira & Kiklades; otherwise E. Aegean Islands (Halki & Rodos)].

S. dependens Rech.f. (*FE* 4: 322), described from the Samaria Gorge in W. Crete, is included - with some doubt - in synonymy of **1**, after Barclay (1986: 35).

S. idaea (Gand.) Lipsch. (*FE* 4: 319) = **2a**.

2. S. mollis M.Bieb., *Fl. taur.-caucas.* 3: 522 (1819) - *FE* 4: 319.
●**a.** subsp. **idaea** (Gand.) Lack in Strid & Kit Tan, *Mount. Fl. Greece* 2: 534 (1991) - *FE* 4: 319 as *S. idaea* (Gand.) Lipsch.
Cr (C, E) - *MAP 443*
Calcareous rocky slopes, clayey soil & fine gravel in dolines; 1400-2450m; fl. 5-7.
C. & E. Crete (Psiloritis & Dikti) - Endemic.
Subsp. *mollis*, given as doubtfully present in the Cretan area in *FE*, was recorded in error for **1** (Barclay, 1986: 36).

65. Senecio L.

●**1. S. fruticulosus** Sm., *Fl. Graec. prodr.* 2: 178 (1813) - *FE* 4: 202.
Cr (W, C, E) - *MAP 444*
Calcareous rocky places, rubble & screes; (1000-)1400-2400m; fl. 6-9.
Crete (Lefka Ori, Psiloritis & Dikti) - Endemic.

2. S. gallicus Chaix in Vill., *Hist. pl. Dauphiné* 1: 371 (1786) - *FE* 4: 203.
Cr (C, E) Ks Kp Sa - *MAP 445*

Calcareous gravel & screes, bare stony ground near sea; 0-1200m; fl. 3-5.
Mainly E. Crete; Karpathos group [S. Europe].

●3. S. gnaphalodes Sieber, *Reise Kreta* 1: 352 (1823) - *FE* 4: 194.
Cr (E) Kp Sa - *MAP 446*
Calcareous cliffs, among rocks, screes, walls of terraces; 50-450m.
E. Crete; Karpathos, Saria - Endemic.

? S. lividus L., *Sp. pl.*: 867 (1753) - *FE* 4: 204.
Doubtfully present in Crete (Greuter, 1974: 160) [W. & C. Mediterranean region].

4. S. squalidus L., *Sp. pl.*: 869 (1753) - *FE* 4: 202.
Cr (W) - *MAP 447*
Calcareous rocky debris beneath cliffs; 350m; fl. 3-5.
W. Crete (S. side) [W., C. & S. Europe].

5. S. vulgaris L., *Sp. pl.*: 867 (1753) - *FE* 4: 204.
Cr (W, C, E) Ks Kp - *MAP 448*
Disturbed ground, maritime sands, flat clayey areas; 0-1600m; fl. 2-6.
Crete (widespread), Kasos, Karpathos [throughout Europe].

66. Serratula L.

1. S. cichoracea (L.) DC., *Prodr.* 6: 670 (1838) - *FE* 4: 251.
●a. subsp. cretica Turrill in *Kew Bull.* 12: 391 (1957) - *FE* 4: 251.
Cr (E) - *MAP 449*
Cliffs, rocks, stony slopes; 200-500m; fl. 6.
E. Crete - Endemic.

67. Silybum Adans.

1. S. marianum (L.) Gaertn., *Fruct. sem. pl.* 2: 378 (1791) - *FE* 4: 249.
Cr (W, C) - *MAP 450*
Rocky & stony ground, waste areas; 0-400m.
W. & C. Crete (N. side) [W., C. & S. Europe].

68. Sonchus L.

1. S. asper (L.) Hill, *Herb. brit.* 1: 47 (1769) - *FE* 4: 327.
Cr (W, C) Kp - *MAP 451*
Olive groves, disturbed ground; 0-650m; fl. 3-5.
a. subsp. asper
Crete [almost throughout Europe].
b. subsp. glaucescens (Jord.) Ball in *J. Linn. Soc. (Bot.)* 16: 548 (1878) - *FE* 4: 327.

Crete [W., C. & S. Europe].
The species sensu lato occurs mainly in W. Crete and also in Karpathos.

2. S. oleraceus L., *Sp. pl.*: 794 (1753) - *FE* 4: 327.
Cr (W, C, E) Ks Kp - *MAP 452*
Olive groves, scrub, cultivated & fallow land, disturbed ground, waste areas; fl. 3-5.
Mainly W. & E. Crete; Kasos, Karpathos [almost throughout Europe].

? S. tenerrimus L., *Sp. pl.*: 794 (1753) - *FE* 4: 327.
Doubtfully present in Crete [S. Europe].

69. Staehelina L.

S. arborea Schreb. (*FE* 4: 217) = 2.

1. S. fruticosa (L.) L., *Syst. nat.* ed.12, 2: 538 (1767) - *FE* 4: 217.
Cr (W, E) Ks Kp Sa - *MAP 453*
Calcareous cliffs; 0-1800m; fl. 9-11.
W. & E. Crete (S. side); Karpathos group [Kiklades; otherwise E. Aegean Islands (Simi)].

●2. S. petiolata (L.) Hilliard & B.L.Burtt in *Notes R. bot. Gdn Edinb.* 32: 384 (1973) - *FE* 4: 217 as *S. arborea* Schreb.
Cr (W, C, E) - *MAP 454*
Calcareous cliffs; 100-1450m; fl. 6-8.
Mainly W. & C. Crete - Endemic.

70. Steptorhamphus Bunge

1. S. tuberosus (Jacq.) Grossh., *Fl. Kavkaza* 4: 258 (1934) - *FE* 4: 328.
Cr (W, C, E) Ks Kp Sa - *MAP 455*
Calcareous rocky banks, rocky ground beneath cliffs; 0-400m; fl. 5.
Crete (sporadic); Karpathos group [S. Balkan peninsula & Aegean region].

71. Tagetes L.

[1. T. minuta] L., *Sp. pl.*: 887 (1753) - *FE* 4: 144.
Cr (W) - *MAP 456*
Naturalized in orchards, orange plantations & other cultivated, irrigated ground; 0-100m; fl. 4-8.
W. Crete [S. Europe; from S. America].
Recorded since *FE* (Yannitsaros, 1979).

72. Tanacetum L.

[1. T. parthenium] (L.) Sch.Bip., *Tanaceteen*: 55 (1844) - *FE* 4: 171.
Cr - *NOT MAPPED*

Introduced, exact status not known.
Crete [W., C. & S. Europe].

73. **Taraxacum** F.H.Wigg.

The following species, with the possible exception of **2**, belong to sect. **Scariosa** Hand.-Mazz. emend. Dahlst., which is represented in *FE* **4**: 334 by the **T. bithynicum** group. Further details are given by Turland (1992*b*: 160).

1. T. aleppicum Dahlst. in *Acta Horti Bergiani* **9**(1): 14 (1926).
Cr (W, E) - *NOT MAPPED*
Crete (Lefka Ori & Dikti) [Greece; otherwise S.W. Asia].

2. T. bithynicum DC., *Prodr.* **7**: 149 (1838) - *FE* **4**: 334.
Cr (W) - *MAP 457*
Under Zelkova trees, calcareous rocky places; 1200-2000m; fl. 8.
W. Crete (Lefka Ori) [S.W. Asia].
The plant dealt with here is the species sensu stricto.

3. T. hellenicum Dahlst. in *Acta Horti Bergiani* **9**(1): 11 (1926).
Cr (C, E) - *MAP 458*
Open phrygana on serpentine, roadside; 200-600m; fl. 3-4.
C. & E. Crete [Mediterranean region].

T. megalorhizon (Forssk.) Hand.-Mazz. (*FE* **4**: 334) is apparently best treated as a nomen confusum (Turland, 1992*b*: 160); most records are probably referable to **4**.

4. T. minimum (V.Brig. ex Guss.) N.Terracc. in *Atti Ist. Incoragg. Sci. nat.* ser.2, **6**: 352 (1869) - *FE* **4**: 335.
Cr (C, E) Kp - *MAP 459*
Rock-crevices, open phrygana, beneath cliffs, bare stony ground, clayey areas, roadsides; 0-900m; fl. 10, 3-4.
C. & E. Crete; Karpathos [Mediterranean region].
The data given here are based on confirmed records only; the species is probably widespread in Crete.

The *T. officinale* group is given for the Cretan area in *FE* **4**: 341. This is based on an old record, for which the name was used in a broad, aggregate sense, referring to the genus as a whole (Greuter et al., 1984*b*: 274).

T. sect. **Scariosa** (*MAP 460*) is widespread in Crete and occurs also in Kasos; most records are probably referable to **4**.

74. **Tolpis** Adans.

1. T. barbata (L.) Gaertn., *Fruct. sem. pl.* **2**: 372 (1791) - *FE* **4**: 306. (Including *T. umbellata* Bertol. - *FE* **5**: 306.)
Cr (W, C) - *MAP 461*
Open sandy ground near sea; fl. 5.
Mainly W. Crete [S. Europe].

2. T. virgata Bertol., *Rar. Lig. pl.* **1**: 15 (1803) - *FE* **4**: 306.
Cr (W, C, E) - *MAP 462*
Rocky clearings in Cupressus woodland, calcareous rocky places & screes, flat clayey areas, maritime sands, fallow fields; 0-2000m.
Crete (sporadic) [Mediterranean region].

75. **Tragopogon** L.

T. hybridus L. (*FE* **4**: 325) = **Geropogon 1**.

●**1. T. lassithicus** Rech.f. in *Denkschr. Akad. Wiss. Wien* **105**(2,1): 156 (1943) - *FE* **4**: 324.
Cr (C, E) - *MAP 463*
Rocky slopes, screes; 1800-2200m.
C. & E. Crete (Psiloritis & Dikti) - Endemic.

2. T. longirostris Bisch. ex Sch.Bip. in Webb & Berthel., *Hist. nat. Iles Canaries* **2**: 469 (1850) - *FE* **4**: 323.
Ks Kp - *MAP 464*
Garigue, phrygana, fallow fields; 0-450m; fl. 4.
Kasos, Karpathos [S.W. Asia].

T. porrifolius subsp. *australis* (Jord.) Nyman (*FE* **4**: 323) = **3**.

3. T. sinuatus Avé-Lall., *Pl. Ital. bor.*: 17 (1829) - *FE* **4**: 323 as *T. porrifolius* subsp. *australis* (Jord.) Nyman.
Cr (W, C, E) - *MAP 465*
Olive groves, rocky places, abandoned fields, maritime sands; 0-450m; fl. 3-5.
Crete (widespread) [Mediterranean region].

76. **Tussilago** L.

1. T. farfara L., *Sp. pl.*: 865 (1753) - *FE* **4**: 186.
Cr (W, C) - *MAP 466*
Sandy and pebbly river-banks, stony soil on roadsides; 100-350m.
W. & C. Crete [almost throughout Europe].
Recorded since *FE* (Greuter et al., 1984*b*: 275)

77. **Tyrimnus** (Cass.) Cass.

1. T. leucographus (L.) Cass. in *Dict. Sci. nat.* **56**: 207 (1828) - *FE* **4**: 244.
Cr (W, C, E) Kp - *MAP 467*

Rocky places, disturbed ground, roadsides; 0-350m; fl. 4-5.
Crete (sporadic); Karpathos [Mediterranean region].

78. Urospermum Scop.

1. U. picroides (L.) Scop. ex F.W.Schmidt, *Samml. phys.-ökon. Aufs.*: 275 (1795) - *FE* **4**: 308.
Cr (W, C, E) Ks Kp Sa - *MAP 468*
Olive groves, rocky places, screes, disturbed ground; 0-450m; fl. 2-5.
Crete (widespread); Karpathos group [mainly Mediterranean region].

Wagenitzia lancifolia (Sieber ex Spreng.) Dostál (*FE* **4**: 301) = **Centaurea 7.**

79. Xanthium L.

[1. X. brasilicum] Vell., *Fl. flumin.*: 399 (1825) - *FE* **4**: 143.
Cr (W) - *MAP 469*
Naturalized in weed communities on humid sandy soil near sea.
W. Crete (W. of Hania).

[2. X. saccharatum] Wallr., *Beitr. bot.* **1**: 238 (1842) - *FE* **4**: 143.
Cr - *NOT MAPPED*
Naturalized.
Crete.

[3. X. spinosum] L., *Sp. pl.*: 987 (1753) - *FE* **4**: 143.
Cr (W, C, E) - *MAP 470*
Naturalized in weed communities.
Mainly W. & C. Crete [C. & S. Europe; from S. America].

"*X. strumarium*" (*FE* **4**: 143) = **1 & 2** (Barclay, 1986: 38).

80. Xeranthemum L.

1. X. inapertum (L.) Mill., *Gard. Dict.* ed.8: no.2 (1768) - *FE* **4**: 212.
Cr - *NOT MAPPED*
Crete [mainly Mediterranean region].

CONVOLVULACEAE

1. Calystegia R.Br.

1. C. sepium (L.) R.Br., *Prodr.*: 483 (1810) - *FE* **3**: 78.
a. subsp. **sepium**
Cr (W, C) - *MAP 471*

Scrub on river-banks, Phragmites beds, damp ground near sea.
W. & C. Crete [most of Europe].

? C. silvatica (Kit.) Griseb., *Spic. fl. rumel.* **2**: 74 (1844) - *FE* **3**: 79.
Doubtfully present in Crete; ?Karpathos [mainly S. Europe].

2. C. soldanella (L.) Roem. & Schult., *Syst. veg.* **4**: 184 (1819) - *FE* **3**: 78.
Cr (W, C) - *MAP 472*
Maritime sands.
W. & C. Crete [coasts of W. & S. Europe].

2. Convolvulus L.

1. C. althaeoides L., *Sp. pl.*: 156 (1753) - *FE* **3**: 82.
Cr (W, C, E) Ks Kp Sa - *MAP 473*
Rocky places, abandoned fields & terraces; 0-500m; fl. 3-6.
Crete (widespread); Karpathos group [S. Europe].
Subsp. *tenuissimus* (Sm.) Stace (*FE* **3**: 82) = **5.**

●2. C. argyrothamnos Greuter in *Bauhinia* **3**: 251 (1967) - *FE* **3**: 80.
Cr (W, E) - *MAP 474*
Calcareous cliffs in gorges; 150-450m.
W. & E. Crete - Endemic.
Endangered species, legally protected, although doubtfully distinct from **8**, appearing morphologically to fall within the range of variation of that species.

3. C. arvensis L., *Sp. pl.*: 153 (1753) - *FE* **3**: 81.
Cr (W, C, E) Kp - *MAP 475*
Marshes, seasonally wet places, cultivated & fallow land, waste areas; 0-450m; fl. 3-5.
Crete (widespread); Karpathos [almost throughout Europe].

? C. cantabrica L., *Sp. pl.*: 158 (1753) - *FE* **3**: 81.
Doubtfully present in Crete [S.C. & S. Europe].

4. C. dorycnium L., *Syst. nat.* ed.10, **2**: 923 (1759) - *FE* **3**: 80.
Cr (W, C, E) Kp - *MAP 476*
Calcareous phrygana, coastal rocks, maritime shingle; 0-100m; fl. 5-7.
Crete (sporadic, coastal); Karpathos [S. Greece & Aegean region].

5. C. elegantissimus Mill., *Gard. Dict.* ed.8: no.22 (1768) - *FE* **3**: 82 as *C. althaeoides* subsp. *tenuissimus* (Sm.) Stace.
Cr (W, C) - *MAP 477*
Phrygana, rocky & sandy places; 0-950m; fl. 3-5.

W. & C. Crete [mainly C. & E. Mediterranean region].

C. lanatus Vahl (*FE* **3**: 80) was almost certainly recorded in error (Greuter, 1974: 158).

6. C. libanoticus Boiss., *Diagn. pl. orient.* ser.1, **11**: 82 (1849) - *FE* **3**: 80.
Cr (C) - *MAP 478*
Flat clayey areas flooded in winter; 1400m.
C. Crete (Nida plain in Psiloritis) [C. & S. Greece; otherwise S.W. Asia].

7. C. lineatus L., *Syst. nat.* ed.10, **2**: 923 (1759) - *FE* **3**: 81.
?Cr Ks ?Kp - *MAP 479*
?Crete; Kasos, ?Karpathos [S. Europe].
Recorded from Kasos & Karpathos by Greuter et al. (1983*a*: 55 as "*C.* (cf.) *lineatus*"); recorded from Kasos - without such ambiguity - by Raus (1990: 27).

8. C. oleifolius Desr. in Lam., *Encycl.* **3**: 552 (1792) - *FE* **3**: 80.
Cr (W, C, E) Ks Kp - *MAP 480*
Phrygana, calcareous rocky places, steep banks, maritime sands & rocks, offshore islets; 0-500m; fl. 4-6, 10-11.
Mainly W. & E. Crete (coastal); Kasos, Karpathos [Malta, S. Greece & Aegean region]. Both subsp. *oleifolius* and subsp. *scopulorum* (Rech.f.) Greuter & Pleger (Greuter et al., 1983*a*: 55) have been recorded from Crete and Karpathos; the distinguishing features are not constant, however, and it seems impossible to define infraspecific taxa satisfactorily within this polymorphic species.

9. C. siculus L., *Sp. pl.*: 156 (1753) - *FE* **3**: 81.
a. subsp. **siculus**
Cr (W, C, E) Ks Kp - *MAP 481*
Step-crevices, among rocks, bases of calcareous cliffs; 0-600m; fl. 3-5.
Crete (sporadic); Kasos, Karpathos [Mediterranean region].

3. Cressa L.

1. C. cretica L., *Sp. pl.*: 223 (1753) - *FE* **3**: 78.
Cr (C, E) Kp - *MAP 482*
Rocky places, maritime sands; 0-300m.
C. & E. Crete; Karpathos [Mediterranean region].

4. Cuscuta L.

●**1. C. atrans** Feinbrun in *Israel J. Bot.* **19**: 22 (1970) - *FE* **3**: 76.
Cr (W) - *MAP 483*
Calcareous open rocky ground, on spiny dwarf shrubs, including Astracantha cretica, Satureja spinosa & Verbascum spinosum; 1850-2100m; fl. 7-8.
Crete (Lefka Ori) - Endemic.
Additionally recorded from Dikti in E. Crete in *MFG* **2**: 15 (also given as possibly occurring in Psiloritis in C. Crete).

? C. brevistyla A.Braun ex A.Rich., *Tent. fl. abyss.* **2**: 79 (1851) - *FE* **3**: 77.
Doubtfully present in Crete (Greuter, 1973*a*: 49) [Mediterranean region].

2. C. epithymum (L.) L., *Syst. veg.* ed.13: 140 (1774) - *FE* **3**: 77.
Cr (W, C, E) - *MAP 484*
Phrygana, maritime sands, usually on dwarf shrubs; 0-300m; fl. 4-5.
Crete (sporadic) [almost throughout Europe].
Subsp. *kotschyi* (Des Moul.) Arcang. (*FE* **3**: 77), recorded from Dikti in E. Crete in *MFG* **2**: 15, is treated as doubtfully distinct from subsp. *epithymum* in *M-Ch* **3**: 9, and is not separated here.

3. C. palaestina Boiss., *Diagn. pl. orient.* ser.1, **11**: 86 (1849) - *FE* **3**: 76.
a. subsp. **palaestina**
Cr Ks Kp - *NOT MAPPED*
Crete; Kasos, Karpathos [mainly E. Mediterranean region].

C. pedicellata Ledeb. (*FE* **3**: 76) was recorded from Karpathos by Greuter et al. (1983*a*: 55 as "*C.* (cf.) *pedicellata*"), but presumably in error, since the record is not repeated in *M-Ch* **3**: 10.

4. C. planiflora Ten., *Fl. napol.* **3**: 250 (1824-1829) - *FE* **3**: 77.
Cr (W, E) - *MAP 485*
Rocky places, recorded on Atractylis gummifera & Centaurea idaea; 300-1800m.
W. & E. Crete [S. Europe].

5. Ipomoea L.

1. I. imperati (Vahl) Griseb., *Cat. pl. Cub.*: 203 (1866) - *FE* **3**: 82 as *I. stolonifera* J.F.Gmel.
Cr (W) - *MAP 486*
Maritime sands; fl. 10.
W. Crete [Azores, Balearic Islands (Cabrera) & S. Italy; otherwise widespread in warm-temperate & tropical regions].

I. indica (Burm.) Merr. (*FE* **3**: 82 as *I. acuminata* (Vahl) Roem. & Schult.) is cultivated for ornament in Crete and has also been recorded as a casual escape (Greuter, 1974: 148).

I. stolonifera J.F.Gmel. (*FE* **3**: 82) = **1.**

CRASSULACEAE

Aeonium arboreum (L.) Webb & Berthel. (*FE* 1: 356) is probably only cultivated.

1. Crassula L.

1. C. alata (Viv.) A.Berger in Engl. & Prantl, *Natürl. PflFam.* ed.2, **18a**: 389 (1930).
Cr (W, C, E) Kp - *MAP 487*
Bare sandy ground & calcareous rocky places near sea, flat bare paths, hard trodden earth, courtyards of Minoan palaces, particularly on winter-wet ground; 0-80m.
Crete (sporadic); Karpathos [Kiklades; otherwise N. Africa & S.W. Asia].
Recorded since *FE* (Greuter & Raus, 1981: 276).

2. C. tillaea Lest.-Garl., *Fl. Jersey*: 87 (1903) - *FE* 1: 351.
Cr (C) - *MAP 488*
Flat clayey area, apparently flooded in winter; 620m.
C. Crete [W. & S. Europe].

3. C. vaillantii (Willd.) Roth, *Enum. pl. phaen. Germ.* **1**: 992 (1827) - *FE* 1: 351.
Cr (W) - *MAP 489*
Water puddles in karstic holes.
W. Crete (Gavdos island) [S. Europe].

2. Rosularia (DC.) Stapf

1. R. serrata (L.) A.Berger in Engl. & Prantl, *Natürl. PflFam.* ed.2, **18a**: 465 (1930) - *FE* 1: 364.
Cr (W, C, E) Ks Kp Sa - *MAP 490*
Calcareous cliffs, crevices & ledges, usually in shade; 50-2000m.
Crete (widespread); Karpathos group [Kithira; otherwise E. Aegean Islands & W. Turkey].

3. Sedum L.

1. S. acre L., *Sp. pl.*: 432 (1753) - *FE* 1: 359.
Cr (E) - *MAP 491*
Calcareous open stony ground; 1300-2000m.
E. Crete (Dikti) [almost throughout Europe].
Cretan plants belong to subsp. *neglectum* (Ten.) Murb., which is treated as doubtfully distinct from subsp. *acre* in *M-Ch* 3: 19, and is not separated here.

2. S. album L., *Sp. pl.*: 430 (1753) - *FE* 1: 360.
Cr (W, C, E) - *MAP 492*
Calcareous rocks, crevices, rubble & screes; 800-2400m.

Crete (mainly Lefka Ori, Kedros, Psiloritis, Kofinas, Dikti & Afendis Kavousi) [most of Europe].
Cretan plants belong to subsp. *athoum* (DC.) Hayek, which is treated as doubtfully distinct from subsp. *album* in *M-Ch* 3: 19, and is not separated here.

3. S. amplexicaule DC. in *Mém. agric. Soc. agric. Dép. Seine* **11**: 12 (1808) - *FE* 1: 359, included in synonymy of *S. tenuifolium* (Sm.) Strobl.
a. subsp. **tenuifolium** (Sm.) Greuter in *Willdenowia* **11**: 277 (1981) - *FE* 1: 359 as *S. tenuifolium* (Sm.) Strobl.
Cr (W, C, E) Kp - *MAP 493*
Calcareous rocky places, gravel & screes; 350-2000m; fl. 5-6.
Crete (widespread, mainly in mountains); Karpathos [Mediterranean region].
"*S. annuum*" (*FE* 1: 362) = **9** & **11** (Greuter et al., 1984b: 276; *MFG* 1: 357).

4. S. caespitosum (Cav.) DC., *Prodr.* **3**: 405 (1828) - *FE* 1: 363.
Cr (C, E) - *MAP 494*
Calcareous rocky phrygana; -850m.
C. & E. Crete [S.C. & S. Europe].
Given for the Cretan area in *FE*, based on records which are referable to **9** (Greuter et al., 1984b: 276). The same authors record the true species from E. Crete (loc. cit.), without commenting on records from C. Crete by Zaffran (1976: 67; 1990: 147).

S. cepaea L. (*FE* 1: 362) was recorded in error (Greuter, 1974: 156).

●**5. S. creticum** C.Presl in *Isis, Jena* **21**: 273 (1828) - *FE* 1: 362.
Cr (W, C, E) Kp Sa - *MAP 495*
Calcareous cliffs & crevices, rock-hollows & debris, bare ground; 0-1600m; fl. 5-6.
Mainly W. & E. Crete; Karpathos, Saria - Endemic.
S. hierapetrae Rech.f. (*FE* 1: 361), which occurs in the mountains of E. Crete, is reduced to varietal rank under *S. creticum* in *MFG* 1: 353, and is not separated here.

S. dasyphyllum L. (*FE* 1: 361) was almost certainly recorded in error (Greuter, 1974: 157).

6. S. delicum (Vierh.) Carlström in *Willdenowia* **15**: 110 (1985) - not cited in *FE*.
Cr (W) - *MAP 496*
Rocky coasts; 0-150m; fl. 4-5.
W. Crete [S. Greece & Kiklades].
Related to **12**.

S. hierapetrae Rech.f. (*FE* 1: 361) see **5**.

7. S. hispanicum L., *Cent. pl.* **1**: 12 (1755) -
FE **1**: 363.
Cr (E) - *MAP 497*
Calcareous rocky places; 800-950m.
E. Crete (Afendis Kavousi); Karpathos [mainly
S.E. Europe].

S. idaeum D.A.Webb (*FE* **1**: 360) = **8a**.

8. S. laconicum Boiss. & Heldr. in Boiss.,
Diagn. pl. orient. ser.1, **6**: 55 (1846) - *FE* **1**:
360.
a. subsp. **insulare** (Rech.f.) Greuter & Rech.f.
in *Boissiera* **13**: 67 (1967) - *FE* **1**: 360 as *S.
idaeum* D.A.Webb.
Cr (W, C, E) - *MAP 498*
*Calcareous open rocky slopes, rubble & screes;
(650-)1450-2350m.*
Crete (mainly Lefka Ori, Psiloritis & Dikti)
[Kithira].

9. S. litoreum Guss., *Pl. rar.*: 185 (1826) - *FE*
1: 362.
Cr (W, C, E) Ks Kp Sa - *MAP 499*
Rocks; 0-1150m.
Mainly E. Crete; Karpathos group [C. & E.
Mediterranean region].

10. S. magellense Ten., *Fl. napol.* **1**: xxvi
(1811-1815) - *FE* **1**: 361.
a. subsp. **olympicum** (Boiss.) Greuter & Burdet
in Greuter, Burdet & G.Long, *Med-Checklist* **3**:
24 (1986) - not cited in *FE*.
Cr (W, C, E) - *MAP 500*
*Calcareous cliffs, rock-crevices, rocky slopes,
flat clayey areas; 1500-2350m.*
Crete (Lefka Ori, Psiloritis & Dikti) [Italy &
Balkan peninsula].
Subsp. *magellense* is confined to Italy and
Algeria (*M-Ch* **3**: 24).

S. ochroleucum Chaix (*FE* **1**: 358) was almost
certainly recorded in error (Greuter, 1974: 157).

S. pallidum M.Bieb. (*FE* **1**: 363) is given for
Crete by Barclay (1986: 40) and for Karpathos
by Greuter et al. (1983a: 55), but all records
from the Aegean region are doubtful according
to Carlström (1985: 113); cf. *MFG* **1**: 358.

●**11. S. praesidis** Runemark & Greuter in
Willdenowia **11**: 18 (1981).
Cr (W, C, E) Ks - *MAP 501*
*Calcareous cliffs, crevices & rocks, phrygana;
0-1500m.*
Crete (widespread); Kasos - Endemic.
Related to **9**.

12. S. rubens L., *Sp. pl.*: 432 (1753) - *FE* **1**:
363.
Cr (W, C, E) Ks Kp - *MAP 502*
*Calcareous rocky places & screes, maritime
sands, stony abandoned fields; 0-2400m.*

Mainly W. Crete; Kasos, Karpathos [W. & S.
Europe].

13. S. sediforme (Jacq.) Pau in *Actas Mems
Congr. Nat. esp.*: 246 (1909) - *FE* **1**: 358.
Cr (W, C, E) Kp - *MAP 503*
Calcareous rocky places; 0-250m.
Crete (sporadic); Karpathos [Mediterranean
region].

? S. stellatum L., *Sp. pl.*: 431 (1753) - *FE* **1**:
362.
Doubtfully present in Crete (Greuter, 1974: 157)
[Mediterranean region].

S. tenuifolium (Sm.) Strobl (*FE* **1**: 359) = **3a**.

14. S. tristriatum Boiss. & Heldr. in Boiss.,
Diagn. pl. orient. ser.1, **10**: 16 (1849) - *FE* **1**:
361.
Cr (W, E) - *MAP 504*
*Calcareous rock-crevices, rubble & screes, flat
clayey areas; 600-2300m; fl. 6-7.*
W. & E. Crete (mainly Lefka Ori & Dikti) [S.
Peloponnisos].

4. Umbilicus DC.

U. chloranthus Heldr. & Sart. ex Boiss. (*FE* **1**:
351) was almost certainly recorded in error
(Greuter, 1974: 157).

U. erectus DC. (*FE* **1**: 352) = **2**.

1. U. horizontalis (Guss.) DC., *Prodr.* **3**: 400
(1828) - *FE* **1**: 352.
Cr (W, C, E) Ks Kp Sa - *MAP 505*
*Cliffs, rock-crevices, old walls; 0-1000m; fl. 4-
5.*
Mainly W. & E. Crete; Karpathos group
[Mediterranean region].

2. U. luteus (Huds.) Webb & Berthel., *Hist.
nat. Iles Canaries* **1**: 177 (1840) - *FE* **1**: 352 as
U. erectus DC.
Cr (C, E) - *MAP 506*
Calcareous cliffs & rock-crevices; 1000-1800m.
C. & E. Crete (Psiloritis & Dikti) [S. Italy & S.
Balkan peninsula].

3. U. parviflorus (Desf.) DC., *Prodr.* **3**: 400
(1828) - *FE* **1**: 351.
Cr (W, C, E) Kp - *MAP 507*
*Calcareous cliffs, rock-hollows, old walls; 0-
1200m; fl. 3-5.*
Mainly W. Crete; Karpathos [S. Greece;
otherwise E. Aegean Islands & S.W. Turkey].

4. U. rupestris (Salisb.) Dandy in Ridd.,
Hedley & W.R.Price, *Fl. Gloucestershire*: 611
(1948) - *FE* **1**: 352.
Cr (W) - *MAP 508*

Mossy rocks in Castanea grove; 500m.
W. Crete [W. & S. Europe].

CRUCIFERAE
(BRASSICACEAE)

1. Aethionema R.Br.

1. A. saxatile (L.) R.Br. in W.T.Aiton, *Hortus kew.* **4**: 80 (1812) - *FE* 1: 322.
a. subsp. creticum (Boiss. & Heldr.)
I.A.Andersson, Carlström, Franzén, Karlén & Nybom in *Willdenowia* **13**: 18 (1983) - *FE* 1: 322, included in synonymy of **1**.
Cr (W, C, E) Kp - *MAP 509*
Calcareous cliffs, rock-crevices & stony slopes; 300-2200m; fl. 3-4.
Crete (widespread, mainly in mountains); Karpathos [S.E. Greece & Aegean region; otherwise W. Turkey].

Alliaria petiolata (M.Bieb.) Cavara & Grande is given for the Cretan area in *FE* 1: 267, although there are no records as a basis for this (Greuter, 1974: 139).

Alyssoides cretica (L.) Medik. (*FE* 1: 296) = **Lutzia 1**.

2. Alyssum L.

A. alyssoides (L.) L. (*FE* 1: 299) was almost certainly recorded in error (Greuter, 1974: 156).

A. corsicum Duby is given for the Cretan area in *FE* 1: 303, although there are no records as a basis for this (Greuter, 1974: 139).

1. A. fallacinum Hausskn. in *Mitt. thüring. bot. Ver.* nov.ser. **3-4**: 114 (1893) - *FE* 1: 303.
Cr (C) - *MAP 510*
Phrygana of Cistus & Sarcopoterium.
C. Crete [Greece].
The plants from Crete have been treated separately as the endemic *A. baldaccii* Vierh. ex Nyár. in *Bul. Grad. bot. Muz. bot. Univ. Cluj* **7**: 123 (1928).

2. A. foliosum Bory & Chaub. in Bory, *Exp. sci. Morée, Bot.*: 185 (1832) - *FE* 1: 300.
Cr (C, E) Kp - *MAP 511*
Soil-patches in calcareous rocky phrygana; 700-1800m; fl. 3-4.
C. & E. Crete (Kedros & Dikti); Karpathos (Kalilimni) [S. Greece & Aegean region; otherwise S.W. Asia].

●**3. A. fragillimum** (Bald.) Rech.f. in *Denkschr. Akad. Wiss. Wien* **105(2,1)**: 77 (1943) - *FE* 1: 304.
Cr (W) - *MAP 512*

Calcareous rock-crevices, rubble & screes, stony & gravelly places; 1800-2400m; fl. 6-7.
W. Crete (Lefka Ori) - Endemic.

●**4. A. idaeum** Boiss. & Heldr. in Boiss., *Diagn. pl. orient.* ser.1, **8**: 35 (1849) - *FE* 1: 302.
Cr (C) - *MAP 513*
Calcareous rubble, mobile & stabilized screes, gravelly places; 1700-2400m; fl. 5-6.
C. Crete (Psiloritis) - Endemic.
Additionally recorded from Dikti in E. Crete in *MFG* 1: 293.

●**5. A. lassiticum** Halácsy, *Consp. fl. graec.* suppl.1: 10 (1908) - *FE* 1: 302.
Cr (E) - *MAP 514*
Calcareous rocky places; 1700-2000m.
E. Crete (Dikti) - Endemic.

A. minus Rothm. (*FE* 1: 300) = **8**.

6. A. minutum Schltdl. ex DC., *Syst. nat.* **2**: 316 (1821) - *FE* 1: 300.
Cr (W, C, E) - *MAP 515*
Calcareous rocky slopes & gravel; 1100-2100m; fl. 4-5.
Crete (Lefka Ori, Psiloritis, Dikti & Afendis Kavousi) [E. & S. Europe].

A. murale Waldst. & Kit. (*FE* 1: 302) was recorded in error (Greuter, 1974: 156).

A. paniculatum Desf. is given for the Cretan area in *M-Ch* 3: 46, but treated as a taxon of uncertain status and presumed extinct (cf. Rechinger, 1943a: 227).

A. saxatile L. (*FE* 1: 299) = **Aurinia 1**.

7. A. siculum Jord., *Diagn. esp. nouv.* **1**: 202 (1864) - not cited in *FE*.
Cr (C, E) - *MAP 516*
Rocky ground, among stones; 850-1700m; fl. 5-6.
C. & E. Crete (Psiloritis, Dikti & Afendis Kavousi area) [Sicily & S. Greece].

8. A. simplex Rudolfi in *J. Bot. Göttingen* **1799(2)**: 290 (1799) - *FE* 1: 300 as *A. minus* Rothm.
Cr (E) Kp - *MAP 517*
Mountain slopes, calcareous screes, open dry stony places; 0-1150m.
E. Crete; Karpathos [E. & S. Europe].

9. A. smyrnaeum C.A.Mey. in *Bull. scient. Acad. imp. Sci. St. Pétersb.* **7**: 132 (1840) - *FE* 1: 300.
Cr (E) - *MAP 518*
Among stones; 1200-1400m.
E. Crete (Dikti) [Kiklades (Naxos); otherwise E. Aegean Islands & W. Turkey].
Recorded since *FE* (Persson, 1971).

●**10. A. sphacioticum** Boiss. & Heldr. in Boiss., *Diagn. pl. orient.* ser.1, **8**: 35 (1849) - *FE* **1**: 302.
Cr (W, C) - *MAP 519*
Calcareous rock-crevices, rubble & mobile screes; 1700-2400m; fl. 4-6(-7).
W. & C. Crete (Lefka Ori & Psiloritis) - Endemic.

11. A. strigosum Banks & Sol. in Russell, *Nat. hist. Aleppo* ed.2, **2**: 257 (1794) - *FE* **1**: 300.
Cr (E) Sa - *MAP 520*
E. Crete (Dionisiades islands); Saria [mainly S.E. Europe].

"*A. umbellatum*" (*FE* **1**: 300) = **7** (Barclay, 1986: 41).

3. Arabidopsis (DC.) Heynh.

1. A. thaliana (L.) Heynh. in Holl & Heynh., *Fl. Sachsen* **1**: 538 (1842) - *FE* **1**: 267.
Cr (W, C) - *MAP 521*
Calcareous rocky slopes, mountain pastures, flat clayey areas; 500-2100m.
W. & C. Crete [almost throughout Europe].

4. Arabis L.

1. A. alpina L., *Sp. pl.*: 664 (1753) - *FE* **1**: 294.
Cr (W, C, E) Kp - *MAP 522*
Calcareous cliffs, crevices, rocky places & screes; 1000-2400m; fl. 4-5.
Crete (Lefka Ori, Kedros, Psiloritis, Dikti & Afendis Kavousi); Karpathos (Kalilimni) [most of Europe].
A. alpina is treated here sensu lato, as plants from both Greece and the Cretan area cannot be referred satisfactorily to either subsp. *alpina* or subsp. *caucasica* (Willd. ex Schltdl.) Briq. (*FE* **1**: 294 as *A. caucasica* Willd. ex Schltdl.); cf. *MFG* **1**: 268.

2. A. auriculata Lam., *Encycl.* **1**: 219 (1783) - *FE* **1**: 293 as *A. recta* Vill.
Cr (W) - *MAP 523*
Calcareous rocky places; 2200m.
W. Crete (Lefka Ori) [C. & S. Europe].
Additionally recorded from Psiloritis in C. Crete in *MFG* **1**: 266.

A. caucasica Willd. ex Schltdl. (*FE* **1**: 294) see **1**.

●**3. A. cretica** Boiss. & Heldr. in Boiss., *Diagn. pl. orient.* ser.1, **8**: 20 (1849) - *FE* **1**: 292 as *A. serpyllifolia* subsp. *cretica* (Boiss. & Heldr.) B.M.G.Jones.
Cr (W, C, E) - *MAP 524*

Calcareous rocky places & crevices; 950-2350m; fl. 3-6(-10).
Crete (Lefka Ori, Psiloritis, Dikti & Afendis Kavousi) - Endemic.

A. longistyla Rech.f. (*FE* **1**: 293) is included in synonymy of **Diplotaxis 1**.

A. muralis Bertol. (*FE* **1**: 292) was recorded in error (Greuter, 1974: 156).

A. recta Vill. (*FE* **1**: 293) = **2**.

A. serpyllifolia subsp. *cretica* (Boiss. & Heldr.) B.M.G.Jones (*FE* **1**: 292) = **3**.

4. A. verna (L.) R.Br. in W.T.Aiton, *Hortus kew.* **4**: 105 (1812) - *FE* **1**: 293.
Cr (W, C, E) Kp - *MAP 525*
Calcareous woodland, scrub, rocks, walls, screes, bare stony ground; 0-1200m; fl. 3-5.
Mainly W. Crete; Karpathos [Mediterranean region].

5. Aubrieta Adans.

1. A. deltoidea (L.) DC., *Syst. nat.* **2**: 294 (1821) - *FE* **1**: 295.
Cr (W, E) - *MAP 526*
Calcareous rocks, crevices, rubble & screes; 1100-2300m; fl. 3-5.
W. Crete (Lefka Ori), one record from E. Crete (Dikti) [mainly Sicily, S. Balkan peninsula & Aegean region].
Given for Karpathos in *FE* **1**: 295 (as var. *microphylla* Boiss.), although there appear to no records upon which this is based.

6. Aurinia Desv.

1. A. saxatilis (L.) Desv. in *J. Bot. Agric. Pharm. Med. Arts Paris* **3**: 162 (1815) - *FE* **1**: 299 as *Alyssum saxatile* L.
a. subsp. **megalocarpa** (Hausskn.) T.R.Dudley in *Jour. Arn. Arb.* **45**: 397 (1964) - *FE* **1**: 299 as *Alyssum saxatile* subsp. *megalocarpum* (Hausskn.) Rech.f.
Cr (W, C) - *MAP 527*
Calcareous cliffs, step-crevices, rocky slopes; 0-550m; fl. 2-4.
W. & C. Crete [S. Italy, Kithira & Kiklades; otherwise E. Aegean Islands & W. Turkey].

7. Biscutella L.

1. B. didyma L., *Sp. pl.*: 653 (1753) - *FE* **1**: 329.
Cr (W, C, E) Ks Kp - *MAP 528*

Rocky places, stony ground beneath cliffs; 0-1100m; fl. 2-5.
Mainly W. & C. Crete; Kasos, Karpathos [Mediterranean region].
Subsp. *columnae* (Ten.) Nyman is given for the Cretan area in *M-Ch* **3**: 63, but as doubtfully distinct from subsp. *didyma*; it is not separated here.

B. laevigata L. is given for the Cretan area in *FE* **1**: 326, although there are no records as a basis for this (Greuter, 1974: 139).

8. Brassica L.

1. B. cretica Lam., *Encycl.* **1**: 747 (1785) - *FE* **1**: 337.
a. subsp. **aegaea** (Heldr. & Halácsy) Snogerup, M.A.Gust. & Bothmer in *Willdenowia* **19**: 291 (1990) - not cited in *FE*.
Cr (E) Ks Kp - *MAP 529*
Calcareous cliffs & offshore islets; 0-1100m.
E. Crete (Dionisiades islands); Kasos, Karpathos [Ionian Islands (Lefkada & Kefallinia) & Aegean region; otherwise S.W. Turkey & Israel].
b. subsp. **cretica** (including var. *nivea* (Boiss. & Spruner) O.E.Schulz - *FE* **1**: 337).
Cr (W, C, E) - *MAP 530*
Calcareous cliffs; 0-1500m; fl. 3-4.
Crete (widespread) [N.& W. Peloponnisos; otherwise Lebanon].

2. B. nigra (L.) W.D.J.Koch in Röhl., *Deutschl. Fl.* ed.3, **4**: 713 (1833) - *FE* **1**: 338.
Cr (W, C, E) Kp - *MAP 531*
Cultivated & fallow land, marshy places, river-beds, disturbed ground; 0-500m; fl. 3-5.
Crete (widespread); Karpathos [most of Europe].
Doubtfully native (*M-Ch* **3**: 71). The immature inflorescences are collected by the local people as a condiment.

3. B. tournefortii Gouan, *Ill. observ. bot.*: 44 (1773) - *FE* **1**: 338.
Cr (W) - *MAP 532*
Weed communities, maritime sands, disturbed ground; 0-400m; fl. 4-5.
W. Crete [Mediterranean region].

9. Bunias L.

1. B. erucago L., *Sp. pl.*: 670 (1753) - *FE* **1**: 269.
Cr (W) - *MAP 533*
Weed communities on stony ground; fl. 3-4.
W. Crete [mostly S. Europe].

10. Cakile Mill.

1. C. maritima Scop., *Fl. carniol.* ed.2, **2**: 35 (1772) - *FE* **1**: 343.
Cr (W, C, E) Ks Kp Sa - *MAP 534*
Maritime sands; fl. 3-6, 9-10.
Crete (widespread); Karpathos group [coasts of most of Europe].

11. Calepina Adans.

1. C. irregularis (Asso) Thell. in Schinz & Keller, *Fl. Schweiz* ed.2, **1**: 218 (1905) - *FE* **1**: 345.
Cr (W) - *MAP 535*
Sandy alluvial soil of river-mouth.
W. Crete (Petres river W. of Rethimno) [W., C. & S. Europe].
Doubtfully native; recorded since *FE* (Greuter et al., 1984*b*: 277).

Camelina alyssum (Mill.) Thell. is given for the Cretan area in *FE* **1**: 315, although there are no records as a basis for this (Greuter, 1974: 139).

C. microcarpa Andrz. ex DC. is given for the Cretan area in *FE* **1**: 315, although there are no records as a basis for this (Greuter, 1974: 139).

C. sativa (L.) Crantz is given for the Cretan area in *FE* **1**: 315, although there are no records as a basis for this (Greuter, 1974: 139).

12. Capsella Medik.

1. C. bursa-pastoris (L.) Medik., *Pfl.-Gatt*: 85 (1792) - *FE* **1**: 316.
Cr (W, C, E) Kp - *MAP 536*
Calcareous slopes, mountain pastures, flat clayey areas, cultivated & fallow land, disturbed ground; 0-1700m; fl. 3-4.
Mainly W. & C. Crete; Karpathos [throughout Europe].

C. rubella Reut. (*FE* **1**: 316) was probably recorded in error (Akeroyd in Greuter & Raus, 1986: 417), and anyway is treated as doubtfully distinct from **1** in *M-Ch* **3**: 76.

13. Cardamine L.

1. C. graeca L., *Sp. pl.*: 655 (1753) - *FE* **1**: 289.
Cr (W, C, E) - *MAP 537*
Calcareous woodland, among rocks in shady places, screes; 500-1300m; fl. 3-5.
Mainly W. Crete [S. Europe].

2. C. hirsuta L., *Sp. pl.*: 655 (1753) - *FE* **1**: 289.
Cr (W, C, E) Kp - *MAP 538*
Olive groves, rocky places, flat clayey areas, cultivated & bare ground; 0-1400m; fl. 3-4.
Mainly W. & C. Crete; Karpathos [almost throughout Europe].

14. Cardaria Desv.

1. C. draba (L.) Desv. in *J. Bot. Agric. Pharm. Med. Arts Paris* **3**: 163 (1815) - *FE* **1**: 333.
a. subsp. **draba**
Cr (W, C, E) Ks Kp - *MAP 539*
Olive groves, vineyards, cultivated & fallow fields, roadsides, waste areas; 0-800m; fl. 3-5.
Crete (sporadic); Kasos, Karpathos [most of Europe].

15. Carrichtera DC.

1. C. annua (L.) DC. in *Mém. Mus. Hist. nat. Paris* **7**: 250 (1821) - *FE* **1**: 342.
Cr (W) Kp - *MAP 540*
Fallow fields, scree; near s.l.; fl. 3-4.
W. Crete (Hora Sfakion); Karpathos [Mediterranean region].
Recorded since *FE* (Greuter & Raus, 1986: 104).

"*Cheiranthus cheiri*" (*FE* **1**: 279) = **Erysimum 1** (cf. Snogerup, 1967).

16. Clypeola L.

1. C. jonthlaspi L., *Sp. pl.*: 652 (1753) - *FE* **1**: 307.
Cr (W, C, E) Kp - *MAP 541*
Calcareous cliffs, crevices, rocky slopes, among stones; 100-2000m; fl. 3-4.
Mainly W. Crete; Karpathos [S. Europe].

17. Coronopus Zinn

[1. C. didymus] (L.) Sm., *Fl. brit.* **2**: 691 (1800) - *FE* **1**: 333.
Cr (W) - *MAP 542*
Possibly naturalized on margins of pavements & as a grass-weed in gardens.
W. Crete [W., C. & S. Europe; from S. America].
Recorded since *FE* (Yannitsaros, 1986: 63).

2. C. squamatus (Forssk.) Asch., *Fl. Brandenburg* **1**: 62 (1860) - *FE* **1**: 333.
Cr - *NOT MAPPED*
Crete [most of Europe].

18. Didesmus Desv.

1. D. aegyptius (L.) Desv. in *J. Bot. Agric. Pharm. Med. Arts Paris* **3**: 160 (1815) - *FE* **1**: 344.
Cr (W, E) Ks Kp - *MAP 543*
Open olive groves, fallow & abandoned fields, roadsides, disturbed ground, maritime rocks; 0-200m; fl. 3-4.
Mainly E. Crete; Kasos, Karpathos [S. Aegean region; otherwise Libya, Egypt & Cyprus].

19. Diplotaxis DC.

1. D. viminea (L.) DC., *Syst. nat.* **2**: 635 (1821) - *FE* **1**: 335. (Including *Arabis longistyla* Rech.f. - *FE* **1**: 293.)
Cr (W, E) Ks Kp - *MAP 544*
Olive groves, caverns of cliffs, open dry stony places, walls, fallow fields; 20-100m; fl. 3-6.
W. & E. Crete; Kasos, Karpathos [mostly S. Europe].
Erroneously regarded as absent from the Cretan area in *FE* (Greuter, 1974: 140).

20. Draba L.

D. bruniifolia Steven (*M-Ch* **3**: 96) see **2**.

●**1. D. cretica** Boiss. & Heldr. in Boiss., *Diagn. pl. orient. ser.1*, **8**: 27 (1849) - *FE* **1**: 309.
Cr (W, C, E) - *MAP 545*
Calcareous rock-crevices & ledges, stabilized screes, stony ground with thin soil layer, flat clayey areas; 1100-2400m; fl. 4-5.
Crete (Lefka Ori, Kedros, Psiloritis, Dikti & Afendis Kavousi) - Endemic.

2. D. heterocoma Fenzl, *Pug. pl. nov. Syr.*: 13 (1842) - *FE* **1**: 310.
Kp - *MAP 546*
1200m.
Karpathos (Kalilimni) [Turkey to Trascaucasia].
Referred to subsp. *heterocoma* in *M-Ch* **3**: 96 (as *D. bruniifolia* subsp. *heterocoma* (Fenzl) Coode & Cullen) and, tentatively, in *MFG* **1**: 315. Subsp. *archipelagi* (O.E.Schulz) Buttler, given as doubtfully present in the Cretan area in *M-Ch*, occurs nearby on the E. Aegean island of Samos and in W. Turkey.

3. D. muralis L., *Sp. pl.*: 642 (1753) - *FE* **1**: 312.
Cr (W) - *MAP 547*
Flat clayey areas; 1050m.
W. Crete (Omalos plain in Lefka Ori) [most of Europe].

21. Drabopsis K.Koch

1. D. nuda (Bél. ex Boiss.) Stapf in *Denkschr. Akad. Wiss. Wien* **51(2)**: 298 (1886).
Cr (W) - *MAP 548*
Somewhat moist stony ground close to snow-patches on N.W.-facing slope; 1800-1850m; fl. 5.
W. Crete (Lefka Ori) [C. Turkey to W. Himalaya].
Recorded since *FE* (Gustavsson, 1977 as *D. verna* K.Koch).

22. Enarthrocarpus Labill.

1. E. arcuatus Labill., *Icon. pl. Syr.* **5**: 4 (1812) - *FE* **1**: 345.
Cr (W, C, E) Kp - *MAP 549*
Sparse low calcareous phrygana, maritime rocks & sands; 0-150m; fl. 3-4.
Crete (sporadic); Karpathos [Greece & Aegean region; otherwise S.W. Asia].

23. Erophila DC.

1. E. praecox (Steven) DC., *Syst. nat.* **2**: 357 (1821) - *FE* **1**: 313 as *E. verna* subsp. *praecox* (Steven) Walters.
Cr (C, E) Kp - *MAP 550*
Calcareous rocky slopes, bare stony ground; 0-1500m; fl. 3-4.
C. & E. Crete; Karpathos [mainly Mediterranean region].

2. E. verna (L.) Chevall., *Fl. gén. env. Paris* **2**: 898 (1827) - *FE* **1**: 312 as *E. verna* (L.) Chevall. subsp. *verna*.
Cr (W) - *MAP 551*
Flat clayey areas; 650-1050m.
W. Crete [most of Europe].
Subsp. *praecox* (Steven) Walters (*FE* **1**: 313) = **1**.

E. verna sensu lato (*MAP 552*), i.e. including **1**, is widespread in Crete.

24. Eruca Mill.

1. E. sativa Mill., *Gard. Dict.* ed.8: no.1 (1768) - *FE* **1**: 340 as *E. vesicaria* subsp. *sativa* (Mill.) Thell.
Cr (W, C, E) Kp - *MAP 553*
Olive groves, cultivated & fallow land; 0-450m; fl. 3-5.
Mainly W. & C. Crete; Karpathos [Mediterranean region].
Subsp. *longirostris* (Uechtr.) Jahand. & Maire is given for the Cretan area in *M-Ch* **3**: 103, but as doubtfully distinct from subsp. *sativa*; it is not separated here.

E. vesicaria subsp. *sativa* (Mill.) Thell. (*FE* **1**: 340) = **1**.

25. Erucaria Gaertn.

1. E. hispanica (L.) Druce in *Rep. Botl Soc. Exch. Club Br. Isl.* **3**: 418 (1914) - *FE* **1**: 343.
Cr (C, E) Kp - *MAP 554*
Fallow fields.
C. & E. Crete; Karpathos [mainly Spain, S. Greece & Aegean region].

26. Erysimum L.

1. E. candicum Snogerup in *Op. bot. Soc. bot. Lund* **13**: 34 (1967).
a. subsp. **candicum**
Cr (W, C, E) - *MAP 555*
Calcareous cliffs; 50-1200m; fl. 3-4.
Crete (widespread) [S.E. Kiklades (Anafi)].
●**b.** subsp. **carpathum** Snogerup in *Op. bot. Soc. bot. Lund* **13**: 38 (1967).
Kp Sa - *MAP 556*
Calcareous cliffs; 50-800m; fl. 3-4.
Karpathos, Saria - Endemic.
Given for Kasos & Karpathos, rather than Karpathos & Saria, by Greuter et al. (1983a: 56); this contradicts other records and is presumably a printing error.

●**2. E. creticum** Boiss. & Heldr. in Boiss., *Diagn. pl. orient.* ser. 2, **1**: 26 (1854) - *FE* **1**: 272.
Cr (E) - *MAP 557*
Rocky banks, debris of gorge-beds, rocky phrygana, roadsides; 0-900(-1300)m; fl. 3-5.
E. Crete - Endemic.
Records from Karpathos are referable to **3** (Raus, 1991: 306).

? E. graecum Boiss. & Heldr. in Boiss., *Diagn. pl. orient.* ser.2, **1**: 27 (1854) - *FE* **1**: 272.
Doubtfully present in Crete (Greuter, 1974: 156) [S. Greece].

3. E. horizontale P.Candargy in *Bull. Soc. bot. Fr.* **44**: 154 (1897).
Kp - *MAP 558*
Rocky banks & phrygana, field-margins; 0-800m; fl. 3-4.
Karpathos [N. Aegean region (Samothraki); otherwise E. Aegean Islands (Lesvos) & ?W. Turkey].
Recorded by Raus (1991: 306).

●**4. E. mutabile** Boiss. & Heldr. in Boiss., *Diagn. pl. orient.* ser.1, **8**: 24 (1849) - *FE* **1**: 272.
Cr (W, E) - *MAP 559*
Dwarf shrub communities above timberline, calcareous rock-debris, screes, crevices, flat clayey areas; (850-)1450-2300m; fl. 4-6.
W. & E. Crete (Lefka Ori & Dikti) - Endemic.

●**5. E. raulinii** Boiss., *Fl. orient.* **1**: 192 (1867) - *FE* **1**: 271.
Cr (W, C) - *MAP 560*
Stony Cupressus woodland, rocky garigue & phrygana, calcareous cliffs, crevices & screes; 400-2200m; fl. 4-6.
W. & C. Crete - Endemic.

27. Fibigia Medik.

1. F. lunarioides (Willd.) Sm., *Fl. graec.* **7**: 22, t.625 (1831) - *FE* **1**: 305.
Cr (C, E) - *MAP 561*
Coastal calcareous cliffs.
C. & E. Crete (Paximadia & Dionisiades islands) [Kiklades; otherwise E. Aegean Islands (Rodos & Halki)].
Recorded since *FE* (Greuter, 1973a: 37).

28. Hirschfeldia Moench

1. H. incana (L.) Lagr.-Foss., *Fl. Tarn Garonne.*: 19 (1847) - *FE* **1**: 342.
Cr (W, C, E) Ks Kp Sa - *MAP 562*
Vineyards, fallow fields, river-beds, maritime rocks & sands, roadsides.
Mainly W. & E. Crete; Karpathos group [S. Europe].
Collected by the local people as a wild vegetable.

29. Hornungia Rchb.

1. H. petraea (L.) Rchb., *Deutschl. Fl.* **1**: 33 (1837) - *FE* **1**: 317.
Cr (W, C, E) Kp - *MAP 563*
Calcareous rock-crevices, open stony ground; 1200-1850m; fl. 4-5.
Crete (Lefka Ori, Kedros, Psiloritis, Dikti & Afendis Kavousi); Karpathos (Kalilimni) [W., C. & S. Europe].

30. Hymenolobus Nutt. ex Torr. & A.Gray

1. H. procumbens (L.) Nutt. ex Torr. & A.Gray, *Fl. N. Amer.* **1**: 117 (1838) - *FE* **1**: 317.

a. subsp. procumbens
Cr (W) Ks Kp - *MAP 564*
Maritime rocks & sands, stony ground & ledges of calcareous cliffs on offshore islets.
W. Crete (Gavdos island); Kasos, Karpathos [mainly S. Europe].
Recorded since *FE* (Greuter & Raus, 1986: 105; Höner & Greuter, 1988: 132).

31. Iberis L.

I. odorata L. (*FE* **1**: 325) was recorded in error (Greuter, 1974: 156).

1. I. sempervirens L., *Sp. pl.*: 648 (1753) - *FE* **1**: 323.
Cr (W) - *MAP 565*
Calcareous rocks; 1850-1900m; fl. 5.
W. Crete (Lefka Ori) [Mediterranean region].

32. Isatis L.

1. I. lusitanica L., *Sp. pl.*: 670 (1753) - *FE* **1**: 269.
Kp - *MAP 566*
Cultivated and fallow terraces; 300m; fl. 3-4.
Karpathos (N. end) [N. Africa & S.W. Asia].
Recorded since *FE* (Greuter, 1974: 147).

33. Lepidium L.

1. L. hirtum (L.) Sm., *Comp. fl. brit.* ed.2: 98 (1816) - *FE* **1**: 331.
"Subsp. *nebrodense*" (*FE* **1**: 331) = subsp. **a** (*MFG* **1**: 335).
a. subsp. oxyotum (DC.) Thell. in *Vjschr. naturf. Ges. Zürich* **51**: 153 (1906) - *FE* **1**: 331.
Cr (W, C, E) - *MAP 567*
Stony Cupressus woodland, calcareous rocky places, screes & gravel, flat clayey areas; (10-)1100-2400m; fl. 4-7.
Crete (Lefka Ori, Akrotiri peninsula, Kedros, Psiloritis & Dikti) [Corsica].

L. ruderale L. is given for the Cretan area in *FE* **1**: 332, although there are no records as a basis for this (Greuter, 1974: 139).

[2. L. sativum] L., *Sp. pl.*: 644 (1753) - *FE* **1**: 331.
[a. subsp. sativum]
Cr (W) - *NOT MAPPED*
Possibly naturalized in waste area.
W. Crete [almost throughout Europe; from Egypt & W. Asia].

3. L. spinosum Ard., *Animadv. bot. spec. Alt.*: 34 (1764) - *FE* **1**: 331.
Cr (W, C, E) Kp - *MAP 568*

Weed communities, roadsides; 0-500m; fl. 4-5.
Crete (sporadic); Karpathos [mainly E.
Mediterranean region].

[4. L. virginicum] L., *Sp. pl.*: 645 (1753) - *FE*
1: 332.
Cr (W) - *MAP 569*
Possibly naturalized in orange plantations.
W. Crete (S.W. of Hania) [most of Europe;
from N. America].
Recorded since *FE* (Yannitsaros, 1979: 104).

34. Lunaria L.

1. L. annua L., *Sp. pl.*: 653 (1753) - *FE* **1**:
296.
a. subsp. **pachyrhiza** (Borbás) Hayek in *Beih.
Repert. nov. Spec. Regni veg.* **30(1)**: 424 (1925)
- *FE* **1**: 296.
Cr (W, C) - *MAP 570*
*Roadside banks, weed communities, near
villages; 200-700m; fl. 3-4.*
W. & C. Crete [S. Italy, Balkan peninsula &
Romania].

35. Lutzia Gand.

1. L. cretica (L.) Greuter & Burdet in
Willdenowia **13**: 94 (1983) - *FE* **1**: 296 as
Alyssoides cretica (L.) Medik.
Cr (W, C, E) Ks Kp - *MAP 571*
Calcareous cliffs; 0-2000m; fl. 2-4.
Mainly C. & E. Crete; Kasos, Karpathos
[Kiklades (Astipalea)].
Given as endemic to the Cretan area in *FE*,
although previously recorded from Astipalea by
Runemark et al. (1960).

36. Malcolmia R.Br.

1. M. africana (L.) R.Br. in W.T.Aiton,
Hortus kew. **4**: 121 (1812) - *FE* **1**: 277.
Cr (C, E) - *MAP 572*
Lygeum steppe, clayey hills, seashores.
C. & E. Crete [S. Europe].

2. M. chia (L.) DC., *Syst. nat.* **2**: 440 (1821) -
FE **1**: 278.
Cr (W, C, E) Ks Kp Sa - *MAP 573*
*Rock-crevices, screes, open sandy or rocky
slopes, phrygana, usually near the coast,
maritime sands; 0-850m; fl. 3-5.*
Crete (widespread); Karpathos group [N.Greece
& Aegean region].

3. M. flexuosa (Sm.) Sm., *Fl. graec.* **7**: 33,
t.634 (1831) - *FE* **1**: 278.
Cr (W, C, E) Ks Kp Sa - *MAP 574*
a. subsp. **flexuosa**
Cr (E) Ks Kp Sa - *NOT MAPPED*

E. Crete; Karpathos group [Kiklades; otherwise
E. Aegean Islands (Rodos) & Cyprus].
b. subsp. **naxensis** (Rech.f.) Stork in *Op. bot.
Soc. bot. Lund* **33**: 35 (1972) - not cited in *FE*.
Cr (W, C) - *MAP 575*
*Calcareous rocks, crevices, rubble & screes
near sea, maritime sands; 0-200m; fl. 3-5.*
Mainly W. Crete [Aegean region].

4. M. nana (DC.) Boiss., *Fl. orient.* **1**: 222
(1867) - *FE* **1**: 278 as *Maresia nana* (DC.) Batt.
Cr (E) - *MAP 576*
Maritime sands.
E. Crete [mainly Mediterranean & Black Sea
coasts].
Recorded since *FE* (Greuter et al., 1984b: 278).

Maresia nana (DC.) Batt. (*FE* **1**: 278) =
Malcolmia 4.

37. Matthiola R.Br.

[1. M. incana] (L.) R.Br. in W.T.Aiton, *Hortus
kew.* **4**: 119 (1812) - *FE* **1**: 280.
[a. subsp. **incana]**
Cr (W) - *MAP 577*
Naturalized on maritime rocks.
W. Crete (near Hania) [coasts of W. & S.
Europe].
Erroneously given as native to the Cretan area in
FE (Greuter, 1974: 156).

2. M. sinuata (L.) R.Br. in W.T.Aiton, *Hortus
kew.* **4**: 120 (1812) - *FE* **1**: 280.
Cr (W, C, E) Ks Kp - *MAP 578*
*Calcareous cliffs, offshore islets; 0-450m; fl. 3-
4.*
Crete (sporadic); Kasos, Karpathos [coasts of
W. & S. Europe].
Erroneously regarded as absent from the Cretan
area in *FE* (Greuter, 1974: 140). Plants from the
Cretan area belong to the Balkan subsp.
glandulosa (Vis.) Vierh., which is treated as
doubtfully distinct from subsp. *sinuata* in *M-Ch*
3: 143, and is not separated here.

3. M. tricuspidata (L.) R.Br. in W.T.Aiton,
Hortus kew. **4**: 120 (1812) - *FE* **1**: 280.
Cr (W, C, E) Kp - *MAP 579*
*Maritime rocks & sands, tops of old walls; fl. 3-
4.*
Crete (mainly N. coast); Karpathos
[Mediterranean region].

38. Nasturtium R.Br.

1. N. officinale R.Br. in W.T.Aiton, *Hortus
kew.* **4**: 111 (1812) - *FE* **1**: 284.
Cr (W, C, E) Kp - *MAP 580*

Fresh water, marshes, ditches & other wet places; 0-1450m; fl. 3-4.
Mainly W. Crete; Karpathos [almost throughout Europe].

39. Neslia Desv.

1. N. apiculata Fisch., Mey. & Avé-Lall., *Index sem. hort. petrop.* **8**: 68 (1842) - *FE* **1**: 316 as *N. paniculata* subsp. *thracica* (Velen.) Bornm.
Cr (W) - *MAP 581*
0-600m.
W. Crete [S. Europe].

N. paniculata subsp. *thracica* (Velen.) Bornm. (*FE* **1**: 316) = **1**.

40. Raphanus L.

1. R. raphanistrum L., *Sp. pl.*: 669 (1753) - *FE* **1**: 346.
a. subsp. **raphanistrum**
Cr (W) - *MAP 582*
Among crops; -1050m.
W. Crete [throughout Europe].

[2. R. sativus] L., *Sp. pl.*: 669 (1753) - *FE* **1**: 346.
Cr (W, C, E) - *MAP 583*
Possibly naturalized in cultivated areas; fl. 4-5.
Crete (sporadic) [widely cultivated in Europe, of uncertain origin].
Recorded by Greuter (1974: 156).

41. Rapistrum Crantz

1. R. rugosum (L.) All., *Fl. pedem.* **1**: 257 (1785) - *FE* **1**: 344. (Including subsp. *linnaeanum* Rouy & Foucaud and subsp. *orientale* (L.) Arcang. - both *FE* **1**: 344.)
Cr (W, E) Ks Kp - *MAP 584*
Roadsides, maritime sands, disturbed ground; fl. 3-5.
W. & E. Crete; Kasos, Karpathos [most of Europe].

42. Ricotia L.

●**1. R. cretica** Boiss. & Heldr. in Boiss., *Diagn. pl. orient.* ser.1, **8**: 29 (1849) - *FE* **1**: 295.
Cr (W, C, E) - *MAP 585*
Calcareous rocks, rubble & screes; 0-1200m; fl. 3-5.
Mainly W. & E. Crete - Endemic.

●**2. R. isatoides** (Barbey) B.L.Burtt in *Kew Bull.* **6**: 131 (1951) - *FE* **1**: 295.
Kp - *MAP 586*
Calcareous screes.
Karpathos - Endemic.
[Plate 1.]

43. Rorippa Scop.

1. R. sylvestris (L.) Besser, *Enum. pl.*: 27 (1821) - *FE* **1**: 283.
a. subsp. **sylvestris**
Cr - *NOT MAPPED*
Crete [almost throughout Europe].

44. Sinapis L.

1. S. alba L., *Sp. pl.*: 668 (1753) - *FE* **1**: 339.
Cr (W, C, E) Kp - *MAP 587*
Olive groves, cultivated & fallow land, roadsides, maritime sands; 0-500m; fl. 3-5.
[**a.** subsp. **alba**]
Possibly naturalized.
Crete; Karpathos [almost throughout Europe].
b. subsp. **dissecta** (Lag.) Bonnier, *Fl. ill. France* **1**: 58 (1912) - *FE* **1**: 339.
Crete [mainly S. Europe].
c. subsp. **mairei** (H.Lindb.) Maire in *Bull. Soc. Hist. nat. Afr. N.* **24**: 197 (1933) - not cited in *FE*
Cretan area [Mediterranean region].
Recorded by Baillargeon in Greuter & Raus (1985: 69).
The species sensu lato is widespread in Crete and occurs also in Karpathos.

2. S. arvensis L., *Sp. pl.*: 668 (1753) - *FE* **1**: 339.
a. subsp. **arvensis**
Cr (C, E) Ks Kp - *MAP 588*
Olive groves, cultivated terraces, flat clayey areas; 200-1400m; fl. 3-4.
C. & E. Crete; Kasos, Karpathos [almost throughout Europe].

45. Sisymbrium L.

1. S. irio L., *Sp. pl.*: 659 (1753) - *FE* **1**: 264.
Cr - *NOT MAPPED*
Crete [almost throughout Europe].

2. S. officinale (L.) Scop., *Fl. carniol.* ed.2, **2**: 26 (1772) - *FE* **1**: 266.
Cr (W, C, E) Kp - *MAP 589*
Olive groves, scrub, disturbed ground; 0-750m; fl. 3-5.
Mainly W. Crete; Karpathos [almost throughout Europe].

3. S. orientale L., *Cent. pl.* **2**: 24 (1756) - *FE*
1: 265.
Cr (W, C, E) Ks Kp - *MAP 590*
Olive groves, vineyards, roadsides, waste areas;
0-450m; fl. 3-4.
Crete (sporadic); Kasos, Karpathos [W., C. &
S. Europe].

4. S. polyceratium L., *Sp. pl.*: 658 (1753) - *FE*
1: 265.
Cr (C) Ks Kp - *MAP 591*
Calcareous rocks.
C. Crete; Kasos, Karpathos [Mediterranean
region].

46. Teesdalia R.Br.

1. T. coronopifolia (J.P.Bergeret) Thell. in
Reprium Spec. nov. Regni veg. **10**: 289 (1912) -
FE **1**: 318.
Cr (W) Kp - *MAP 592*
Flat clayey areas, fallow fields; 700-1050m; fl.
3-4.
W. Crete (Omalos plain in Lefka Ori);
Karpathos (Lastos plain E. of Kalilimni) [S.
Europe].

47. Thlaspi L.

●**1. T. creticum** (Degen & Ják.) Greuter &
Burdet in *Willdenowia* **13**: 95 (1983) - not cited
in *FE*.
Cr (W, C, E) - *MAP 593*
Calcareous rocky places & gravel; 1450-2400m;
fl. 5-6.
Crete (Lefka Ori, Psiloritis & Dikti) - Endemic.

"*T. graecum*" (*FE* **1**: 320) = **1** (Greuter, 1974:
156).

T. microphyllum Boiss. & Orph. (*FE* **1**: 320)
was recorded in error (Greuter, 1974: 156).

2. T. perfoliatum L., *Sp. pl.*: 646 (1753) - *FE*
1: 319.
a. subsp. perfoliatum
Cr (W, C) Kp - *MAP 594*
Calcareous rocky places, mountain pastures;
300-2200m; fl. 4-5.
W. & C. Crete (mainly Lefka Ori, Kedros &
Psiloritis); Karpathos [almost throughout
Europe].

●**3. T. zaffranii** (F.K.Mey.) Greuter & Burdet
in *Willdenowia* **15**: 420 (1986).
Cr (W) - *MAP 595*
Calcareous screes; 1500-1700m.
W. Crete (Lefka Ori) - Endemic.
Described since *FE*, as *Noccaea zaffranii*
F.K.Mey. (Meyer, 1986).

CUCURBITACEAE

1. Bryonia L.

1. B. cretica L., *Sp. pl.*: 1013 (1753) - *FE* **2**:
297.
a. subsp. cretica
Cr (W, C, E) Ks Kp Sa - *MAP 596*
Olive groves, scrub, rocky places, garden walls;
0-600m; fl. 3-5.
Crete (widespread, rarer towards E.); Karpathos
group [Aegean region].

2. Ecballium A.Rich.

1. E. elaterium (L.) A.Rich. in Bory, *Dict.*
class. hist. nat. **6**: 19 (1824) - *FE* **2**: 297.
Cr (W, C, E) Kp - *MAP 597*
Waste areas & roadsides, especially in &
around villages; 0-700m; fl. 3-5.
Crete (widespread); Karpathos [S. Europe].

CYNOMORIACEAE

Cynomorium coccineum L. (*FE* **1**: 75) was
almost certainly recorded in error (Greuter,
1974: 154).

DATISCACEAE

1. Datisca L.

1. D. cannabina L., *Sp. pl.*: 1037 (1753) - *FE*
2: 296.
Cr (W) - *MAP 598*
Moist stream-banks in woodland; 1000m.
W. Crete (Lefka Ori) [S.W. Asia to Himalaya].

DIPSACACEAE

1. Cephalaria Schrad.

1. C. squamiflora (Sieber) Greuter in
Candollea **22**: 235 (1967) - *FE* **4**: 57.
a. subsp. squamiflora
Cr (W) Kp - *MAP 599*
Calcareous cliffs; 1150-1750m; fl. 7-8.
W. Crete (Lefka Ori); Karpathos (Kalilimni)
[Kiklades (Amorgos); otherwise E. Aegean
Islands (Ikaria)].

2. Knautia L.

1. K. integrifolia (L.) Bertol., *Fl. ital.* **2**: 32
(1835) - *FE* **4**: 67.
Cr (W, C, E) Kp - *MAP 600*

a. subsp. **mimica** (Borbás) Greuter in *Boissiera* **13**: 130 (1967) - not cited in *FE*.
Phrygana, rocky places; 0-750m; fl. 4-5.
Mainly W. & C. Crete [Albania & Greece].
The species sensu lato occurs also in Karpathos.

3. Lomelosia Raf.

● **1. L. albocincta** (Greuter) Greuter & Burdet in *Willldenowia* **15**: 73 (1985) - *FE* **4**: 69 as *Scabiosa albocincta* Greuter.
Cr (W, C) - *MAP 601*
Calcareous cliffs; 10-1500m; fl. 8.
W. & C. Crete - Endemic.

2. L. brachiata (Sm.) Greuter & Burdet in *Willdenowia* **15**: 73 (1985) - *FE* **4**: 74 as *Tremastelma palaestinum* (L.) Janch.
Cr (W, E) Kp - *MAP 602*
Rocky phrygana, abandoned terraces; 0-1800m; fl. 4-5.
Mainly W. Crete; Karpathos [Italy, Balkan peninsula & Aegean region].

3. L. divaricata (Jacq.) Greuter & Burdet in *Willdenowia* **15**: 74 (1985) - *FE* **4**: 71 as *Scabiosa sicula* L.
Cr (W, E) Kp - *MAP 603*
Calcareous rocky places, open stony ground; fl. 5.
W. & E. Crete; Karpathos [Mediterranean region].

● **4. L. minoana** (P.H.Davis) Greuter & Burdet in *Willdenowia* **15**: 74 (1985) - *FE* **4**: 69 as *Scabiosa minoana* (P.H.Davis) Greuter.
a. subsp. **asterusica** (Greuter) Greuter & Burdet in *Willdenowia* **15**: 75 (1985) - not cited in *FE*.
Cr (C) - *MAP 604*
Calcareous cliffs; 1150-1200m.
C. Crete (Kofinas) - Endemic.
b. subsp. **minoana**
Cr (E) - *MAP 605*
Calcareous cliffs; 450-1500m.
E. Crete (Dikti) - Endemic.

● **5. L. sphaciotica** (Roem. & Schult.) Greuter & Burdet in *Willdenowia* **15**: 76 (1985) - *FE* **4**: 70 as *Scabiosa sphaciotica* Roem. & Schult.
Cr (W, C, E) - *MAP 606*
Calcareous rock-crevices, stabilized screes, flat clayey areas; 1400-2400m; fl. 7-8.
Crete (Lefka Ori, Psiloritis & Dikti) - Endemic.

6. L. variifolia (Boiss.) Greuter & Burdet in *Willdenowia* **15**: 76 (1985) - *FE* **4**: 69 as *Scabiosa variifolia* Boiss.
Kp Sa - *MAP 607*

Calcareous cliffs & step-crevices; 0-1200m; fl. 7.
Karpathos, Saria [E. Aegean Islands (Simi, Halki & Rodos) & S.W. Turkey].

4. Pterocephalus Adans.

1. P. brevis Coult., *Mém. Dipsac.*: 32 (1823) - *FE* **4**: 68.
Kp - *MAP 608*
Karpathos [S.W. Asia].

P. papposus (L.) Coult. (*FE* **4**: 68) = **2**.

2. P. plumosus (L.) Coult., *Mém. Dipsac.*: 31 (1823) - *FE* **4**: 68 as *P. papposus* (L.) Coult.
Cr (W, C, E) Kp Sa - *MAP 609*
Phrygana, rocky places, screes, Lygeum steppe; 0-600m; fl. 4-5.
Mainly W. Crete; Karpathos, Saria [E. Mediterranean region].

Scabiosa albocincta Greuter (*FE* **4**: 69) = **Lomelosia 1**.

S. atropurpurea L. (*FE* **4**: 71) = **Sixalix 1**.

S. atropurpurea subsp. *chaniotica* Rech.f. (Rechinger, 1943*b*: 137; Barclay, 1986: 47) is included - with some doubt - in synonymy of **Sixalix 1a**, after *M-Ch* **3**: 197.

S. minoana (P.H.Davis) Greuter (*FE* **4**: 69) = **Lomelosia 4**.

S. sicula L. (*FE* **4**: 71) = **Lomelosia 3**.

S. sphaciotica Roem. & Schult. (*FE* **4**: 70) = **Lomelosia 5**.

S. variifolia Boiss. (*FE* **4**: 69) = **Lomelosia 6**.

5. Sixalix Raf.

1. S. atropurpurea (L.) Greuter & Burdet in *Willdenowia* **15**: 76 (1985) - *FE* **4**: 71 as *Scabiosa atropurpurea* L.
a. subsp. **maritima** (L.) Greuter & Burdet in *Willdenowia* **15**: 76 (1985) - *FE* **4**: 71, included in synonymy of *Scabiosa atropurpurea* L. (?Including *Scabiosa atropurpurea* subsp. *chaniotica* Rech.f. - not cited in *FE*.)
Cr (W, C, E) Kp - *MAP 610*
Among ancient ruins, roadsides.
Crete (sporadic); Karpathos [Mediterranean region].

Tremastelma palaestinum (L.) Janch. (*FE* **4**: 74) = **Lomelosia 2**.

ELAEAGNACEAE

1. Elaeagnus L.

[1. E. angustifolia] L., *Sp. pl.*: 121 (1753) - *FE*
2: 261.
Cr - *NOT MAPPED*
*Cultivated for ornament & hedges and
naturalized.*
Crete [C. & S. Europe; from temperate Asia].

ELATINACEAE

1. Elatine L.

1. E. alsinastrum L., *Sp. pl.*: 368 (1753) - *FE*
2: 296.
Cr - *NOT MAPPED*
*Flat clayey areas in dolines, periodically
waterlogged.*
Crete [most of Europe].

ERICACEAE

1. Arbutus L.

1. A. andrachne L., *Syst. nat.* ed.10, 2: 1024
(1759) - *FE* 3: 11.
Cr (W, C, E) - *MAP 611*
*Garigue with Cistus, calcareous cliff; 0-600m;
fl. 4.*
Crete (sporadic) [mainly S. Albania, Greece &
Aegean region].

2. A. unedo L., *Sp. pl.*: 395 (1753) - *FE* 3: 11.
Cr (W, C) - *MAP 612*
*Woodland and maquis on non-calcareous
substrata; 50-750m; fl. 10-11, rarely 4.*
W. & C. Crete; Karpathos [W. Europe &
Mediterranean region].

Hybrid:

A. andrachne x A. unedo = A. x
andrachnoides Link, *Enum. hort. berol. alt.* 1:
395 (1821) - *FE* 3: 11.
Calcareous hill; 600m.
W. Crete.
Recorded by Rechinger (1943b: 106).

2. Erica L.

1. E. arborea L., *Sp. pl.*: 353 (1753) - *FE* 3: 7.
Cr (W, C, E) - *MAP 613*
*Light woodland and maquis on non-calcareous
substrata; 0-850m; fl. 3-4.*
Mainly W. Crete [S.W. Europe &
Mediterranean region].

2. E. manipuliflora Salisb. in *Trans. Linn. Soc.
Lond.* 6: 344 (1802) - *FE* 3: 7.
Cr (W, C, E) Ks Kp Sa - *MAP 614*
*Light woodland, maquis, garigue, phrygana,
calcareous cliffs, open rocky & sandy ground; 0-
2000m; fl. 8-11.*
Crete (widespread); Karpathos group [C. & E.
Mediterranean region].

EUPHORBIACEAE

1. Andrachne L.

1. A. telephioides L., *Sp. pl.*: 1014 (1753) - *FE*
2: 211.
Cr (W, C, E) Ks Kp - *MAP 615*
*Calcareous rocky slopes, crevices & rubble, flat
clayey areas; 60-2400m; fl. 4-7.*
Crete (mainly in mountains); Kasos, Karpathos
[Mediterranean region].
Plants from high altitudes in Crete (1800-
2400m) have been described as subsp.
oreocretensis Aldén (Aldén, 1982), which is
treated as doubtfully distinct from subsp.
telephioides in *M-Ch* 3: 205, and is not
separated here. Plants from two localities at
lower altitudes (600m & 1400m) have features
intermediate between subsp. *oreocretensis* and
the lowland subsp. *telephioides* (Greuter et al.,
1984b: 278).

2. Chrozophora A.Juss.

1. C. obliqua (Vahl) A.Juss. ex Spreng., *Syst.
veg.* 3: 850 (1826) - *FE* 2: 211.
Cr (W) - *MAP 616*
Maritime sands.
W. Crete [Mediterranean region].

2. C. tinctoria (L.) A.Juss., *Euphorb. gen.*: 84
(1824) - *FE* 2: 211.
Cr (W, C) Kp - *MAP 617*
Dry stream-beds, fallow fields, waste areas.
W. & C. Crete; Karpathos [S. Europe].

3. Euphorbia L.

1. E. acanthothamnos Heldr. & Sart. ex
Boiss., *Diagn. pl. orient.* ser.2, 4: 86 (1859) -
FE 2: 220.
Cr (W, C, E) Ks Kp Sa - *MAP 618*
*Garigue, phrygana, rocky places, flat clayey
areas; 0-2000m; fl. 3-5.*
Crete (widespread); Karpathos group
[?Jugoslavia, Greece & Aegean region].

"*E. akenocarpa*" (*FE* 2: 217) = 23 (Barclay
186: 49).

2. E. aleppica L., *Sp. pl.*: 458 (1753) - *FE* 2: 221.
?Cr Ks - *MAP 619*
?Crete; Kasos [Mediterranean region].
Doubtful occurrence in the Cretan area confirmed since *FE* (Greuter, 1974: 146).

"*E. apios*" (*FE* 2: 219) = **7** (Greuter, 1973a: 28).

3. E. chamaesyce L., *Sp. pl.*: 455 (1753) - *FE* 2: 216. (Including subsp. *massiliensis* (DC.) Thell. - *FE* 2: 216.)
Cr (W, C, E) - *MAP 620*
Fallow fields, bare ground; fl. -10.
Crete (sporadic) [S. Europe].

4. E. characias L., *Sp. pl.*: 463 (1753) - *FE* 2: 226.
Cr (W, C, E) Kp Sa - *MAP 621*
Open woodland, olive groves, scrub, garigue, open rocky slopes, screes, abandoned cultivated land; 0-1200m; fl. 2-4.
Crete (widespread); Karpathos (N. end), Saria [Mediterranean region].
The plants from Crete belong to *E. characias* sensu stricto, which occurs in the W. & C. Mediterranean region, whereas those from Karpathos and Saria belong to *E. melapetala* Guss., which is otherwise known only from Sicily. *E. veneta* Willd. (*FE* 2: 226 as *E. characias* subsp. *wulfenii* (Hoppe ex W.D.J.Koch) A.R.Sm.) does not occur in the Cretan area. Both *E. melapetala* and *E. veneta* are treated as doubtfully distinct from *E. characias* in *M-Ch* **3**: 208-209, and are not separated here.

5. E. deflexa Sm., *Fl. Graec. prodr.* **1**: 328 (1809) - *FE* 2: 223.
Cr (E) - *MAP 622*
Calcareous rocky places; 1600-2100m.
E. Crete (Dikti) [C. Greece & Aegean region].

6. E. dendroides L., *Sp. pl.*: 462 (1753) - *FE* 2: 216.
Cr (W, C, E) Ks Kp Sa - *MAP 623*
Calcareous cliffs & rocky places, sometimes forming scrub on rocky slopes; 0-400m; fl. 3-4.
Mainly W. Crete; Karpathos group [Mediterranean region].

7. E. dimorphocaulon P.H.Davis in *Phyton, Horn* **1**: 196 (1949) - *FE* 2: 219.
Cr (W, C, E) - *MAP 624*
Rock-crevices & phrygana; 0-800m; fl. 9-11.
Crete (widespread, N. side) [S. Turkey & Cyprus].

8. E. exigua L., *Sp. pl.*: 456 (1753) - *FE* 2: 222.
Cr (W) Kp - *MAP 625*

Fallow fields, burnt garigue, sandy places near sea, bare & moist ground; 0-550m; fl. 3-4.
W. Crete; Karpathos [most of Europe].

9. E. falcata L., *Sp. pl.*: 456 (1753) - *FE* 2: 222.
a. subsp. **falcata**
Cr (C, E) Kp - *MAP 626*
Olive groves, Lygeum steppe, abandoned cultivated land.
C. & E. Crete; Karpathos [mainly C. & S. Europe].

10. E. helioscopia L., *Sp. pl.*: 459 (1753) - *FE* 2: 221.
Cr (W, C, E) Ks Kp - *MAP 627*
Cultivated & fallow land, disturbed ground, waste areas; 0-600m; fl. 3-4.
Crete (sporadic); Kasos, Karpathos [almost throughout Europe].

11. E. herniariifolia Willd., *Sp. pl.*: **2**: 902 (1799) - *FE* 2: 224.
Cr (W, C, E) - *MAP 628*
Calcareous rocky places, rubble & screes; 1400-2400m.
Crete (Lefka Ori, Psiloritis & Afendis Kavousi) [Albania & Greece; otherwise S.W. Asia].

12. E. hirsuta L., *Amoen. acad.* **4**: 483 (1759) - *FE* 2: 220 as *E. pubescens* Vahl.
Cr (W, C, E) - *MAP 629*
Marshes, river-mouths, often brackish.
Crete (sporadic) [S. Europe].

13. E. microsphaera Boiss., *Diagn. pl. orient.* ser.1, **7**: 87 (1846) - *FE* 2: 217.
Kp - *MAP 630*
Karpathos [S.W. Asia].
Recorded since *FE* (Greuter et al., 1983a: 57).

"*E. myrsinites*" (*FE* 2: 221) = **19** (Greuter, 1965: 170).

14. E. oblongata Griseb., *Spic. fl. rumel.* **1**: 136 (1843) - *FE* 2: 218.
Cr (W) - *MAP 631*
Dry river-bed.
W. Crete (S.W. of Hania) [mainly S. Balkan peninsula & Aegean region].

15. E. paralias L., *Sp. pl.*: 458 (1753) - *FE* 2: 225.
Cr (W, C, E) Ks Kp - *MAP 632*
Maritime sands & gravel; fl. 4-5.
Crete (sporadic); Kasos, Karpathos [coasts of W. & S. Europe].

16. E. peplis L., *Sp. pl.*: 455 (1753) - *FE* 2: 216.
Cr (W, C, E) Kp Sa - *MAP 633*
Maritime sands & shingle; fl. 5-9.
Crete (sporadic); Karpathos, Saria [coasts of W.

& S. Europe].

17. E. peplus L., *Sp. pl.*: 456 (1753) - *FE* 2: 222.
Cr (W, C, E) Ks Kp - *MAP 634*
Fallow fields, bare stony & sandy ground; 0-450m; fl. 3-4.
Mainly W. Crete; Kasos, Karpathos [almost throughout Europe].

18. E. platyphyllos L., *Sp. pl.*: 460 (1753) - *FE* 2: 220.
Cr (W) - *MAP 635*
W. Crete [W., C. & S. Europe].

E. pubescens Vahl (*FE* 2: 220) = **12**.

●**19. E. rechingeri** Greuter in *Candollea* 20: 172 (1965) - *FE* 2: 221.
Cr (W) - *MAP 636*
Calcareous rock-crevices, rubble & screes; 1800-2300m; fl. 4-5.
Crete (Lefka Ori) - Endemic.

E. rigida M.Bieb. (*FE* 2: 221) was recorded in error (Greuter, 1974: 155).

? E. segetalis L., *Sp. pl.*: 458 (1753) - *FE* 2: 222.
Doubtfully present in Crete [C. & S.W. Europe & C. Mediterranean region].

●**20. E. sultan-hassei** Strid, Bentzer, Bothmer, Engstrand & M.A.Gust. in *Willdenowia* 19: 63 (1989).
Cr (W) - *MAP 637*
Calcareous cliffs in gorges; 0-500m; fl. 3.
W. Crete (S. side) - Endemic.
[Plate 4.] Superficially resembling **6**, but with branches more slender and capsules tuberculate; more closely related to *E. hierosolymitana* Boiss., from S.W. Asia, and *E. bivonae* Steud. (*FE* 2: 220), from N. Africa, Sicily, Malta and the small island of Karavi E. of Peloponnisos.

21. E. taurinensis All., *Fl. pedem.* 1: 287 (1785) - *FE* 2: 222.
Cr - *NOT MAPPED*
Crete [S. Europe].

22. E. terracina L., *Sp. pl.* ed.2: 654 (1762) - *FE* 2: 226.
Cr - *NOT MAPPED*
Crete [Mediterranean region].

23. E. valerianifolia Lam., *Encycl.* 2: 435 (1788) - not cited in *FE*.
Cr - *NOT MAPPED*
Crete [Greece; otherwise Libya & S.W. Asia].

4. Mercurialis L.

1. M. annua L., *Sp. pl.*: 1035 (1753) - *FE* 2: 212.
Cr (W, C, E) Ks Kp Sa - *MAP 638*
Olive groves, gorge-beds, maritime sands, among ruins & near walls, waste areas in towns; 0-450m; fl. 1-4.
Crete (widespread); Karpathos group [most of Europe].

5. Ricinus L.

[1. R. communis] L., *Sp. pl.*: 1007 (1753) - *FE* 2: 213.
Cr (W, C, E) - *MAP 639*
Cultivated for ornament and naturalized in waste areas.
Crete (widespread) [S.C. & S. Europe; from tropics].

FAGACEAE

1. Castanea Mill.

1. C. sativa Mill., *Gard. Dict.* ed.8: no.1 (1768) - *FE* 1: 61.
Cr (W) - *MAP 640*
Woodland, moist valleys, on non-calcareous substrata.
W. Crete [mainly W., C. & S. Europe].
Doubtfully native (*Atlas FE* 3: 66).

2. Quercus L.

Q. brachyphylla Kotschy (*FE* 1: 64) is included in synonymy of **4**.

? Q. cerris L., *Sp. pl.*: 997 (1753) - *FE* 1: 63.
Doubtfully present in Crete (Greuter, 1974: 154) [mainly S.C. & S. Europe].

1. Q. coccifera L., *Sp. pl.*: 995 (1753) - *FE* 1: 62.
Cr (W, C, E) Kp - *MAP 641*
Woodland, maquis, scrub, garigue; 0-1600m; fl. 3-4.
Crete (widespread); Karpathos [Mediterranean region].

2. Q. ilex L., *Sp. pl.*: 995 (1753) - *FE* 1: 62.
Cr (W, C, E) Kp - *MAP 642*
Woodland, maquis, humid valleys, calcareous cliffs; 300-800m; fl. 4.
Mainly W. & C. Crete; Karpathos [mainly Mediterranean region].

3. Q. ithaburensis Decne. in *Annls Sci. nat.* ser.2 (Bot.), 4: 348 (1835) - not cited in *FE*.

a. subsp. **macrolepis** (Kotschy) Hedge & Yalt. in *Willdenowia* **11**: 42 (1981) - *FE* **1**: 63 as *Q. macrolepis* Kotschy.
Cr (W, C, E) - *MAP 643*
Woodland, olive groves, maquis, scrub, often as isolated trees in cultivated areas; 150-650m; fl. 4-5.
Mainly W. & C. Crete [S.E. Italy, Albania, Greece & Aegean region].
Formerly extensively cultivated in Europe, and unlikely to be native in Crete (*Atlas FE* **3**: 70).

Q. macrolepis Kotschy (*FE* **1**: 63) = **3a**.

4. Q. pubescens Willd., *Berlin. Baumz.*: 279 (1796) - *FE* **1**: 64. (Including *Q. brachyphylla* Kotschy - *FE* **1**: 64.)
Cr (W, C, E) - *MAP 644*
Woodland, maquis, scrub, often as isolated trees in cultivated areas; 300-750m; fl. 4-5.
Mainly W. & C. Crete [W., C. & S. Europe].
Subsp. *crispata* (Steven) Greuter & Burdet is given for the Cretan area in *M-Ch* **3**: 230, but as doubtfully distinct from subsp. *pubescens*; it is not separated here.

FRANKENIACEAE

1. Frankenia L.

1. F. hirsuta L., *Sp. pl.*: 331 (1753) - *FE* **2**: 295.
Cr (W, C, E) Ks Kp - *MAP 645*
Maritime rocks & sands; fl. 4.
Mainly C. & E. Crete; Kasos, Karpathos [S.E. Europe & Mediterranean region].

2. F. pulverulenta L., *Sp. pl.*: 332 (1753) - *FE* **2**: 295.
a. subsp. **pulverulenta**
Cr (W, C, E) Ks Kp - *MAP 646*
Maritime rocks & sandy ground; fl. 3-6.
Crete (sporadic); Kasos, Karpathos [S.E. & S. Europe].

GENTIANACEAE

1. Blackstonia Huds.

1. B. acuminata (W.D.J.Koch & Ziz) Domin in *Rozpr. ceské Akad. Ved Umeni* **43(2)**: 6 (1933) - *FE* **3**: 56, included in synonymy of *B. perfoliata* subsp. *serotina* (W.D.J.Koch ex Rchb.) Vollm.
a. subsp. **acuminata**
Cr (W) - *MAP 647*
W. Crete (Fasas valley) [Mediterranean region]. Recorded by Zeltner (1978: 107).

2. B. perfoliata (L.) Huds., *Fl. angl.*: 146 (1762) - *FE* **3**: 56.
Cr (W, C, E) Ks Kp Sa - *MAP 648*
Stream-banks, damp rocks, moist bare ground; 0-950m; fl. 4-5.
a. subsp. **intermedia** (Ten.) Zeltner in *Bull. Soc. neuchâtel. Sci. nat.* **93**: 45 (1970) - not cited in *FE*.
Crete [Mediterranean region].
b. subsp. **perfoliata**
W. Crete (Fasas valley) [W., C. & S. Europe]. The species sensu lato occurs mainly in W. & C. Crete and also in the Karpathos group; most records are probably referable to subsp. **a** (cf. Zeltner, 1978).

2. Centaurium Hill

1. C. erythraea Rafn, *Danm. Holst. Fl.* **2**: 75 (1800) - *FE* **3**: 57.
Cr (W, C) Kp - *MAP 649*
Calcareous rocky places, roadside banks; 0-650m.
a. subsp. **erythraea**
Crete [most of Europe].
b. subsp. **rhodense** (Boiss. & Reut.) Melderis in *Bot. J. Linn. Soc.* **65**: 234 (1972) - *FE* **3**: 58.
Crete; Karpathos [C. & E. Mediterranean region].
c. subsp. **rumelicum** (Velen.) Melderis in *Bot. J. Linn. Soc.* **65**: 232 (1972) - *FE* **3**: 58.
Crete [Mediterranean region].

2. C. maritimum (L.) Fritsch in *Mitt. naturw. Ver. Univ. Wien* **5**: 97 (1907) - *FE* **3**: 59.
Cr (W, C, E) Kp - *MAP 650*
Maquis, dry river-beds, damp ground near sea; 0-250m; fl. 4.
Crete (sporadic); Karpathos [W. & S. Europe].

3. C. pulchellum (Sw.) Druce, *Fl. Berkshire*: 342 (1898) - *FE* **3**: 59.
Cr (W, C, E) Kp - *MAP 651*
Calcareous rocky places near coast, moist & bare ground, stream-banks; 0-300(-1650)m; fl. 3-4.
Crete (sporadic); Karpathos [almost throughout Europe].

4. C. spicatum (L.) Fritsch in *Mitt. naturw. Ver. Univ. Wien* **5**: 97 (1907) - *FE* **3**: 59.
Cr (W, C, E) - *MAP 652*
Marshy places, calcareous open stony ground near coast.
Crete (sporadic) [S. Europe].
C. subspicatum (Velen.) Ronniger is given for the Cretan area in *M-Ch* **3**: 239, but as doubtfully distinct from *C. spicatum*; it is not separated here.

C. subspicatum (Velen.) Ronniger (*FE* **3**: 59)

see **4**.

5. C. tenuiflorum (Hoffmanns. & Link) Fritsch in *Mitt. naturw. Ver. Univ. Wien* **5**: 97 (1907) - *FE* **3**: 59.
Cr (W, C, E) Ks Kp Sa - *MAP 653*
Rocky places, damp & saline ground near sea, waste areas; 0-950m; fl. 8.
a. subsp. **acutiflorum** (Schott) Zeltner in *Bull. Soc. neuchâtel. Sci. nat.* **93**: 94 (1970) - *FE* **3**: 59.
Crete [Mediterranean region].
b. subsp. **tenuiflorum**
Crete; Kasos [W. & S. Europe].
The species sensu lato occurs mainly in W. Crete and also in the Karpathos group.

GERANIACEAE

1. Erodium L'Hér.

? **E. acaule** (L.) Bech. & Thell. in *Reprium Spec. nov. Regni veg.* **25**: 215 (1928) - *FE* **2**: 203.
Doubtfully present in Crete (Greuter, 1974: 156) [Mediterranean region].

1. E. botrys (Cav.) Bertol., *Amoen. ital.*: 35 (1819) - *FE* **2**: 201.
Cr (W) - *MAP 654*
Karstic ground.
W. Crete [S. Europe].

2. E. chium (L.) Willd., *Phytographia* **1**: 10 (1795) - *FE* **2**: 200.
a. subsp. **chium**
Ks Kp Sa - *MAP 655*
Step-crevices of cliffs & stony ground beneath; 0-300m; fl. 3-4.
Karpathos group [Mediterranean region].

3. E. ciconium (L.) L'Hér. in Aiton, *Hort. kew.* **2**: 414 (1789) - *FE* **2**: 201.
Cr (W, E) - *MAP 656*
Calcareous rocky places, gorge-beds; 0-500m.
W. & E. Crete [mainly S. Europe].
Greuter (1974: 156) considered the species doubtfully present, giving as a basis for his opinion an old record cited by Rechinger (1943a: 281); he did not comment, however, on a later record (Rechinger, 1943b: 84). The species has since been recorded by Strasser (1988: 19, 23, 27).

4. E. cicutarium (L.) L'Hér. in Aiton, *Hort. kew.* **2**: 414 (1789) - *FE* **2**: 202 as *E. cicutarium* (L.) L'Hér. subsp. *cicutarium*.
Cr (W, C, E) Ks Kp Sa - *MAP 657*
Calcareous open stony ground, maritime sands & rubble, flat clayey areas; 0-1900m; fl. 3-5.
Mainly W. & E. Crete; Karpathos group [almost throughout Europe].

5. E. crassifolium L'Hér. in Aiton, *Hort. kew.* **2**: 414 (1789) - *FE* **2**: 204 as *E. hirtum* (Forssk.) Willd.
Cr (E) - *MAP 658*
Lygeum steppe, superficially hardened sandy soil near sea; 10-60m; fl. 3-4.
E. Crete (Ierapetra area) [N. Africa & S.W. Asia].
Considered by Greuter to be native to Crete, as part of the relict desert-like element of the flora (1973a: 41).

6. E. gruinum (L.) L'Hér. in Aiton, *Hort. kew.* **2**: 415 (1789) - *FE* **2**: 201.
Cr (W, C, E) Ks Kp Sa - *MAP 659*
Olive groves, coastal phrygana, river-beds; 0-1200m; fl. 3-4.
Mainly W. & E. Crete; Karpathos group [Sicily & Aegean region].

E. hirtum (Forssk.) Willd. (*FE* **2**: 204) = **5**.

7. E. laciniatum (Cav.) Willd., *Sp. pl.*: **3**: 633 (1800) - *FE* **2**: 200.
a. subsp. **laciniatum**
Cr (W, C, E) - *MAP 660*
Maritime sands, gorge-beds; 0-750m; fl. 3-4.
Crete (sporadic) [Mediterranean region].

8. E. malacoides (L.) L'Hér. in Aiton, *Hort. kew.* **2**: 415 (1789) - *FE* **2**: 200.
Cr (W, C, E) Ks Kp - *MAP 661*
Olive groves, rocky places; 50-750m; fl. 3-5.
Mainly W. & E. Crete; Kasos, Karpathos [S. Europe].

9. E. moschatum (L.) L'Hér. in Aiton, *Hort. kew.* **2**: 414 (1789) - *FE* **2**: 203.
Cr (W, E) Kp - *MAP 662*
Olive groves, stony ground; 50-650m; fl. 3-5.
W. & E. Crete; Karpathos [W., C. & S. Europe].

10. E. neuradifolium Delile in *Mém. Acad. Sci. Lett. Montpellier*, Sect. Méd. **1**: 425 (1853) - not cited in *FE*.
Cr (E) Ks Kp - *MAP 663*
Maritime sands, rocks & rubble.
E. Crete; Kasos, Karpathos [Spain & Greece; otherwise N. Africa & S.W. Asia].
Recorded by Greuter et al. (1983a: 58), Barclay (1986: 51), Christodoulakis et al. (1990: 432) and Raus (1990: 28). Previously recorded by Rechinger (1943a: 280 as "*E. subtrilobum*", b: 84 as "*E. subtrilobum* var. *glanduliferum*").

2. Geranium L.

G. brutium Gasp. (*FE* **2**: 198) = **G. molle** subsp. **brutium**.

1. G. columbinum L., *Sp. pl.*: 682 (1753) - *FE* 2: 198.
Cr (W, C, E) - MAP 664
Calcareous rocky places; 350-1350m; fl. 4-5.
Crete (sporadic) [almost throughout Europe].

2. G. dissectum L., *Cent. pl.* 1: 21 (1755) - *FE* 2: 198.
Cr (W, C) Kp - MAP 665
Marshes, damp ground, rocky places; 0-650m; fl. 4-5.
W. & C. Crete; Karpathos [almost throughout Europe].

3. G. lucidum L., *Sp. pl.*: 682 (1753) - *FE* 2: 198.
Cr (W, C, E) Kp - MAP 666
Calcareous woodland, rocky places, screes; 0-1400m; fl. 3-5.
Mainly W. Crete; Karpathos [most of Europe].

4. G. molle L., *Sp. pl.*: 682 (1753) - *FE* 2: 198.
? subsp. **brutium** (Gasp.) Graebn. in Asch. & Graebn., *Syn. mitteleur. Fl.* 7: 53 (1913) - *FE* 2: 198 as *G. brutium* Gasp.
Doubtfully present in Crete (Greuter, 1974: 156) [S. Italy, Sicily & Balkan peninsula].
a. subsp. molle
Cr (W, C, E) Kp - MAP 667
Olive groves, gorge-beds, among rocks; 0-2100m; fl. 3-5.
Crete (widespread); Karpathos [almost throughout Europe].
Literature records of the species sensu lato have here been referred to subsp. **a**.

5. G. purpureum Vill., *Fl. delph.*: 72 (1786) - *FE* 2: 198.
Cr (W, C, E) Ks Kp Sa - MAP 668
Calcareous woodland, olive groves, gorge-beds, among rocks; 0-400m; fl. 3-5.
Mainly W. Crete; Karpathos group [W. & S. Europe].

? **G. pusillum** Burm.f., *Spec. bot. Geran.*: 27 (1759) - *FE* 2: 198.
Doubtfully present in Crete (Greuter, 1974: 156) [almost throughout Europe].

6. G. robertianum L., *Sp. pl.*: 681 (1753) - *FE* 2: 198.
Cr - NOT MAPPED
Crete [almost throughout Europe].

7. G. rotundifolium L., *Sp. pl.*: 683 (1753) - *FE* 2: 198.
Cr (W, C, E) Ks Kp - MAP 669
Olive groves, gorge-beds, among rocks, flat clayey areas; 0-2000m; fl. 3-5.
Mainly W. & C. Crete; Kasos, Karpathos [most of Europe].

8. G. tuberosum L., *Sp. pl.*: 680 (1753) - *FE* 2: 197.
a. subsp. tuberosum
Cr (C, E) Kp - MAP 670
Cultivated & fallow fields, weed communities in cultivated areas; 0-800m; fl. 3-4.
C. & E. Crete; Karpathos [S. Europe].

GLOBULARIACEAE

1. Globularia L.

1. G. alypum L., *Sp. pl.*: 95 (1753) - *FE* 3: 283.
Cr (W, C) - MAP 671
Open rocky phrygana, sandy hills; 0-100m; fl. 4-5.
W. & C. Crete (Gavdos island & Gulf of Mesara area) [Mediterranean region].

GUTTIFERAE
(HYPERICACEAE)

1. Hypericum L.

●**1. H. aciferum** (Greuter) N.Robson in *Feddes Reprium* 74: 23 (1967) - *FE* 2: 264.
Cr (W) - MAP 672
Shady calcareous cliffs & boulders near sea; 0-50m; fl. 6-10.
W. Crete (W. of Hora Sfakion) - Endemic.
[Plate 4.] Endangered species, legally protected.

2. H. aegypticum L., *Sp. pl.*: 784 (1753) - *FE* 2: 264.
Cr (W, E) - MAP 673
Calcareous coastal cliffs & phrygana; 0-100m; fl. 3-4.
W. & E. Crete (Akrotiri peninsula & W. of Sitia) [Mediterranean region].

●**3. H. amblycalyx** Coustur. & Gand. in *Bull. Soc. bot. Fr.* 63: 14 (1917) - *FE* 2: 264.
Cr (E) - MAP 674
Calcareous cliffs, steep rocky banks; 0-1000m; fl. 4-5.
E. Crete - Endemic.
Endemic status not noted in *FE*.

4. H. cuisinii Barbey in *Bull. Soc. vaud. Sci. nat.* 21: 220 (1886) - *FE* 2: 266.
Ks Kp Sa - MAP 675
Calcareous cliffs & rock-crevices; 0-1150m.
Karpathos group [E. Aegean Islands].

5. H. empetrifolium Willd., *Sp. pl.*: 3: 1452 (1802) - *FE* 2: 264.
Cr (W, C, E) Kp - MAP 676.
a. subsp. empetrifolium
Cr (W, C, E) Kp - MAP 677

Woodland, maquis, garigue; -800m; fl. 4-5.
Crete (widespread); Karpathos [N. Albania,
Greece & Aegean region].
● **b.** subsp. **oliganthum** (Rech.f.) I.Hagemann
in *Pl. Syst. Evol.* **155**: 186 (1987) - not cited in
FE.
Cr (W, C, E) - *MAP 678*
*Pinus brutia woodland, phrygana, rocky places;
0-1250m; fl. 4-5.*
Mainly W. & E. Crete - Endemic.
● **c.** subsp. **tortuosum** (Rech.f.) I.Hagemann in
Pl. Syst. Evol. **155**: 186 (1987) - not cited in
FE.
Cr (W, C) - *MAP 679*
*Calcareous rock-crevices, flat clayey areas;
1400-2300m; fl. 5-8.*
W. & C. Crete (Lefka Ori & Psiloritis) -
Endemic.

6. H. hircinum L., *Sp. pl.*: 784 (1753) - *FE* **2**:
263.
Cr (W, C, E) - *MAP 680*
*Stream-banks & springs in woodland & maquis,
damp cliff-ledges by springs, gorge-beds; 0-
1000m.*
a. subsp. **albimontanum** (Greuter) N.Robson in
Bull. Br. Mus. nat. Hist. (Bot.) **12**: 313 (1985).
Cr (W, E) - *NOT MAPPED*
W. & E. Crete [Peloponnisos & Kiklades
(Andros); otherwise E. Aegean Islands (Samos)
& Cyprus].
Described since *FE*, as *H. hircinum* var.
albimontanum Greuter (Greuter, 1975a: 25).
b. subsp. **majus** (Aiton) N.Robson in *Bull. Br.
Mus. nat. Hist. (Bot.)* **12**: 310 (1985) - not cited
in *FE*.
Cr (E) - *NOT MAPPED*
E. Crete (Afendis Kavousi) [W. Europe &
Mediterranean region].
The species sensu lato occurs mainly in W.
Crete.

● **7. H. jovis** Greuter, *Colloque OPTIMA Crète,
Guide Excurs.*: 25 (1975).
Cr (C) - *MAP 681*
Calcareous cliffs; 550-1500m; fl. 4-5.
C. Crete - Endemic.
The central Cretan vicariant of **3**.

● **8. H. kelleri** Bald. in *Malphigia* **9**: 67 (1895)
- *FE* **2**: 267.
Cr (W, C) - *MAP 682*
*Flat clayey areas & field-margins; (300-)1050-
2000m; fl. 6-7.*
Mainly W. Crete (mainly Lefka Ori) - Endemic.
Somewhat similar to **11**, but ecologically
restricted to flat clayey ground (e.g. in dolines)
and apparently not closely related (cf. *MFG* **1**:
607).

9. H. perfoliatum L., *Syst. nat.* ed.12, **2**: 510
(1767) - *FE* **2**: 266.
Cr (W, C, E) - *MAP 683*
*Phrygana, Lygeum steppe, rocky places,
abandoned fields; 0-600m; fl. 4-6.*
Crete (sporadic) [Mediterranean region].

10. H. perforatum L., *Sp. pl.*: 785 (1753) - *FE*
2: 269.
Cr (W, C) Kp - *MAP 684*
Rocky places, old dry-stone walls; 50-400m.
W. & C. Crete; Karpathos [almost throughout
Europe].
Subsp. *veronense* (Schrank) A.Fröhl. is given
for the Cretan area in *M-Ch* **3**: 271, but as
doubtfully distinct from subsp. *perforatum*; it is
not separated here.

H. tetrapterum Fr. (*FE* **2**: 268) was recorded in
error (Greuter, 1974: 156).

● **11. H. trichocaulon** Boiss. & Heldr. in
Boiss., *Diagn. pl. orient.* ser.1, **8**: 110 (1849) -
FE **2**: 267.
Cr (W, C) - *MAP 685*
*Phrygana, calcareous rocky places & ledges,
flat clayey areas; (10-)350-1900m; fl. 4-6.*
W. & C. Crete (mainly Lefka Ori, Kedros &
Psiloritis) - Endemic.

12. H. triquetrifolium Turra, *Farsetia*: 12
(1765) - *FE* **2**: 269.
Cr (W, C, E) Ks Kp - *MAP 686*
*Cultivated & fallow fields, roadsides, waste
areas; 0-400m; fl. (5-)6-9.*
Crete (widespread); Kasos, Karpathos
[Mediterranean region].

Hybrids:

H. empetrifolium x H. jovis
C. Crete (Kofinas).
Putative; recorded by Greuter et al. (1984b:
279).

H. kelleri x H. trichocaulon
On schist; 330m.
W. Crete.
Recorded by Rechinger (1949: 200).

HALORAGACEAE

1. Myriophyllum L.

1. M. spicatum L., *Sp. pl.*: 992 (1753) - *FE* **2**:
312.
Cr (W, C) - *MAP 687*
Fresh water.
W. & C. Crete [almost throughout Europe].

HIPPURIDACEAE

Hippuris vulgaris L. is given for the Cretan area in *FE* **2**: 313, although there are no records as a basis for this (Greuter, 1974: 139).

JUGLANDACEAE

Juglans regia L. is erroneously given as native to the Cretan area in *FE* **1**: 56 (Greuter, 1974: 154); it is cultivated only.

LABIATAE
(LAMIACEAE)

Acinos alpinus (L.) Moench (*FE* **3**: 165) = **Satureja 1**.

"*A. rotundifolius*" (*FE* **3**: 166) = **Satureja 5** (*M-Ch* **3**: 339).

1. Ajuga L.

1. A. chamaepitys (L.) Schreb., *Pl. verticill. unilab. gen. sp.*: 24 (1773) - *FE* **3**: 129.
a. subsp. **chia** (Schreb.) Arcang., *Comp. fl. ital.*: 560 (1882) - *FE* **3**: 129.
Cr (W) - *MAP 688*
Calcareous scree; 250m.
W. Crete (Korikos peninsula) [E.C. & S.E. Europe].

2. A. iva (L.) Schreb., *Pl. verticill. unilab. gen. sp.*: 25 (1773) - *FE* **3**: 129.
Cr (E) Ks Kp - *MAP 689*
E. Crete; Kasos, Karpathos [S. Europe].

3. A. orientalis L., *Sp. pl.*: 561 (1753) - *FE* **3**: 128.
Cr (W) - *MAP 690*
Among rocks of gorge-bed; 220m.
W. Crete (near Kastelli Kissamou) [mainly S.E. Europe].
Recorded since *FE* (Greuter et al., 1984*b*: 279).

2. Ballota L.

1. B. acetabulosa (L.) Benth., *Labiat. gen. spec.*: 595 (1834) - *FE* **3**: 150.
Cr (W) Ks Kp - *MAP 691*
River-beds, waste areas; near s.l.; fl. 4.
W. Crete; Kasos, Karpathos [E. & S. Greece & Aegean region; otherwise E. Aegean Islands & W. Turkey].

2. B. nigra L., *Sp. pl.*: 582 (1753) - *FE* **3**: 150.
a. subsp. **uncinata** (Fiori & Bég.) Patzak in *Annln naturh. Mus. Wien* **62**: 64 (1958) - *FE* **3**: 151.
Cr (W, C) - *MAP 692*

Roadsides, waste areas, villages, animal enclosures; 0-450m; fl. 4-6.
W. & C. Crete [S. Europe].

3. B. pseudodictamnus (L.) Benth., *Labiat. gen. spec.*: 594 (1834) - *FE* **3**: 150.
a. subsp. **pseudodictamnus**
Cr (W, C, E) - *MAP 693*
Steep rocky slopes, phrygana; 0-700m.
Crete (widespread, rarer towards E.) [S. Aegean region].

Calamintha cretica (L.) Lam. (*FE* **3**: 167) = **Satureja 4**.

C. incana (Sm.) Boiss. (*FE* **3**: 167) = **Satureja 6**.

"*C. nepeta*" (*FE* **3**: 166) = **Satureja 2** (Barclay, 1986: 57).

Clinopodium vulgare L. (*FE* **3**: 167) = **Satureja 13**.

3. Coridothymus Rchb.f.

1. C. capitatus (L.) Rchb.f. in *Öst. bot. Wbl.* **7**: 161 (1857) - *FE* **3**: 174 as *Thymus capitatus* (L.) Hoffmanns. & Link.
Cr (W, C, E) Ks Kp Sa - *MAP 694*
Pinus brutia woodland, dry phrygana, rocky places, maritime sands; 0-2000m; fl. 6-8.
Crete (widespread); Karpathos group [Mediterranean region].

4. Lamium L.

1. L. amplexicaule L., *Sp. pl.*: 579 (1753) - *FE* **3**: 148.
a. subsp. **amplexicaule**
Cr (W, C, E) Ks Kp - *MAP 695*
Rocky places, mountain pastures, cultivated terraces, disturbed ground; 0-2200m; fl. 3-5.
Mainly W. & C. Crete; Kasos, Karpathos [almost throughout Europe].

? L. bifidum Cirillo, *Pl. rar. neapol.* **1**: 22 (1788) - *FE* **3**: 148.
Subsp. *albimontanum* Rech.f. (*FE* **3**: 148) is included in synonymy of **4**.
Subsp. **bifidum**
Doubtfully present in Crete (Greuter, 1974: 159) [S. Europe].

2. L. garganicum L., *Sp. pl.* ed.2: 808 (1763) - *FE* **3**: 147.
a. subsp. **striatum** (Sm.) Hayek in *Beih. Repert. nov. Spec. Regni veg.* **30(2)**: 275 (1929) - *FE* **3**: 147, included in synonymy of subsp. *garganicum*.
Cr (W, C, E) - *MAP 696*

Calcareous rocky places; c. 1700m; fl. 5.
Crete (Lefka Ori, Kedros & Dikti) [Albania,
Bulgaria, Greece & Aegean region].

3. L. moschatum Mill., *Gard. Dict.* ed.8: no.4
(1768) - *FE* **3**: 148.
Cr Kp - *NOT MAPPED*
Crete; Karpathos [E. Balkan peninsula &
Aegean region].

4. L. purpureum L., *Sp. pl.*: 579 (1753) - *FE*
3: 148. (Including *L. bifidum* subsp.
albimontanum Rech.f. - *FE* **3**: 148.)
Cr (W) - *MAP 697*
*Calcareous garigue, grazed karstic land,
stream-beds; 1050-1600m; fl. 4.*
W. Crete (Lefka Ori) [almost throughout
Europe].

5. Lavandula L.

1. L. stoechas L., *Sp. pl.*: 573 (1753) - *FE* **3**:
187.
a. subsp. **stoechas**
Cr (W) - *MAP 698*
*Garigue & grassy places on non-calcareous
substrata, schistose cliffs; 50-650m; fl. 3-4.*
W. Crete [Mediterranean region].

6. Marrubium L.

1. M. vulgare L., *Sp. pl.*: 583 (1753) - *FE* **3**:
138.
Cr (W, C, E) Ks Kp - *MAP 699*
*Waste places, villages, animal enclosures; 0-
600m; fl. 4-5.*
Crete (widespread); Kasos, Karpathos [most of
Europe].

7. Melissa L.

1. M. officinalis L., *Sp. pl.*: 592 (1753) - *FE* **3**:
162.
a. subsp. **altissima** (Sm.) Arcang., *Comp. fl.
ital.* ed.2, 427: (1894) - *FE* **3**: 163.
Cr (W, C, E) Kp - *MAP 700*
*Olive groves, maquis, stream-banks, rocky
places, waste areas; -500m.*
Crete (sporadic); Karpathos [S. Europe].
[b. subsp. **officinalis]**
Cr - *NOT MAPPED*
Possibly naturalized.
Crete [most of Europe].
Recorded by Barclay (1986: 55).

8. Mentha L.

1. M. aquatica L., *Sp. pl.*: 576 (1753) - *FE* **3**:
185.
Cr (W, C, E) Kp - *MAP 701*

*Marshes, streams, springs, ditches & other wet
places; 0-400m.*
Crete (sporadic); Karpathos [almost throughout
Europe].

2. M. longifolia (L.) Huds., *Fl. angl.*: 221
(1762) - *FE* **3**: 186.
Cr (W, C) - *MAP 702*
*Marshes, streams, ditches, springs & other wet
places; 0-800m.*
W. & C. Crete [Most of Europe].
Cretan plants belong to subsp. *typhoides* (Briq.)
Harley, which is treated as doubtfully distinct
from subsp. *longifolia* in *M-Ch* **3**: 298, and is
not separated here.

M. microphylla K.Koch (*FE* **3**: 186) see **4**.

3. M. pulegium L., *Sp. pl.*: 577 (1753) - *FE* **3**:
184.
Cr (W, C, E) Kp - *MAP 703*
*Marshy & damp places, lake-shore, springs,
ditches, flat clayey areas in dolines flooded in
winter; 0-1300m; fl. 5-6.*
Mainly W. & C. Crete; Karpathos [W., C. & S.
Europe].
Both subsp. *pulegium* and subsp. *erinoides*
(Heldr.) Kokkini have been recorded from Crete
(Barclay, 1986: 55); the latter is otherwise
known from the Kiklades (Greuter et al., 1984b:
280), but is treated as doubtfully distinct in *M-
Ch* **3**: 297, and is not separated here.

4. M. spicata L., *Sp. pl.*: 576 (1753) - *FE* **3**:
186.
Cr (W, C, E) Kp - *MAP 704*
*Marshes, streams, springs & other wet places;
0-1600m.*
Crete (sporadic); Karpathos [most of Europe].
Both subsp. *spicata* (= *M. viridis* (L.) L.) and
subsp. *condensata* (Briq.) Greuter & Burdet (*FE*
3: 186 as *M. microphylla* K.Koch) have been
recorded from Crete and Karpathos (Greuter et
al., 1983a: 58; Barclay, 1986: 55); the latter is
known from the C. & E. Mediterranean region,
but is treated as doubtfully distinct in *M-Ch* **3**:
298, and is not separated here.

? M. suaveolens Ehrh., *Beitr. Naturk.* **7**: 149
(1792) - *FE* **3**: 185.
Doubtfully present in Crete (Greuter, 1974: 159)
[mainly W., C. & S. Europe].

Hybrids:

M. aquatica x **M. spicata** subsp. **condensata** =
M. x reverchonii Briq. in *Bull. Soc. bot.
Genève* **5**: 67 (1889) - *FE* **3**: 185 as *M. x
pyramidalis* Ten.
Moist place.
W. Crete.
Recorded by Petrak (in Rechinger, 1943b: 129).

M. aquatica x **M. spicata** subsp. **spicata** = **M. x piperita** L., *Sp. pl.*: 576 (1753) - *FE* 3: 185.
Doubtfully present in Crete (Greuter, 1974: 159).

M. spicata subsp. **condensata** x **M. suaveolens** = **M. x digenea** Briq. ex Petrak in *Denkschr. Akad. Wiss. Wien* 105(1): 543 (1943).
Recorded from Crete by Petrak (in Rechinger, 1943*b*: 127), but this is considered doubtful by Greuter (1974: 159).

M. spicata subsp. **spicata** x **M. suaveolens** = **M. x villosa** Huds., *Fl. angl.* ed.2: 250 (1778) - *FE* 3: 186.
Recorded from Crete by Petrak (in Rechinger, 1943*b*: 128), but this is considered doubtful by Greuter (1974: 159).

Micromeria graeca (L.) Benth. ex Rchb. (*FE* 3: 169) = **Satureja graeca**.

M. hispida Boiss. & Heldr. ex Benth. (*FE* 3: 168) = **Satureja 3**.

M. juliana (L.) Benth. ex Rchb. (*FE* 3: 169) = **Satureja 7**.

"*M. microphylla*" (*FE* 3: 168) = **Satureja 10** (Greuter, 1974: 159).

M. myrtifolia Boiss. & Hohen. (*FE* 3: 169) = **Satureja 8**.

M. nervosa (Desf.) Benth. (*FE* 3: 169) = **Satureja 9**.

M. sphaciotica Boiss. & Heldr. ex Benth. (*FE* 3: 168) = **Satureja 10**.

M. tapeinantha Rech.f. (*FE* 3: 169) is included - with some doubt - in synonymy of **Satureja 9**, after *M-Ch* 3: 338.

9. Nepeta L.

1. N. melissifolia Lam., *Encycl.* 1: 711 (1785) - *FE* 3: 160.
Cr (E) - MAP 705
Calcareous cliffs & rocky places; 0-500m; fl. 3-4.
E. Crete [Kiklades].

2. N. scordotis L., *Cent. pl.* 2: 20 (1756) - *FE* 3: 159.
Cr (W) - MAP 706
Calcareous scree, roadside bank; -200m; fl. 3-4.
W. Crete [S. Aegean region].

●**3. N. sphaciotica** P.H.Davis in *Notes R. bot. Gdn Edinb.* 21: 136 (1953) - *FE* 3: 159.
Cr (W) - MAP 707
Calcareous rocky slopes & stabilized screes; 2200-2300m; fl. 8.

W. Crete (Lefka Ori) - Endemic.
[Plate 4.] Endangered species, legally protected. Overgrazing by sheep is said to prevent production of seed (Greuter, 1973*a*: 52).

Ocimum basilicum L. (not cited in *FE*) is cultivated in Crete and has also been recorded as a casual escape (Rechinger, 1943*a*: 548).

10. Origanum L.

1. O. calcaratum Juss., *Gen. pl.*: 115 (1789) - *FE* 3: 172 as *O. tournefortii* Aiton.
Cr (E) - MAP 708
Calcareous cliffs; 450-500m; fl. 8.
E. Crete (S.E. of Sitia) [Kiklades; otherwise E. Aegean Islands (Halki)].

●**2. O. dictamnus** L., *Sp. pl.*: 589 (1753) - *FE* 3: 172.
Cr (W, C, E) - MAP 709
Calcareous cliffs, crevices & rubble, gorge-beds, often in shade; 0-1900m; fl. 6-10.
Crete (widespread, rarer towards E.) - Endemic. Vulnerable species, legally protected. Known as *diktamos* to the local people, who make an infusion from the dried leaves and inflorescences. The plant is commercially cultivated at the S.W. edge of the Dikti massif, and is occasionally seen in gardens elsewhere. Recorded in error from Greece, and as a casual from Malta (*M-Ch* 3: 305). A record from S.W. Turkey is considered referable to a related (but unidentified) species by Ietswaart (in Davis, 1982: 312).

"*O. heracleoticum*" (*FE* 3: 171) = **6a** (Barclay, 1986: 56).

●**3. O. microphyllum** (Benth.) Vogel in *Linnaea* 15: 76 (1841) - *FE* 3: 172.
Cr (W, E) - MAP 710
Calcareous open woodland, garigue, rocky places & crevices; 400-1800m; fl. 6-9.
W. & E. Crete (Lefka Ori & Dikti) - Endemic.

4. O. onites L., *Sp. pl.*: 590 (1753) - *FE* 3: 172.
Cr (W, C, E) Kp Sa - MAP 711
Calcareous cliffs, steep banks, scrub, garigue; 0-700m; fl. 4-5.
Mainly C. & E. Crete; Karpathos, Saria [Sicily, Malta, Greece & Aegean region].

O. tournefortii Aiton (*FE* 3: 172) = **1**.

●**5. O. vetteri** Briq. & Barbey in Stefani, Fors.-Major & Barbey, *Karpathos*: 124 (1895) - *FE* 3: 172.
Kp - MAP 712
Shady crevices in rock-faces & cliffs, growing

through *Erica manipuliflora* cushions and among
moss & stones beneath cliffs; *1000-1200m; fl. 7.*
Karpathos (Kalilimni) - Endemic.
[Plate 4.]

6. O. vulgare L., *Sp. pl.*: 590 (1753) - *FE* **3**:
171.

a. subsp. **hirtum** (Link) Ietsw. in *Leiden Bot.*
ser.4: 112 (1980) - *FE* **3**: 171, included in
synonymy of *O. heracleoticum* L.
Cr (W, C) - *MAP 713*
Olive groves, rocky & damp places; 0-1500m;
fl. 6-8.
W. & C. Crete [Balkan peninsula & Aegean
region].
Collected by the local people for culinary use.

Hybrid:

O. microphyllum x **O. vulgare** subsp. **hirtum**
= **O. x minoanum** P.H.Davis in *Notes R. bot.*
Gdn Edinb. **21**: 137 (1953) - *FE* **3**: 172.
Dry bushy slopes; 170-1500m; fl. 6-8.
W. & E. Crete.
Described from Crete; recorded earlier by
Rechinger (1943*b*: 125; 1949: 209 as *Majorana*
leptoclados Rech.f.)

11. Phlomis L.

1. P. cretica C.Presl in J.& C.Presl, *Delic.*
prag.: 84 (1822) - *FE* **3**: 145.
Cr (W, C) - *MAP 714*
Clearings in Quercus coccifera woodland,
garigue; 0-1250m; fl. 3-5.
W. & C. Crete [S. Greece; otherwise E. Aegean
Islands (Rodos) & S.W. Turkey (Marmaris
peninsula)].

2. P. floccosa D.Don in *Bot. Reg.* **15**: t.1300
(1830) - *FE* **3**: 145.
Ks Kp - *MAP 715*
Scrub, garigue; 0-900m; fl. 3-4.
Kasos, Karpathos [Tunisia, Libya & Egypt].
Recorded from Kasos since *FE* (Greuter et al.,
1983*a*: 58). *P. floccosa* is described in *FE* as a
"dwarf shrub up to 35cm"; this is somewhat
misleading, however, as plants in Karpathos
often reach 1m in height.

3. P. fruticosa L., *Sp. pl.*: 584 (1753) - *FE* **3**:
145.
Cr (W, C) - *MAP 716*
Scrub, garigue, calcareous rocky places; 0-
1050m; fl. 4-6.
W. & C. Crete [Mediterranean region].

●**4. P. lanata** Willd., *Enum. pl., Suppl.*: 41
(1814) - *FE* **3**: 145.
Cr (W, C, E) - *MAP 717*
Rocky clearings in Cupressus woodland,

garigue, phrygana, cliffs, gorge-beds & other
rocky places; 0-1600m; fl. 4-5.
Mainly C. & E. Crete - ?Endemic [doubtfully
also in Italy].

●**5. P. pichleri** Vierh. in *Öst. bot. Z.* **65**: 232
(1915) - *FE* **3**: 145.
Ks Kp Sa - *MAP 718*
Scrub, garigue, rocky gorge-beds; 0-800m; fl. 4-
5.
Karpathos group - Endemic.
Recorded from Saria since *FE* (Greuter et al.,
1983*a*: 58).

Hybrids:

P. cretica x **P. fruticosa** = **P. x cytherea**
Rech.f. in *Boissiera* **13**: 115 (1967).
Phrygana; 300-500m; fl. 4-5.
W. & C. Crete.
Recorded by Turland (1992*b*: 161).

P. cretica x **P. lanata** = **P. x commixta**
Rech.f. in *Denkschr. Akad. Wiss. Wien*
105(2,1): 119 (1943).
Clearings of Quercus coccifera woodland;
800m.
C. Crete (Psiloritis).
Described from Crete.

P. floccosa x **P. pichleri** = **P. x vierhapperi**
Rech.f. in *Annln naturh. Mus. Wien* **47**: 149
(1936).
Described from Karpathos.

P. fruticosa x **P. lanata** = **P. x sieberi** Vierh.
in *Öst. bot. Z.* **65**: 231 (1915).
Described from Crete.

12. Prasium L.

1. P. majus L., *Sp. pl.*: 601 (1753) - *FE* **3**: 137.
Cr (W, C, E) Ks Kp Sa - *MAP 719*
Scrub, calcareous rocky places, maritime sands;
0-400m; fl. 3-5.
Crete (widespread); Karpathos group
[Mediterranean region].

13. Prunella L.

●**1. P. cretensis** Gand. in *Bull. Soc. bot. Fr.*
62: 156 (1916) - *FE* **3**: 162, included in
synonymy of **2**.
Cr (W, C) - *MAP 720*
Open stony ground, flat clayey areas; 1500-
1600m.
W. & C. Crete (Lefka Ori & Psiloritis) -
Endemic.

2. P. laciniata (L.) L., *Sp. pl.* ed.2: 837 (1763)
- *FE* **3**: 162.
Cr (W, C) - *MAP 721*

Grassy terraced slopes, fallow fields, among paving stones on path; 100-500m; fl. 4-5.
W. & C. Crete [W., C. & S. Europe].

3. P. vulgaris L., *Sp. pl.*: 600 (1753) - *FE* **3**: 162.
Cr (W) - *MAP 722*
Damp stream-banks beneath Platanus trees; 500-600m; fl. 3-4.
W. Crete [almost throughout Europe].

14. Rosmarinus L.

1. R. officinalis L., *Sp. pl.*: 23 (1753) - *FE* **3**: 187.
Cr (W, C, E) Kp - *MAP 723*
Villages and cultivated areas nearby; 300-550m; fl. 3-10.
Crete (sporadic); Karpathos [Mediterranean region].
Occasionally cultivated and doubtfully native; probably only planted in Karpathos.

15. Salvia L.

1. S. fruticosa Mill., *Gard. Dict.* ed.8: no.5 (1768) - *FE* **3**: 189 as *S. triloba* L.f.
Cr (W, C, E) Ks Kp - *MAP 724*
Clearings in Pinus brutia woodland, olive groves, scrub, garigue; 0-700m; fl. 3-5.
Crete (widespread); Kasos, Karpathos [Mediterranean region].

2. S. pomifera L., *Sp. pl.*: 24 (1753) - *FE* **3**: 190.
a. subsp. pomifera
Cr (W, C) - *MAP 725*
Pinus brutia woodland, calcareous scrub, garigue & rocky places; 200-1200m; fl. 5-6.
Mainly W. Crete [S. Greece & S. Aegean region].

3. S. pratensis L., *Sp. pl.*: 25 (1753) - *FE* **3**: 191.
Cr (W) - *MAP 726*
Deciduous Quercus groves, abandoned fields; 400m; fl. 5-6.
W. Crete (S. of Rethimno) [most of Europe].
Recorded since *FE*, as doubtfully native (Greuter et al., 1984b: 281). Cretan plants belong to subsp. *haematodes* (L.) Briq., which is otherwise known from S. Italy, but is treated as doubtfully distinct from subsp. *pratensis* in *M-Ch* **3**: 319, and is not separated here.

S. triloba L.f. (*FE* **3**: 189) = **1**.

4. S. verbenaca L., *Sp. pl.*: 25 (1753) - *FE* **3**: 192.
Cr (W, C, E) Ks Kp Sa - *MAP 727*

Fallow fields, disturbed ground; 0-700m; fl. 2-6, 9-11.
Crete (widespread); Karpathos group [W. & S. Europe].

5. S. viridis L., *Sp. pl.*: 24 (1753) - *FE* **3**: 192.
Cr (W, C, E) Ks Kp Sa - *MAP 728*
Phrygana, calcareous rocky places, open stony ground; 0-250m; fl. 4-5.
Mainly W. & E. Crete; Karpathos group [S. Europe].

16. Satureja L.

1. S. alpina (L.) Scheele in *Flora, Jena* **26**: 577 (1843) - *FE* **3**: 165 as *Acinos alpinus* (L.) Moench.
a. subsp. meridionalis (Nyman) Greuter & Burdet in *Willldenowia* **14**: 302 (1984) - *FE* **3**: 166 as *Acinos alpinus* subsp. *meridionalis* (Nyman) P.W.Ball.
Cr (W, C, E) - *MAP 729*
Calcareous rocky places; 450-2350m; fl. 5-6.
Crete (Lefka Ori, Psiloritis & Dikti) [S. Europe].

2. S. calamintha (L.) Scheele in *Flora, Jena* **26**: 577 (1843) - *FE* **3** 166, included in synonymy of *Calamintha nepeta* (L.) Savi.
Cr (W, C, E) - *MAP 730*
Scrub, ditches, streams, springs, other shady & moist places; 0-400m; fl. 8-11.
Mainly W. & C. Crete [S. Europe].

●**3. S. candica** Greuter & Burdet in *Willldenowia* **14**: 302 (1984) - *FE* **3**: 168 as *Micromeria hispida* Boiss. & Heldr. ex Benth.
Cr (C, E) - *MAP 731*
Calcareous rocky places & crevices; 300-1700m.
C. & E. Crete (Psiloritis & Afendis Kavousi) - Endemic.

●**4. S. cretica** (L.) Briq. in Engl. & Prantl, *Natürl. PflFam.* **IV(3a)**: 302 (1896) - *FE* **3**: 167 as *Calamintha cretica* (L.) Lam.
Cr (W) - *MAP 732*
Calcareous cliffs, crevices, rubble of gorge-beds, other rocky places; 0-1900m.
W. Crete (mainly Lefka Ori) - Endemic.

? **S. graeca** L., *Sp. pl.*: 568 (1753) - *FE* **3**: 169 as *Micromeria graeca* (L.) Benth. ex Rchb.
Doubtfully present in Crete (Greuter, 1974: 159) [Mediterranean region].

5. S. graveolens (M.Bieb.) Caruel in Parl., *Fl. ital.* **6**: 143 (1884) - *FE* **3**: 166 as "*Acinos rotundifolius*".
Cr (W, C, E) Kp - *MAP 733*
Calcareous open rocky phrygana; 150-700m; fl. 4-5.

Crete (sporadic); Karpathos [S. Europe].

6. S. insularis Greuter & Burdet in *Willdenowia* **14**: 304 (1984) - *FE* **3**: 167 as *Calamintha incana* (Sm.) Boiss.
Kp - *MAP 734*
Growing through Sarcopoterium spinosum bushes, rocky gorge-bed; c. 300m.
Karpathos [S. Greece & Aegean region; otherwise Libya & S.W. Asia].
Erroneously given as doubtfully present in the Cretan area in *FE* (Greuter, 1974: 140).

7. S. juliana L., *Sp. pl.*: 567 (1753) - *FE* **3**: 169 as *Micromeria juliana* (L.) Benth. ex Rchb.
Cr (W, C, E) Kp - *MAP 735*
Pinus brutia woodland, calcareous rocky places & crevices; 0-2200m.
Crete (widespread); Karpathos [Mediterranean region].

8. S. myrtifolia (Boiss. & Hohen.) Greuter & Burdet in *Willdenowia* **14**: 305 (1984) - *FE* **3**: 169 as *Micromeria myrtifolia* Boiss. & Hohen.
Cr (W, E) Kp - *MAP 736*
Phrygana, rocky places; 0-400m.
W. & E. Crete; Karpathos [Greece & Aegean region; otherwise S.W. Asia].

9. S. nervosa Desf., *Fl. atlant.* **2**: 9 (1798) - *FE* **3**: 169 as *Micromeria nervosa* (Desf.) Benth. (?Including *Micromeria tapeinantha* Rech.f. - *FE* **3**: 169.)
Cr (W, C, E) Ks Kp Sa - *MAP 737*
Olive groves, phrygana, rocky places, open stony ground; 0-600m; fl. 4-5.
Crete (widespread); Karpathos group [Mediterranean region].

●**10. S. sphaciotica** (Boiss. & Heldr. ex Benth.) Greuter & Burdet in *Willdenowia* **14**: 306 (1984) - *FE* **3**: 168 as *Micromeria sphaciotica* Boiss. & Heldr. ex Benth.
Cr (W) Kp - *MAP 738*
Calcareous rocky places; fl. -10.
W. Crete; Karpathos - Endemic.

11. S. spinosa L., *Cent. pl.* **2**: 19 (1756) - *FE* **3**: 164.
Cr (W, C, E) - *MAP 739*
Calcareous open rocky slopes & screes; 1200-2400m; fl. 7-8.
Crete (Lefka Ori, Psiloritis & Dikti) [E. Aegean Islands (Samos) & S.W. Anatolia].
Not endemic to Crete as given in *FE* (cf. Davis, 1982: 320).

12. S. thymbra L., *Sp. pl.*: 567 (1753) - *FE* **3**: 164.
Cr (W, C, E) Ks Kp - *MAP 740*
Open Pinus brutia woodland, maquis, garigue, phrygana, maritime sands; 0-1500m; fl. 3-6.

Crete (widespread); Kasos, Karpathos [S. Sardinia & Aegean region].

13. S. vulgaris (L.) Fritsch, *Exkursionsfl. Oesterreich*: 477 (1897) - *FE* **3**: 167 as *Clinopodium vulgare* L.
a. subsp. **orientalis** (Bothmer) Greuter & Burdet in *Willdenowia* **14**: 306 (1984) - *FE* **3**: 167, included in synonymy of *Clinopodium vulgare* subsp. *arundanum* (Boiss.) Nyman.
Cr (W) - *MAP 741*
Platanus woodland, maquis, on non-calcareous substrata; 500-600m; fl. 5.
W. Crete [mainly C. & E. Mediterranean region].

17. Scutellaria L.

●**1. S. hirta** Sm., *Fl. Graec. prodr.* **1**: 425 (1809) - *FE* **3**: 136.
Cr (W, C, E) - *MAP 742*
Calcareous rock-crevices, rubble & screes; 800-2400m; fl. 5-8.
Crete (Lefka Ori, Kedros, Psiloritis, Dikti & Afendis Kavousi) - Endemic.

●**2. S. sieberi** Benth. in DC., *Prodr.* **12**: 420 (1848) - *FE* **3**: 136.
Cr (W, C, E) - *MAP 743*
Scrub, calcareous cliffs, crevices, ledges, rocky places & screes; 0-950m; fl. 4-6.
Crete (widespread) - Endemic.

18. Sideritis L.

1. S. curvidens Stapf in *Denkschr. Akad. Wiss. Wien* **50(2)**: 100 (1885) - *FE* **3**: 143.
Cr (W, C, E) Ks Kp Sa - *MAP 744*
Cupressus woodland, phrygana, calcareous rocky places, crevices, screes, sandy fields; 0-500m; fl. 4.
Crete (widespread); Karpathos group [Greece & Aegean region; otherwise Libya & S.W. Asia].

2. S. syriaca L., *Sp. pl.*: 574 (1753) - *FE* **3**: 142.
●**a.** subsp. **syriaca**
Cr (W, C, E) - *MAP 745*
Calcareous open rocky slopes; 800-2000m; fl. 7-8.
Crete (mainly Lefka Ori, Psiloritis & Afendis Kavousi) - Endemic.
Additionally recorded from Dikti in E. Crete in *MFG* **2**: 85. Known as *malotira* to the local people, who make an infusion from the dried inflorescences.

19. Stachys L.

1. S. arvensis (L.) L., *Sp. pl.* ed.2: 814 (1763)

- *FE* **3**: 157.
Cr (W, E) Kp - *MAP 746*
Rocks, stony ground beneath cliffs; 0-450m; fl.
4.
Mainly W. Crete; Karpathos [W., C. & S.
Europe].

2. S. cretica L., *Sp. pl.*: 581 (1753) - *FE* **3**:
153.
a. subsp. cretica
Cr (W, C, E) - *MAP 747*
Olive groves, rocky places, maritime sands,
roadsides; 0-700m; fl. 4-5.
Mainly W. & C. Crete [Albania, Greece &
Aegean region].

●**3. S. mucronata** Sieber ex Spreng., *Syst.*
veg. 2: 733 (1825) - *FE* **3**: 155.
Cr (E) Ks Kp - *MAP 748*
Calcareous phrygana; 0-1200m; fl. 7.
E. Crete; Kasos, Karpathos - Endemic.

4. S. ocymastrum (L.) Briq., *Lab. Alp. mar.*:
252 (1893) - *FE* **3**: 157.
Cr (W) - *MAP 749*
Roadsides, waste areas; 0-200m; fl. 4.
W. Crete [Mediterranean region].

5. S. spinosa L., *Sp. pl.*: 581 (1753) - *FE* **3**:
156.
Cr (W, C, E) Kp - *MAP 750*
Phrygana, rocky places, abandoned fields,
seashores; 0-800m; fl. 5-6.
Mainly W. & E. Crete; Karpathos [S.E.
Kiklades].

6. S. spinulosa Sm., *Fl. Graec. prodr.* 1: 410
(1809) - *FE* **3**: 157.
Cr (W, C) - *MAP 751*
Olive groves, calcareous cliffs, rocky places,
weed communities; 50-550m; fl. 4-5.
Mainly W. Crete [Balkan peninsula; otherwise
E. Aegean Islands & W. Turkey].

7. S. tournefortii Poir. in Lam., *Encycl.* **13**:
227 (1817) - *FE* **3**: 153.
Cr (W) - *MAP 752*
Coastal phrygana, calcareous rocky places; 0-
200m; fl. 4.
W. Crete (N. side) [Libya].

20. Teucrium L.

●**1. T. alpestre** Sm., *Fl. Graec. prodr.* 1: 395
(1809) - *FE* **3**: 134 as *T. alpestre* Sm. subsp.
alpestre.
Cr (W, C, E) - *MAP 753*
Calcareous cliffs, crevices & rocks, phrygana,
flat clayey areas; 0-2200m; fl. 6-8.
Crete (widespread) - Endemic.
Subsp. *gracile* (Barbey & Fors.-Major) D.Wood
(*FE* **3**: 134) = **7**.

2. T. brevifolium Schreb., *Pl. verticill. unilab.*
gen. sp.: 27 (1773) - *FE* **3**: 130.
Cr (W, E) Ks Kp Sa - *MAP 754*
Garigue, phrygana, rocky places; 0-400m; fl. 3-
4.
W. & E. Crete; Karpathos group [S. Aegean
region; otherwise N.E. Libya, N.W. Egypt, E.
Aegean Islands & S.W. Turkey].

3. T. capitatum L., *Sp. pl.*: 566 (1753) - *FE* **3**:
134 as *T. polium* subsp. *capitatum* (L.) Arcang.
Cr (C) - *MAP 755*
Calcareous garigue & phrygana, rocky places,
maritime sands; 0-600m.
C. Crete (N. side) [S. Europe].

●**4. T. cuneifolium** Sm., *Fl. Graec. prodr.* **1**:
395 (1809) - *FE* **3**: 133.
Cr (W) - *MAP 756*
Calcareous cliffs & rock-crevices; 50-600m; fl.
5.
W. Crete (S. side) - Endemic.

5. T. divaricatum Sieber ex Heldr. in *Herb.*
graec. norm.: no.290 (1857) - *FE* **3**: 132.
a. subsp. divaricatum
Cr (W, C, E) Ks Kp Sa - *MAP 757*
Calcareous cliffs & stony ground beneath,
crevices, rocky places; 0-1200m; fl. 5-7.
Crete (widespread, rarer towards E.); Karpathos
group [E. Greece; otherwise S.W. Asia].

6. T. flavum L., *Sp. pl.*: 565 (1753) - *FE* **3**:
132.
a. subsp. gymnocalyx Rech.f. in *Bot. Arch.*,
Berlin **42**: 397 (1941) - *FE* **3**: 133.
Cr (W) - *MAP 758*
Rock-crevices; 200-300m.
W. Crete (Samaria gorge) [S.E. Greece].
Regarded as absent from the Cretan area in *FE*,
although previously recorded by Rechinger
(1943b: 114).
b. subsp. hellenicum Rech.f. in *Bot. Arch.*,
Berlin **42**: 397 (1941) - *FE* **3**: 133.
Cr (C, E) - *MAP 759*
Phrygana; -1000m.
C. & E. Crete [Greece; otherwise ?E. Aegean
islands (Rodos) & W. Turkey].

●**7. T. gracile** Barbey & Fors.-Major in
Stefani, Fors.-Major & Barbey, *Karpathos*: 127
(1895) - *FE* **3**: 134 as *T. alpestre* subsp. *gracile*
(Barbey & Fors.-Major) D.Wood.
Cr (E) Ks Kp Sa - *MAP 760*
Calcareous cliffs, schistose hillsides; fl. 7.
E. Crete; Karpathos group - Endemic.
Recorded from the Dionisiades islands by
Christodoulakis et al. (1990: 433), who also
give the species as occurring on the main island
of Crete (E. division, without locality, op. cit.:
440).

T. heliotropifolium Barbey (*FE* **3**: 131) = **10a**.

8. T. massiliense L., *Sp. pl.* ed.2: 789 (1763) -
FE **3**: 131.
Cr (W) - *MAP 761*
*Damp maquis, rocky places, on non-calcareous
substrata; 300-500m.*
W. Crete [W. Mediterranean region].

9. T. microphyllum Desf. in *Annls Mus. Hist.
nat. Paris* **10**: 300 (1807) - *FE* **3**: 133.
Cr (W, C, E) Kp - *MAP 762*
*Pinus brutia woodland, calcareous phrygana,
rocky places & crevices; 0-700m; fl. 5-6.*
Crete (widespread); Karpathos [S. Aegean
region].

10. T. montbretii Benth. in *Annls Sci. nat.*
ser.2 (Bot.), **6**: 56 (1836) - *FE* **3**: 131.
a. subsp. **heliotropifolium** (Barbey) P.H.Davis
in *Notes R. bot. Gdn Edinb.* **21**: 138 (1953) - *FE*
3: 131 as *T. heliotropifolium* Barbey.
Kp Sa - *MAP 763*
*Crevices of calcareous cliffs, particularly
beneath overhangs & in caverns; 0-550m; fl. 7.*
Karpathos, Saria [E. Aegean Islands (Simi) &
S.W. Turkey (Marmaris peninsula)].
Recorded from outside the Cretan area since *FE*
(Carlström, 1987: 107, 239).

"*T. polium*" (Barclay, 1986: 58) = **3**. "*T.
polium*" is also given for Kasos & Karpathos by
Greuter et al. (1983*a*: 59), but the record cited
from Kasos (Davis, 1953: 139) is referable to **7**
(Raus, 1990: 29). The occurrence in Karpathos
requires confirmation.

T. polium subsp. *capitatum* (L.) Arcang. (*FE* **3**:
134) = **3**.

11. T. scordium L., *Sp. pl.*: 565 (1753) - *FE* **3**:
132.
a. subsp. **scordioides** (Schreb.) Arcang., *Comp.
fl. ital.*: 559 (1882) - *FE* **3**: 132.
Cr (W, C, E) - *MAP 764*
Marshy places, damp ditches; 0-400m; fl. 7.
Crete (sporadic) [S. Europe].

21 Thymbra L.

●**1. T. calostachya** (Rech.f.) Rech.f. in
Kulturpflanze, Beih. **3**: 64 (1962) - *FE* **3**: 170.
Cr (E) - *MAP 765*
*Calcareous cliffs & steep rocky slopes in gorges;
0-250m; fl. 5.*
E. Crete (S. side) - Endemic.
[Plate 5.]

22. Thymus L.

T. capitatus (L.) Hoffmanns. & Link (*FE* **3**:
174) = **Coridothymus 1**.

1. T. leucotrichus Halácsy, *Consp. fl. graec.* **2**:
561 (1902) - *FE* **3**: 176.
a. subsp. **leucotrichus**
Cr (W) - *MAP 766*
*Calcareous rubble, open stony ground; 1550-
2100m.*
W. Crete (Lefka Ori) [Greece; otherwise S.W.
Asia].

LAURACEAE

1. Laurus L.

1. L. nobilis L., *Sp. pl.*: 369 (1753) - *FE* **1**:
246.
Cr (W, C) - *MAP 767*
*Woodland, olive groves, scrub, calcareous cliff;
50-550m; fl. 3-4.*
W. & C. Crete [Mediterranean region].

LEGUMINOSAE
(FABACEAE)

Acacia farnesiana (L.) Willd. (*FE* **2**: 84) is
given for the Cretan area - as a casual - in *M-Ch*
4: 2, based on an old record from C. Crete cited
by Rechinger (1943*b*: 91), who questioned
whether it was merely cultivated or becoming
established as an escape. It is probably only
cultivated. Other species of *Acacia* are
frequently planted as ornamentals, especially for
roadside landscaping and as street trees.

1. Anagyris L.

1. A. foetida L., *Sp. pl.*: 374 (1753) - *FE* **2**: 85.
Cr (W, C, E) Ks Kp Sa - *MAP 768*
*Olive groves, scrub, roadsides, waste areas; 0-
400m; fl. 3(-4).*
Mainly W. & C. Crete; Karpathos group
[Mediterranean region].

2. Anthyllis L.

1. A. aegaea Turrill in *Kew Bull.* **1939**: 189
(1939) - *FE* **2**: 178.
Cr (E) - *MAP 769*
Calcareous coastal cliffs; 400m; fl. 4-5.
E. Crete (W. of Sitia) [Kiklades].

A. barba-jovis L. (*FE* **2**: 178) was recorded in
error (Greuter, 1974: 158).

2. A. hermanniae L., *Sp. pl.*: 720 (1753) - *FE*
2: 178.
Cr (W, C, E) Kp Sa - *MAP 770*
*Pinus brutia woodland, maquis, garigue,
phrygana, cliffs, open stony ground near sea,*

maritime sands; 0-600m; fl. 4-5.
Mainly W. & E. Crete; Karpathos, Saria
[Mediterranean region].

A. tetraphylla L. (*FE* 2: 181) = **Tripodion 1**.

3. A. vulneraria L., *Sp. pl.*: 719 (1753) - *FE* 2: 179.
a. subsp. **rubriflora** (DC.) Arcang., *Comp. fl. ital.*: 178 (1882) - *FE* 2: 181 as subsp. *praepropera* (A.Kern.) Bornm.
Cr (W, C, E) Ks Kp Sa - *MAP 771*
Calcareous garigue & phrygana, rocky places, soil-filled hollows, flat clayey areas; 50-2050m; fl. 3-5.
Mainly W. & E. Crete; Karpathos group
[mainly C. & E. Mediterranean region].

3. Astracantha Podlech

●**1. A. cretica** (Lam.) Podlech in *Mitt. bot. StSamml. Münch.* **19**: 8 (1983) - *FE* 2: 117 as *Astragalus creticus* Lam. subsp. *creticus*.
Cr (C, E) - *MAP 772*
Calcareous open rocky slopes, flat clayey areas, often gregarious above timberline; (700-)1200-2100m; fl. 6-8.
C. & E. Crete (Kedros, Psiloritis, Dikti & Afendis Kavousi) - ?Endemic [possibly also in E. Aegean Islands (Samos) & S.W. Turkey].

4. Astragalus L.

1. A. angustifolius Lam., *Encycl.* **1**: 321 (1783) - *FE* 2: 119.
a. subsp. **angustifolius**
Cr (W, C, E) - *MAP 773*
Calcareous open rocky slopes, flat clayey areas, often gregarious above timberline; 1200-2200m; fl. 6-8.
Crete (Lefka Ori, Kedros, Psiloritis & Dikti) [Balkan peninsula].

2. A. austro-aegaeus Rech.f. in *Phyton, Horn* **1**: 202 (1949) - *FE* 2: 114.
Ks Kp - *MAP 774*
Garigue, phrygana, margins of olive groves; 0-600m; fl. 3-4.
Kasos, Karpathos [E. Aegean islands (Rodos)].

3. A. boeticus L., *Sp. pl.*: 758 (1753) - *FE* 2: 111.
Cr Kp - *NOT MAPPED*
Crete; Karpathos [Mediterranean region].

A. creticus Lam. subsp. *creticus* (*FE* 2: 117) = **Astracantha 1**.

4. A. depressus L., *Cent. pl.* **2**: 29 (1756) - *FE* 2: 115.

a. subsp. **depressus**
Cr (W, C, E) - *MAP 775*
Calcareous rock-crevices, open rocky ground, flat clayey areas; 1200-2100m; fl. 4-5.
Crete (Lefka Ori, Psiloritis & Dikti) [S. Europe].

5. A. echinatus Murray, *Prodr. stirp. gott.*: 222 (1770) - *FE* 2: 113.
Cr Kp - *NOT MAPPED*
Crete; Karpathos [Mediterranean region].

6. A. epiglottis L., *Sp. pl.*: 759 (1753) - *FE* 2: 113.
a. subsp. **epiglottis**
Kp - *MAP 776*
Karpathos [Mediterranean region].

A. haarbachii Spruner ex Boiss. (*FE* 2: 112) was almost certainly recorded in error (Greuter, 1974: 157).

7. A. hamosus L., *Sp. pl.*: 758 (1753) - *FE* 2: 113.
Cr (W, C, E) Ks Kp - *MAP 777*
Olive terraces, scrub, open ground, clayey hills; 0-600m; fl. 3-4.
Crete (sporadic); Kasos, Karpathos [S. Europe].

●**8. A. idaeus** Bunge in *Mém. Acad. Sci. St. Petersb.* **11**(16): 107 (1868) - *FE* 2: 121.
Cr (C, E) - *NOT MAPPED*
C. & E. Crete (Psiloritis & Dikti) - Endemic. The species is apparently known only from two collections made over a century ago (*MFG* **1**: 472).

●**9. A. nummularius** Lam., *Encycl.* **1**: 317 (1783) - *FE* 2: 116.
Cr (E) - *MAP 778*
Calcareous open rocky ground, bare patches in dwarf shrub communities; 1100-2148m; fl. 5.
E. Crete (Dikti) - Endemic.

10. A. pelecinus (L.) Barneby in *Mem. N. Y. bot. Gdn* **13**: 26 (1964) - *FE* 2: 127 as *Biserrula pelecinus* L.
Cr (W, E) Ks Kp - *MAP 779*
Bare & stony places; fl. 4.
W. & E. Crete; Kasos, Karpathos [Mediterranean region].

11. A. peregrinus Vahl, *Symb. bot.* **1**: 57 (1790) - *FE* 2: 112.
a. subsp. **peregrinus**
Cr (E) - *NOT MAPPED*
E. Crete (Koufonisi island) [S. Kiklades; otherwise Libya, Egypt, Sinai & adjacent S.W. Asia].

12. A. sinaicus Boiss., *Diagn. pl. orient. ser.1*, **9**: 57 (1849) - *FE* 2: 113.
Cr (E) Kp - *MAP 780*

Sandy places.
E. Crete (Gaidouronisi island); Karpathos
[mainly S. Jugoslavia, Greece & Aegean
region].

Biserrula pelecinus L. (*FE* **2**: 127) =
Astragalus 10.

5. Bituminaria Fabr.

1. B. bituminosa (L.) C.H.Stirt. in *Bothalia* **13**:
318 (1981) - *FE* **2**: 127 as *Psoralea bituminosa*
L.
Cr (W, C, E) Ks Kp Sa - *MAP 781*
*Pinus brutia woodland, olive groves, rocky
places, maritime sands, roadsides, waste areas;
0-750m; fl. 3-9.*
Crete (widespread); Karpathos group [S.
Europe].

6. Calicotome Link

1. C. villosa (Poir.) Link in *Neues J. Bot.* **2(2)**:
51 (1808) - *FE* **2**: 86.
Cr (W, C, E) - *MAP 782*
*Maquis, scrub, garigue, maritime sands; 0-
1600m; fl. 3-4.*
Crete (widespread) [Mediterranean region].

7. Ceratonia L.

1. C. siliqua L., *Sp. pl.*: 1026 (1753) - *FE* **2**:
83.
Cr (W, C, E) Ks Kp - *MAP 783*
Olive groves, scrub, garigue; 0-700m; fl. 9-12.
Crete (widespread); Kasos, Karpathos
[Mediterranean region].

Cercis siliquastrum L. is given for the Cretan
area in *FE* **2**: 83; there are no records as a basis
for this (Greuter, 1974: 139), although the
species is planted on roadsides and as a street
tree in towns.

8. Chamaecytisus Link

1. C. creticus (Boiss. & Heldr.) Rothm. in
Feddes Reprium Spec. nov. veg. **53**: 144 (1944)
- *FE* **2**: 90. (Including *C. subidaeus* (Gand.)
Rothm. - *FE* **2**: 91.)
Cr (W, C, E) - *MAP 784*
*Light woodland, maquis, phrygana, rocky
places, usually on non-calcareous substrata;
400-1600m; fl. 4-5.*
Mainly W. & C. Crete [S. Peloponnisos].
Recorded from Peloponnisos since *FE*
(Boratynski et al., 1983: 36).

C. subidaeus (Gand.) Rothm. (*FE* **2**: 91) is
included in synonymy of **1**.

9. Cicer L.

C. arietinum L. (*FE* **2**: 128) is cultivated in
Crete for its edible seeds and has also been
recorded as a casual escape (Rechinger, 1943a:
322).

1. C. incisum (Willd.) K.Malý in Asch. &
Graebn., *Syn. mitteleur. Fl.* **6(2)**: 900 (1909) -
FE **2**: 128.
Cr (W, C, E) - *MAP 785*
*Calcareous rubble & screes; 1500-2400m; fl. 6-
9.*
Crete (Lefka Ori, Psiloritis & Dikti) [C. & S.
Greece; otherwise S.W. Asia].

10. Coronilla L.

C. cretica L. (*FE* **2**: 183) = **Securigera 1**.

C. emerus subsp. *emeroides* (Boiss. & Spruner)
Hayek (*FE* **2**: 183) was almost certainly
recorded in error (Greuter, 1974: 158).

C. globosa Lam. (*FE* **2**: 183) = **Securigera 2**.

C. rostrata Boiss. & Spruner (*FE* **2**: 183) =
Securigera 3.

1. C. scorpioides (L.) W.D.J.Koch, *Syn. fl.
germ. helv.*: 188 (1835) - *FE* **2**: 183.
Cr (W, C, E) Ks Kp Sa - *MAP 786*
*Olive groves, cultivated & fallow land,
seashores; 0-750m; fl. 3-5.*
Mainly W. & E. Crete; Karpathos group [S.
Europe].

2. C. valentina L., *Sp. pl.*: 742 (1753) - *FE* **2**:
183. (Including subsp. *glauca* (L.) Batt. - *FE* **2**:
183.)
Cr (C, E) Kp Sa - *MAP 787*
*Calcareous cliffs, rocks & screes; 500-700m; fl.
4.*
C. & E. Crete; Karpathos, Saria [Mediterranean
region].

C. varia L. (*FE* **2**: 183) was almost certainly
recorded in error (Greuter, 1974: 158).

11. Dorycnium Mill.

1. D. hirsutum (L.) Ser. in DC., *Prodr.* **2**: 208
(1825) - *FE* **2**: 172.
Cr (W) Kp - *MAP 788*
W. Crete (Gavdos island); Karpathos
[Mediterranean region].

2. D. rectum (L.) Ser. in DC., *Prodr.* **2**: 208
(1825) - *FE* **2**: 172.
Cr (W, C, E) - *MAP 789*

Platanus woodland, streams, marshes, ditches & other damp ground; 0-500m; fl. 5-6.
Mainly W. & C. Crete [Mediterranean region].

12. Ebenus L.

●**1. E. cretica** L., *Sp. pl.*: 764 (1753) - *FE* 2: 191.
Cr (W, C, E) - *MAP 790*
Cliffs, steep banks, rarely in phrygana; 0-800m; fl. 4-5.
Crete (widespread) - Endemic.

13. Genista L.

1. G. acanthoclada DC., *Prodr.* 2: 146 (1825) - *FE* 2: 100.
a. subsp. **acanthoclada**
Cr (W, C, E) Kp - *MAP 791*
Light woodland, maquis, garigue, phrygana, maritime sands; 0-850m; fl. 4-6.
Crete (widespread); Karpathos [Greece & Aegean region; otherwise Libya, E. Aegean Islands & Turkey].

2. G. fasselata Decne. in *Annls Sci. nat.* ser.2 (Bot.), 4: 360 (1835) - *FE* 2: 100.
Ks Kp - *MAP 792*
Kasos, Karpathos [S.W. Asia].

3. G. monspessulana (L.) L.A.S.Johnson in *Contr. N. S. W. Natn. Herb.* 3: 98 (1962) - *FE* 2: 93 as *Teline monspessulana* (L.) K.Koch.
Cr (W, C) - *MAP 793*
Maquis, stream-banks beneath Platanus trees, humid valleys, on non-calcareous substrata; 150-600m; fl. 3-4.
W. & C. Crete [mainly Mediterranean region].
Recorded since *FE* (Strasser, 1989: 1, 7, 11; Turland, 1992a: 350).

Gleditsia triacanthos L. (*FE* 2: 84) is given for the Cretan area - as a casual - in *M-Ch* 4: 105, based on an old record from C. Crete cited by Greuter (1973a: 42), who speculated that it perhaps referred to the beginnings of naturalization, rather than cultivated plants.

14. Glycyrrhiza L.

G. echinata L. (*FE* 2: 127) was almost certainly recorded in error (Greuter, 1974: 157).

[**1. G. glabra**] L., *Sp. pl.*: 742 (1753) - *FE* 2: 127.
Cr (C, E) - *MAP 794*
Naturalized on roadsides near coast.
Mainly C. Crete [C., E. & S. Europe].
Erroneously given as native to the Cretan area in *FE* (Greuter, 1974: 157).

15. Hedysarum L.

1. H. spinosissimum L., *Sp. pl.*: 750 (1753) - *FE* 2: 186.
a. subsp. **spinosissimum**
Cr (E) Ks Kp - *MAP 795*
Open stony ground, sandy places near sea; 0-350m; fl. 3-4.
E. Crete; Kasos, Karpathos [Mediterranean region].

16. Hippocrepis L.

1. H. biflora Spreng., *Pl. min. cogn. pug.* 2: 73 (1815) - *FE* 2: 185 as "*H. unisiliquosa*".
Cr (W, C, E) Ks Kp - *MAP 796*
Soil-patches in garigue, rocky places; 0-200m; fl. 3-4.
Mainly W. & E. Crete; Kasos, Karpathos [S. Europe].

2. H. ciliata Willd. in *Magazin Ges. naturf. Fr. Berl.* 2: 173 (1808) - *FE* 2: 185.
Cr (W, E) Ks Kp - *MAP 797*
Rocky places, maritime sands; 0-300m.
W. & E. Crete; Kasos, Karpathos [S. Europe].

3. H. cyclocarpa Murb. in *Acta Univ. lund.* 33(12): 80 (1897).
Ks Kp - *MAP 798*
Calcareous rocky phrygana with flat clayey areas, abandoned terraces, cliff; 0-350m; fl. 3-4.
Kasos, Karpathos [Tunisia, Libya & Egypt].
Recorded since *FE* (Höner, 1986).

4. H. multisiliquosa L., *Sp. pl.*: 744 (1753) - *FE* 2: 185.
Kp - *MAP 799*
Calcareous rocks with Pistacia lentiscus; 200-250m.
Karpathos [Mediterranean region].
Recorded since *FE* (Greuter, 1974: 148).

5. H. unisiliquosa L., *Sp. pl.*: 744 (1753).
a. subsp. **unisiliquosa**
Kp - *MAP 800*
Karpathos [E. Peloponnisos & Kiklades (Sikinos); otherwise S.W. Asia].
"*H. unisiliquosa*" as given in *FE* 2: 185 is referable to **1** (Greuter et al., 1984b: 282). The true species is recorded from Karpathos by Greuter & Raus (1987: 443), based on a collection made by Pichler in 1880.

17. Hymenocarpos Savi

1. H. circinnatus (L.) Savi, *Fl. pis.* 2: 205 (1798) - *FE* 2: 177.
Cr (W, C, E) Ks Kp - *MAP 801*

Olive groves, open stony ground, screes, soil-filled hollows, maritime sands; 0-650m; fl. 3-5.
Mainly W. & C. Crete; Kasos, Karpathos [S. Europe].

18. Lathyrus L.

1. L. amphicarpos L., *Sp. pl.*: 729 (1753) - *FE* 2: 142.
Cr (W) Kp - *MAP 802*
Calcareous open stony ground.
W. Crete; Karpathos [Mediterranean region].
Erroneously given as doubtfully present in the Cretan area in *FE* (Greuter, 1974: 140).

? L. angulatus L., *Sp. pl.*: 731 (1753) - *FE* 2: 142.
Doubtfully present in Crete (Greuter, 1974: 157) [mainly Mediterranean region].

2. L. annuus L., *Demonstr. pl.*: 20 (1753) - *FE* 2: 142.
Cr (W, C, E) Kp - *MAP 803*
Olive groves, cultivated terraces, roadsides, ditches, damp ground near sea; 0-450m; fl. 3-5.
Crete (sporadic); Karpathos [Mediterranean region].

3. L. aphaca L., *Sp. pl.*: 729 (1753) - *FE* 2: 143.
Cr (W, C, E) Ks Kp - *MAP 804*
Olive groves, vineyards, cultivated fields, calcareous screes; 0-750m; fl. 4-5.
Crete (sporadic); Kasos, Karpathos [W., C. & S. Europe].

L. articulatus L. (*FE* 2: 142) is included in synonymy of **5**.

4. L. cicera L., *Sp. pl.*: 730 (1753) - *FE* 2: 142.
Cr (W) Ks Kp - *MAP 805*
Olive groves, mountain plain; 400-1050m.
W. Crete; Kasos, Karpathos [S. Europe].
Occurring as a native plant as well as cultivated.

5. L. clymenum L., *Sp. pl.*: 732 (1753) - *FE* 2: 142. (Including *L. articulatus* L. - *FE* 2: 142.)
Cr (C, E) Kp - *MAP 806*
Olive terraces; 50-350m; fl. 3-4.
C. & E. Crete; Karpathos [Mediterranean region].

? L. grandiflorus Sm., *Fl. Graec. prodr.* 2: 67 (1813) - *FE* 2: 141.
Doubtfully present in Crete (Greuter, 1974: 157) [S. Italy, Sicily & S. half of Balkan peninsula].

6. L. hierosolymitanus Boiss., *Diagn. pl. orient.* ser.1, **9**: 127 (1849) - *FE* 2: 142.
Cr (W, E) Kp - *MAP 807*
Among crops; fl. 4.
W. & E. Crete; Karpathos [N.E. Greece &

Kiklades; otherwise S.W. Asia].

? L. hirsutus L., *Sp. pl.*: 732 (1753) - *FE* 2: 142.
Doubtfully present in Crete (Greuter, 1974: 157) [C. & S. Europe].

7. L. laxiflorus (Desf.) Kuntze in *Trudy imp. S.-Peterb. bot. Sada* **10**: 185 (1887) - *FE* 2: 140.
a. subsp. **laxiflorus**
Cr (W, C) - *MAP 808*
Margins of woodland & maquis, rocky places; 100-1600m; fl. 4-5.
W. & C. Crete [mainly S.E. Europe].

●**8. L. neurolobus** Boiss. & Heldr. in Boiss., *Diagn. pl. orient.* ser.1, **9**: 125 (1849) - *FE* 2: 140.
Cr (W) - *MAP 809*
Marshes, streams & springs in woodland & maquis, moist shady rocks; 50-300m; fl. 5-7.
W. Crete - Endemic.
[Plate 5.]

9. L. ochrus (L.) DC. in Lam. & DC., *Fl. franç.* ed.3, **4**: 578 (1805) - *FE* 2: 142.
Cr (W) Kp - *MAP 810*
Olive groves, ditches, also frequently cultivated; 0-500m; fl. 3-5.
W. Crete; Karpathos [S. Europe].
Doubtfully native (*M-Ch* 4: 121).

[10. L. sativus] L., *Sp. pl.*: 730 (1753) - *FE* 2: 142.
Cr - *NOT MAPPED*
Cultivated and possibly naturalized.
Crete [C., E. & S. Europe, of unknown origin].

11. L. saxatilis (Vent.) Vis., *Fl. dalmat.* 3: 330 (1851) - *FE* 2: 141.
Cr (W, E) Ks Kp - *MAP 811*
Calcareous rocks, roadside banks; 50-400m; fl. 4.
W. & E. Crete; Kasos, Karpathos [mainly Mediterranean region].

12. L. setifolius L., *Sp. pl.*: 731 (1753) - *FE* 2: 142.
Cr (W, C, E) Ks Kp - *MAP 812*
Garigue, phrygana, stony ground; 50-1350m; fl. 3-5.
Mainly W. Crete; Kasos, Karpathos [S. Europe].

13. L. sphaericus Retz., *Observ. bot.* 3: 39 (1784) - *FE* 2: 141.
Cr (E) Kp - *MAP 813*
Olive groves.
E. Crete; Karpathos [mainly S. Europe].

L. stenophyllus Boiss. & Heldr. (*FE* 2: 142) was recorded in error (Greuter, 1974: 157).

19. Lens Mill.

[1. L. culinaris] Medik. in *Vorles. Churpfälz. phys.-ökon. Ges.* **2**: 361 (1787) - *FE* 2: 136.
Cr Kp - *NOT MAPPED*
Cultivated for its edible seeds and possibly naturalized in fallow fields; 50-200m; fl. 3-4.
Crete; Karpathos [C., E. & S. Europe; of unknown origin].

2. L. ervoides (Brign.) Grande in *Boll. Orto bot., Napoli* **5**: 58 (1918) - *FE* 2: 136.
Cr (E) - *MAP 814*
Gorge-bed.
E. Crete [S. Europe].

3. L. nigricans (M.Bieb.) Godr., *Fl. Lorraine* **1**: 173 (1843) - *FE* 2: 136.
Cr Ks Kp - *NOT MAPPED*
Crete; Kasos, Karpathos [S. Europe].

20. Lotus L.

1. L. angustissimus L., *Sp. pl.*: 774 (1753) - *FE* 2: 175.
Cr (W) Kp - *MAP 815*
Platanus woodland, rocks, fallow fields, maritime sands; 0-1050m.
W. Crete; Karpathos [mainly S. Europe].

2. L. conimbricensis Brot., *Phytogr. Lusitan. select.*: 59 (1800) - *FE* 2: 175.
Cr (W, C) Kp - *MAP 816*
Flat clayey areas, fallow fields, on non-calcareous substrata; 0-1050m; fl. 4-5.
W. & C. Crete; Karpathos [Mediterranean region].

3. L. corniculatus L., *Sp. pl.*: 775 (1753) - *FE* 2: 174.
Cr (W, C, E) - *MAP 817*
Marshes, ditches, damp ground, sandy places, vineyards; 0-700m; fl. 4.
Crete (sporadic) [almost throughout Europe].

4. L. cytisoides L., *Sp. pl.*: 776 (1753) - *FE* 2: 176.
Cr (W, C, E) Ks Kp Sa - *MAP 818*
Phrygana, maritime sands & rocks; 0-200m; fl. 3-5.
Mainly W. & E. Crete; Karpathos group [Mediterranean region].

5. L. edulis L., *Sp. pl.*: 774 (1753) - *FE* 2: 175.
Cr (W, C, E) Ks Kp - *MAP 819*
Vineyards, coastal phrygana, soil-filled hollows, maritime sands & rocks, fallow fields; 0-400m; fl. 3-4.
Crete (widespread, rarer towards E.); Kasos, Karpathos [Mediterranean region].

6. L. glaber Mill., *Gard. Dict.* ed.8: no.3 (1768) - *FE* 2: 174 as *L. tenuis* Waldst. & Kit. ex Willd.
Cr (W) - *MAP 820*
Damp places.
W. Crete (W. of Hania) [most of Europe].

7. L. halophilus Boiss. & Spruner in Boiss., *Diagn. pl. orient.* ser.1, **2**: 37 (1843) - *FE* 2: 176.
Cr (W, C, E) Ks Kp - *MAP 821*
Olive groves, calcareous phrygana, maritime sands; 0-800m; fl. 3-5.
Crete (widespread); Kasos, Karpathos [Mediterranean region].

8. L. ornithopodioides L., *Sp. pl.*: 775 (1753) - *FE* 2: 176.
Cr (W, C, E) Ks Kp Sa - *MAP 822*
Quercus woodland, olive groves, rocky & sandy places, maritime sands; 0-500m; fl. 4-5.
Mainly W. Crete; Karpathos group [S. Europe].

9. L. palustris Willd., *Sp. pl.*: **3**: 1394 (1802) - *FE* 2: 175.
Cr (W, C, E) Kp - *MAP 823*
Marshy places.
Crete (sporadic); Karpathos [Greece & Aegean region; otherwise N. Africa & S.W. Asia].

10. L. parviflorus Desf., *Fl. atlant.* **2**: 206 (1799) - *FE* 2: 175.
Cr (W) - *MAP 824*
Grassy places, dry river-beds; 0-400m.
W. Crete [S. Europe].

11. L. pedunculatus Cav., *Icon.* **2**: 52 (1793) - *FE* 2: 175 as *L. uliginosus* Schkuhr.
Cr (W) - *MAP 825*
Seasonally wet places, brackish marshes, damp grassland.
W. Crete [W., C. & S. Europe].

12. L. peregrinus L., *Sp. pl.*: 774 (1753) - *FE* 2: 176.
Cr (W, C, E) Ks Kp Sa - *MAP 826*
Olive groves, vineyards, seashores; 0-100m; fl. 4-5.
Crete (sporadic); Karpathos group [Sicily (Linosa), Greece & Aegean region].

13. L. preslii Ten., *Fl. napol.* **5**: 160 (1835-1836) - *FE* 2: 175.
Cretan area [Mediterranean region].
Recorded since *FE* (Lassen in Greuter & Raus, 1987: 444).

L. tenuis Waldst. & Kit. ex Willd. (*FE* 2: 174) = **6**.

L. uliginosus Schkuhr (*FE* 2: 175) = **11**.

21. Lupinus L.

1. L. albus L., *Sp. pl.*: 721 (1753) - *FE* 2: 105.
a. subsp. albus
Cr (W, E) - *MAP 827*
Cultivated & fallow land; 600-1050m.
W. & E. Crete [C. & S. Europe].
Doubtfully native.
b. subsp. graecus (Boiss. & Spruner) Franco & P.Silva in *Feddes Reprium* **79**: 52 (1968) - *FE* 2: 105.
Cr - *NOT MAPPED*
Crete [Balkan peninsula & Aegean region].

2. L. angustifolius L., *Sp. pl.*: 721 (1753) - *FE* 2: 105.
Cr (W, C) Kp - *MAP 828*
Open stony ground; -600m.
W. & C. Crete; Karpathos [S. Europe].

3. L. micranthus Guss., *Fl. sicul. prodr.* **2**: 400 (1828-1832) - *FE* 2: 105.
Cr (W, E) Kp - *MAP 829*
Olive groves, fallow fields; 25-500m; fl. 3-5.
W. & E. Crete; Karpathos [Mediterranean region].

4. L. pilosus L., *Syst. veg.* ed.13: 545 (1774) - *FE* 2: 106 as *L. varius* subsp. *orientalis* Franco & P.Silva.
Cr (W, C) - *MAP 830*
Olive groves, fallow fields, also occasionally cultivated for its seeds; 0-750m; fl. 3-4.
W. & C. Crete [Greece & Aegean region; otherwise S.W. Asia].

L. varius subsp. *orientalis* Franco & P.Silva (*FE* 2: 106) = **4**.

22. Medicago L.

"*M. aculeata*" (*FE* **2**: 156) = **7** (Greuter in Greuter & Rechinger, 1967: 81).

1. M. arabica (L.) Huds., *Fl. angl.*: 288 (1762) - *FE* 2: 156.
Cr (W, C) - *MAP 831*
Light woodland, olive groves; 0-500m; fl. 4-5.
W. & C. Crete [mainly S. Europe].
Erroneously regarded as absent from the Cretan area in *FE* (Greuter, 1974: 140).

2. M. arborea L., *Sp. pl.*: 778 (1753) - *FE* 2: 155.
Cr (W, C, E) Ks Kp - *MAP 832*
Native on calcareous cliffs & offshore islets of Kasos & Karpathos, also planted and naturalized on roadsides & field-margins in both Crete & Karpathos; 0-500m; fl. 2-5.
Crete (sporadic); Kasos, Karpathos [Mediterranean region].

3. M. ciliaris (L.) All., *Fl. pedem.* **1**: 315 (1785) - *FE* 2: 155.
Cr (C) - *MAP 833*
Olive groves, terraces under Quercus pubescens, open grassland; 200-650m.
C. Crete [Mediterranean region].
Recorded since *FE* (Lesins & Lesins, 1979: 211).

4. M. constricta Durieu in *Act. Soc. linn. Bordeaux* **29**: 15 (1873) - not cited in *FE*.
Cr (W) - *MAP 834*
Calcareous rocky places.
W. Crete (Akrotiri peninsula) [Bulgaria, Greece & Aegean region].

5. M. coronata (L.) Bartal., *Cat. piante Siena*: 61 (1776) - *FE* 2: 157.
Cr (W, C, E) Kp Kp Sa - *MAP 835*
Calcareous rock-ledges & crevices, soil-pockets in rocks, open stony ground; 0-500m; fl. 4.
Mainly W. Crete; Karpathos group [Mediterranean region].

6. M. disciformis DC., *Cat. pl. horti monsp.*: 124 (1813) - *FE* 2: 157.
Cr (W) Ks Kp - *MAP 836*
Calcareous rocky places, open stony ground near sea.
W. Crete; Kasos, Karpathos [Mediterranean region].

7. M. doliata Carmign. in *G. Pisano* **12**: 48 (1810) - *FE* 2: 156 as "*M. aculeata*".
Cr - *NOT MAPPED*
Crete [Mediterranean region].

[8. M. falcata] L., *Sp. pl.*: 779 (1753) - *FE* 2: 154 as *M. sativa* subsp. *falcata* (L.) Arcang.
Cr (W, E) - *MAP 837*
Cultivated for fodder and possibly naturalized in fields & along field-margins; -800m; fl. 6.
W. & E. Crete [most of Europe].

"*M. globosa*" (*FE* **2**: 156) = **4** (Barclay, 1986: 64).

9. M. heyniana Greuter in *Candollea* **25**: 190 (1970).
Kp - *MAP 838*
Clayey soil-patches in low sparse phrygana on calcareous rocky ground; 750-900m.
Karpathos [Kiklades (Amorgos); otherwise E. Aegean Islands (Tilos & Rodos) & S.W. Turkey (Marmaris peninsula)].

10. M. littoralis Rohde ex Loisel., *Notes fl. France*: 118 (1810) - *FE* 2: 156.
Cr (W, C, E) Ks Kp - *MAP 839*
Mostly on maritime rocks & sands; 0-200m.
Mainly W. & E. Crete; Kasos, Karpathos [mainly Mediterranean region].

11. M. lupulina L., *Sp. pl.*: 779 (1753) - *FE 2*: 154.
Cr (W, E) Kp - *MAP 840*
Vineyards, calcareous rocky places, flat clayey areas; 800-2000m.
Mainly W. Crete; Karpathos [almost throughout Europe].

12. M. marina L., *Sp. pl.*: 779 (1753) - *FE 2*: 156.
Cr (W, C, E) Ks Kp - *MAP 841*
Maritime sands; fl. 3-5.
Crete (widespread); Kasos, Karpathos [coasts of W. & S. Europe].

13. M. minima (L.) L., *Fl. angl.*: 21 (1754) - *FE 2*: 157.
Cr (W, C, E) Ks Kp - *MAP 842*
River-beds, roadside banks, open stony ground near sea; 0-400m.
Crete (sporadic); Kasos, Karpathos [most of Europe].

14. M. monspeliaca (L.) Trautv. in *Bull. scient. Acad. imp. Sci. St. Pétersb.* **8**: 272 (1841) - *FE 2*: 152 as *Trigonella monspeliaca* L.
Cr (W, C, E) Ks Kp Sa - *MAP 843*
Burnt phrygana, bare stony & sandy ground, maritime sands & rocks; 0-1750m; fl. 3-4.
Crete (widespread); Karpathos group [C. & S. Europe].

15. M. murex Willd., *Sp. pl.*: **3**: 1410 (1802) - *FE 2*: 156.
Cr (W, C, E) - *MAP 844*
Olive groves, calcareous rocky places, cultivated land; 0-400m.
Crete (sporadic) [Mediterranean region].

16. M. orbicularis (L.) Bartal., *Cat. piante Siena*: 60 (1776) - *FE 2*: 155.
Cr (W, C, E) Ks Kp - *MAP 845*
Rocky & sandy places, bare ground; 0-450m; fl. 4.
Crete (widespread); Kasos, Karpathos [S. Europe].

17. M. polymorpha L., *Sp. pl.*: 779 (1753) - *FE 2*: 156.
Cr (W, C, E) Ks Kp - *MAP 846*
Olive groves, margins of maquis, vineyards, screes, dry river-beds, maritime sands & rocks, coastal saline ground; 0-400m; fl. 4.
Mainly W. Crete; Kasos, Karpathos [mainly S. Europe].

18. M. praecox DC., *Cat. pl. horti monsp.*: 123 (1813) - *FE 2*: 157.
Cr (W, C, E) - *MAP 847*
Weed communities on trodden ground; 0-1300m.
Crete (sporadic) [Mediterranean region].
Recorded since *FE* (Lesins & Lesins, 1979:

193).

19. M. rigidula (L.) All., *Fl. pedem.* **1**: 316 (1785) - *FE 2*: 156.
Cr (W, C) Kp - *MAP 848*
Rocky & sandy places; 50-1400m.
W. & C. Crete; Karpathos [S. Europe].

20. M. rugosa Desr. in Lam., *Encycl.* **3**: 632 (1792) - *FE 2*: 155.
Cr (E) Ks Kp - *MAP 849*
Weed communities, cultivated land; 50-400m; fl. 4.
E. Crete; Kasos, Karpathos [Mediterranean region].

[21. M. sativa] L., *Sp. pl.*: 778 (1753) - *FE 2*: 154.
[a. subsp. sativa]
Cr (W, C, E) Kp - *MAP 850*
Cultivated for fodder and naturalized; fl. 4-6.
Crete (sporadic); Karpathos [almost throughout Europe].
Subsp. *falcata* (L.) Arcang. (*FE 2*: 154) = **8**.

22. M. scutellata (L.) Mill., *Gard. Dict.* ed.8: no.2 (1768) - *FE 2*: 155.
Cr (W) Kp - *MAP 851*
Open stony ground; 0-100m; fl. 4.
W. Crete; Karpathos [S. Europe].

●**23. M. strasseri** Greuter, Matthäs & Risse in *Willdenowia* **12**: 201 (1982).
Cr (W, C, E) - *MAP 852*
Calcareous cliffs, mainly in gorges; 30-400m; fl. 4.
Crete (sporadic, N. side) - Endemic.
[Plate 5.] Related and similar to **2**, but generally smaller.

24. M. truncatula Gaertn., *Fruct. sem. pl.* **2**: 350 (1791) - *FE 2*: 156.
Cr (W, E) Ks Kp - *MAP 853*
Rocky & sandy places, seashores; 0-600m.
W. & E. Crete; Kasos, Karpathos [mainly Mediterranean region].

25. M. tuberculata (Retz.) Willd., *Sp. pl.*: **3**: 1410 (1802) - *FE 2*: 156 as *M. turbinata* (L.) All.
Cr (W, E) Ks Kp - *MAP 854*
Fallow fields, open stony ground.
W. & E. Crete; Kasos, Karpathos [Mediterranean region].

M. turbinata (L.) All. (*FE 2*: 156) = **25**.

23. Melilotus Mill.

1. M. graecus (Boiss. & Spruner) Lassen in *Willdenowia* **16**: 445 (1987) - *FE 2*: 151 as *Trigonella graeca* (Boiss. & Spruner) Boiss.
Cr (W, C, E) - *MAP 855*

Calcareous cliffs, ledges of steep rocky slopes, rubble in gorges, cultivated, bare & disturbed ground; 0-500m; fl. 3-5.
Mainly W. & C. Crete [W. & S. Greece].
Cretan plants have been confused with *M. creticus* (L.) Desr. *(FE 2*: 151 as *Trigonella cretica* (L.) Boiss.), which occurs in the E. Aegean Islands and W. Turkey, but not Crete (cf. Greuter in Greuter & Rechinger, 1967: 76).

2. M. indicus (L.) All., *Fl. pedem.* **1**: 308 (1785) - *FE 2*: 149.
Cr (W, C, E) Kp - *MAP 856*
Vineyards, river-beds, roadsides, seashores.
Crete (sporadic); Karpathos [W., C. & S. Europe].

3. M. italicus (L.) Lam., *Fl. franç.* **2**: 594 (1779) - *FE 2*: 149.
Cr (W) Kp - *MAP 857*
Step-crevices of cliffs, roadsides; 350m.
W. Crete; Karpathos [Mediterranean region].

4. M. messanensis (L.) All., *Fl. pedem.* **1**: 309 (1785) - *FE 2*: 150.
Cr (E) - *MAP 858*
Sandy vineyard.
E. Crete [Mediterranean region].
Erroneously regarded as absent from the Cretan area in *FE* (Greuter, 1974: 140).

5. M. neapolitanus Ten., *Fl. napol.* **1**: lxii (1811-1815) - *FE 2*: 149.
Cr (W, C) Kp - *MAP 859*
Rocks near coast.
W. & C. Crete; Karpathos [S. Europe].

? M. segetalis (Brot.) Ser. in DC., *Prodr.* **2**: 187 (1825) - *FE 2*: 150.
Doubtfully present in Crete (Greuter, 1974: 158) [Mediterranean region].

6. M. sulcatus Desf., *Fl. Atl.* **2**: 193 (1799) - *FE 2*: 150.
Cr (W, C) Ks - *MAP 860*
Roadside banks.
W. & C. Crete; Kasos [Mediterranean region].

24. Onobrychis Mill.

1. O. aequidentata (Sm.) d'Urv. in *Mém. Soc. linn. Paris* **1**: 346 (1822) - *FE 2*: 191.
Cr (W, C, E) Ks Kp - *MAP 861*
Phrygana, rocky places; 0-500m; fl. 3-5.
Crete (sporadic); Kasos, Karpathos [Mediterranean region].

2. O. caput-galli (L.) Lam., *Fl. franç.* **2**: 651 (1779) - *FE 2*: 191.
Cr (W, C, E) Ks Kp - *MAP 862*
Rocky places, dry river-beds, maritime sands; 0-100m; fl. 3-5.

Mainly W. & E. Crete; Kasos, Karpathos [Mediterranean region].

O. crista-galli (L.) Lam. *(FE 2*: 191) was almost certainly recorded in error (Greuter, 1974: 158).

O. shahpurensis Rech.f., described from Iran, is given for the Cretan area - as endemic - in *M-Ch* **4**: 154. Its inclusion there is an obvious error.

●**3. O. sphaciotica** Greuter in *Candollea* **20**: 213 (1965) - *FE 2*: 189.
Cr (W) - *MAP 863*
Calcareous cliffs; 1300-1750m; fl. 6-7.
W. Crete (Lefka Ori) - Endemic.

25. Ononis L.

1. O. diffusa Ten., *Fl. napol.* **1**: xli (1811-1815) - *FE 2*: 148.
Cr - *NOT MAPPED*
Crete [Mediterranean region].

2. O. mitissima L., *Sp. pl.*: 717 (1753) - *FE 2*: 148.
Cr (C) Kp - *MAP 864*
Phrygana; 10-50m.
C. Crete (Dia island); Karpathos [Mediterranean region].

3. O. natrix L., *Sp. pl.*: 717 (1753) - *FE 2*: 144.
a. subsp. hispanica (L.f.) Cout., *Fl. Portugal*: 331 (1913) - *FE 2*: 145.
Cr (W, C, E) - *MAP 865*
Maritime sands; fl. 3-7.
Crete (S. coast, Gavdos & Gaidouronisi islands) [W. & E. Mediterranean region].
Erroneously regarded as absent from the Cretan area in *FE* (Greuter, 1974: 140).
Subsp. *natrix* *(FE 2*: 144) was recorded in error (Greuter, 1974: 157).
b. subsp. ramosissima (Desf.) Batt. in Batt. & Trab., *Fl. Algérie* **1**: 213 (1889) - *FE 2*: 145.
Kp - *MAP 866*
Garigue, phrygana, maritime sands; 0-700m; fl. 3-4.
Karpathos [mainly W. & C. Mediterranean region].
Erroneously regarded as absent from the Cretan area in *FE* (Greuter, 1974: 140).

4. O. ornithopodioides L., *Sp. pl.*: 718 (1753) - *FE 2*: 145.
Cr (W, E) Ks Kp - *MAP 867*
Rocky slopes, soil-pockets among rocks; 0-300m; fl. 3-4.
W. & E. Crete; Kasos, Karpathos [Mediterranean region].
Erroneously regarded as absent from the Cretan

area in *FE* (Greuter, 1974: 140).

5. O. pubescens L., *Mant. pl. alt.*: 267 (1771) - *FE* 2: 145.
Cr (W, C, E) - MAP 868
Scrub, Lygeum steppe, maritime rocks; 0-100m.
Crete (sporadic) [Mediterranean region].

6. O. reclinata L., *Sp. pl.* ed.2: 1011 (1763) - *FE* 2: 145.
Cr (W, C, E) Ks Kp - MAP 869
Burnt garigue, rocky & sandy places, screes, maritime sands, bare ground; 0-350m; fl. 3-5.
Crete (widespread, coastal); Kasos, Karpathos [W. & S. Europe].

7. O. serrata Forssk., *Fl. aegypt.-arab.*: 130 (1775) - *FE* 2: 148.
Kp - MAP 870
Maritime sands.
Karpathos [Sicily (Linosa); otherwise N. Africa & S.W. Asia].

8. O. sieberi Besser ex DC., *Prodr.* 2: 162 (1825) - *FE* 2: 146 as *O. viscosa* subsp. *sieberi* (Besser ex DC.) Sirj.
Cr (C, E) - MAP 871
Lygeum steppe, stony stream deposits; fl. 4.
C. & E. Crete (S. side) [C. & E. Mediterranean region].

9. O. spinosa L., *Sp. pl.*: 716 (1753) - *FE* 2: 147.
a. subsp. **diacantha** (Sieber ex Rchb.) Greuter in *Boissiera* 13: 75 (1967) - *FE* 2: 147, included in synonymy of subsp. *antiquorum* (L.) Arcang.
Cr (W, C, E) Kp - MAP 872
Open Quercus coccifera woodland, phrygana, rocky places, flat clayey areas, fallow fields; 0-1900m; fl. 5-8.
Crete (widespread); Karpathos [S. Aegean region].

O. variegata L. (*FE* 2: 147) was almost certainly recorded in error (Greuter, 1974: 157).

●**10. O. verae** Sirj. in *Beih. bot. Zbl.* 49(2): 517 (1932) - *FE* 2: 145.
Cr (W) - MAP 873
Pinus brutia woodland, calcareous rocky places; 300-500m; fl. 4.
W. Crete - Endemic.
[Plate 5.]

11. O. viscosa L., *Sp. pl.*: 718 (1753) - *FE* 2: 145.
a. subsp. **breviflora** (DC.) Nyman, *Consp. fl. eur.* 161 (1878) - *FE* 2: 146.
Cr (W, C, E) Ks Kp Sa - MAP 874
Rocky places, river-beds, disturbed ground; 0-350m; fl. 4-5.
Crete (sporadic); Karpathos group [Mediterranean region].

Subsp. *sieberi* (Besser ex DC.) Sirj. (*FE* 2: 146) = **8**.

26. Ornithopus L.

1. O. compressus L., *Sp. pl.*: 744 (1753) - *FE* 2: 182.
Cr (W, C) - MAP 875
Calcareous rocky places, dry river-beds, fallow fields; 50-1050m; fl. 4.
W. & C. Crete [S. Europe].

2. O. pinnatus (Mill.) Druce in *J. Bot., Lond.* 45: 420 (1907) - *FE* 2: 182.
Cr - NOT MAPPED
Crete [W. Europe & Mediterranean region].
Erroneously regarded as absent from the Cretan area in *FE* (Greuter, 1974: 140).

27. Pisum L.

1. P. sativum L., *Sp. pl.*: 727 (1753) - *FE* 2: 143.
a. subsp. **humile** (Holmboe) Greuter, Matthäs & Risse in *Willdenowia* 14: 283 (1984).
Cr (C) - MAP 876
Step-crevices of cliffs; 400m.
C. Crete (W. of Iraklio) [Libya, Egypt & S.W. Asia].
Recorded since *FE* (Greuter, 1973a: 42).
[b. subsp. sativum]
Cr (W, E) Kp - MAP 877
Cultivated for fodder and its edible seeds and possibly naturalized in fallow fields; 0-550m; fl. 3-4.
W. & E. Crete; Karpathos [mainly S. Europe].
Regarded as absent from the Cretan area in *FE*, although previously recorded by Rechinger (1943a: 337).

Psoralea bituminosa L. (*FE* 2: 127) = **Bituminaria 1**.

28. Scorpiurus L.

1. S. muricatus L., *Sp. pl.*: 745 (1753) - *FE* 2: 185.
Cr (W, C, E) Ks Kp - MAP 878
Calcareous rocky places, maritime sands & rocks; 0-700m; fl. 3-4.
Crete (widespread); Kasos, Karpathos [S. Europe].

29. Securigera DC.

1. S. cretica (L.) Lassen in *Willdenowia* 19: 60 (1989) - *FE* 2: 183 as *Coronilla cretica* L.
Cr (W, C) Kp - MAP 879

Weed communities, roadsides; fl. 4.
W. & C. Crete; Karpathos [mainly S.E.
Europe].

●**2. S. globosa** (Lam.) Lassen in *Willdenowia*
19: 60 (1989) - *FE* **2**: 183 as *Coronilla globosa*
Lam.
Cr (W, C, E) - MAP 880
*Calcareous cliffs & rocky debris below, stream
deposits; 0-500m; fl. 4-6.*
Crete (widespread) - Endemic.

3. S. parviflora (Desv.) Lassen in *Willdenowia*
19: 60 (1989) - *FE* **2**: 183 as *Coronilla rostrata*
Boiss. & Spruner.
Cr (W) Kp - MAP 881
*Olive groves, grassy phrygana, rocky places; 0-
450m; fl. 4.*
W. Crete; Karpathos [mainly Greece & Aegean
region; otherwise S.W. Asia].

4. S. securidaca (L.) Degen & Dörfl. in
Denkschr. Akad. Wiss. Wien **64**: 718 (1897) -
FE **2**: 177.
Cr (W, C, E) Kp Sa - MAP 882
*Olive groves, rocky places, gorge-beds,
maritime sands; 0-450m; fl. 3-5.*
Crete (widespread); Karpathos, Saria [S.
Europe].

30. Spartium L.

1. S. junceum L., *Sp. pl.*: 708 (1753) - *FE* **2**:
101.
Cr (W, C, E) Kp - MAP 883
*Roadside banks, watercourses, also planted for
ornament; 0-500m; fl. 4-5.*
Crete (widespread); Karpathos [mainly
Mediterranean region].

31. Tetragonolobus Scop.

1. T. purpureus Moench, *Methodus*: 164
(1794) - *FE* **2**: 177.
Cr (W, C, E) Ks Kp - MAP 884
*Olive groves, fallow fields, seashores, disturbed
ground, waste areas; 0-500m; fl. 3-5.*
Crete (sporadic); Kasos, Karpathos [S. Europe].

32. Trifolium L.

T. alexandrinum L. (*FE* **2**: 171) has been
recorded from W. Crete (W. of Hania), as a
probable casual relic of cultivation (Greuter,
1973a: 43).

1. T. angustifolium L., *Sp. pl.*: 769 (1753) -
FE **2**: 170.
Cr (W, C, E) Ks Kp - MAP 885

*Olive groves, rocky places, gorge-beds,
maritime sands; 0-450m; fl. 3-5.*
Crete (widespread); Kasos, Karpathos [S.
Europe].
T. pamphylicum Boiss. & Heldr., otherwise
known from Turkey & Cyprus, is given for the
Cretan area in *M-Ch* **4**: 179, but as doubtfully
distinct from *T. angustifolium*; it is not separated
here.

2. T. arvense L., *Sp. pl.*: 769 (1753) - *FE* **2**:
167.
Cr (W, C) Kp - MAP 886
*Rocky places, cliffs, weed communities; 50-
1700m; fl. 4.*
Mainly W. Crete; Karpathos [almost throughout
Europe].

? T. aurantiacum Boiss. & Spruner in Boiss.,
Diagn. pl. orient. ser.1, **2**: 33 (1843) - *FE* **2**:
166.
Doubtfully present in Crete (Greuter, 1974: 158)
[Greece].

●**3. T. barbeyi** Gibelli & Belli in *Atti Accad.
Sci. Torino* **22**: 610 (1887) - *FE* **2**: 169.
Kp - MAP 887
Grassy places.
Karpathos - Endemic.
Erroneously given as occurring also on the E.
Aegean island of Rodos in *FE* (Carlström, 1987:
73).

4. T. bocconei Savi in *Atti Accad. ital. Firenze*
1: 191 (1808) - *FE* **2**: 167.
Cr Kp - NOT MAPPED
Crete; Karpathos [W. & S. Europe].

5. T. boissieri Guss., *Fl. sicul. syn.* **2**: 858
(1845) - *FE* **2**: 165.
Cr (W) Kp Sa - MAP 888
Calcareous rocky places; 300-400m.
W. Crete; Karpathos, Saria [Spain, Greece &
Aegean region; otherwise S.W. Asia].

6. T. campestre Schreb. in Sturm, *Deutschl. Fl.*
Abt.1, Band 4: Heft 16 (1804) - *FE* **2**: 166.
(Including *T. lagrangei* Boiss. - *FE* **2**: 165.)
Cr (W, C, E) Ks Kp Sa - MAP 889
*Platanus woodland, olive groves, rocky & sandy
places, soil-filled hollows; 0-600m; fl. 3-5.*
Crete (widespread); Karpathos group [almost
throughout Europe].

7. T. cherleri L., *Demonstr. pl.*: 21 (1753) - *FE*
2: 169.
Cr (W) Kp - MAP 890
Doline; (-1800)m.
W. Crete; Karpathos [S. Europe].

8. T. clypeatum L., *Sp. pl.*: 769 (1753) - *FE* **2**:
172.
Kp - MAP 891

Olive groves, phrygana, cultivated terraces,
weed communities, roadsides; 0-550m; fl. 3-4.
Karpathos [S.W. Asia].
Given also for Crete - as doubtfully present - by
Barclay (1986: 66), but apparently not recorded
on the island since the early 19th century (cf.
Rechinger, 1943*a*: 365).

9. T. dasyurum C.Presl, *Symb. bot.* **1**: 53
(1831) - *FE* **2**: 168.
Cr (E) Ks Kp - *MAP 892*
Fallow fields; 300-600m.
E. Crete; Kasos, Karpathos [Greece & Aegean
region; otherwise Libya, Egypt & S.W. Asia].

10. T. filiforme L., *Sp. pl.*: 773 (1753) - *FE* **2**:
166 as *T. micranthum* Viv.
Cr Kp - *NOT MAPPED*
Flat clayey areas in dolines.
Crete; Karpathos [W. & S. Europe].
Recorded from Crete by Egli (1989; 1991).

11. T. fragiferum L., *Sp. pl.*: 772 (1753) - *FE*
2: 165.
Cr (W, C, E) - *MAP 893*
Cupressus woodland, bare ground, tracks; 300-
500m; fl. 4-5.
Crete (sporadic) [almost throughout Europe].

12. T. glomeratum L., *Sp. pl.*: 770 (1753) - *FE*
2: 164.
Cr (W, C) - *MAP 894*
Platanus woodland, rocky places, fallow fields;
0-1050m.
Mainly W. Crete [W. & S. Europe].

13. T. grandiflorum Schreb. in *Nova Acta*
physico-med. **3**: 477 (1767) - *FE* **2**: 165 as *T.*
speciosum Willd.
Cr (W, C) Kp - *MAP 895*
Calcareous rocky places & ledges, rubble of
gorge-beds; 50-1400m; fl. 3-5.
W. & C. Crete; Karpathos [C. & E.
Mediterranean region].

T. hirtum All. (*FE* **2**: 169) was almost certainly
recorded in error (Greuter, 1974: 158).

T. hybridum L. is given for the Cretan area in
FE **2**: 162, although there are no records as a
basis for this (Greuter, 1974: 139).

T. incarnatum L. is given for the Cretan area in
FE **2**: 168, although there are no records as a
basis for this (Greuter, 1974: 139).

14. T. infamia-ponertii Greuter in *Candollea*
31: 215 (1976) - *FE* **2**: 170 as *T. intermedium*
Guss.
Cr (W, C, E) Ks Kp - *MAP 896*
Calcareous rocky places, soil-filled hollows,
sandy places.

Crete (sporadic); Kasos, Karpathos
[Mediterranean region].

T. lagrangei Boiss. (*FE* **2**: 165) is included in
synonymy of **6**.

15. T. lappaceum L., *Sp. pl.*: 768 (1753) - *FE*
2: 169.
Cr (C, E) Kp - *MAP 897*
Calcareous rocky slopes, river-beds; 0-1100m.
C. & E. Crete; Karpathos [S. Europe].
Erroneously regarded as absent from the Cretan
area in *FE* (Greuter, 1974: 140).

16. T. leucanthum M.Bieb., *Fl. taur.-caucas.*
2: 214 (1808) - *FE* **2**: 171.
Kp - *MAP 898*
Karpathos [S. Europe].

17. T. ligusticum Balb. ex Loisel., *Fl. gall.*:
731 (1807) - *FE* **2**: 167.
Cr (W) - *MAP 899*
Platanus woodland on non-calcareous
substratum; 600m.
W. Crete [mainly Mediterranean region].
Regarded as absent from the Cretan area in *FE*,
although previously recorded by Rechinger
(1943*b*: 96); cf. Greuter (1973*a*: 44).

T. michelianum Savi, given as doubtfully present
in the Cretan area in *FE* **2**: 163, is absent
according to *M-Ch* **4**: 186.

T. micranthum Viv. (*FE* **2**: 166) = **10**.

18. T. nigrescens Viv., *Fl. ital. fragm.*: 12
(1808) - *FE* **2**: 163.
Cr (W, C, E) Kp - *MAP 900*
Phrygana, rocky places, flat clayey areas,
coastal saline ground; 0-1050m.
a. subsp. **nigrescens**
Cretan area [S. Europe].
b. subsp. **petrisavii** (Clementi) Holmboe in
Bergens Mus. Skr. ser.2, **1**(2): 106 (1914) - *FE*
2: 163.
Cretan area [C. & E. Mediterranean region].
The species sensu lato occurs mainly in W.
Crete and also in Karpathos.

19. T. ornithopodioides L., *Sp. pl.*: 766 (1753)
- *FE* **2**: 161.
Cr - *NOT MAPPED*
Flat clayey areas in dolines, periodically
waterlogged.
Crete [mainly W. Europe].
Recorded since *FE* (Egli, 1989; 1991: 325).

20. T. pallidum Waldst. & Kit., *Descr. icon.*
pl. Hung. **1**: 35 (1801) - *FE* **2**: 169.
Cr (W, C) - *MAP 901*
Rocks.
W. & C. Crete [S. Europe].

T. pamphylicum Boiss. & Heldr. (*M-Ch* **4**: 179) see **1**.

21. T. patens Schreb. in Sturm, *Deutschl. Fl.* Abt.1, Band 4: Heft 16 (1804) - *FE* **2**: 166.
Cr - *NOT MAPPED*
Crete [C. & S. Europe].

22. T. physodes Steven ex M.Bieb., *Fl. taur.-caucas.* **2**: 217 (1808) - *FE* **2**: 164. (Including *T. rechingeri* Rothm. and *T. sclerorrhizum* Boiss. - both *FE* **2**: 164.)
Cr (W, C, E) Ks Kp - *MAP 902*
Platanus woodland, olive groves, calcareous rocky places; 200-600m; fl. 4.
Crete (sporadic); Kasos, Karpathos [Mediterranean region].

●**23. T. praetermissum** Greuter, Pleger & Raus in *Willdenowia* **13**: 61 (1983).
Cr (C) Kp - *MAP 903*
Calcareous rocks & ledges; 100-950m.
C. Crete (E. of Iraklio); Karpathos (Kalilimni) - Endemic.

T. rechingeri Rothm. (*FE* **2**: 164) is included in synonymy of **22**.

24. T. repens L., *Sp. pl.*: 767 (1753) - *FE* **2**: 162.
Cr (W, C, E) - *MAP 904*
Seasonally wet places, damp grassland, rocky places, flat clayey areas; 50-1600m.
Crete (sporadic) [almost throughout Europe].
Subsp. *orphanideum* (Boiss.) Coombe (*FE* **2**: 162) is doubtfully present in Crete (Greuter, 1974: 158), and anyway is doubtfully distinct from subsp. *repens* (*M-Ch* **4**: 190).

25. T. resupinatum L., *Sp. pl.*: 771 (1753) - *FE* **2**: 165.
Cr (W) Kp - *MAP 905*
Maritime sands, coastal saline ground.
W. Crete; Karpathos [W., C. & S. Europe].

26. T. scabrum L., *Sp. pl.*: 770 (1753) - *FE* **2**: 167.
Cr (W, C, E) Ks Kp Sa - *MAP 906*
Rocky places, maritime sands & rocks; 0-350m; fl. 3-4.
Crete (widespread, rarer towards E.); Karpathos group [W. & S. Europe].

T. sclerorrhizum Boiss. (*FE* **2**: 164) is included in synonymy of **22**.

T. smyrnaeum Boiss. (*FE* **2**: 171) was recorded in error (Greuter, 1974: 158).

T. speciosum Willd. (*FE* **2**: 165) = **13**.

27. T. spumosum L., *Sp. pl.*: 771 (1753) - *FE* **2**: 164.
Cr (W) Kp - *MAP 907*

Gorge.
W. Crete; Karpathos [Mediterranean region].

28. T. squamosum L., *Amoen. acad.* **4**: 105 (1759) - *FE* **2**: 171.
Cr - *NOT MAPPED*
Crete [W. Europe & Mediterranean region].

29. T. stellatum L., *Sp. pl.*: 769 (1753) - *FE* **2**: 168.
Cr (W, C, E) Ks Kp - *MAP 908*
Soil-patches in garigue & phrygana, open stony ground, roadsides; 0-1350m; fl. 3-5.
Crete (widespread); Kasos, Karpathos [Mediterranean region].

30. T. subterraneum L., *Sp. pl.*: 767 (1753) - *FE* **2**: 172.
Cr (W, C) Kp - *MAP 909*
Olive groves, fallow fields, flat clayey areas; 0-1050m; fl. 4-5.
W. & C. Crete; Karpathos [W. & S. Europe].
Subsp. *oxaloides* Nyman is given for the Cretan area in *M-Ch* **4**: 192, but as doubtfully distinct from subsp. *subterraneum*; it is not separated here.

31. T. suffocatum L., *Mant. pl. alt.*: 276 (1771) - *FE* **2**: 164.
Cr (W) Ks Kp - *MAP 910*
W. Crete; Kasos, Karpathos [W. & S. Europe].

32. T. tenuifolium Ten., *Fl. napol.* **1**: xliv (1811-1815) - *FE* **2**: 167.
Cr (W) - *MAP 911*
Phrygana, rocks; -400m.
W. Crete [S. Italy, Sicily, Balkan peninsula & Aegean region].

33. T. tomentosum L., *Sp. pl.*: 771 (1753) - *FE* **2**: 165.
Cr (W, C, E) Ks Kp - *MAP 912*
Rocky places, dry river-beds, fields & field-margins; 0-1300m; fl. 3-4.
Mainly W. Crete; Kasos, Karpathos [mainly Mediterranean region].

34. T. uniflorum L., *Sp. pl.*: 771 (1753) - *FE* **2**: 164.
Cr (W, C, E) Ks Kp - *MAP 913*
Open phrygana, rocky places & crevices, flat clayey areas, maritime sands, trodden ground; 0-2400m; fl. 3-5.
Crete (widespread); Kasos, Karpathos [C. & E. Mediterranean region].

T. vesiculosum Savi is given for the Cretan area in *FE* **2**: 164, although there are no records as a basis for this (Greuter, 1974: 139).

33. Trigonella L.

1. T. balansae Boiss. & Reut. in Boiss., *Diagn. pl. orient.* ser.2, **5**: 79 (1856) - *FE* **2**: 151.
Cr (W, C, E) Ks Kp Sa - *MAP 914*
Mostly maritime rocks & sandy places; fl. 3-4.
Crete (mainly N. coast); Karpathos group [S. Greece & Aegean region; otherwise S.W. Asia].

"T. corniculata" (*FE* **2**: 151) = *T. esculenta* Willd., recorded in error from the Cretan area (*M-Ch* **4**: 195).

"T. cretica" (*FE* **2**: 151) = **Melilotus 1** (Greuter in Greuter & Rechinger, 1967: 76).

[2. T. foenum-graecum] L., *Sp. pl.*: 777 (1753) - *FE* **2**: 152.
Cr - *NOT MAPPED*
Cultivated and possibly naturalized.
Crete [mainly C. & S. Europe; ?from S.W. Asia].

3. T. gladiata Steven ex M.Bieb., *Fl. taur.-caucas.* **2**: 222 (1808) - *FE* **2**: 152.
Cr Kp - *NOT MAPPED*
Crete; Karpathos [S. Europe].

T. monspeliaca L. (*FE* **2**: 152) = **Medicago 14**.

4. T. rechingeri Sirj. in *Öst. bot. Z.* **85**: 58 (1936) - *FE* **2**: 151.
Cr (E) Ks Kp - *MAP 915*
Maritime rocks on offshore islets.
E. Crete (Dionisiades islands); Kasos, Karpathos [S.E. Kiklades; otherwise E. Aegean Islands (Tilos)].

5. T. spinosa L., *Sp. pl.*: 777 (1753) - *FE* **2**: 151.
Cr (W) Ks - *MAP 916*
Dry ground on coast; fl. 4.
W. Crete; Kasos [E. Aegean Islands (Rodos) & S.W. Asia].
Recorded from Kasos since *FE* (Greuter et al., 1983a: 62).

34. Tripodion Medik.

1. T. tetraphyllum (L.) Fourr. in *Annls Soc. linn. Lyon* ser.2, **16**: 359 (1868) - *FE* **2**: 181 as *Anthyllis tetraphylla* L.
Cr (W, C, E) Ks Kp - *MAP 917*
Olive groves, fallow & abandoned land, soil-filled hollows, bare ground; 0-500m; fl. 3-4.
Crete (widespread); Kasos, Karpathos [Mediterranean region].

35. Vicia L.

1. V. bithynica (L.) L., *Syst. nat.* ed.10, **2**: 1166 (1759) - *FE* **2**: 135.
Cr (W, C) Kp - *MAP 918*
Shady rocks, grassy places, disturbed ground; fl. 3-5.
W. & C. Crete; Karpathos [W. & S. Europe].

V. cracca L. is given for the Cretan area in *FE* **2**: 131, although there are no records as a basis for this (Greuter, 1974: 139).

2. V. cretica Boiss. & Heldr. in Boiss., *Diagn. pl. orient.* ser.1, **9**: 118 (1849) - *FE* **2**: 132.
Cr (W, C, E) Kp - *MAP 919*
Phrygana, rocky places, often growing through dwarf shrubs; 0-650m; fl. 3-5.
Mainly W. Crete; Karpathos [S.E. Greece & S. Aegean region; otherwise S.W. Asia].

V. dalmatica A.Kern. (*FE* **2**: 131) = **13a**.

[3. V. ervilia] (L.) Willd., *Sp. pl.*: **3**: 1103 (1802) - *FE* **2**: 133.
Cr (C) Ks Kp - *MAP 920*
Cultivated for fodder and possibly naturalized on open stony ground.
C. Crete; Kasos, Karpathos [S. Europe].
Erroneously given as native to the Cretan area in *FE* (Greuter, 1974: 157).

V. faba L. (*FE* **2**: 135) is cultivated for its edible seeds in both Crete and Karpathos and also occurs as a casual escape.

? V. grandiflora Scop., *Fl. carniol.* ed.2, **2**: 65 (1772) - *FE* **2**: 134.
Doubtfully present in Crete [mainly C. & S.E. Europe].

4. V. hybrida L., *Sp. pl.*: 737 (1753) - *FE* **2**: 135.
Cr (W, C, E) Kp - *MAP 921*
Olive groves, rocky places, weed communities, roadsides, waste areas; 0-750m; fl. 3-5.
Mainly W. & C. Crete; Karpathos [S. Europe].

5. V. lathyroides L., *Sp. pl.*: 736 (1753) - *FE* **2**: 135.
Cr (W, C) Ks Kp - *MAP 922*
Open stony ground; 550-1400m.
W. & C. Crete; Kasos, Karpathos [most of Europe].

V. laxiflora Brot. (Barclay, 1986: 68) = **8**.

6. V. lutea L., *Sp. pl.*: 736 (1753) - *FE* **2**: 135.
Cr (W) - *MAP 923*
Olive groves, grassy places, roadsides; 0-300m; fl. 4-5.
W. Crete [W., C. & S. Europe].

7. V. narbonensis L., *Sp. pl.*: 737 (1753) - *FE* **2**: 135.
Cr (E) - *NOT MAPPED*
E. Crete [mainly S. Europe].
Recorded since *FE* (Schäfer, 1973: 213, 219).

8. V. parviflora Cav. in *An. Cienc. nat. Madrid*
4: 73 (1801) - *FE* **2**: 133 as "*V. tenuissima*".
Cr (W) - *MAP 924*
Low scrub, rocky places, river-beds; 50-650m.
W. Crete [S. Europe].
Erroneously regarded as absent from the Cretan
area in *FE* (Greuter, 1974: 140 as "*V. tenuissima*").

9. V. peregrina L., *Sp. pl.*: 737 (1753) - *FE* **2**:
135.
Cr (W, C, E) - *MAP 925*
Scrub, garigue, maritime sands; 0-500m.
Crete (sporadic) [S. Europe].

? V. pinetorum Boiss. & Spruner in Boiss.,
Diagn. pl. orient. ser.1, **2**: 104 (1843) - *FE* **2**:
131.
Doubtfully present in Crete (Greuter, 1974: 157)
[S. Aegean region].

10. V. pubescens (DC.) Link, *Handbuch* **2**: 190
(1831) - *FE* **2**: 133.
Cr (W, C) Kp - *MAP 926*
*Platanus woodland, stream-banks in maquis,
rocky places; 175-600m; fl. 3-4.*
W. & C. Crete; Karpathos [S. Europe].

11. V. sativa L., *Sp. pl.*: 736 (1753) - *FE* **2**:
134.
Cr (W, C, E) Ks Kp - *MAP 927*
*Olive groves, cultivated, fallow & abandoned
land, also frequently cultivated for fodder; 0-
1050m; fl. 3-5.*
? subsp. amphicarpa (L.) Batt. in Batt. &
Trab., *Fl. Algérie* **1**: 268 (1889) - *FE* **2**: 134.
Doubtfully present in Crete [S. Europe]..
a. subsp. cordata (Wulfen ex Hoppe) Batt. in
Batt. & Trab., *Fl. Algérie* **1**: 267 (1889) - *FE* **2**:
135.
Crete [S. Europe].
b. subsp. macrocarpa (Moris) Arcang., *Comp.
fl. ital.*: 201 (1882) - *FE* **2**: 135.
Cultivated and doubtfully native.
c. subsp. nigra (L.) Ehrh. in *Hannover. Mag.*
18: 229 (1780) - *FE* **2**: 134.
Crete [throughout Europe].
[d. subsp. sativa]
Cultivated and naturalized.
Crete [almost throughout Europe].
The species sensu lato occurs mainly in W. &
C. Crete and also in Kasos & Karpathos.

12. V. sibthorpii Boiss., *Diagn. pl. orient.*
ser.1, **9**: 122 (1849) - *FE* **2**: 131.
Cr (E) - *MAP 928*
Sandy vineyard.
E. Crete (near Ierapetra) [Greece & Aegean
region].

13. V. tenuifolia Roth, *Tent. fl. Germ.* **1**: 309
(1788) - *FE* **2**: 131.
a. subsp. dalmatica (A.Kern.) Greuter in
Willldenowia **16**: 114 (1986) - *FE* **2**: 131 as *V.
dalmatica* A.Kern.
Cr (W) Ks Kp - *MAP 929*
Olive groves, fallow fields; 450-1050m; fl. 4-5.
W. Crete (Omalos plain in Lefka Ori); Kasos,
Karpathos [S.E. Europe].
Additionally recorded from Kedros in C. Crete
in *MFG* **1**: 485 (as *V. cracca* subsp. *stenophylla*
(Velen.) C.D.Preston).
Subsp. *tenuifolia*, given as doubtfully present in
the Cretan area in *FE*, was recorded in error for
subsp. **a** (Barclay, 1986: 69).

? V. tetrasperma (L.) Schreb., *Spic. fl. lips.*:
26 (1771) - *FE* **2**: 133.
Doubtfully present in Crete (Greuter, 1974: 157)
[almost throughout Europe].

14. V. villosa Roth, *Tent. fl. Germ.* **2(2)**: 182
(1793) - *FE* **2**: 132.
a. subsp. microphylla (d'Urv.) P.W.Ball in
Feddes Reprium **79**: 45 (1968) - *FE* **2**: 132.
Cr (W) Ks Sa - *MAP 930*
W. Crete; Kasos, Saria [S. Greece & Aegean
region; otherwise Libya, Egypt & S.W. Asia].
b. subsp. varia (Host) Corb., *Nouv. Fl.
Normand.*: 181 (1894) - *FE* **2**: 132.
Cr (W, C) Kp - *MAP 931*
*Olive groves, cultivated terraces, calcareous
rocky places; 0-1050m; fl. 4.*
W. & C. Crete; Karpathos [most of Europe].

LENTIBULARIACEAE

1. Utricularia L.

U. australis R.Br. (*FE* **3**: 297) see note under **1**.

1. U. vulgaris L., *Sp. pl.*: 18 (1753) - *FE* **3**:
297.
Cr (W) - *MAP 932*
Fresh water.
W. Crete (Agia lake & river to N.W.) [most of
Europe].
The precise identity of Cretan plants is
uncertain; they are provisionally referred to this
species until confirmation is available. The
possibility that they belong instead to *U.
australis* R.Br. (*FE* **3**: 297) cannot entirely be
ruled out (Greuter, 1973a: 51-52).

LINACEAE

1. Linum L.

1. L. arboreum L., *Sp. pl.*: 279 (1753) - *FE* **2**:
206. (Including *L. caespitosum* Sm. - *FE* **2**: 206

and *L. doerfleri* Rech.f. - *FE* **2**: 207.)
Cr (W, C, E) Ks Kp Sa - *MAP 933*
*Calcareous cliffs, crevices & ledges, steep rocky
banks of road cuttings, rarely in phrygana on
rocky slopes; 0-2000m; fl. 1-7.*
Mainly W. & E. Crete; Karpathos group [S.E.
Kiklades (Astipalea); otherwise E. Aegean
Islands (Simi, Halki & Rodos) & S.W. Turkey
(Marmaris peninsula)].

2. L. bienne Mill., *Gard. Dict.* ed.8: no.8
(1768) - *FE* **2**: 209.
Cr (W, C, E) Ks Kp - *MAP 934*
*Coastal phrygana, gorge-beds, damp ditches,
maritime sands, roadsides; 0-550m; fl. 3-5.*
Crete (widespread); Kasos, Karpathos [W. & S.
Europe].

L. caespitosum Sm. (*FE* **2**: 206) is included in
synonymy of **1**.

3. L. corymbulosum Rchb., *Fl. germ. excurs.*:
834 (1832) - *FE* **2**: 210 as *L. strictum* subsp.
corymbulosum (Rchb.) Rouy.
Cr (W, E) Kp - *MAP 935*
Calcareous rocks, clayey hills; 200-950m.
W. & E. Crete; Karpathos [S. Europe].

4. L. decumbens Desf., *Fl. atlant.* **1**: 278
(1798) - *FE* **2**: 209.
Ks Kp Sa - *MAP 936*
Calcareous open phrygana; fl. 4.
Karpathos group [Mediterranean region].
Erroneously regarded as absent from the Cretan
area in *FE* (Greuter, 1974: 140).

L. doerfleri Rech.f. (*FE* **2**: 207) is included in
synonymy of **1**.

5. L. nodiflorum L., *Sp. pl.*: 280 (1753) - *FE*
2: 208.
Cr (W, E) Kp - *MAP 937*
Dry olive groves, dry roadsides; 0-100m; fl. 4-5.
W. & E. Crete; Karpathos [mainly
Mediterranean region].

6. L. pubescens Banks & Sol. in Russell, *Nat.
hist. Aleppo* ed.2, **2**: 268 (1794) - *FE* **2**: 210.
Cr (W) - *MAP 938*
*Bare ground in phrygana, calcareous rocky
places; 25-300m; fl. 4-5.*
W. Crete [Albania & Greece; otherwise S.W.
Asia].
Cretan plants belong to subsp. *sibthorpianum*
(Margot & Reut.) P.H.Davis, which is treated
as doubtfully distinct from subsp. *pubescens* in
M-Ch **4**: 224, and is not separated here.

7. L. strictum L., *Sp. pl.*: 279 (1753) - *FE* **2**:
210 as *L. strictum* L. subsp. *strictum.*
Cr (W, C, E) Ks Kp Sa - *MAP 939*
*Soil-patches in phrygana, rocky & sandy places;
0-150m; fl. 4-5.*

Crete (sporadic); Karpathos group [S. Europe].
The plants from the Cretan area belong to subsp.
spicatum (Pers.) Nyman, which is treated as
doubtfully distinct from subsp. *strictum* in *M-Ch*
4: 224, and is not separated here.
Subsp. *corymbulosum* (Rchb.) Rouy (*FE* **2**: 210)
= **3**.

8. L. trigynum L., *Sp. pl.*: 279 (1753) - *FE* **2**:
210.
Cr (W) - *MAP 940*
*Margins of maquis, rocky places, dry river-beds,
sandy places near sea; 0-300m.*
W. Crete [mainly S. Europe].

[9. L. usitatissimum] L., *Sp. pl.*: 277 (1753) -
FE **2**: 209.
Cr (W) Kp - *MAP 941*
Cultivated and naturalized.
W. Crete; Karpathos [almost throughout
Europe, of uncertain origin].

2. Radiola Hill

1. R. linoides Roth, *Tent. fl. Germ.* **2(1)**: 199
(1789) - *FE* **2**: 211.
Cr (W) - *MAP 942*
Along ditches, damp ground; 50-1050m.
W. Crete [most of Europe].
Recorded since *FE* (Gradstein & Smittenberg,
1968).

LORANTHACEAE

1. Viscum L.

1. V. album L., *Sp. pl.*: 1023 (1753) - *FE* **1**:
72.
Cr (E) - *MAP 943*
*Pinus brutia woodland, on the branches of the
trees; 600-700m.*
E. Crete (Afendis Kavousi) [C. & S. Europe].
Cretan plants belong to subsp. *austriacum*
(Wiesb.) Vollm. (*FE* **1**: 73), which is treated as
doubtfully distinct from subsp. *album* in *M-Ch*
4: 227, and is not separated here. Erroneously
given as "subsp. *abietis*" by Barclay (1986: 70).

LYTHRACEAE

1. Lythrum L.

1. L. borysthenicum (Schrank) Litv. in
Majevski, *Fl. sred. Ross.* ed.5: 209 (1917) - *FE*
2: 302.
Cr (C) - *MAP 944*
*Flat clayey area, apparently flooded in winter;
620m.*
C. Crete [mainly S. Europe].

2. L. hyssopifolia L., *Sp. pl.*: 447 (1753) - *FE*
2: 301.
Cr (W, C) Ks Kp - *MAP 945*
Marshes, seasonally wet places, ditches; 0-
500m; fl. 3-5.
W. & C. Crete; Kasos, Karpathos [most of
Europe].

3. L. junceum Banks & Sol. in Russell, *Nat.*
hist. Aleppo ed.2, 2: 253 (1794) - *FE* 2: 301.
Cr (W, C, E) Kp - *MAP 946*
Marshes, seasonally wet places, streams,
ditches, springs; 0-700m; fl. 3-5.
Crete (widespread); Karpathos [mainly
Mediterranean region].

? L. portula (L.) D.A.Webb in *Feddes Reprium*
74: 13 (1967) - *FE* 2: 302.
Doubtfully present in Crete (Greuter et al.,
1984b: 284) [almost throughout Europe].

MALVACEAE

1. Abutilon Mill.

1. A. theophrasti Medik., *Malvenfam.*: 28
(1787) - *FE* 2: 254.
Cr (W) - *MAP 947*
Waste areas; 0-25m; fl. 8-10.
W. Crete [mainly S.E. Europe & Mediterranean
region].
Given as doubtfully present in Crete by Greuter
(1974: 156), but occurrence confirmed - as
doubtfully native - by Turland (1992b: 161).

2. Alcea L.

1. A. biennis Winterl, *Index hort. bot. Univ.*
Hung.: [3] (1788) - *FE* 2: 254 as *A. pallida*
(Willd.) Waldst. & Kit.
Cr (W, C) - *MAP 948*
Step-crevices of calcareous cliffs, roadsides; 0-
700m; fl. 6-8.
W. & C. Crete [mainly Balkan peninsula;
otherwise S.W. Asia].
Cretan plants belong to *A. cretica* (Weinm.)
Greuter (*FE* 2: 254 as *A. pallida* subsp. *cretica*
(Weinm.) D.A.Webb), which is treated as
doubtfully distinct from *A. biennis* in *M-Ch* 4:
232, and is not separated here.

A. pallida (Willd.) Waldst. & Kit. (*FE* 2: 254)
= **1.**

2. A. setosa (Boiss.) Alef. in *Öst. bot. Z.* 12:
255 (1862) - *FE* 2: 254.
Cr - *NOT MAPPED*
Crete [Italy, Jugoslavia & Turkey-in-Europe;
otherwise S.W. Asia].

3. Althaea L.

1. A. hirsuta L., *Sp. pl.*: 687 (1753) - *FE* 2:
253.
Cr - *NOT MAPPED*
Crete [mainly S. Europe].

4. Gossypium L.

G. arboreum L. (*FE* 2: 255) was recorded
historically, but is doubtfully still present
(Greuter, 1973a: 39).

G. barbadense L. (*FE* 2: 255) was recorded
historically, but probably in error (Greuter,
1974: 156).

[1. G. herbaceum] L., *Sp. pl.*: 693 (1753) - *FE*
2: 255.
Cr - *NOT MAPPED*
Cultivated and naturalized.
Crete [S. Europe; probably from W. Pakistan].

G. hirsutum L. (*FE* 2: 255) was recorded
historically, but probably in error (Greuter,
1974: 156).

5. Hibiscus L.

H. cannabinus L. (*FE* 2: 256) is cultivated only.

1. H. trionum L., *Sp. pl.*: 697 (1753) - *FE* 2:
256.
Cr (W) - *MAP 949*
W. Crete [mainly C. & S. Europe].

6. Lavatera L.

1. L. arborea L., *Sp. pl.*: 690 (1753) - *FE* 2:
252.
Cr (W, E) Ks Kp - *MAP 950*
Maritime rocks on offshore islets.
W. & E. Crete (Gramvousa island, Prasonisi
islet near Elafonisi island & Fotia islet E. of
Ierapetra); Kasos, Karpathos [coastal W. Europe
& Mediterranean region].

2. L. bryoniifolia Mill., *Gard. Dict.* ed.8:
no.11 (1768) - *FE* 2: 252.
Cr (W, C, E) - *MAP 951*
Olive groves, rocky places, roadsides, fallow &
abandoned land, burnt & waste areas; 0-450m;
fl. 5-6.
Crete (widespread, rarer in E.) [?Italy, Greece
& Aegean region; otherwise Libya & S.W.
Asia; extinct in Sicily].

3. L. cretica L., *Sp. pl.*: 691 (1753) - *FE* 2:
251.
Cr (W, C, E) Kp - *MAP 952*

Olive groves, vineyards, fallow fields, waste areas; 0-450m; fl. 3-5.
Crete (sporadic); Karpathos [W. Europe & Mediterranean region].

4. L. punctata All., *Auct. fl. pedem.*: 26 (1789) - *FE* **2**: 252.
Cr - *NOT MAPPED*
Crete [Mediterranean region].

Malope malacoides L. (*FE* **2**: 249) was almost certainly recorded in error (Greuter, 1974: 156).

7. Malva L.

1. M. aegyptia L., *Sp. pl.*: 690 (1753) - *FE* **2**: 250.
Cr (W, E) Ks Kp - *MAP 953*
Sparse phrygana & bare stony ground near sea, calcareous screes, maritime sands; 0-250m; fl. 3-4.
W. & E. Crete; Kasos, Karpathos [Spain & Aegean region; otherwise N. Africa & S.W. Asia].

2. M. cretica Cav., *Diss.*: 67 (1786) - *FE* **2**: 250.
a. subsp. **cretica**
Cr (W, C, E) Kp - *MAP 954*
Calcareous open phrygana, screes, rocky & sandy places near sea; 0-600m; fl. 3-5.
Mainly W. Crete; Karpathos [Mediterranean region].

3. M. nicaeensis All., *Fl. pedem.* **2**: 40 (1785) - *FE* **2**: 251.
Cr Ks Kp - *NOT MAPPED*
Crete; Kasos, Karpathos [S. Europe].

4. M. parviflora L., *Demonstr. pl.*: 18 (1753) - *FE* **2**: 251.
Cr (W, E) Ks Kp - *MAP 955*
Maritime sands, bare ground, waste areas; 0-200m; fl. 3-4.
W. & E. Crete; Kasos, Karpathos [mainly Mediterranean region].

5. M. sylvestris L., *Sp. pl.*: 689 (1753) - *FE* **2**: 250.
Cr (W, C, E) Ks Kp Sa - *MAP 956*
Olive groves, vineyards, rocky places, flat clayey areas, maritime sands, disturbed ground, roadsides, waste areas; 0-1400m; fl. 2-6.
Crete (widespread); Karpathos group [almost throughout Europe].

MELIACEAE

1. Melia L.

[1. M. azederach] L., *Sp. pl.*: 384 (1753) - *FE* **2**: 231.

Cr - *NOT MAPPED*
Planted for ornament, especially on roadsides, and possibly naturalized.
Crete [Mediterranean region; from S. & E. Asia].

MOLLUGINACEAE

1. Glinus L.

1. G. lotoides L., *Sp. pl.*: 463 (1753) - *FE* **1**: 114.
Cr (W) - *NOT MAPPED*
W. Crete [S. Europe].

MORACEAE

1. Ficus L.

1. F. carica L., *Sp. pl.*: 1059 (1753) - *FE* **1**: 67.
Cr (W, C, E) Ks Kp - *MAP 957*
Calcareous cliffs, olive groves, cultivated areas, roadsides; 0-600m.
Crete (widespread); Kasos, Karpathos [mainly S. Europe].
Given as doubtfully native in *FE*, but considered native in *M-Ch* **4**: 242 and in *Atlas FE* **3**: 85 (except in Kasos, where status is shown as doubtful).

2. Morus L.

[1. M. alba] L., *Sp. pl.*: 986 (1753) - *FE* **1**: 66.
Cr - *NOT MAPPED*
Widely planted in and around towns & villages and possibly naturalized.
Crete [mainly S. Europe; from China].

M. nigra L. (*FE* **1**: 66) is probably only planted.

MYRTACEAE

1. Myrtus L.

1. M. communis L., *Sp. pl.*: 471 (1753) - *FE* **2**: 303.
a. subsp. **communis**
Cr (W, C, E) Ks Kp - *MAP 958*
Olive groves, scrub, watercourses, damp ground; 0-500m; fl. 4-6.
Mainly W. & C. Crete; Kasos, Karpathos [mainly Mediterranean region].
? subsp. **tarentina** (L.) Nyman, *Consp. fl. eur.*: 245 (1879) - *FE* **2**: 304.
Doubtfully present in Crete (Greuter, 1974: 158) [W. & C. Mediterranean region].

Literature records of the species sensu lato have here been referred to subsp. **a**.

NYCTAGINACEAE

Mirabilis jalapa L. (*FE* **1**: 111) has been recorded from Karpathos as a casual escape from cultivation (Greuter et al., 1983*a*: 63); it is also cultivated for ornament in Crete.

NYMPHAEACEAE

Nymphaea alba L. (*FE* **1**: 205) is presumed extinct, having been recorded historically in W. Crete, but never since (Greuter, 1973*a*: 35). The species is distributed almost throughout Europe, occurring in still and slow-moving fresh water.

OLEACEAE

1. Fraxinus L.

1. F. ornus L., *Sp. pl.*: 1057 (1753) - *FE* **3**: 53.
Cr (W) - *MAP 959*
Humid stream valleys with Platanus & Quercus ilex; 300m; fl. 4.
W. Crete (Fasas valley) [C. & S. Europe].
Recorded since *FE* (Turland, 1992*a*: 351).

2. Olea L.

1. O. europaea L., *Sp. pl.*: 8 (1753) - *FE* **3**: 55.
Cr (W, C, E) Ks Kp - *MAPS 960, 961 & 962*
Woodland, scrub, garigue, calcareous cliffs & rocky places, also extensively cultivated and escaping; 0-700m; fl. 5.
Crete (widespread); Kasos, Karpathos [mainly Mediterranean region].
Native plants belong to subsp. *oleaster* (Hoffmanns. & Link) Negodi (*FE* **3**: 55 as var. *sylvestris* Brot.), which is treated as doubtfully distinct from cultivated subsp. *europaea* in *M-Ch* **4**: 248, and is not separated here. Such native plants are frequently used as grafting stock for cultivated olives.

3. Phillyrea L.

1. P. latifolia L., *Sp. pl.*: 8 (1753) - *FE* **3**: 55.
Cr (W, C, E) Ks Kp - *MAP 963*
Woodland, maquis, scrub, rocky places; 50-700m.
Mainly W. & C. Crete; Kasos, Karpathos

[Mediterranean region].

ONAGRACEAE

1. Epilobium L.

1. E. hirsutum L., *Sp. pl.*: 347 (1753) - *FE* **2**: 309.
Cr (W, C) - *MAP 964*
Ditches & other wet places; fl. 5.
W. & C. Crete [almost throughout Europe].

2. E. lanceolatum Sebast. & Mauri, *Fl. roman. prodr.*: 138 (1818) - *FE* **2**: 310.
Cr (W) - *MAP 965*
Shady wet rocks beneath Castanea trees; 500m.
W. Crete [W., C. & S. Europe].
Recorded since *FE* (Greuter, 1973*a*: 44).

3. E. parviflorum Schreb., *Spic. fl. lips.*: 146 (1771) - *FE* **2**: 309.
Cr (W) Kp - *MAP 966*
Roadside ditch; 150m; fl. 9.
W. Crete; Karpathos [almost throughout Europe].

? E. tetragonum L., *Sp. pl.*: 348 (1753) - *FE* **2**: 310.
Subsp. **tetragonum**
Doubtfully present in Crete (Greuter, 1974: 158) [almost throughout Europe].

OROBANCHACEAE

1. Cistanche Hoffmanns. & Link

1. C. phelypaea (L.) Cout., *Fl. Portugal*: 571 (1913) - *FE* **3**: 286.
Cr (E) Ks - *MAP 967*
Calcareous rocky places & maritime sands on offshore islets, on Atriplex halimus & Suaeda vera.
E. Crete (Mikronisi islet E. of Gaidouronisi island, Koufonisi & Dionisiades islands); Kasos (islet W. of Armathia island) [Portugal & Spain; otherwise N. Africa & S.W. Asia].

2. Orobanche L.

1. O. alba Stephan ex Willd., *Sp. pl.*: 3: 450 (1800) - *FE* **3**: 290.
Cr - *NOT MAPPED*
Crete [mainly W., C. & S. Europe].

2. O. canescens C.Presl in J.& C.Presl, *Delic. prag.*: 72 (1822) - *FE* **3**: 291.
Cr (W) - *MAP 968*

*Waste area, on Chrysanthemum coronarium;
250m; fl. 4.*
W. Crete [?Corsica, Sardinia, Sicily, Italy &
Greece].
Given as erroneously recorded from the Cretan
area in *M-Ch* **4**: 258; occurrence is confirmed
here — Ep. Agios Vasilios: Mirthios,
22.4.1992, *M.J.Y.Foley* 187 (herb.
M.J.Y.Foley!, LANC) - rev. A.Gilli (Wien).

3. O. cernua Loefl., *Iter hispan.*: 152 (1758) -
FE **3**: 289.
Cr Kp - *NOT MAPPED*
Crete; Karpathos [mainly S. Europe].
Subsp. *cumana* (Wallr.) Soó is given for the
Cretan area in *M-Ch* **4**: 258, but as doubtfully
distinct from subsp. *cernua*; it is not separated
here.

"*O. coelestis*" (*FE* **3**: 288, recorded from Kasos)
= **10** (Raus, 1991: 305).

4. O. crenata Forssk., *Fl. aegypt.-arab.*: 113
(1775) - *FE* **3**: 290.
Cr (W, C, E) Kp - *MAP 969*
*Open stony ground, cultivated areas, gardens,
on Vicia faba; 0-1650m; fl. 4.*
Crete (sporadic); Karpathos [S. Europe].

5. O. gracilis Sm. in *Trans. Linn. Soc. Lond.* **4**:
172 (1798) - *FE* **3**: 293.
Cr - *NOT MAPPED*
Crete [W., C. & S. Europe].

6. O. grisebachii Reut. in DC., *Prodr.* **11**: 28
(1847) - *FE* **3**: 291.
Cr Ks Kp ?Sa - *NOT MAPPED*
Crete; Kasos, Karpathos, ?Saria [Greece &
Aegean region; otherwise Egypt & S.W. Asia].

7. O. hederae Duby, *Bot. gall.* **1**: 350 (1828) -
FE **3**: 292.
Cr (W, C, E) - *MAP 970*
*Woodland & other shady places, on Hedera
helix; 0-800m; fl. 4-5.*
Crete (sporadic) [W., C. & S. Europe].
Recorded since *FE* (Greuter et al., 1984*b*: 285).

8. O. lavandulacea Rchb., *Iconogr. bot. pl.
crit.* **7**: 48 (1829) - *FE* **3**: 288.
Cr (W) - *MAP 971*
*Open areas in olive groves, banks by paths, on
Bituminaria bituminosa; 0-100m; fl. 4-5.*
W. Crete [Mediterranean region].
Regarded as absent from the Cretan area in *FE*,
although doubtful records already existed
(Greuter, 1974: 159); occurrence since
confirmed by Turland (1992*a*: 351).

"*O. loricata*" (*FE* **3**: 291, recorded from Saria
as "*O. picridis*") ? = **6** (Greuter et al., 1983*a*:
63).

O. oxyloba (Reut.) Beck (*FE* **3**: 288), recorded

by Greuter (1973*a*: 52), is included in synonymy
of **10b**.

9. O. pubescens d'Urv. in *Mém. Soc. linn.
Paris* **1**: 332 (1822) - *FE* **3**: 290.
Cr (W, C, E) Ks Kp - *MAP 972*
*Olive groves, phrygana, rocky places &
crevices, maritime sands, roadsides, waste
areas, mostly on Pseudorlaya pumila, Scandix
pecten-veneris & Tordylium apulum; 0-2000m;
fl. 3-4.*
Mainly W. Crete; Kasos, Karpathos [mainly
S.E. Europe].

? O. purpurea Jacq., *Enum. stirp. Vindob.*: 108
(1762) - *FE* **3**: 289.
Doubtfully present in Crete [mainly W., C. &
S. Europe].

10. O. ramosa L., *Sp. pl.*: 633 (1753) - *FE* **3**:
288.
Cr (W, C, E) Ks Kp - *MAP 973*
Phrygana, rocky places; 0-2000m; fl. 4.
a. subsp. **mutelii** (F.W.Schultz) Cout., *Fl.
Portugal*: 566 (1913) - *FE* **3**: 288.
Crete [S. Europe].
b. subsp. **nana** (Reut.) Cout., *Fl. Portugal*: 566
(1913) - *FE* **3**: 288. (Including *O. oxyloba*
(Reut.) Beck - *FE* **3**: 288.)
Crete [S. Europe].
c. subsp. **ramosa**
Crete [mainly C. & S. Europe].
The species sensu lato is sporadic in Crete and
occurs also in Kasos & Karpathos.

11. O. sanguinea C.Presl in J.& C.Presl, *Delic.
prag.*: 71 (1822) - *FE* **3**: 293.
Cr (W) Ks Kp - *MAP 974*
*Rocky & sandy places, mainly on offshore islets,
on Lotus cytisoides.*
W. Crete (Elafonisi island, coast W. of
Paleohora & islet off W. coast of Akrotiri
peninsula); Kasos, Karpathos [Mediterranean
region].

O. schultzii Mutel is doubtfully present in the
Cretan area (*FE* **3**: 288), and anyway is treated
as doubtfully distinct from **10** in *M-Ch* **4**: 263.

OXALIDACEAE

1. Oxalis L.

1. O. corniculata L., *Sp. pl.*: 435 (1753) - *FE*
2: 192.
Cr (W) - *MAP 975*
*Bare ground in olive groves, cracks in
pavements; 0-450m; fl. 4.*
W. Crete [W., C. & S. Europe].

[2. O. debilis] Kunth in Humb., Bonpl. &
Kunth, *Nov. gen. sp.* **5**: 236 (1822) - *FE* **2**: 193.

(Including *O. corymbosa* DC. - *FE* 2: 193.)
Cr (W) - *MAP 976*
Naturalized as a weed at small harbour.
W. Crete (near Kastelli Kissamou) [W. Europe;
from S. America].
Recorded since *FE* (Greuter, 1973a: 40).

[3. O. pes-caprae] L., *Sp. pl.*: 434 (1753) - *FE*
2: 193.
Cr (W, C, E) Ks Kp - *MAP 977*
*Extensively naturalized and a troublesome weed
in olive groves and other cultivated ground,
sometimes invading more natural habitats such
as woodland and rock-crevices; 0-600m; fl. 2-5.*
Crete (widespread); Kasos, Karpathos [W.
Europe & Mediterranean region; from S.
Africa].

PAEONIACEAE

1. Paeonia L.

1. P. clusii Stern & Stearn in *Curtis's bot. Mag.*
162: t.9594 (1940) - *FE* 1: 243.
● **a. subsp. clusii**
Cr (W, C, E) Kp - *MAP 978*
*Calcareous woodland, olive groves, scrub,
garigue, rocky places; 100-1450m; fl. 3-5.*
Crete (mainly Lefka Ori & Dikti areas);
Karpathos - Endemic.
More frequent in Karpathos than in Crete. *P.
clusii* occurs outside the Cretan area on the E.
Aegean island of Rodos, as subsp. *rhodia*
(Stearn) Tzanoud. (= *P. rhodia* Stearn).

P. mascula (L.) Mill. (*FE* 1: 244) was almost
certainly recorded in error (Greuter, 1974: 155),
perhaps for pink-flowered variants of **1a**, which
are known to occur in Crete.

PAPAVERACEAE

Chelidonium majus L. is given for the Cretan
area in *FE* 1: 251, although there are no records
as a basis for this (Greuter, 1974: 139).

1. Corydalis DC.

"*C. rutifolia*" (*FE* 1: 253) = **1** (*Atlas FE* 9: 66).

● **1. C. uniflora** (Sieber) Nyman, *Syll. fl. Eur.*:
185 (1855) - *FE* 1: 253.
Cr (W, C, E) - *MAP 979*
*Open calcareous rocky places, rubble, screes,
flat clayey areas; 1400-2400m; fl. 4-6.*
Crete (Lefka Ori, Psiloritis & Dikti) - Endemic.
A record from the Kikladean island of Andros
(Lidén, 1988: 363) is considered doubtful in *M-
Ch* **4**: 272.

2. Fumaria L.

1. F. capreolata L., *Sp. pl.*: 701 (1753) - *FE* 1:
256.
Cr (W) - *NOT MAPPED*
W. Crete [W., C. & S. Europe].
Additionally recorded from W./C. Crete in *Atlas
FE* **9**: 86.

"*F. densiflora*", given as doubtfully present in
Crete by Greuter et al. (1984b: 285), = **7a**
(*Atlas FE* **9**: 94).

F. flabellata Gasp. (*FE* 1: 256) was recorded in
error (Lidén, 1986: 66).

2. F. gaillardotii Boiss., *Fl. orient.* **1**: 139
(1867) - *FE* 1: 256.
Cr (W, E) - *NOT MAPPED*
W. & E. Crete [Mediterranean region].

3. F. judaica Boiss., *Diagn. pl. orient.* ser.1, **8**:
15 (1849) - *FE* 1: 256.
a. subsp. judaica
Cr (E) Kp - *NOT MAPPED*
E. Crete; Karpathos [C. & E. Mediterranean
region].

"*F. kralikii*" (Greuter, 1974: 140; Greuter et al.,
1983a: 64) is almost certainly referable to **7a**
(*Atlas FE* **9**: 93).

4. F. macrocarpa Parl., *Pl. nov.*: 5 (1842) - *FE*
1: 256.
a. subsp. macrocarpa
Cr (W, C, E) Ks Kp - *MAP 980*
*Olive groves, calcareous rocky ground beneath
cliffs, screes; 100-550m; fl. 3-4.*
Crete (sporadic); Kasos, Karpathos [mainly E.
Mediterranean region].

5. F. officinalis L., *Sp. pl.*: 700 (1753) - *FE* 1:
258.
a. subsp. officinalis
Cr (W, C, E) Kp - *MAP 981*
Cultivated ground; fl. 3-4.
Crete (sporadic); Karpathos [almost throughout
Europe].
Erroneously regarded as absent from the Cretan
area in *FE* (Greuter, 1974: 140).

6. F. parviflora Lam., *Encycl.* **2**: 567 (1788) -
FE 1: 258.
Cr (W, C, E) Ks Kp - *NOT MAPPED*
Crete; Kasos, Karpathos [W., C. & S. Europe].

7. F. petteri Rchb., *Icon. fl. germ. helv.* **3**: 1
(1838-1839) - *FE* 1: 257.
a. subsp. petteri (including subsp. *thuretii*
(Boiss.) Pugsley - *FE* 1: 257).
Cr (W, C) Ks Kp - *MAP 982*
W. & C. Crete; Kasos, Karpathos [mainly
Balkan peninsula].

Recorded since *FE* (Greuter, 1973*a*: 36).

3. Glaucium Mill.

1. G. corniculatum (L.) Rudolph, *Fl. jen.*: 13 (1781) - *FE* **1**: 251.
a. subsp. **corniculatum**
Cr (C, E) Kp - *MAP 983*
Garigue, disturbed bare stony ground; 0-50m; fl. 4-5.
C. & E. Crete; Karpathos [mainly C. & S. Europe].

2. G. flavum Crantz, *Stirp. austr. fasc.* **2**: 133 (1763) - *FE* **1**: 251.
Cr (W, C, E) - *MAP 984*
Rock-faces & steep rocky banks exposed by road building, rubble heaps, stony & sandy places near sea; 0-300m; fl. 3-5.
Crete (widespread) [W., C. & S. Europe].

"*G. leiocarpum*" (*FE* **1**: 251) = 2 (*M-Ch* **4**: 280).

4. Hypecoum L.

H. glaucescens Guss. (Barclay, 1986: 75; Greuter et al., 1983*a*: 64) is included in synonymy of **1a**.

1. H. procumbens L., *Sp. pl.*: 124 (1753) - *FE* **1**: 252.
a. subsp. **procumbens** (including *H. glaucescens* Guss. - not cited in *FE*).
Cr (W, C, E) Ks Kp - *MAP 985*
Maritime sands; fl. 3-5.
Crete (sporadic); Kasos, Karpathos [S. Europe].
Subsp. *atropunctatum* Å.E.Dahl is erroneously recorded from the Cretan area in *M-Ch* **4**: 282, based on Dahl (1989), who gives no such occurrence.

2. H. torulosum Å.E.Dahl in *Pl. Syst. Evol.* **163**: 268 (1989).
Cr (E) Kp - *NOT MAPPED*
Maritime sands; fl. 3-5.
E. Crete; Karpathos [Mediterranean region].
It is possible that some records for **1** and for *H. glaucescens* in fact belong here.

5. Papaver L.

1. P. apulum Ten., *Fl. neapol. prodr. app. quinta*: 16 (1826) - *FE* **1**: 249.
Cr (W, C, E) - *MAP 986*
Crete (sporadic) [S. Italy, Sicily, Balkan peninsula & Aegean region].
Regarded as absent from the Cretan area in *FE*, although previously recorded by Meikle (1957);

cf. Greuter (1973*a*: 36).

2. P. argemone L., *Sp. pl.*: 506 (1753) - *FE* **1**: 248.
a. subsp. **nigrotinctum** (Fedde) Kadereit in *Notes R. bot. Gdn Edinb.* **44**: 37 (1986) - *FE* **1**: 249 as *P. nigrotinctum* Fedde.
Ks Kp - *MAP 987*
Among crops in cultivated land; 300m; fl. 4.
Kasos, Karpathos [?N.W. Jugoslavia, Peloponnisos, Evvia & Kiklades; otherwise E. Aegean Islands & S.W. Turkey].
Recorded since *FE* (Greuter, 1974: 147; *Atlas FE* **9**: 38).
Subsp. *argemone* is not known to occur (cf. *Atlas FE* **9**: 38-39).

P. commutatum Fisch. & C.A.Mey. (*FE* **1**: 248) was almost certainly recorded in error (Greuter, 1974: 155).

P. dubium L. (*FE* **1**: 248) is not given for the Cretan area in *Atlas FE* **9**: 34-37, although that work gives subsp. *laevigatum* (M.Bieb.) Pawł. as doubtfully present in Crete, after Greuter et al. (1984*b*: 285), who state "There undisputedly is a particular taxon of the *Papaver dubium* aggregate occurring in Crete....but its identification with *P. laevigatum* is open to dispute". These plants, together with records of *P. dubium*, should be referred to **5**, which is the only taxon in the *P. dubium* group known to occur in the Cretan area.

3. P. guerlekense Stapf in *Denkschr. Akad. Wiss. Wien* **51**: 359 (1886) - not cited in *FE*. (Including *P. stipitatum* Fedde - *FE* **1**: 248.)
Cr (E) Kp - *NOT MAPPED*
E. Crete; Karpathos [Aegean region; otherwise S.W. Asia].
Recorded by Kadereit (1988: 263) and *Atlas FE* **9**: 33. Related to **6**.

4. P. hybridum L., *Sp. pl.*: 506 (1753) - *FE* **1**: 249.
Cr (W, C, E) Ks Kp - *MAP 988*
Calcareous open stony ground.
Crete (sporadic); Kasos, Karpathos [most of Europe].

P. laevigatum M.Bieb. (Barclay, 1986: 75) see note under *P. dubium*.

P. pseudo-haussknechtii Fedde (Greuter, 1973*a*: 35; Barclay, 1986: 75) is included in synonymy of **6**.

5. P. purpureomarginatum Kadereit in *Notes R. bot. Gdn Edinb.* **45**: 235 (1988).
Cr (W, C, E) Ks Kp Sa - *MAP 989*
Calcareous rocky places & gravel; 0-450m; fl. 4-5.
Mainly W. Crete; Karpathos group [S. Greece

& Aegean region; otherwise S.W. Asia].
Related to *P. dubium* L.

6. P. rhoeas L., *Sp. pl.*: 507 (1753) - *FE* **1**:
248. (Including *P. pseudo-haussknechtii* Fedde -
not cited in *FE*.)
Cr (W, C, E) Ks Kp Sa - *MAP 990*
*Cultivated & fallow land, rocky places, screes,
bare & disturbed ground; 0-600m; fl. 3-5.*
Crete (widespread); Karpathos group [almost
throughout Europe].

7. P. somniferum L., *Sp. pl.*: 508 (1753) - *FE*
1: 247.
? subsp. **setigerum** (DC.) Arcang., *Comp. fl.
ital.*: 25 (1882) - *FE* **1**: 247.
Doubtfully present in Crete (Greuter, 1974: 155)
[Mediterranean region].
[**a.** subsp. **somniferum**]
Cr - *NOT MAPPED*
Cultivated and possibly naturalized.
Crete [most of Europe].

6. Roemeria Medik.

1. R. hybrida (L.) DC., *Syst. nat.* **2**: 92 (1821)
- *FE* **1**: 251.
a. subsp. **hybrida**
Cr (W) Kp - *MAP 991*
W. Crete; Karpathos [mainly S. Europe].
Additionally recorded from W./C. Crete in *Atlas
FE* **9**: 56.

PEDALIACEAE

1. Sesamum L.

[**1. S. indicum**] L., *Sp. pl.*: 634 (1753) - *FE* **3**:
284.
Cr - *NOT MAPPED*
Cultivated and possibly naturalized.
Crete [S.E. Europe & Mediterranean region;
probably from S.E. Asia].
Recorded by Rechinger (1943a: 491).

PHYTOLACCACEAE

1. Phytolacca L.

[**1. P. americana**] L., *Sp. pl.*: 441 (1753) - *FE*
1: 112.
Cr (W, C) - *MAP 992*
*Naturalized in shady places, usually beneath
cultivated trees such as olives & oranges; 100-
300m; fl. 6-7.*
W. & C. Crete [C. & S. Europe; from N.
America].

PLANTAGINACEAE

1. Plantago L.

1. P. afra L., *Sp. pl.* ed.2: 168 (1762) - *FE* **4**:
44.
Cr (W, C, E) Ks Kp Sa - *MAP 993*
*Rocky places, gorge-beds, abandoned terraces,
roadsides, maritime sands & rocks, bare &
saline ground; 0-500m; fl. 3-5.*
Mainly W. & E. Crete; Karpathos group [S.
Europe].

2. P. albicans L., *Sp. pl.*: 114 (1753) - *FE* **4**:
43.
Cr (E) Kp - *MAP 994*
*Olive groves on clayey soil, Lygeum steppe,
open bare stony & clayey ground, maritime
sands; 0-350m; fl. 3-4.*
E. Crete; Karpathos [Mediterranean region].

3. P. altissima L., *Sp. pl.* ed.2: 164 (1762) - *FE*
4: 42.
Cr (C) - *MAP 995*
C. Crete (S. of Iraklio) [C. Europe & Balkan
peninsula].

4. P. amplexicaulis Cav., *Icon. Descr.* **2**: 22
(1793) - *FE* **4**: 42.
a. subsp. **amplexicaulis**
Cr (E) Kp - *MAP 996*
*Calcareous rocky places, open stony ground
near sea, waste areas; 0-200m; fl. 3-4.*
E. Crete; Karpathos [S. Spain, S. Italy & S.
Aegean region; otherwise N. Africa & Cyprus].

5. P. arenaria Waldst. & Kit., *Pl. Rar. Hung.*
1: 51 (1801) - *FE* **4**: 43.
Cr (W) - *MAP 997*
*Coastal phrygana, maritime sands, margins of
cultivated land.*
W. Crete [C., E. & S. Europe].

6. P. bellardii All., *Fl. pedem.* **1**: 82 (1785) -
FE **4**: 43.
Cr (W, C, E) Ks Kp - *MAP 998*
*Phrygana, rocky places, maritime sands &
gravel; 0-500m; fl. 4-5.*
Mainly W. Crete; Kasos, Karpathos [S.
Europe].
Both subsp. *bellardii* and subsp. *deflexa* (Pilg.)
Rech.f. (*FE* **4**: 43) have been recorded (Greuter
et al., 1983a: 64; Barclay, 1986: 76), although
the latter is treated as doubtfully distinct in *M-
Ch* **4**: 298, and is not separated here.

? **P. coronopus** L., *Sp. pl.*: 115 (1753) - *FE* **4**:
40 as *P. coronopus* L. subsp. *coronopus*.
Doubtfully present in Crete (Greuter, 1974: 159)
[mainly W. & S. Europe].
Subsp. *commutata* (Guss.) Pilg. (*FE* **4**: 40) =
12a.

7. P. cretica L., *Sp. pl.*: 114 (1753) - *FE* **4**: 43.
Cr (W, C, E) Ks Kp Sa - *MAP 999*
Calcareous rocky places, open dry stony ground on coast, seashores; 0-700m; fl. 4-5.
Crete (sporadic); Karpathos group [S. Aegean region; otherwise S.W. Asia].

8. P. lagopus L., *Sp. pl.*: 114 (1753) - *FE* **4**: 43.
Cr (W, C, E) Ks Kp Sa - *MAP 1000*
Rocky places, maritime sands & rocks, bare ground; 0-550m; fl. 3-5.
Crete (widespread); Karpathos group [S. Europe].

9. P. lanceolata L., *Sp. pl.*: 113 (1753) - *FE* **4**: 42.
Cr (W, C, E) Kp - *MAP 1001*
Olive groves, marshy places, ditches, damp ground, clayey pastures, rocky places; 0-2000m; fl. 3-5.
Crete (sporadic); Karpathos [almost throughout Europe].

10. P. major L., *Sp. pl.*: 112 (1753) - *FE* **4**: 39.
Cr (W, C) Kp - *MAP 1002*.
a. subsp. **intermedia** (Gilib.) Lange, *Haandb. Danske fl.* ed.2: 714 (1869) - *FE* **4**: 39.
Cr (W, C) - *MAP 1003*
Marshes, springs, damp ground; 0-400m.
W. & C. Crete [most of Europe].
b. subsp. **major**
Cr (W, C) - *MAP 1004*
Olive groves, damp ditches; 0-450m; fl. 4-6.
Mainly W. Crete [almost throughout Europe].
The species sensu lato occurs also in Karpathos.

11. P. squarrosa Murray in *Commentat. Soc. Scient. gotting.* **4**: 38 (1782) - *FE* **4**: 43.
Cr (W) Kp - *MAP 1005*
Maritime sands.
W. Crete (Elafonisi & Gavdos islands); Karpathos [Aegean region; otherwise Libya, Egypt, Sinai & S.W. Asia].

12. P. weldenii Rchb., *Fl. germ. excurs.*: 396 (1831).
a. subsp. **weldenii** - *FE* **4**: 40 as *P. coronopus* subsp. *commutata* (Guss.) Pilg.
Cr (W, C, E) Ks Kp Sa - *MAP 1006*
Rocky places, seashores, bare & damp ground; 0-1050m; fl. 3-5.
Crete (sporadic); Karpathos group [Mediterranean region].

PLATANACEAE

1. Platanus L.

1. P. orientalis L., *Sp. pl.*: 999 (1753) - *FE* **1**: 384.

Cr (W, C, E) Kp - *MAP 1007*
Along rivers, streams, by springs, often planted for shade in & near villages; 0-1200m; fl. 4.
Crete (widespread, rarer towards E.); Karpathos [Italy, Sicily & Balkan peninsula].

PLUMBAGINACEAE

1. Acantholimon Boiss.

A. androsaceum (Jaub. & Spach) Boiss. (*FE* **3**: 30) is included in synonymy of **1**.

1. A. ulicinum (Willd. ex Schult.) Boiss. in DC., *Prodr.* **12**: 627 (1848) - not cited in *FE*. (Including *A. androsaceum* (Jaub. & Spach) Boiss. - *FE* **3**: 30.)
Cr (W, C) - *MAP 1008*
Calcareous open rocky slopes, flat clayey areas; 1650-2300m; fl. 6-8(-10).
W. & C. Crete (Lefka Ori & Psiloritis) [Jugoslavia, Albania & Greece; otherwise S.W. Asia].

2. Limoniastrum Heist. ex Fabr.

1. L. monopetalum (L.) Boiss. in DC., *Prodr.* **12**: 689 (1848) - *FE* **3**: 51.
Cr (E) - *MAP 1009*
Maritime sands & rocks.
E. Crete (Gaidouronisi island) [Mediterranean region].
Also occasionally cultivated for ornament in coastal areas.

3. Limonium Mill.

1. L. aucheri (Girard) Greuter & Burdet in *Willdenowia* **19**: 39 (1989) - not cited in *FE*.
Cr (E) - *MAP 1010*
Calcareous maritime rocks.
E. Crete (Dragonada in Dionisiades islands) [Kiklades; otherwise E. Aegean islands (Rodos) & Cyprus].
Recorded by Rechinger (1943*a*: 104 as *L. ocymifolium* var. *bellidifolium* (Sm.) Rech.f.)
Related to **9**.

L. avei (De Not.) Brullo & Erben (*M-Ch* **4**: 329) see **4**.

●**2. L. carpathum** (Rech.f.) Rech.f. in *Denkschr. Akad. Wiss. Wien* **105(1)**: 427 (1943) - *FE* **3**: 46.
Kp - *MAP 1011*
Calcareous maritime cliffs; fl. 6.
Karpathos - Endemic.
[Plate 6.]

3. L. doerfleri (Halácsy) Rech.f. in *Denkschr. Akad. Wiss. Wien* **105(1)**: 427 (1943) - *FE* **3**: 47 as *L. ramosissimum* subsp. *doerfleri* (Halácsy) Pignatti.
Ks - *MAP 1012*
Kasos (islet off N.E. cape) [Kiklades].
Recorded since *FE* (Raus, 1990: 30).

4. L. echioides (L.) Mill., *Gard. Dict.* ed.8: no.11 (1768) - *FE* **3**: 50.
Cr (W, C, E) Ks Kp - *MAP 1013*
Lygeum steppe, maritime sands & rocks; fl. 6.
Mainly E. Crete; Kasos, Karpathos [Mediterranean region].
L. avei (De Not.) Brullo & Erben, recorded from Gavdos island off the S. coast of W. Crete by Brullo (1988: 17), is given for the Cretan area in *M-Ch* **4**: 329, but as doubtfully distinct from **4**; it is not separated here.

5. L. frederici (Barbey) Rech.f. in *Denkschr. Akad. Wiss. Wien* **105(1)**: 427 (1943) - *FE* **3**: 45.
Cr (W, E) Kp Sa - *MAP 1014*
Calcareous maritime cliffs, rocks & crevices; 0-50m; fl. 7.
W. & E. Crete (Agria Gramvousa & Gramvousa islands, Korikos & Rodopos peninsulas & Dionisiades islands); Karpathos, Saria [S.E. Kiklades].

6. L. graecum (Poir.) Rech.f. in *Denkschr. Akad. Wiss. Wien* **105(1)**: 427 (1943) - *FE* **3**: 46 as *L. graecum* (Poir.) Rech.f. subsp. *graecum*.
Cr (W, E) Ks - *MAP 1015*
Maritime sands & rocks; 0-150m; fl. 7-9.
W. & E. Crete; Kasos [S. Greece & S. Aegean region; otherwise S.W. Asia].

●**7. L. hierapetrae** Rech.f. in *Denkschr. Akad. Wiss. Wien* **105(2,1)**: 104 (1943) - not cited in *FE*.
Cr (E) - *MAP 1016*
Maritime sands; fl. 5.
E. Crete (W. of Ierapetra) - Endemic.
[Plate 6.] Related to **9**.

8. L. hyssopifolium (Girard) Rech.f. in *Denkschr. Akad. Wiss. Wien* **105(1)**: 427 (1943) - *FE* **3**: 46, included in synonymy of *L. graecum* (Poir.) Rech.f. subsp. *graecum*.
Cr Ks Kp Sa - *NOT MAPPED*
Coastal rocks, damp sand & shingle; fl. 7.
Crete; Karpathos group [S. Greece & Aegean region].

9. L. ocymifolium (Poir.) Kuntze, *Revis. gen. pl.* **1**: 396 (1891) - *FE* **3**: 47.
Cr (W, C) - *MAP 1017*
Open stony ground near sea.
W. & C. Crete [S. Greece; otherwise E. Aegean Islands].

Regarded as absent from the Cretan area in *FE*, although previously recorded (cf. Greuter in Greuter & Rechinger, 1967: 97).
"*L. oleifolium*" (*FE* **3**: 46) = **14** (Bokhari & Edmondson in Davis, 1982: 470).

10. L. pigadiense (Rech.f.) Rech.f. in *Denkschr. Akad. Wiss. Wien* **105(1)**: 427 (1943) - *FE* **3**: 46, included in synonymy of *L. graecum* (Poir.) Rech.f. subsp. *graecum*.
Cr (E) Kp - *MAP 1018*
Calcareous maritime cliffs & rocks; fl. 6.
E. Crete (Fotia islet E. of Ierapetra); Karpathos [S. Aegean region].

11. L. sieberi (Boiss.) Kuntze, *Revis. gen. pl.* **1**: 396 (1891) - *FE* **3**: 46, included in synonymy of *L. graecum* (Poir.) Rech.f. subsp. *graecum*.
Cr (W, C, E) Kp - *MAP 1019*
Maritime sands & rocks.
Crete (sporadic); Karpathos [S. Greece; otherwise S.W. Asia].

12. L. sinuatum (L.) Mill., *Gard. Dict.* ed.8: no.6 (1768) - *FE* **3**: 40.
a. subsp. **sinuatum**
Cr (W, C, E) Kp - *MAP 1020*
Maritime sands & rocks; fl. 4-5.
Crete (N. coast); Karpathos [Mediterranean region].
Plants are sometimes collected as a wild salad vegetable by the local people.

●**13. L. sitiacum** Rech.f. in *Denkschr. Akad. Wiss. Wien* **105(2,1)**: 103 (1943) - not cited in *FE*.
Cr (E) Ks - *MAP 1021*
Calcareous maritime rocks; fl. 5.
E. Crete (Sideros peninsula & Dionisiades islands); Kasos (islet to N.) - Endemic.
Related to **11**.

14. L. virgatum (Willd.) Fourr. in *Annls Soc. linn. Lyon* ser.2, **17**: 141 (1869).
Cr (C, E) Kp - *MAP 1022*
Lygeum steppe, maritime sands.
C. & E. Crete; Karpathos [W. Europe & Mediterranean region].
Erroneously included in synonymy of *L. oleifolium* Mill. in *FE* **3**: 46 (Bokhari & Edmondson in Davis, 1982: 470).

L. vulgare subsp. *serotinum* (Rchb.) Gams (*FE* **3**: 42) was almost certainly recorded in error (Greuter, 1974: 158).

4. Plumbago L.

[1. P. auriculata] Lam., *Encycl.* **2**: 270 (1786) - *FE* **3**: 30.
Cr (C) - *MAP 1023*

Cultivated for ornament and naturalized among ancient ruins.
C. Crete (S. of Iraklio) [S. Europe; from S. Africa].
Recorded by Greuter (1973a: 47).

P. europaea L. is given as occurring in the Cretan area in *FE* **3**: 30, although the only record within the last 70 years (Rechinger, 1943b: 103) is referred to **1** by Greuter (1973a: 47).

POLYGALACEAE

1. Polygala L.

1. P. monspeliaca L., *Sp. pl.*: 702 (1753) - *FE* **2**: 233.
Cr (W, C, E) Kp - *MAP 1024*
Phrygana; 100-400m; fl. 3-4.
Crete (sporadic); Karpathos [Mediterranean region].

2. P. venulosa Sm., *Fl. Graec. prodr.* **2**: 52 (1813) - *FE* **2**: 233.
Cr (W, C, E) Ks Kp - *MAP 1025*
Scrub, phrygana; 0-1200m; fl. 3-5.
Crete (sporadic); Kasos, Karpathos [S. Greece & Aegean region; otherwise S.W. Asia].

POLYGONACEAE

1. Atraphaxis L.

1. A. billardieri Jaub. & Spach, *Ill. pl. orient.* **2**: 14, 17 (1844) - *FE* **1**: 89.
Cr (W, C) - *MAP 1026*
Calcareous screes; c. 1300m; fl. 5-6.
W. & C. Crete (Lefka Ori & Psiloritis) [C. & E. Greece; otherwise S.W. Asia].

Bilderdykia convolvulus (L.) Dumort. (*FE* **1**: 81) = Fallopia **1**.

2. Emex Campd.

1. E. spinosa (L.) Campd., *Monogr. Rumex*: 58 (1819) - *FE* **1**: 89.
Cr (W, C, E) Ks Kp - *MAP 1027*
Maritime sands, bare & disturbed ground, waste areas; fl. 3-4.
Crete (sporadic, coastal); Kasos, Karpathos [mainly Mediterranean region].

3. Fallopia Adans.

1. F. convolvulus (L.) A.Löve in *Taxon* **19**: 300 (1970) - *FE* **1**: 81 as *Bilderdykia convolvulus*

(L.) Dumort.
Cr (W, E) - *MAP 1028*
Gorge, dry roadside; 0-1000m.
W. & E. Crete [almost throughout Europe].

4. Persicaria (L.) Mill.

1. P. lanigera (R.Br.) Soják in *Preslia* **46**: 153 (1974).
Cr (W, C) - *MAP 1029*
Muddy & gravelly river-banks, wet roadside ditch; 0-30m; fl. 4, 9-12.
W. & C. Crete [old world tropics extending to Egypt, Israel & Jordan].
Recorded since *FE* (Akeroyd & Preston, 1987: 365); considered doubtfully native by Akeroyd (1987: 256).

2. P. salicifolia (Brouss. ex Willd.) Assenov in Jordanov, *Fl. Nar. Rep. Balg.* **3**: 243 (1966) - *FE* **1**: 79 as *Polygonum salicifolium* Brouss. ex Willd.
Cr (W, C) - *MAP 1030*
Shallow fresh water, rivers, streams & other wet places; 0-200m; fl. 4-5, 9.
W. & C. Crete [S. Europe].

5. Polygonum L.

1. P. arenastrum Boreau, *Fl. centre France* ed.3, **2**: 559 (1857) - *FE* **1**: 79.
Cr (W, E) - *MAP 1031*
Flat clayey areas; 1300-1700m.
W. & E. Crete (Lefka Ori & Afendis Kavousi) [most of Europe].
Recorded by Greuter (1973a: 27) and Zaffran (1976: 20; 1990: 77).
Additionally recorded from Dikti in E. Crete in *MFG* **1**: 63.

2. P. aviculare L., *Sp. pl.*: 362 (1753) - *FE* **1**: 78.
Cr (W, C, E) - *MAP 1032*
Mountain pastures, flat clayey areas, maritime shingle, bare & disturbed ground; 0-1850m; fl. 4.
Mainly W. Crete [probably throughout Europe].

3. P. equisetiforme Sm., *Fl. Graec. prodr.* **1**: 266 (1809) - *FE* **1**: 77.
Cr (W, C, E) - *MAP 1033*
Olive groves, roadsides, among ancient ruins; fl. 5-8.
Mainly C. Crete [Mediterranean region].

●**4. P. idaeum** Hayek in *Beih. Repert. nov. Spec. Regni veg.* **30(1)**: 110 (1924) - *FE* **1**: 77.
Cr (C, E) - *MAP 1034*
Flat clayey areas, dominant over much of the Nida plain in Psiloritis; 1400-1900m; fl. 7-10.

C. & E. Crete (Psiloritis & Dikti) - Endemic.
Records from Greece (S. Peloponnisos & Evvia)
are referable to *P. aviculare* var. *nanum* (Bory)
Boiss. (Akeroyd & Preston, 1987: 365).

5. P. longipes Halácsy & Charrel in *Öst. bot. Z.*
40: 164 (1890) - *FE* **1**: 77.
Cr (W) - *MAP 1035*
*Flat clayey areas in mountains, also as a garden
weed.*
W. Crete [S. Balkan peninsula & Aegean
region].
Recorded by Greuter (1973*a*: 27).

6. P. maritimum L., *Sp. pl.*: 361 (1753) - *FE*
1: 77.
Cr (W, C, E) Ks Kp - *MAP 1036*
Maritime sands; fl. 6.
Crete (sporadic); Kasos, Karpathos [coasts of
Atlantic, Mediterranean & Black Sea].

P. salicifolium Brouss. ex Willd. (*FE* **1**: 79) =
Persicaria 2.

6. Rumex L.

1. R. acetosella L., *Sp. pl.*: 338 (1753) - *FE* **1**:
83.
a. subsp. **acetoselloides** (Balansa) Nijs in
Feddes Reprium **95**: 60 (1984) - not cited in *FE.*
Cr (W, C, E) - *MAP 1037*
Crete (sporadic) [mainly Balkan peninsula &
Aegean region].

2. R. bucephalophorus L., *Sp. pl.*: 336 (1753)
- *FE* **1**: 88.
a. subsp. **bucephalophorus** (including subsp.
graecus (Steinh.) Rech.f. - *FE* **1**: 89).
Cr (W) - *MAP 1038*
*Platanus woodland, olive groves, rocky places,
maritime sands; 0-600m.*
W. Crete [Mediterranean region].
b. subsp. **gallicus** (Steinh.) Rech.f. in *Bot.
Notiser 1939*: 497 (1939) - *FE* **1**: 88, included in
synonymy of subsp. **a.**
Cr (W, C, E) Kp - *MAP 1039*
*Calcareous rocky places & screes, maritime
sands, bare ground; 0-600m; fl. 3-5.*
Crete (sporadic); Karpathos [Mediterranean
region].
Subsp. *gallicus* is represented in the Cretan area
by var. **aegaeus** (Rech.f.) Maire (*FE* **1**: 89 as
subsp. *aegaeus* Rech.f.), which occurs mainly in
the Aegean region.

3. R. conglomeratus Murray, *Prodr. stirp.
gott.*: 52 (1770) - *FE* **1**: 87.
Cr (W, C, E) - *MAP 1040*
*Shallow fresh water, streams, ditches, marshes,
seasonally wet places, damp grassland; 0-200m.*
Crete (sporadic) [almost throughout Europe].

4. R. pulcher L., *Sp. pl.*: 336 (1753) - *FE* **1**:
87.
Cr (W, C, E) Ks Kp Sa - *MAP 1041*
a. subsp. **anodontus** (Hausskn.) Rech.f. in
Beih. bot. Zbl. **49(2)**: 34 (1932) - *FE* **1**: 87.
Cr - *NOT MAPPED*
Crete [Aegean region; otherwise N. Africa &
S.W. Asia].
b. subsp. **pulcher**
Cr (W) Kp - *MAP 1042*
Calcareous rocks.
W. Crete; Karpathos [mainly W. & S. Europe].
c. subsp. **raulinii** (Boiss.) Rech.f. in *Beih. bot.
Zbl.* **49(2)**: 39 (1932) - *FE* **1**: 87.
Cr (W) - *MAP 1043*
Rocky places; -500m.
W. Crete [Bulgaria, Greece & Aegean region;
otherwise E. Aegean Islands & Turkey].
d. subsp. **woodsii** (De Not.) Arcang., *Comp. fl.
ital.*: 585 (1882) - *FE* **1**: 87 as subsp.
divaricatus (L.) Murb.
Cr (W, C, E) Kp - *MAP 1044*
*Scrub, marshes, damp places, ditches, sandy
places, flat clayey areas; 0-1400m.*
Crete (sporadic); Karpathos [S. Europe].
The species sensu lato occurs mainly in W. &
C. Crete and also in Kasos & Saria.

5. R. tuberosus L., *Sp. pl.* ed.2: 481 (1762) -
FE **1**: 84.
a. subsp. **creticus** Rech.f. in *Candollea* **12**: 30
(1949) - *FE* **1**: 84.
Cr (W, C, E) Ks Kp - *MAP 1045*
*Calcareous rocky places & crevices; 0-1450m;
fl. 3-4.*
Crete (widespread); Kasos, Karpathos [Greece
& Aegean region; otherwise E. Aegean Islands
& W. Turkey].
Erroneously regarded as absent from the Cretan
area in *FE* (Greuter, 1974: 140).

Hybrid:

R. conglomeratus x **R. pulcher** subsp. **woodsii**
Ditches.
W. Crete (S.W. of Hania).
Recorded by Rechinger (1943*b*: 65).

PORTULACACEAE

1. Montia L.

1. M. minor C.C.Gmel., *Fl. bad.* **1**: 301 (1805)
- *FE* **1**: 115 as *M. fontana* subsp.
chondrosperma (Fenzl) Walters.
Cr (W) - *MAP 1046*
*Muddy gravel in running water near a spring;
1050m.*
W. Crete (Omalos plain in Lefka Ori) [W., C.
& S. Europe].

Recorded since *FE* (Greuter, 1973a: 30).

2. Portulaca L.

1. P. oleracea L., *Sp. pl.*: 445 (1753) - *FE* **1**: 114.
a. subsp. **oleracea**
Cr (W, C, E) Kp - *MAP 1047*
Bare disturbed ground, occasionally cultivated as a salad plant; 0-100m; fl. 8-10.
Mainly W. & C. Crete; Karpathos [mainly C. & S. Europe].
Erroneously regarded as absent from the Cretan area in *FE* (Greuter, 1974: 140). Doubtfully native in Europe (*Atlas FE* **5**: 108).

PRIMULACEAE

1. Anagallis L.

1. A. arvensis L., *Sp. pl.*: 148 (1753) - *FE* **3**: 28.
Cr (W, C, E) Ks Kp Sa - *MAP 1048*
Olive groves, open rocky & sandy places, gorge-beds, Lygeum steppe, cultivated & fallow land; 0-700m; fl. 3-5.
Mainly W. & C. Crete; Karpathos group [almost throughout Europe].
Subsp. *latifolia* (L.) Arcang. is given for the Cretan area in *M-Ch* **4**: 370, but as doubtfully distinct from subsp. *arvensis*; it is not separated here.

2. A. foemina Mill., *Gard. Dict.* ed.8: no.2 (1768) - *FE* **3**: 28.
Cr (W, C) - *MAP 1049*
W. & C. Crete [W., C. & S. Europe].

3. A. tenella (L.) L., *Syst. veg.* ed.13: 165 (1774) - *FE* **3**: 28.
Cr (W) - *MAP 1050*
Marshy places, moist shady rocks.
W. Crete (Agia lake & Fasas valley) [mainly W. Europe].

2. Asterolinon Hoffmanns. & Link

1. A. linum-stellatum (L.) Duby in DC., *Prodr.* **8**: 68 (1844) - *FE* **3**: 27.
Cr (W, C, E) Ks Kp - *MAP 1051*
Bare soil-patches in phrygana, sandy places near coast; 0-850m; fl. 4-5.
Mainly W. & C. Crete; Kasos, Karpathos [W. & S. Europe].

3. Cyclamen L.

●**1. C. creticum** (Dörfl.) Hildebr. in *Beih. bot. Zbl.* **19(2)**: 367 (1906) - *FE* **3**: 25.
Cr (W, C, E) Kp - *MAP 1052*

Woodland, maquis, scrub, stream-banks, shady rocky places, screes; 0-1050m; fl. 3-5.
Mainly W. Crete; Karpathos - Endemic.
Recorded from Karpathos since *FE* (Greuter et al., 1983a: 65). Given for Cyprus - as an introduction - in *M-Ch* **4**: 376.

2. C. graecum Link in *Linnaea* **9**: 573 (1835) - *FE* **3**: 25.
Cr (W, C, E) - *MAP 1053*
Calcareous rocky places & crevices; 0-600m; fl. 8-11.
Mainly W. Crete [Greece & Aegean region; otherwise S.W. Asia].

? C. hederifolium Aiton, *Hort. kew.* **1**: 196 (1789) - *FE* **3**: 25.
Doubtfully present in Crete (Greuter, 1974: 158) [S. Europe].

3. C. persicum Mill., *Gard. Dict.* ed.8: no.3 (1768) - *FE* **3**: 26.
?Cr Kp - *MAP 1054*
Calcareous rocky slope above maritime cliffs; 60m; fl. 3-4.
?Crete; Karpathos [Algeria, Tunisia & S.W. Asia].
In Europe known with certainty only from Karpathos. A record from the Sideros peninsula in E. Crete (anon., 1989) lacks firm evidence, and all previous Cretan records are very doubtful (Greuter et al., 1984b: 286). Records from Athos in N.E. Greece (as given in *FE*) are erroneous (*M-Ch* **4**: 376).

4. Lysimachia L.

1. L. serpyllifolia Schreb. in *Nova Acta Acad. Caesar. Leop. Carol.* **4**: 144 (1770) - *FE* **3**: 26.
Cr (W, C, E) - *MAP 1055*
Woodland, garigue, rocky places, screes; (10-)550-2200m; fl. 4-8.
Crete (widespread, mainly in mountains) [C. & S. Greece].

5. Primula L.

1. P. vulgaris Huds., *Fl. angl.*: 70 (1762) - *FE* **3**: 16.
a. subsp. **vulgaris**
Cr (W) - *MAP 1056*
Castanea & Platanus woodland, damp banks with ferns, shady & rocky places by streams; 400-600m; fl. 3-4.
W. Crete [most of Europe].

6. Samolus L.

1. S. valerandi L., *Sp. pl.*: 171 (1753) - *FE* **3**: 29.
Cr (W, C, E) Kp - *MAP 1057*

Platanus woodland, springs, marshes, moist rocks, damp bare earth; 0-1700m; fl. 4-10.
Crete (widespread); Karpathos [most of Europe].

PUNICACEAE

1. Punica L.

[**1. P. granatum**] L., *Sp. pl.*: 472 (1753) - *FE* 2: 305.
Cr (W) Ks Kp - *MAP 1058*
Cultivated as a fruit tree and naturalized.
W. Crete; Kasos, Karpathos [S. Europe; from S.W. Asia].

RAFFLESIACEAE

1. Cytinus L.

1. C. hypocistis (L.) L., *Syst. nat.* ed.12, 2: 602 (1767) - *FE* 1: 75.
a. subsp. **clusii** Nyman, *Consp. fl. eur.*: 645 (1881) - *FE* 1: 75 as *C. ruber* Fritsch.
Cr (W, C, E) Ks Kp - *MAP 1059*
Woodland, maquis & garigue, on Cistus creticus; 100-800m; fl. 4-5.
Crete (sporadic); Kasos, Karpathos [Mediterranean region].
Regarded as absent from the Cretan area in *FE*, although previously recorded by Rechinger (1943*b*: 73); cf. Greuter (1973*a*: 34).
b. subsp. **hypocistis** (including subsp. *orientalis* Wettst. - *FE* 1: 75).
Cr (W, C, E) Kp - *MAP 1060*
Woodland, maquis & garigue, on Cistus parviflorus & C. salviifolius; 150-550m; fl. 4-5.
Crete (sporadic); Karpathos [S.W. Europe & Mediterranean region].

RANUNCULACEAE

1. Adonis L.

"*A. aestivalis*" (*FE* 1: 223) = **2a** (Greuter et al., 1984*b*: 286).

1. A. annua L., *Sp. pl.*: 547 (1753) - *FE* 1: 222.
a. subsp. **cupaniana** (Guss.) C.Steinb. in *Webbia* 25: 324 (1971) - *FE* 1: 223, included in synonymy of **2**.
Kp - *MAP 1061*
Cultivated fields; 300m; fl. 3-4.
Karpathos (N. end) [mainly Mediterranean region].
Records of "*A. annua*" from Crete are referable to **2a** (Greuter et al., 1984*b*: 286).

2. A. microcarpa DC., *Syst. nat.* 1: 223 (1817) - *FE* 1: 223.
a. subsp. **cretica** (Huth) Vierh. in *Öst. bot. Z.* **84**: 127 (1935) - not cited in *FE*.
Cr (W, C, E) - *MAP 1062*
Calcareous rocky places, fallow fields, open stony ground; 0-350m; fl. 3-4.
Mainly W. Crete [?Italy, Kiklades; otherwise S.W. Asia].
b. subsp. **microcarpa**
Ks - *MAP 1063*
Cultivated & abandoned terraces; 20-220m.
Kasos [S. Europe].
Given as doubtfully present in Crete by Barclay (1986: 81), but not known to occur there according to Greuter & Raus (1989: 43).

2. Anemone L.

A. blanda Schott & Kotschy is given as doubtfully present in the Cretan area in *FE* 1: 218, although there are no records as a basis for this (Greuter, 1974: 139).

1. A. coronaria L., *Sp. pl.*: 539 (1753) - *FE* 1: 219.
Cr (W, C, E) Kp - *MAP 1064*
Olive groves, fallow & abandoned fields, flat clayey areas; 0-1050m; fl. 2-4.
Mainly W. & C. Crete; Karpathos [Mediterranean region].

2. A. hortensis L., *Sp. pl.*: 540 (1753) - *FE* 1: 219.
a. subsp. **heldreichii** (Boiss.) Rech.f. in *Denkschr. Akad. Wiss. Wien* 105(2,1): 74 (1943) - not cited in *FE*.
Cr (W, C, E) Kp - *MAP 1065*
Calcareous open woodland, olive groves, scrub, garigue, phrygana, rocky places; 0-1850m; fl. 2-4.
Mainly W. Crete; Karpathos.
Also given as occurring in the floristic territory of Greece in *M-Ch* 4: 394, but with no reference to any records from that area. The species is erroneously regarded as absent from the Cretan area in *FE* (Greuter, 1974: 140).

A. pavonina Lam. is given for the Cretan area in *FE* 1: 219, although there are no records as a basis for this (Greuter, 1974: 139).

3. Clematis L.

1. C. cirrhosa L., *Sp. pl.*: 544 (1753) - *FE* 1: 221.
Cr (W, C, E) Ks Kp Sa - *MAP 1066*
Woodland, scrub, rocky places, old dry-stone walls; 0-750m; fl. 10-2(-4).

Crete (widespread); Karpathos group [S. Europe].

●2. **C. elisabethae-carolae** Greuter in *Candollea* **20**: 213 (1965).
Cr (W) - *MAP 1067*
Deep hollows, flutings & crevices in calcareous rocks; 1250-1850m; fl. 6-7.
W. Crete (Lefka Ori) - Endemic.
[Plate 6.] Related to *C. flammula* L.

? C. flammula L., *Sp. pl.*: 544 (1753) - *FE* **1**: 221.
Doubtfully present in Crete (Greuter, 1974: 155) [S. Europe].

C. viticella L. is given for the Cretan area in *FE* **1**: 221, although there are no records as a basis for this (Greuter, 1974: 139).

4. Consolida (DC.) Gray

"*C. ambigua*" (*FE* **1**: 217) = **1** (*Atlas FE* **8**: 70).

1. C. ajacis (L.) Schur in *Verh. Mitt. siebenb. Ver. Naturw.* **4**: 47 (1853) - *FE* **1**: 217 as "*C. ambigua*".
Cr (W) - *MAP 1068*
Bare ground in waste areas; near s.l.; fl. 7.
W. Crete [mainly C. Europe & Mediterranean region].

5. Delphinium L.

1. D. peregrinum L., *Sp. pl.*: 531 (1753) - *FE* **1**: 215.
Cr (W) Kp - *MAP 1069*
Sandy soil in very open phrygana; near s.l.
W. Crete (coast opposite Elafonisi island); Karpathos [C. & E. Mediterranean region].

2. D. staphisagria L., *Sp. pl.*: 531 (1753) - *FE* **1**: 216.
Cr (W, C, E) Kp - *MAP 1070*
Stony Cupressus woodland, rocky gorge-beds, rocky places near streams, among ruined buildings; 0-500m; fl. 4-6.
Mainly W. Crete; Karpathos [Mediterranean region].

6. Garidella L.

1. G. nigellastrum L., *Sp. pl.*: 425 (1753) - *FE* **1**: 210.
Cr (W, C, E) - *MAP 1071*
Olive groves, calcareous rocky garigue; fl. 4-5.
Crete (sporadic) [mainly Spain & France; otherwise S.W. Asia].

2. G. unguicularis Poir., *Encycl., Suppl.* **2**: 709 (1812).
Cr (W, C, E) - *MAP 1072*

Sparsely vegetated ground in olive groves, phrygana; 30-500m; fl. -10.
Crete (sporadic) [S.W. Asia].
Recorded since *FE* (Strid, 1969).

7. Myosurus L.

1. M. minimus L., *Sp. pl.*: 284 (1753) - *FE* **1**: 238.
Cr - *NOT MAPPED*
Flat clayey areas in dolines, periodically waterlogged.
Crete [most of Europe].
Recorded since *FE* (Egli, 1989; 1991: 325).

8. Nigella L.

1. N. arvensis L., *Sp. pl.*: 534 (1753) - *FE* **1**: 209.
a. subsp. **brevifolia** Strid in *Op. bot. Soc. bot. Lund* **28**: 44 (1970).
Cr (W, C) - *MAP 1073*
Cultivated soil in open olive grove; 50m; fl. 6-8.
W. & C. Crete [S. Peloponnisos (Elafonisi island); otherwise E. Aegean Islands (Halki & Rodos)].
Recently recorded from C. Crete, confirming occurrence on the island (Turland, 1992*b*: 162); the two previous collections (both from W. Crete) were made over a century ago.

●2. **N. carpatha** Strid in *Op. bot. Soc. bot. Lund* **28**: 49 (1970).
Ks Kp - *MAP 1074*
Stony slopes with poorly developed phrygana; 20-70m; fl. 5-7.
Kasos, Karpathos - Endemic.

"*N. cretica*" (*FE* **1**: 209) = **1a** (Strid, 1970).

3. N. damascena L., *Sp. pl.*: 534 (1753) - *FE* **1**: 210.
Cr (W, C) - *MAP 1075*
Olive groves, garigue & rocky places; 0-350m; fl. 4-5.
W. & C. Crete [mainly C. & S. Europe].

"*N. degenii*" (*FE* **1**: 209) = **2** (Strid, 1970).

4. N. doerfleri Vierh. in *Magy. bot. Lap.* **25**: 147 (1926) - *FE* **1**: 210.
Cr (W, C, E) - *MAP 1076*
Calcareous rocky garigue, phrygana, flat clayey areas; 50-400m; fl. 4-5.
Crete (sporadic) [S. Aegean region].
The description in *FE* is misleading, having been based on a herbarium sheet mostly made up of **5** (Strid, 1970).

5. N. fumariifolia Kotschy in Unger & Kotschy, *Ins. Cypern.*: 319 (1865) - *FE* **1**: 210.
Cr (C, E) Ks Kp - *MAP 1077*

Phrygana, among stones; 0-100m.
C. & E. Crete; Kasos, Karpathos [Kiklades
(Paros & Andiparos); otherwise ?E. Aegean
Islands (Rodos) & Cyprus].
Recorded from Crete since *FE* (Strid, 1965*b*).
Full distributional details are given by Greuter
(1973*a*: 35). Occurrence in Rodos is considered
doubtful by Carlström (1987: 46).

N. sativa L. (*FE* 1: 210) was historically
recorded as being rarely cultivated (Rechinger,
1943*a*: 179).

6. N. stricta Strid in *Op. bot. Soc. bot. Lund*
28: 48 (1970).
Cr (W) - *MAP 1078*
Between shrubs on maritime sands; fl. 4-5.
W. Crete (S.W. part) [Kithira].

9. Ranunculus L.

? R. aquatilis L., *Sp. pl.*: 556 (1753) - *FE* 1:
237.
Doubtfully present in Crete (Greuter, 1974: 155)
[most of Europe].

1. R. arvensis L., *Sp. pl.*: 555 (1753) - *FE* 1:
230.
Cr (W, C, E) Kp - *MAP 1079*
Cultivated & fallow fields; 400-750m; fl. 4-5.
Crete (sporadic); Karpathos [most of Europe].

2. R. asiaticus L., *Sp. pl.*: 552 (1753) - *FE* 1:
232.
Cr (W, C, E) Ks Kp - *MAP 1080*
*Phrygana, rocky places, cultivated, fallow &
abandoned land; 0-750m; fl. 3-5.*
Crete (widespread, rarer towards E.); Kasos,
Karpathos [S.E. Kiklades; otherwise Libya,
Egypt, Sinai & S.W. Asia].
The majority of plants in Crete have white
flowers, often tinged with pink; less frequent are
yellow-flowered variants, while red are very rare.
In Karpathos, however, the colour variants exist
in more balanced proportions. The species also
occurs as an introduction in Italy and the Ionian
Island of Kefallinia (*M-Ch* **4**: 422; *Atlas FE* **8**:
161).

3. R. brevifolius Ten., *Fl. napol.* **1**: lxviii
(1811-1815) - *FE* 1: 234. (Including subsp.
pindicus (Hausskn.) E.Mayer - *FE* 1: 234.)
Cr (W, C) - *MAP 1081*
*Calcareous rubble & stabilized screes; 1800-
2400m; fl. 4-5.*
W. & C. Crete (Lefka Ori & Psiloritis) [C.
Italy, W. & S. Balkan peninsula].
The species is not divided here, after Davis (in
Davis, 1965: 153) and *MFG* **1**: 222, where it is
stated that the features separating subsp.
brevifolius and subsp. *pindicus* show a wide

range of overlap.

4. R. bulbosus L., *Sp. pl.*: 554 (1753) - *FE* 1:
229.
a. subsp. **aleae** (Willk.) Rouy & Foucaud, *Fl.
France* **1**: 106 (1893) - *FE* 1: 229. (Including *R.
neapolitanus* Ten. - *FE* 1: 229.)
Cr (W, C, E) Kp - *MAP 1082*
*Woodland, stream-banks, ditches, marshes &
other moist shady places; 0-1200m; fl. 3-5.*
Mainly W. Crete; Karpathos [S. Europe].

5. R. bullatus L., *Sp. pl.*: 550 (1753) - *FE* 1:
234.
Cr (W, C, E) Kp - *MAP 1083*
*Calcareous rocky garigue, phrygana, soil-
pockets in & among rocks, stabilized screes; 50-
700m; fl. 10-11.*
Crete (widespread, rarer towards E.); Karpathos
[Mediterranean region].

6. R. chius DC., *Syst. nat.* **1**: 299 (1817) - *FE*
1: 230.
Cr (W, C) Kp - *MAP 1084*
*Olive groves, scrub, damp places, bare stony &
disturbed ground; 0-1100m; fl. 3-5.*
W. & C. Crete; Karpathos [mainly
Mediterranean region].

7. R. creticus L., *Sp. pl.*: 550 (1753) - *FE* 1:
231.
Cr (W, C, E) Kp - *MAP 1085*
*Calcareous cliffs & shady rocky places; 0-
1300m; fl. 3-4.*
Crete (widespread, rarer towards E.); Karpathos
[Kiklades; otherwise E. Aegean Islands & S.W.
Turkey].

●**8. R. cupreus** Boiss. & Heldr. in Boiss.,
Diagn. pl. orient. ser.1, **8**: 3 (1849) - *FE* 1:
231.
Cr (W, C, E) Kp - *MAP 1086*
*Calcareous rock-crevices & ledges, soil-pockets
among rocks, screes, open stony ground; 0-
2200m; fl. 3-5.*
Crete (sporadic); Karpathos (Kalilimni) -
Endemic.
Recorded here as new for Karpathos.

"*R. demissus*" (*FE* 1: 229) = **3**, according to
Barclay (1986: 82), but see note under *R.
sartorianus*.

9. R. ficaria L., *Sp. pl.*: 550 (1753) - *FE* 1:
233.
a. subsp. **chrysocephalus** P.D.Sell in *Bot. J.
Linn. Soc.* **106**: 117 (1991).
Cr (W, C, E) - *MAP 1087*
*Woodland, olive groves, cultivated & fallow
fields, damp ground; 0-1050m; fl. 2-4.*
Mainly W. Crete [Greece; otherwise Cyprus].
Differs from subsp. *ficariiformis* (F.W.Schultz)

Rouy & Foucaud (*FE* 1: 234), to which Cretan plants were previously referred, in its lack of axillary bulbils and even more showy appearance (Sell, 1991).

10. R. ficarioides Bory & Chaub., *Nouv. fl. Pélop.*: 34 (1838) - *FE* 1: 234.
Kp - *MAP 1088*
Beneath Acer & Crataegus bushes, soil-pockets among calcareous rocks, flat clayey areas, abandoned fields; 700-1215m; fl. 3-4.
Karpathos [C. & S. Greece; otherwise S.W. Asia].
Regarded as absent from the Cretan area in *FE*, although previously recorded by Rechinger (1943a: 185); cf. Greuter et al. (1983a: 66).

11. R. gracilis E.D.Clarke, *Travels* 2(2): 336 (1814) - *FE* 1: 230.
Cr (W, C) Kp - *MAP 1089*
Calcareous woodland, garigue, rock-crevices, soil-pockets among rocks, abandoned fields; 100-1850m; fl. 3-5.
Mainly W. Crete; Karpathos [mainly Italy & Balkan peninsula].

12. R. lateriflorus DC., *Syst. nat.* 1: 251 (1817) - *FE* 1: 236.
Cr (W) - *MAP 1090*
Damp ground, flooded in winter; 1050m.
W. Crete (Omalos plain in Lefka Ori) [C., S.E. & S. Europe].

13. R. marginatus d'Urv. in *Mém. Soc. linn. Paris* 1: 318 (1822) - *FE* 1: 230.
Cr (W, C, E) Kp - *MAP 1091*
Marshes & other wet places; 0-750m; fl. 3-5.
Crete (sporadic); Karpathos [mainly Mediterranean region].

14. R. muricatus L., *Sp. pl.*: 555 (1753) - *FE* 1: 230.
Cr (W, C, E) Kp - *MAP 1092*
Olive groves, marshy places, ditches, moist bare ground; 0-750m; fl. 3-5.
Mainly W. Crete; Karpathos [S. Europe].

R. neapolitanus Ten. (*FE* 1: 229) is included in synonymy of **4a**.

15. R. ophioglossifolius Vill., *Hist. pl. Dauphiné* 3(2): 731 (1789) - *FE* 1: 235.
Cr (W) - *MAP 1093*
Marshes; fl. 3-5.
W. Crete [mainly S. Europe].
Additionally recorded from W./C. Crete in *Atlas FE* 8: 200.

16. R. paludosus Poir., *Voy. Barbarie* 2: 184 (1789) - *FE* 1: 231.
Cr (W, C, E) Kp - *MAP 1094*
Rocky places, flat clayey areas, abandoned

fields, bare soil, often damp in winter; 50-1050m; fl. 3-5.
Mainly W. Crete; Karpathos [W. Europe & Mediterranean region].

17. R. peltatus Schrank, *Baier. Fl.* 2: 103 (1789) - *FE* 1: 237.
Cr (W) Kp - *MAP 1095*
a. subsp. **fucoides** (Freyn) Muñoz Garm. in *An. Inst. bot. A.J.Cavanilles* 41: 477 (1985) - *FE* 1: 237, included in synonymy of *R. baudotii* Godr.
Fresh water.
W. Crete (Omalos plain in Lefka Ori) [Mediterranean region].
The species sensu lato occurs also in Karpathos.

●**18. R. radinotrichus** Greuter & Strid in *Willdenowia* 11: 267 (1981).
Cr (W) - *MAP 1096*
Calcareous cliffs, crevices, screes & fine rocky debris, facing N. to E.; 1850-2300m; fl. 4-7.
W. Crete (Lefka Ori) - Endemic.
[Plate 6.] Possibly related to *R. fenzlii* Boiss. from S.E. Turkey (Greuter & Strid, op. cit.)

R. rumelicus Griseb. is recorded from E. Crete in *Atlas FE* 8: 149, but with no further details. It otherwise occurs in the Balkan peninsula, E. Aegean Islands, Turkey and Cyprus.

R. saniculifolius Viv. (Greuter, 1973a: 35; Greuter et al., 1983a: 66) = **17**.

"*R. sardous*" (*FE* 1: 230) = **13** (*Atlas FE* 8: 141).

R. sartorianus Boiss. & Heldr. is given as doubtfully present in Crete in *MFG* 1: 216 and *Atlas FE* 8: 131, based on an old record of "*R. demissus*" (Rechinger, 1943a: 192). However, the same record is referred to **3** by Barclay (1986: 82).

19. R. sprunerianus Boiss., *Diagn. pl. orient.* ser.1, 1: 64 (1843) - *FE* 1: 231.
Cr (W, C, E) Kp - *MAP 1097*
Calcareous garigue, soil-pockets among rocks, cultivated & fallow fields; 700-1650m; fl. 4-5.
Crete (in mountains); Karpathos [Balkan peninsula & S. Aegean region].

20. R. subhomophyllus (Halácsy) Vierh. in *Öst. bot. Z.* 84: 131 (1935) - *FE* 1: 231.
Cr (W, C, ?E) ?Kp - *MAP 1098*
Calcareous rocky places & crevices, shady soil-pockets in rocks; 1300-1700m; fl. 4.
Crete (Lefka Ori, Psiloritis & ?Afendis Kavousi); ?Karpathos (Kalilimni) [Peloponnisos; otherwise E. Aegean Islands (Samos)].
Records from Afendis Kavousi and Kalilimni require confirmation, since they are possibly the

result of confusion with the similar **8**, which occurs commonly at both localities.

21. R. trichophyllus Chaix, *Pl. Vap.*: 31 (1785) - *FE* **1**: 237.
a. subsp. **trichophyllus**
Cr (W, C, E) - *MAP 1099*
Still & slow-moving fresh water; 200-900m; fl. 4-5.
Crete (sporadic) [almost throughout Europe].

22. R. velutinus Ten., *Semina* **1825**: 12 (1825) - *FE* **1**: 226.
Cr (W) - *MAP 1100*
Marshes & damp ground near sea; fl. 4-5.
W. Crete [Mediterranean region].
Given by Greuter (1974: 155) as almost certainly recorded in error, but occurrence since confirmed by Turland (1992*a*: 352).

Thalictrum minus L. is given for the Cretan area in *FE* **1**: 241, although there are no records as a basis for this (Greuter, 1974: 139).

RESEDACEAE

1. Reseda L.

1. R. alba L., *Sp. pl.*: 449 (1753) - *FE* **1**: 347.
Cr (W, C) Ks Kp - *MAP 1101*
Fallow fields, banks, old walls; 0-450m; fl. 3-4.
W. & C. Crete; Kasos, Karpathos [mainly S. Europe].

R. arabica Boiss. (*FE* **1**: 349) was almost certainly recorded in error (Greuter, 1974: 156).

2. R. lutea L., *Sp. pl.*: 449 (1753) - *FE* **1**: 348.
a. subsp. **lutea**
Cr (W, C, E) Ks Kp - *MAP 1102*
Rocky & sandy places, roadsides, waste areas; fl. 4.
Crete (sporadic); Kasos, Karpathos [W., C. & S. Europe].

3. R. luteola L., *Sp. pl.*: 448 (1753) - *FE* **1**: 347.
Cr (W, C, E) Kp - *MAP 1103*
Garigue, rocky & sandy places, bare ground; 0-600m; fl. 4.
Mainly W. & C. Crete; Karpathos [W., C. & S. Europe].

"*R. orientalis*" (*FE* **1**: 348) = **4** (*M-Ch* **4**: 450).

4. R. odorata L., *Syst. nat.* ed.10, **2**: 1046 (1759) - *FE* **1**: 348.
Cr (W) - *MAP 1104*
Karstic ground.
W. Crete (Gavdos island) [C. & S. Europe].

RHAMNACEAE

1. Rhamnus L.

1. R. alaternus L., *Sp. pl.*: 193 (1753) - *FE* **2**: 244.
a. subsp. **alaternus**
Cr (W, C) Kp - *MAP 1105*
Scrub, gorges.
W. & C. Crete; Karpathos [Mediterranean region].
Erroneously regarded as absent from the Cretan area in *FE* (Greuter, 1974: 140).

2. R. lycioides L., *Sp. pl.* ed.2: 279 (1762) - *FE* **2**: 244.
Subsp. *graeca* (Boiss. & Reut.) Tutin (Barclay, 1986: 83) was recorded in error (Greuter in Greuter & Rechinger, 1967: 67).
a. subsp. **oleoides** (L.) Jahand. & Maire, *Cat. pl. Maroc.* **2**: 476 (1932) - *FE* **2**: 244.
(Including *R. oleoides* subsp. *microphylla* (Halácsy) P.H.Davis - not cited in *FE*.)
Cr (W, C, E) Ks Kp Sa - *MAP 1106*
Quercus coccifera woodland, garigue, calcareous cliffs & rocky places; 0-1250m; fl. 4-5.
Crete (widespread); Karpathos group [Mediterranean region].

R. oleoides subsp. *microphylla* (Halácsy) P.H.Davis (Barclay, 1986: 83) is included in synonymy of **2a**.

R. prunifolia Sm. (*FE* **2**: 245) = **3a**.

3. R. saxatilis Jacq., *Enum. stirp. Vindob.*: 39 (1762) - *FE* **2**: 244.
a. subsp. **prunifolia** (Sm.) Aldén in Strid, *Mount. Fl. Greece* **1**: 586 (1986) - *FE* **2**: 245 as *R. prunifolia* Sm.
Cr (W, C, E) - *MAP 1107*
Calcareous open rocky places; 1400-2200m.
Crete (Lefka Ori, Psiloritis & Dikti) [Jugoslavia, Greece; otherwise E. Aegean Islands (Lesvos & Hios)].
Recorded from two localities at lower altitudes (possibly as low as 300m) in *MFG* **1**: 586.

Zizyphus jujuba Mill. (*FE* **2**: 243) = *Z. zizyphus*.

Z. zizyphus (L.) Meikle (*FE* **2**: 243 as *Z. jujuba* Mill.) occurs in Crete as a casual relic of cultivation.

ROSACEAE

1. Agrimonia L.

1. A. eupatoria L., *Sp. pl.*: 448 (1753) - *FE* **2**:

32.
Kp - *MAP 1108*
Karpathos [almost throughout Europe].
Recorded since *FE* (Greuter, 1974: 148).

2. Amelanchier Medik.

1. A. ovalis Medik., *Gesch. Bot.*: 79 (1793) -
FE 2: 71.
a. subsp. **cretica** (Willd.) Maire & Petitm.,
Etud. pl. vasc. Grèce: 80 (1908) - *FE* 2: 71 as
A. ovalis var. *cretica* (Willd.) Fiori.
Cr (C) - *MAP 1109*
Calcareous cliffs; 1500m.
C. Crete (Psiloritis) [Sicily & Greece].
Additionally recorded from the Lefka Ori in W.
Crete in *MFG* 1: 437.

3. Aphanes L.

1. A. arvensis L., *Sp. pl.*: 123 (1753) - *FE* 2:
64.
Cr (W, C) Kp - *MAP 1110*
*Calcareous rocky phrygana, exposures of bare
soil; 500-700m.*
W. & C. Crete; Karpathos [W., C. & S.
Europe].

4. Cotoneaster Medik.

1. C. nummularia Fisch. & C.A.Mey., *Index
sem. hort. petrop.* 2: 34 (1836) - *FE* 2: 73.
Cr (W, C, E) - *MAP 1111*
*Calcareous open scrub on rocky slopes & in
ravines; 1300-1800m; fl. 5-6.*
Crete (Lefka Ori, Kedros, Dikti & Afendis
Kavousi) [S.W. Asia].
Additionally recorded from Psiloritis in C. Crete
in *MFG* 1: 440.

5. Crataegus L.

1. C. azarolus var. **aronia** L., *Sp. pl.*: 477
(1753) - *FE* 2: 77.
Cr (W, C) - *MAP 1112*
*Scrub, occasionally as isolated trees in
phrygana; 20-650m; fl. 4.*
Mainly C. Crete [S.W. Asia].
The species occurs elsewhere in S. Europe as
var. *azarolus*, which is cultivated for its edible
fruits and is locally naturalized. There appear to
be no records from the Cretan area which
unambiguously refer to var. *azarolus*.

"*C. heldreichii*" (*FE* 2: 76) = **2b** (Barclay,
1986: 84).

"*C. laciniata*" (*FE* 2: 77) = **2b** (Barclay, 1986:
84).

2. C. monogyna Jacq., *Fl. austriac.* 3: 50
(1775) - *FE* 2: 75.
●**a.** subsp. **aegeica** (Pojark.) Franco in *Feddes
Reprium* **79**: 37 (1968) - *FE* 2: 76.
Kp - *MAP 1113*
*Calcareous scrub & garigue, occasionally
forming small stands of stunted trees; 700-950m.*
Karpathos (Kalilimni) - ?Endemic [possibly in
N. Aegean region (Thasos) & E. Aegean islands
(Ikaria)].
According to Byatt (1976: 290), Greuter
considers the populations in Karpathos to be
distinct, since all plants there are similar and
have many distinct characters. Byatt, however,
is not convinced that they vary from other plants
of *C. monogyna* sufficiently to justify their
separation.
b. subsp. **azarella** (Griseb.) Franco in *Collnea
bot. Barcinone* 7: 471 (1968) - *FE* 2: 76.
Cr (W, C, E) - *MAP 1114*
*Cupressus woodland, rocky places, gorge-beds,
field-margins; 100-1500m; fl. 3-4.*
Mainly W. & C. Crete [Spain, Italy, Sicily, &
S.E. Europe].

Eriobotrya japonica (Thunb.) Lindl. (*FE*: 71)
is probably only cultivated.

6. Potentilla L.

1. P. reptans L., *Sp. pl.*: 499 (1753) - *FE* 2:
45.
Cr (W, C, E) - *MAP 1115*
Marshy places, springs; 0-400m.
Crete (sporadic) [almost throughout Europe].

2. P. speciosa Willd., *Sp. pl.*: 2: 1110 (1800) -
FE 2: 46.
Cr (W, C, E) - *MAP 1116*
Calcareous cliffs & rock-crevices; 1500-2100m.
Crete (Lefka Ori, rarer in Psiloritis & Dikti)
[W. & S. Balkan peninsula].

7. Prunus L.

P. armeniaca L. (*FE* 2: 78) is cultivated only.

P. dulcis (Mill.) D.A.Webb (*FE* 2: 78) is
probably only cultivated.

P. persica (L.) Batsch (*FE* 2: 78) is cultivated
only.

1. P. prostrata Labill., *Icon. pl. Syr.* 1: 15
(1791) - *FE* 2: 79.
Cr (W, C, E) - *MAP 1117*
*Calcareous open rocky slopes, flat clayey areas;
1300-2300m; fl. 4-6.*
Crete (Lefka Ori, Kedros, Psiloritis, Dikti &
Afendis Kavousi) [Mediterranean region].

2. P. webbii (Spach) Vierh. in *Öst. bot. Z.* **65**: 21 (1915) - *FE* **2**: 78.
Cr (W, C, E) Kp - *MAP 1118*
Olive groves, calcareous cliffs & rocky places; 0-900m; fl. 2-3.
Mainly W. & C. Crete; Karpathos [S. Italy & Balkan peninsula].

8. Pyrus L.

P. amygdaliformis Vill. (*FE* **2**: 66) = **2**.

[1. P. communis] L., *Sp. pl.*: 479, 1200 (1753) - *FE* **2**: 66.
Cr Kp - *NOT MAPPED*
Cultivated as a fruit tree and possibly naturalized.
Crete; Karpathos [most of Europe].
Recorded by Rechinger (1943a: 308-309, b: 91) and Greuter et al. (1983a: 66).

2. P. spinosa Forssk., *Fl. aegypt.-arab.*: 27 (1775) - *FE* **2**: 66 as *P. amygdaliformis* Vill.
Cr (W, C, E) Kp - *MAP 1119*
Woodland, olive groves, maquis, scrub, garigue, rocky places, flat clayey areas, field-margins; 0-1500m; fl. 3-4.
Crete (widespread); Karpathos [Mediterranean region].
Wild individuals are frequently used as a grafting stock for various cultivated fruit trees.

9. Rosa L.

1. R. agrestis Savi, *Fl. pis.* **1**: 475 (1798) - *FE* **2**: 31.
Cr (E) - *MAP 1120*
Heavily grazed phrygana, pebbly alluvial soil in gorge; 950-1100m.
E. Crete (Dikti) [most of Europe].
Regarded as absent from the Cretan area in *FE*, although previously recorded by Rechinger (1943a: 306); occurrence since confirmed by Greuter et al. (1984b: 287).

2. R. canina L., *Sp. pl.*: 491 (1753) - *FE* **2**: 29. (Including *R. corymbifera* Borkh. - *FE* **2**: 30.)
Cr (C, E) - *MAP 1121*
Scrub, calcareous rocky places; 750-1000m; fl. 4-5.
C. & E. Crete [almost throughout Europe].

R. corymbifera Borkh. (*FE* **2**: 30) is included in synonymy of **2**.

3. R. dumalis Bechst., *Forstbot.*: 939 (1810), emend. Boulenger in *Bull. Soc. r. Bot. Belg.* **59**:

113 (1927) - *FE* **2**: 30 as *R. caesia* Sm.
a. subsp. **dumalis**
Cr (W) - *MAP 1122*
Calcareous cliffs; 1750m.
W. Crete (Lefka Ori) [mainly C. Europe].
Recorded since *FE* (Greuter et al., 1984b: 287).

R. glutinosa Sm. (*FE* **2**: 32) = **5**.

4. R. heckeliana Tratt., *Rosac. monogr.* **2**: 85 (1823) - *FE* **2**: 31.
a. subsp. **heckeliana**
Cr (W) - *NOT MAPPED*
W. Crete (Lefka Ori) [Sicily & Balkan peninsula].

R. moschata Herrm. (*FE* **2**: 27) was almost certainly recorded in error (Greuter, 1974: 157).

? R. pouzinii Tratt., *Rosac. monogr.* **2**: 112 (1823) - *FE* **2**: 29.
Doubtfully present in Crete (Greuter, 1974: 157) [Mediterranean region].

5. R. pulverulenta M.Bieb., *Fl. taur.-caucas.* **1**: 399 (1808) - *FE* **2**: 32 as *R. glutinosa* Sm.
Cr (W) - *MAP 1123*
Calcareous rocky places; 1700m.
W. Crete (Lefka Ori) [C. & E. Mediterranean region].
Additionally recorded from Psiloritis in C. Crete in *MFG* **1**: 398.

6. R. sempervirens L., *Sp. pl.*: 492 (1753) - *FE* **2**: 27.
Cr (W, C) - *MAP 1124*
Woodland, scrub, maquis; 50-550m; fl. 4-6.
W. & C. Crete [S.W. Europe & Mediterranean region].

Hybrid:

R. heckeliana x R. pulverulenta
W. Crete (Lefka Ori).
Recorded in *MFG* **1**: 399.

10. Rubus L.

"*R. canescens*" (*FE* **2**: 17) = **1** (Barclay, 1986: 85).

1. R. sanctus Schreb., *Icon. descr. pl.* **1**: 15 (1766) - not cited in *FE*. (Including *R. ulmifolius* Schott - *FE* **2**: 15.)
Cr (W, C, E) Kp - *MAP 1125*
Woodland, scrub, hedges, stream-banks, ditches, roadsides; 0-1050m; fl. 5-7.
Crete (widespread, rarer in E.); Karpathos [W., C. & S. Europe].

R. ulmifolius Schott (*FE* **2**: 15) is included in synonymy of **1**.

11. Sanguisorba L.

●**1. S. cretica** Hayek in *Öst. bot. Z.* **64**: 358 (1914) - *FE* 2: 34.
Cr (W) - *MAP 1126*
Calcareous cliffs; 50-1200m; fl. 5-6.
W. Crete (S. side) - Endemic.

2. S. minor Scop., *Fl. carniol.* ed.2, **1**: 110 (1772) - *FE* 2: 34.
Cr (W, C, E) Ks Kp Sa - *MAP 1127*.
a. subsp. **muricata** (Spach) Briq., *Prodr. fl. Corse* **2**(1): 210 (1913) - *FE* 2: 34.
Cr (W, C, E) - *MAP 1128*
Olive groves, vineyards, flat clayey areas; 50-1400m; fl. 4.
Crete (sporadic) [mainly C. & S. Europe].
b. subsp. **verrucosa** (Ehrenb. ex Decne.) Holmboe in *Bergens Mus. Skr.* ser.2, **1**(2): 100 (1914) - *FE* 2: 34 as subsp. *magnolii* (Spach) Briq.
Cr (W, C) Ks Kp Sa - *MAP 1129*
Olive groves, grassy roadsides, areas of cultivation; 0-800m; fl. 4-5.
W. & C. Crete; Karpathos group [Mediterranean region].

12. Sarcopoterium Spach

1. S. spinosum (L.) Spach in *Annls Sci. nat.* ser.3 (Bot.), **5**: 43 (1846) - *FE* 2: 34.
Cr (W, C, E) Ks Kp Sa - *MAP 1130*
Garigue, phrygana; 0-2000m; fl. 3-5.
Crete (widespread); Karpathos group [Mediterranean region].

13. Sorbus L.

1. S. aria (L.) Crantz, *Stirp. austr. fasc.* **2**: 46 (1763) - *FE* 2: 68.
a. subsp. **cretica** (Lindl.) Holmboe in *Bergens Mus. Skr.* ser.2, **1**(2): 100 (1914) - *FE* 2: 68 as *S. graeca* (Spach) Kotschy.
Cr (W) - *MAP 1131*
Calcareous cliffs; 1750-1900m.
W. Crete (Lefka Ori) [Mediterranean region].

S. graeca (Spach) Kotschy (*FE* 2: 68) = **1a**.

2. S. umbellata (Desf.) Fritsch in *Sched. Flor. exsicc. Austro-Hung.* **7**: 18 (1896) - *FE* 2: 69.
a. subsp. **umbellata**
Cr (C, E) - *MAP 1132*
Calcareous cliffs, one occurrence on a vineyard terrace; 900-1500m.
C. & E. Crete (Kedros, Psiloritis, Kofinas, Dikti & Afendis Kavousi) [Balkan peninsula & Romania].
Recorded since *FE* (Greuter et al., 1984*b*: 288).

A putative hybrid between the two species, recorded from the Lefka Ori in *MFG* **1**: 435, is considered doubtful by Greuter et al. (1984*b*: 288).

RUBIACEAE

1. Asperula L.

1. A. arvensis L., *Sp. pl.*: 103 (1753) - *FE* **4**: 13.
Cr (E) - *MAP 1133*
Cultivated & fallow fields; 850-1100m; fl. 5-6.
E. Crete (Dikti) [most of Europe].
Recorded since *FE* (Greuter et al., 1984*b*: 288).

●**2. A. crassula** Greuter & Zaffran in *Willdenowia* **14**: 289 (1984).
Cr (E) - *MAP 1134*
Calcareous open phrygana on rocky ground with Lygeum spartum; 20-160m; fl. 5.
E. Crete (Sideros peninsula) - Endemic.

A. cynanchica L. is given for the Cretan area in *FE* **4**: 10, although there are no records as a basis for this (Greuter et al., 1984*b*: 289).

●**3. A. idaea** Halácsy, *Consp. fl. graec.* **1**: 737 (1901) - *FE* **4**: 7.
Cr (W, C, E) - *MAP 1135*
Calcareous cliffs, rocky slopes, screes, flat clayey areas, often growing through spiny dwarf shrubs; 1200-2300m; fl. 6-8.
Crete (Lefka Ori, Psiloritis & Dikti) - Endemic.

A. incana Sm. (*FE* **4**: 11) = **4**.

●**4. A. pubescens** (Willd.) Ehrend. & Schönb.-Tem. in Strid & Kit Tan, *Mount. Fl. Greece* **2**: 295 (1991) - *FE* **4**: 11 as *A. incana* Sm.
Cr (W, C, E) - *MAP 1136*
Calcareous cliffs, crevices & rocky places; 0-2000m; fl. 4-5.
Mainly W. & C. Crete - Endemic.

●**5. A. rigida** Sm., *Fl. Graec. prodr.* **1**: 89 (1806) - *FE* **4**: 13.
Cr (W, C, E) - *MAP 1137*
Cliffs & rocky places; 0-1900m; fl. 4.
Crete (widespread) - Endemic.

6. A. taygetea Boiss. & Heldr. in Boiss., *Diagn. pl. orient.* ser.1, **10**: 60 (1849) - *FE* **4**: 11.
Cr (W) - *MAP 1138*
Calcareous cliffs & rock-crevices; 150-250m; fl. 4-5.
W. Crete (Korikos & Rodopos peninsulas) [Peloponnisos, Kithira & Andikithira].

7. A. tournefortii Sieber ex Spreng., *Syst. veg.* **1**: 395 (1824) - *FE* **4**: 13.
Cr (W, C, E) Sa - *MAP 1139*

Calcareous cliffs; 50-800m; fl. 5.
C. & E. Crete, one locality in W. Crete
(Rodopos peninsula); Saria [Kiklades; otherwise
E. Aegean Islands (Halki & Rodos)].

2. Crucianella L.

1. C. angustifolia L., *Sp. pl.*: 108 (1753) - *FE*
4: 4.
Cr (W, E) - *MAP 1140*
Rocky places; 700-1300m.
W. & E. Crete [S. Europe].

2. C. imbricata Boiss., *Diagn. pl. orient.* ser.1,
10: 59 (1849) - *FE* **4**: 4.
Cr - *NOT MAPPED*
Crete [S.W. Asia].

3. C. latifolia L., *Sp. pl.*: 109 (1753) - *FE* **4**: 4.
Cr (W, C, E) Ks Kp - *MAP 1141*
*Pinus brutia woodland, calcareous rocky places,
maritime sands & rocks; 0-600m; fl. 4-6.*
Mainly W. Crete; Kasos, Karpathos [S.
Europe].

4. C. macrostachya Boiss., *Diagn. pl. orient.*
ser.1, **3**: 27 (1843) - *FE* **4**: 4.
Cr (C) - *MAP 1142*
Maritime rocks.
C. Crete [S.W. Asia].

3. Galium L.

G. album Mill. (*FE* **4**: 24) is not known to occur
(cf. Krendl, 1987).

1. G. amorginum Halácsy, *Consp. fl. graec.* **1**:
712 (1901) - *FE* **4**: 26.
Kp - *MAP 1143*
Calcareous rock-crevices & ledges; 200-1100m.
Karpathos [S. Kiklades (Folegandros, Keros &
Amorgos)].
A record from the Lefka Ori in W. Crete
(Greuter, 1973a: 55) is referred to **14** by Krendl
(1987: 147).

2. G. aparine L., *Sp. pl.*: 108 (1753) - *FE* **4**:
35.
Cr (W, C, E) Ks Kp - *MAP 1144*
*Rocky places, weed communities; 0-1200m; fl.
3-5.*
Mainly W. & C. Crete; Kasos, Karpathos
[throughout Europe].

3. G. brevifolium Sm., *Fl. Graec. prodr.* **1**: 95
(1806).
a. subsp. **insulare** Ehrend. & Schönb.-Tem. in
Notes R. bot. Gdn Edinb. **37**: 260 (1979).
Kp - *MAP 1145*
Karpathos [E. Aegean Islands & W. Turkey].
Recorded since *FE* (Ehrendorfer & Schönbeck-
Temesy in Davis, 1982: 841).

4. G. canum Req. ex DC., *Prodr.* **4**: 602
(1830) - *FE* **4**: 34.
a. subsp. **ovatum** Ehrend. in *Öst. bot. Z.* **105**:
256 (1958) - *FE* **4**: 34.
Cr (E) Kp Sa - *MAP 1146*
*Calcareous cliffs, usually coastal, sometimes
beneath overhangs; 0-600m; fl. 7.*
E. Crete (Sideros peninsula); Karpathos, Saria
[E. Aegean Islands & Turkey].
Recorded from Crete since *FE* (Greuter et al.,
1984b: 290).

5. G. citraceum Boiss., *Pl. Taygeti Heldr. exs.*
(1845) - not cited in *FE*.
Cr (W, E) - *MAP 1147*
Rock-crevices; 50-1150m; fl. 6-8.
W. & E. Crete [C. Greece, Evvia & S.
Peloponnisos].
Recorded by Krendl (1987: 39). Belonging to
the *G. mollugo* group, together with species **1**,
8, 11, 14, 17 & **19**.

6. G. debile Desv., *Observ. pl. Angers*: 134
(1818) - *FE* **4**: 21.
Cr (W) - *MAP 1148*
*Shallow fresh water, streams, marshes,
seasonally wet places, damp grassland; 0-300m.*
W. Crete [W. & S. Europe].

7. G. divaricatum Pourr. ex Lam., *Encycl.* **2**:
580 (1788) - *FE* **4**: 36.
Cr (W) - *MAP 1149*
Fallow fields; 1050m.
W. Crete (Omalos plain in Lefka Ori) [mainly
S. Europe].

? **G. elongatum** C.Presl in J.& C.Presl, *Delic.
prag.*: 119 (1822) - *FE* **4**: 21.
Doubtfully present in Crete (Greuter, 1974: 160)
[most of Europe].

●**8. G. extensum** Krendl in *Bot. Chronika* **6-7**:
89 (1987).
Cr (W, C, E) - *MAP 1150*
*Cliffs, stream-banks, roadside banks; 125-
1400m.*
Crete (sporadic) - Endemic.
Belonging to the *G. mollugo* group, together
with species **1, 5, 11, 14, 17** & **19**.

●**9. G. fruticosum** Willd., *Sp. pl.*: **1**: 585
(1798) - *FE* **4**: 20.
Cr (W, C) - *MAP 1151*
*Calcareous cliffs, shady rocks, thicket with
Rubus bushes, garigue; 50-1250(-1800)m; fl. 6.*
W. & C. Crete - Endemic.

10. G. graecum L., *Mant. pl.*: 38 (1767) - *FE*
4: 34.
a. subsp. **graecum**
Cr (W, C, E) - *MAP 1152*
Cliffs, crevices & rocky places, often coastal; 0-

700(-1800)m.
Crete (widespread) [E. Aegean Islands & S.W. Turkey].
●**b.** subsp. **pseudocanum** Ehrend. in *Öst. bot. Z.* **105**: 254 (1958) - *FE* **4**: 34.
Cr (C, E) - *MAP 1153*
Calcareous cliffs & rock-crevices, often coastal; 0-750m.
Mainly E. Crete - Endemic.

11. G. heldreichii Halácsy in *Öst. bot. Z.* **47**: 94 (1897) - *FE* **4**: 23.
Cr (W, C, E) - *MAP 1154*
Scrub; 20-600m.
Crete (sporadic) [Greece & Aegean region; otherwise E. Aegean Islands & W. Turkey].

12. G. incanum Sm., *Fl. Graec. prodr.* **1**: 91 (1806) - *FE* **4**: 29.
●**a.** subsp. **creticum** Ehrend. in *Öst. bot. Z.* **98**: 453 (1951) - *FE* **4**: 29.
Cr (E) - *MAP 1155*
Calcareous rocks, screes & stony ground; 1500-2148m.
E. Crete (Dikti) - Endemic.
Additionally recorded from the Lefka Ori in W. Crete in *MFG* **2**: 323.

●**13. G. incrassatum** Halácsy, *Consp. fl. graec.* **1**: 724 (1901) - *FE* **4**: 35.
Cr (W) - *NOT MAPPED*
W. Crete - Endemic.

●**14. G. incurvum** Sm., *Fl. Graec. prodr.* **1**: 92 (1806) - *FE* **4**: 26.
Cr (W, C) - *MAP 1156*
Calcareous cliffs, rock-crevices, stony slopes, screes, often in garigue of Berberis & Juniperus oxycedrus; 1200-2200m; fl. 8.
W. & C. Crete (Lefka Ori & Psiloritis) - Endemic.

15. G. monachinii Boiss. & Heldr. in Boiss., *Diagn. pl. orient.* ser.1, **10**: 67 (1849) - *FE* **4**: 34.
Cr (W, C, E) Kp - *MAP 1157*
Rocky slopes with open woodland, phrygana; 1100-2100m; fl. 4-5.
Crete (Lefka Ori, Kedros, Psiloritis & Afendis Kavousi); Karpathos [S.E. Greece (Attiki & Salamina)].

16. G. murale (L.) All., *Fl. pedem.* **1**: 8 (1785) - *FE* **4**: 36.
Cr (W, C, E) Ks Kp - *MAP 1158*
Rocky places, bare ground; 0-2100m; fl. 4-5.
Crete (widespread); Kasos, Karpathos [S.W. Europe & Mediterranean region].

17. G. peloponnesiacum Ehrend. & Krendl in *Bot. J. Linn. Soc.* **68**: 271 (1974) - *FE* **4**: 26.
Cr (W) - *MAP 1159*

1400m.
W. Crete (Lefka Ori) [Ionian Islands (Kefallinia), Peloponnisos & Kithira].
Recorded since *FE* (Krendl, 1987: 37).

G. rivale (Sm.) Griseb. (*FE* **4**: 20) was almost certainly recorded in error (Greuter, 1974: 159 as *Asperula rivalis* Sm.)

18. G. rotundifolium L., *Sp. pl.*: 108 (1753) - *FE* **4**: 19.
Cr (W) - *MAP 1160*
Riparian Platanus woodland.
W. Crete (Fasas valley) [W., C. & S. Europe].

19. G. samothracicum Rech.f. in *Beih. Repert. nov. Spec. Regni veg.* **100**: 134 (1938) - *FE* **4**: 24.
Cr (W, C, E) - *MAP 1161*
Calcareous rocky slopes & screes, often among spiny dwarf shrubs; (200-)850-2200m; fl. 6-8.
Crete (mainly Lefka Ori, Psiloritis, Dikti & Afendis Kavousi) [N. Aegean region (Samothraki)].

20. G. setaceum Lam., *Encycl.* **2**: 584 (1788) - *FE* **4**: 34. (Including subsp. *decaisnei* (Boiss.) Ehrend. - *FE* **4**: 34.)
Cr (W, C, E) Kp Sa - *MAP 1162*
Calcareous rocky places & screes, Lygeum steppe; 0-700m; fl. 4.
Mainly W. & E. Crete; Karpathos, Saria [Mediterranean region].

? G. spurium L., *Sp. pl.*: 106 (1753) - *FE* **4**: 35.
Doubtfully present in Crete (Greuter, 1974: 160) [most of Europe].

G. suberosum Sm. was recorded from Crete in error for **Asperula 5** (Ehrendorfer & Krendl in *FE* **4**: 13).

21. G. tricornutum Dandy in *Watsonia* **4**: 47 (1957) - *FE* **4**: 35.
Cr (W, C, E) Ks Kp - *MAP 1163*
Cultivated fields & terraces, maritime sands; 0-500m; fl. 3-5.
Crete (sporadic); Kasos, Karpathos [most of Europe].

22. G. verrucosum Huds. in *Phil. Trans. R. Soc.* **56**: 251 (1767) - *FE* **4**: 35.
Cr Ks - *NOT MAPPED*
Crete; Kasos [C. & S. Europe].

23. G. verticillatum Danthoine ex Lam., *Encycl.* **2**: 585 (1788) - *FE* **4**: 36.
Cr (W, C, E) Kp - *MAP 1164*
Calcareous rocky places; 1000-2150m.
Crete (Lefka Ori, Psiloritis & Dikti); Karpathos [S.E. Europe & Mediterranean region].

4. Putoria Pers.

1. P. calabrica (L.f.) DC., *Prodr.* **4**: 577 (1830) - *FE* **4**: 3.
Cr (W) Kp - *MAP 1165*
Calcareous light woodland, rocky places; 0-2000m; fl. 7-10.
W. Crete; Karpathos [Mediterranean region].

5. Rubia L.

1. R. peregrina L., *Sp. pl.*: 109 (1753) - *FE* **4**: 38.
Cr (W, C, E) Kp - *MAP 1166*
Woodland, maquis; 350-600m.
Mainly W. & C. Crete; Karpathos [W. & S. Europe].

2. R. tenuifolia d'Urv., *Enum. pl. Ponti-Eux.*: 17 (1822) - *FE* **4**: 38.
Cr (C, E) Kp Sa - *MAP 1167*
Garigue, rocky places, gorge-beds, open ground near sea; 0-500m; fl. 4.
C. & E. Crete; Karpathos, Saria [S. Greece & Aegean region].
Both subsp. *tenuifolia* and subsp. *brachypoda* (Boiss.) Ehrend. & Schönb.-Tem. are given for Crete by Ehrendorfer & Schönbeck-Temesy (in Davis, 1982: 859). Further distributional data for the two taxa within the Cretan area are lacking, however, and the species is not divided here.

[3. R. tinctorum] L., *Sp. pl.*: 109 (1753) - *FE* **4**: 38.
Cr (W, E) Kp - *MAP 1168*
Rarely cultivated and locally naturalized in olive groves, on field-margins, near seashore; 0-300m.
W. & E. Crete; Karpathos [C. & S. Europe; from W. & C. Asia].

6. Sherardia L.

1. S. arvensis L., *Sp. pl.*: 102 (1753) - *FE* **4**: 3.
Cr (W, C, E) Ks Kp - *MAP 1169*
Rocky places, cultivated & fallow land; 0-850m; fl. 3-5.
Mainly W. & C. Crete; Kasos, Karpathos [almost throughout Europe].

7. Valantia L.

1. V. aprica (Sm.) Boiss. & Heldr. in Boiss., *Diagn. pl. orient.* ser.1, **10**: 72 (1849) - *FE* **4**: 37.
Cr (W, C, E) - *MAP 1170*
Calcareous rubble & screes, rocky places, flat clayey areas; 1100-2400m; fl. 6.
Crete (Lefka Ori, Psiloritis & Dikti) [S. Albania & Greece].

2. V. hispida L., *Syst. nat.* ed.10, **2**: 1307 (1759) - *FE* **4**: 38.
Cr (W, C, E) Ks Kp Sa - *MAP 1171*
Calcareous rocky places, screes, stony ground beneath cliffs, maritime sands & rocks; 0-350m; fl. 4.
Mainly W. & E. Crete; Karpathos group [Mediterranean region].

3. V. muralis L., *Sp. pl.*: 1051 (1753) - *FE* **4**: 38.
Cr (W, C, E) Ks Kp - *MAP 1172*
Open stony ground, soil-filled hollows, maritime sands & rocks; 0-1600m; fl. 4-5.
Mainly W. Crete; Kasos, Karpathos [Mediterranean region].

RUTACEAE

Haplophyllum buxbaumii (Poir.) G.Don (*FE* **2**: 228) was recorded in error (Greuter, 1974: 156).

1. Ruta L.

1. R. chalepensis L., *Mant. pl.*: 69 (1767) - *FE* **2**: 227.
a. subsp. chalepensis
Cr (W, C, E) Kp ?Sa - *MAP 1173*
Calcareous rocky places & crevices, gorge-beds; 0-600m; fl. 4-5.
Mainly W. Crete; Karpathos, ?Saria [S. Europe].
b. subsp. fumariifolia (Boiss. & Heldr.) Nyman, *Consp. fl. eur.*: 143 (1878) - *FE* **2**: 227 as *R. fumariifolia* Boiss. & Heldr.
Cr (E) Ks Kp - *MAP 1174*
Calcareous rocky places.
E. Crete (Sideros peninsula & Dionisiades islands); Kasos, Karpathos [Kithira & Andikithira].

R. fumariifolia Boiss. & Heldr. (*FE* **2**: 227) = **1b.**

SALICACEAE

Populus alba L. was recorded for the Cretan area - as an introduction - by Greuter (1974: 154); it is probably only planted.

P. nigra L. is erroneously given as native to the Cretan area in *FE* **1**: 55 (Greuter, 1974: 154); it is probably only planted.

1. Salix L.

1. S. alba L., *Sp. pl.*: 1021 (1753) - *FE* 1: 45.
Cr (W, C) - *MAP 1175*
River-banks, streams, marshy places; 0-250m;
fl. 3-4.
W. & C. Crete [most of Europe].
Subsp. *micans* (Andersson) Rech.f. (*FE* 1: 45)
was recorded from W. Crete (W. of Hania) by
Rechinger (1943*b*: 63); other records cannot,
however, be referred to a particular subspecies
with any certainty, and the species is not divided
here. *S. alba* is considered doubtfully native in
Crete in *Atlas FE* 3: 15.

SANTALACEAE

1. Osyris L.

1. O. alba L., *Sp. pl.*: 1022 (1753) - *FE* 1: 70.
Cr (W, C, E) - *MAP 1176*
Scrub, rocky places, gorge-beds; 0-750m; fl. 4.
Crete (widespread) [S. Europe].

2. Thesium L.

1. T. bergeri Zucc. in *Abh. bayer. Akad. Wiss.*
2: 324 (1837) - *FE* 1: 72.
Cr (W, C, E) Ks Kp - *MAP 1177*
Pinus brutia woodland, calcareous rocky places
& screes; 0-2000m; fl. 4-5.
Mainly W. Crete; Kasos, Karpathos [S. Balkan
peninsula & Aegean region].

T. divaricatum Jan ex Mert. & W.D.J.Koch is
given for the Cretan area in *FE* 1: 72, although
there are no records as a basis for this (Greuter,
1974: 139).

2. T. humile Vahl, *Symb. bot.* 3: 43 (1794) -
FE 1: 72.
Cr (W, E) Ks Kp - *MAP 1178*
Calcareous open stony ground; 150-400m.
W. & E. Crete; Kasos, Karpathos
[Mediterranean region].
Additionally recorded from W./C. Crete in *Atlas*
FE 3: 107.

SAXIFRAGACEAE

1. Ribes L.

1. R. uva-crispa L., *Sp. pl.*: 201 (1753) - *FE* 1:
383.
a. subsp. **austro-europaeum** (Bornm.) Bech. in
Reprium Spec. nov. Regni veg. 27: 228 (1930) -
not cited in *FE*.
Cr (C, E) - *MAP 1179*
Calcareous open rocky slopes, mountain
summits & dolines; 1300-1800m.

C. & E. Crete (Kedros, Dikti & Afendis
Kavousi) [S. Europe].

2. Saxifraga L.

1. S. chrysosplenifolia Boiss., *Diagn. pl.*
orient. ser.1, 3: 20 (1843) - *FE* 1: 369.
Cr (W, C, E) - *MAP 1180*
Calcareous woodland, rocky places & crevices;
250-1700m; fl. 3-4.
Mainly W. & C. Crete [S. Balkan peninsula &
Aegean region].

2. S. graeca Boiss., *Fl. orient.* 2: 87 (1872) -
FE 1: 376.
Cr (W) - *MAP 1181*
Mountain ridge, mostly in shelter of Cupressus
trees; 1250-1350m.
W. Crete (Lefka Ori) [S. Italy, Sicily & Balkan
peninsula].
Recorded since *FE* (Greuter, 1973*a*: 42).

3. S. hederacea L., *Sp. pl.*: 405 (1753) - *FE* 1:
370.
Cr (W, C, E) Kp - *MAP 1182*
Caverns, hollows & crevices in calcareous cliffs;
200-1550m; fl. 3-5.
Crete (sporadic); Karpathos [Sicily, Jugoslavia
& Greece].

S. rotundifolia L. (*FE* 1: 369) was recorded in
error (Greuter, 1974: 157).

4. S. tridactylites L., *Sp. pl.*: 404 (1753) - *FE*
1: 370.
Cr (C) Kp - *MAP 1183*
Calcareous rocky places; 700-1777m; fl. 4.
C. Crete (Kedros & Psiloritis); Karpathos
(Kalilimni) [almost throughout Europe].
Additionally recorded from Kofinas in C. Crete
in *MFG* 1: 367.

SCROPHULARIACEAE

1. Antirrhinum L.

[1. A. majus] L., *Sp. pl.*: 617 (1753) - *FE* 3:
223.
Cr (C) Kp - *MAP 1184*
Cultivated for ornament and possibly naturalized
in rocky places; fl. 4-5.
C. Crete; Karpathos [W., C. & S. Europe].
"*A. siculum*" (*FE* 3: 223) = 1 (Barclay, 1986:
89).

2. Bellardia All.

1. B. trixago (L.) All., *Fl. pedem.* 1: 61 (1785)
- *FE* 3: 269.
Cr (W, C, E) Ks Kp - *MAP 1185*

Stony clearings in woodland, olive groves, fallow & abandoned fields, sandy ground near sea; 0-850m; fl. 4-5.
Crete (sporadic); Kasos, Karpathos [S. Europe].

3. Chaenorhinum (DC.) Rchb.

●1. C. idaeum Rech.f. in *Denkschr. Akad. Wiss. Wien* 105(2,1): 111 (1943) - *FE* 3: 226 as *C. minus* subsp. *idaeum* (Rech.f.) R.Fern.
Cr (C, E) - *MAP 1186*
Flat clayey areas, open stony ground; 1700-2200m; fl. 6-7.
C. & E. Crete (Psiloritis & Dikti) - Endemic.

C. minus subsp. *idaeum* (Rech.f.) R.Fern. (*FE* 3: 226) = 1.

C. minus (L.) Lange subsp. *minus* (*FE* 3: 226) is not known to occur (cf. Rechinger, 1943b: 111).

2. C. rubrifolium (Robill. & Castagne ex DC.) Fourr. in *Annls Soc. linn. Lyon* nov. ser., 17: 127 (1869) - *FE* 3: 226.
a. subsp. rubrifolium
Cr (W) - *MAP 1187*
Calcareous rocky debris in gorge-beds; 0-400m; fl. 4-5.
W. Crete (S. side) [Mediterranean region].
Recorded since *FE* (Zaffran, 1976: 157; 1990: 289; Turland, 1992a: 352).

4. Cymbalaria Hill

1. C. longipes (Boiss. & Heldr.) A.Chev. in *Bull. Soc. bot. Fr.* 83: 641 (1937) - *FE* 3: 237.
Cr (W, E) Kp Sa - *MAP 1188*
Calcareous rock-crevices; fl. 3-4.
W. & E. Crete (Korikos & Sideros peninsulas); Karpathos, Saria [S. Aegean region; otherwise S.W. Asia].

2. C. microcalyx (Boiss.) Wettst. in Engl. & Prantl, *Natürl. PflFam.* IV(3b): 58 (1891) - *FE* 3: 238.
a. subsp. dodekanesi Greuter in *Boissiera* 13: 108 (1967) - *FE* 3: 238.
Cr (E) Kp Sa - *MAP 1189*
Calcareous cliffs & rock-crevices, maritime gravel; 0-1200m; fl. 3-7.
E. Crete (Sideros peninsula); Karpathos, Saria [E. Aegean Islands].
Given as doubtfully present in Crete by Barclay (1986: 89), but occurrence since confirmed (Turland, 1992b: 162).
b. subsp. microcalyx
Cr (W) - *MAP 1190*
Calcareous cliffs & rock-crevices, among pebbles on beaches; 0-30m; fl. 3-4.
W. Crete (W. coast) [S. & E. Peloponnisos &

Kithira].
Recorded since *FE* (Greuter, 1975b: 19).

[3. C. muralis] P.Gaertn., B.Mey. & Scherb., *Oekon. Fl. Wetterau* 2: 397 (1800) - *FE* 3: 237.
[a. subsp. muralis]
Cr (W, C) - *MAP 1191*
Naturalized on old walls & pavements; 0-500m; fl. 4-8.
W. & C. Crete [W., C. & S. Europe].

5. Euphrasia L.

1. E. salisburgensis Funck ex Hoppe in *Bot. Taschenb.* 1794: 190 (1794) - *FE* 3: 266.
a. subsp. salisburgensis
Cr (W) - *MAP 1192*
Rocky places; 1800-1900m.
W. Crete (Lefka Ori) [C. & S.E. Europe].

6. Kickxia Dumort.

1. K. commutata (Bernh. ex Rchb.) Fritsch, *Excursionsfl. Oesterreich*: 492 (1897) - *FE* 3: 238.
a. subsp. graeca (Bory & Chaub.) R.Fern. in *Bot. J. Linn. Soc.* 64: 74 (1971) - *FE* 3: 238.
Cr (W, C) Kp - *MAP 1193*
Rocky places; 0-600m.
Mainly W. Crete; Karpathos [S. Balkan peninsula & Aegean region].

2. K. elatine (L.) Dumort., *Fl. belg.*: 35 (1827) - *FE* 3: 238.
a. subsp. sieberi (Rchb.) Hayek in *Beih. Repert. nov. Spec. Regni veg.* 30(2): 144 (1929) - *FE* 3: 238 as subsp. *crinita* (Mabille) Greuter.
Cr (W, C, E) Kp Sa - *MAP 1194*
Olive groves, scrub, rocky & sandy places, fallow fields; 0-1250m; fl. 5.
Crete (sporadic); Karpathos, Saria [S. Europe].

3. K. spuria (L.) Dumort., *Fl. belg.*: 35 (1827) - *FE* 3: 239.
a. subsp. integrifolia (Brot.) R.Fern. in *Bot. J. Linn. Soc.* 64: 74 (1971) - *FE* 3: 239.
Cr (W, C) - *MAP 1195*
Quercus pubescens woodland, olive groves, sparsely vegetated ground; 200-600m.
W. & C. Crete [S. Europe].

7. Linaria Mill.

1. L. chalepensis (L.) Mill., *Gard. Dict.* ed.8: no.12 (1768) - *FE* 3: 231.
Cr (W, C) Kp - *MAP 1196*
Olive groves, cultivated & fallow land; 0-200m; fl. 3-4.
W. & C. Crete; Karpathos [Mediterranean

region].

2. L. micrantha (Cav.) Hoffmanns. & Link, *Fl. portug.* **1**: 258 (1813) - *FE* **3**: 236.
Cr - NOT MAPPED
Crete [Mediterranean region].

3. L. pelisseriana (L.) Mill., *Gard. Dict.* ed.8: no.11 (1768) - *FE* **3**: 232.
Cr (W, C) Ks Kp - MAP 1197
Olive groves, rocky places, fallow fields; 0-1050m; fl. 3-4.
Mainly W. Crete; Kasos, Karpathos [W. Europe & Mediterranean region].

4. L. simplex (Willd.) DC. in Lam. & DC., *Fl. franç.* ed.3, **3**: 588 (1805) - *FE* **3**: 236.
Cr (W, C, E) Kp - MAP 1198
Calcareous rocky debris of gorge-beds, open stony ground; 0-750m; fl. 4.
Crete (sporadic); Karpathos [S. Europe].

5. L. triphylla (L.) Mill., *Gard. Dict.* ed.8: no.2 (1768) - *FE* **3**: 230.
Cr (W) - MAP 1199
W. Crete (Gavdos island) [Mediterranean region].

8. Misopates Raf.

1. M. orontium (L.) Raf., *Autik. bot.*: 158 (1840) - *FE* **3**: 224.
Cr (W, C, E) Ks Kp Sa - MAP 1200
Olive groves, rocky places, cultivated & fallow fields, maritime sands; 0-600m; fl. 3-5.
Crete (sporadic); Karpathos group [W., C. & S. Europe].

9. Odontites Ludw.

1. O. linkii Heldr. & Sart. ex Boiss., *Diagn. pl. orient.* ser.2, **3**: 177 (1856) - *FE* **3**: 268.
a. subsp. **cretica** (Boiss.) Greuter in *Annls Mus. Goulandris* **1**: 51 (1973) - *FE* **3**: 268, included in synonymy of **1**.
Cr (W, C, E) Kp - MAP 1201
Calcareous cliffs & rock-crevices; 50-1900m; fl. 10.
Crete (sporadic); Karpathos [E. Aegean Islands (Halki)].

10. Parentucellia Viv.

1. P. latifolia (L.) Caruel in Parl., *Fl. ital.* **6**: 480 (1885) - *FE* **3**: 269.
a. subsp. **latifolia**
Cr (W, C, E) Kp - MAP 1202
Bare soil-patches in phrygana, fallow & abandoned fields, open sandy ground near sea; 0-1050m; fl. 3-5.

Mainly W. Crete; Karpathos [mainly S. Europe].

2. P. viscosa (L.) Caruel in Parl., *Fl. ital.* **6**: 482 (1885) - *FE* **3**: 269.
Cr (W, C, E) Kp - MAP 1203
Damp ground, fallow & abandoned fields; 0-500m; fl. 4-5.
Crete (sporadic); Karpathos [W. & S. Europe].

11. Scrophularia L.

1. S. auriculata L., *Sp. pl.*: 620 (1753) - *FE* **3**: 219.
Cr (W, C) - MAP 1204
Stream-banks, wet ditches; fl. 4-5.
W. & C. Crete [W. Europe & Mediterranean region].

2. S. heterophylla Willd., *Sp. pl.*: **3**: 274 (1802) - *FE* **3**: 219 as *S. heterophylla* Willd. subsp. *heterophylla*.
Cr (W) - MAP 1205
Calcareous cliffs & steep rocks; 0-400m.
W. Crete (N.W. part) [S. Jugoslavia, Greece & Aegean region].

3. S. lucida L., *Syst. nat.* ed.10, **2**: 1114 (1759) - *FE* **3**: 219.
Cr (W, C, E) Ks Kp - MAP 1206
Cliffs & stony ground beneath, steep banks, rocky places, old walls; 50-2000m; fl. 3-5.
Crete (widespread); Kasos, Karpathos [S.E.France, S.E.Italy, Greece & Aegean region; otherwise S.W. Asia].
Plants from the Cretan area belong to subsp. *filicifolia* (Mill.) Rech.f., which is otherwise known from S. Greece, but which is not, according to *MFG* 2: 192, a well-characterized taxon, either geographically or morphologically. It is not separated here.

4. S. peregrina L., *Sp. pl.*: 621 (1753) - *FE* **3**: 218.
Cr (W, C, E) Ks Kp Sa - MAP 1207
Olive groves, weed communities, rocky places, screes; 0-800m; fl. 3-5.
Mainly W. Crete; Karpathos group [Mediterranean region].

12. Sibthorpia L.

1. S. europaea L., *Sp. pl.*: 631 (1753) - *FE* **3**: 252.
Cr (W) - MAP 1208
Small humid valleys in shade of Castanea trees, damp banks with ferns, on non-calcareous substrata; 400-600m.
W. Crete [W. Europe & Greece].

13. Verbascum L.

● **1. V. arcturus** L., *Sp. pl.*: 178 (1753) - *FE* **3**: 209.
Cr (W, C) - *MAP 1209*
Calcareous cliffs, old stone walls; 0-900m; fl. 3-5.
Mainly W. Crete - Endemic.

2. V. macrurum Ten., *Fl. neapol. prodr. app. quinta*: 9 (1826) - *FE* **3**: 211.
Cr (W, C, E) - *MAP 1210*
Open hillsides & rocky places, flat clayey areas, roadsides, waste areas; 0-1050m; fl. 4-8.
Crete (widespread, rarer towards E.) [S. Italy, Sicily & S. Greece].

? V. mucronatum Lam., *Encycl.* **4**: 218 (1797) - *FE* **3**: 214.
Doubtfully present in Crete [Turkey-in-Europe; otherwise E. Aegean Islands (Lesvos) & Turkey].

3. V. sinuatum L., *Sp. pl.*: 178 (1753) - *FE* **3**: 213.
Cr (W, C, E) Ks Kp - *MAP 1211*
Olive groves, fallow fields, roadsides, waste areas; 0-600m; fl. 5-6.
Crete (widespread); Kasos, Karpathos [S. Europe].

● **4. V. spinosum** L., *Cent. pl.* **2**: 10 (1756) - *FE* **3**: 208.
Cr (W, E) - *MAP 1212*
Garigue, phrygana, dwarf shrub communities, rocky & open gravelly places, screes, flat clayey areas; 0-2200m; fl. 5-8.
W. Crete, one record from E. Crete - Endemic.

Hybrids:

V. macrurum x V. sinuatum
Roadside.
W. Crete.
Recorded by Greuter (1973a: 50).

V. sinuatum x V. spinosum = V. x atchleyanum Rech.f. in *Mitt. thüring. bot. Ges.* **2**: 53 (1960).
Calcareous stony ground in gorge.
W. Crete.
Described from Crete, based on a record by Murbeck (1936: 36); also recorded by Rechinger (1943a: 470; 1949: 206) and Zaffran (1990: 287).

14. Veronica L.

1. V. acinifolia L., *Sp. pl.* ed.2: 19 (1762) - *FE* **3**: 248.
Cr - *NOT MAPPED*
Crete [W., S.C., & S. Europe].

2. V. agrestis L., *Sp. pl.*: 13 (1753) - *FE* **3**: 249.
Cr - *NOT MAPPED*
Crete [most of Europe].

3. V. anagallis-aquatica L., *Sp. pl.*: 12 (1753) - *FE* **3**: 248.
a. subsp. anagallis-aquatica
Cr (W, C, E) Kp - *MAP 1213*
Shallow fresh water, wet marshes; 0-200m; fl. 4, 10.
Crete (sporadic); Karpathos [almost throughout Europe].

4. V. arvensis L., *Sp. pl.*: 13 (1753) - *FE* **3**: 249.
Cr (W, C, E) Kp - *MAP 1214*
Open stony ground, flat clayey areas, roadside banks; 0-2200m.
Crete (sporadic); Karpathos [almost throughout Europe].

5. V. beccabunga L., *Sp. pl.*: 12 (1753) - *FE* **3**: 248.
a. subsp. beccabunga
Cr (C) - *MAP 1215*
Wet place in gorge; 600m.
C. Crete [almost throughout Europe].
Recorded since *FE* (Greuter, 1973a: 51).

6. V. cymbalaria Bodard, *Mém. Vér. cymb.*: 3 (1798) - *FE* **3**: 250.
Cr (W, C, E) Ks Kp Sa - *MAP 1216*
Olive groves, rocky places, old stone walls, flat clayey areas; 50-1450m; fl. 3-5.
Mainly W. Crete; Karpathos group [S. Europe].
Some records are possibly referable to **13**.

7. V. glauca Sm., *Fl. Graec. prodr.* **1**: 9 (1806) - *FE* **3**: 249.
a. subsp. glauca
Cr (W) - *NOT MAPPED*
W. Crete [Greece (especially Attiki)].
Not collected in Crete for over a century (cf. *MFG* **2**: 227).
b. subsp. kavusica (Rech.f.) M.A.Fisch. in Strid & Kit Tan, *Mount. Fl. Greece* **2**: 228 (1991) - *FE* **3**: 248 as *V. kavusica* Rech.f.
Cr (W, C, E) - *MAP 1217*
Calcareous cliffs, stony slopes, rubble & screes; 1000-2200m; fl. 4-6.
Crete (Lefka Ori, Kedros, Psiloritis, Kofinas & Afendis Kavousi) [Ionian Islands (Kefallinia)].

8. V. hederifolia L., *Sp. pl.*: 13 (1753) - *FE* **3**: 250 as *V. hederifolia* L. subsp. *hederifolia*.
Cr (C) - *MAP 1218*
Beneath Berberis bushes on calcareous slopes; 1450-1777m.
C. Crete (Kedros & Psiloritis) [most of Europe].
Doubtful occurrence confirmed since *FE* (Greuter et al., 1984b: 291).

V. kavusica Rech.f. (*FE* **3**: 248) = **7b**.

[9. V. persica] Poir. in Lam., *Encycl.* **8**: 542 (1808) - *FE* **3**: 250.
Cr (W, C) - *MAP 1219*
Naturalized on open sandy ground & alluvial deposits near sea; fl. 4.
W. & C. Crete [almost throughout Europe; from S.W. Asia].

10. V. polita Fr., *Novit. fl. svec.*: 63 (1819) - *FE* **3**: 250.
Cr (W) - *MAP 1220*
Weed communities, cultivated fields, waste areas, old stone walls; 100-500m; fl. 4-5.
W. Crete [almost throughout Europe].

"*V. praecox*" (*FE* **3**: 248) = **7b** (Greuter et al., 1984*b*: 291-292).

11. V. sartoriana Boiss. & Heldr. in Boiss., *Diagn. pl. orient.* ser.2, **3**: 171 (1856) - *FE* **3**: 249.
Cr (W, E) - *MAP 1221*
Among rocks in Cupressus woodland, screes; 1300-1750m.
W. & E. Crete (Lefka Ori & Dikti) [Greece & Aegean region].

12. V. thymifolia Sm., *Fl. Graec. prodr.* **1**: 6 (1806) - *FE* **3**: 246.
Cr (W, C, E) - *MAP 1222*
Open rocky places, calcareous rubble; 1500-2350m; fl. 4-6.
Crete (Lefka Ori, Psiloritis & Dikti) [C. & S. Greece].

13. V. trichadena Jord. & Fourr., *Brev. pl. nov.* **1**: 42 (1866) - not cited in *FE*.
Cr - *NOT MAPPED*
Crete [Balearic Islands, Sicily, Malta & Greece; otherwise E. Aegean Islands (Samos & Rodos) & S.W. Turkey].
Recorded in *MFG* **2**: 234. Very closely related to **6**, differing in having shorter hairs on calyces and capsules (cf. *MFG*).

14. V. triloba (Opiz) Wiesb. in *Öst. bot. Z.* **28**: 217 (1878) - *FE* **3**: 250 as *V. hederifolia* subsp. *triloba* (Opiz) Celak.
Cr (C, E) - *MAP 1223*
Calcareous slopes & screes; 1400m.
C. & E. Crete (Psiloritis & Afendis Kavousi) [S.C. & S. Europe].
Recorded since *FE* (Greuter et al., 1984*b*: 291).

SIMAROUBACEAE

1. Ailanthus Desf.

[1. A. altissima] (Mill.) Swingle in *J. Wash. Acad. Sci.* **6**: 490 (1916) - *FE* **2**: 231.

Cr (W, C, E) - *MAP 1224*
Naturalized on roadsides; 0-100m; fl. 5-6.
Mainly W. & C. Crete [W., C. & S. Europe; from China].
Recorded since *FE* (Greuter, 1973*a*: 41).

SOLANACEAE

Datura innoxia Mill. (*FE* **3**: 200) has been recorded from Elounda in E. Crete, as a probable casual escape from cultivation (Greuter, 1974: 149).

D. stramonium L. (*FE* **3**: 200) occurs in Crete as a casual.

1. Hyoscyamus L.

1. H. albus L., *Sp. pl.*: 180 (1753) - *FE* **3**: 195.
Cr (W, C, E) Ks Kp - *MAP 1225*
Old walls; 0-500m; fl. 3-5.
Crete (widespread); Kasos, Karpathos [S. Europe].

[2. H. aureus] L., *Sp. pl.*: 180 (1753) - *FE* **3**: 195.
Cr (C) - *MAP 1226*
Naturalized on old walls; fl. (1-)2-3(-4).
C. Crete (Iraklio town) [from Egypt, Sinai & S.W. Asia].

? H. niger L., *Sp. pl.*: 179 (1753) - *FE* **3**: 195.
Doubtfully present in Crete (Greuter, 1974: 159) [almost throughout Europe].

2. Lycium L.

L. barbarum L. (*FE* **3**: 194) is probably only cultivated.

"*L. europaeum*" (*FE* **3**: 194) = **1** (Greuter et al., 1984*b*: 292).

"*L. intricatum*" (*FE* **3**: 194) = **1** (Greuter et al., loc. cit.)

1. L. schweinfurthii Dammer in *Bot. Jb.* **48**: 224 (1912) - *FE* **3**: 194.
Cr (W, C, E) Ks Kp - *MAP 1227*
Earthy maritime cliffs, low scrub & open stony ground near sea, maritime sands & rubble; 0-200m.
Mainly C. & E. Crete; Kasos, Karpathos [Sicily & Aegean region; otherwise N. Africa & S.W. Asia].

3. Mandragora L.

1. M. autumnalis Bertol., *Elench. pl. hort. bot. bon.*: 6 (1820) - *FE* **3**: 200.
Cr (W, C, E) Ks Kp - *MAP 1228*

*Scrub, rocky places & crevices, bare ground; 0-
500m; fl. 3-5, 10.*
Crete (widespread); Kasos, Karpathos
[Mediterranean region].

4. Nicotiana L.

[1. N. glauca] Graham in *Edinb. New phil. J.* **5**:
175 (1828) - *FE* **3**: 201.
Cr (W, C, E) - *MAP 1229*
Naturalized in waste areas; fl. 2-10.
Crete (sporadic) [Mediterranean region; from
Argentina & Bolivia].

N. rustica L. is given as doubtfully present in
the Cretan area in *FE* **3**: 201, although there
appear to be no records as a basis for this.

N. tabacum L. (*FE* **3**: 201) is probably only
cultivated.

5. Solanum L.

[1. S. elaeagnifolium] Cav., *Icon.* **3**: 22 (1795)
- *FE* **3**: 199.
Cr (W, C) - *MAP 1230*
Naturalized on bare sandy ground near sea.
W. & C. Crete [Greece; from temperate S.
America].
Recorded since *FE* (Yannitsaros & Economidou,
1974: 114).

2. S. luteum Mill., *Gard. Dict.* ed.8: no.3
(1768) - *FE* **3**: 197.
Cr (W, E) Kp - *MAP 1231*
*Rocky places, damp ground, open stony ground
near sea; 0-400m; fl. 3-5..*
a. subsp. **alatum** (Moench) Dostál, *Kvetena
CSR*: 1270 (1949) - *FE* **3**: 198.
Crete [W., C. & S. Europe].
b. subsp. **luteum**
Crete; Karpathos [W., C. & S. Europe].

3. S. nigrum L., *Sp. pl.*: 186 (1753) - *FE* **3**:
197.
Cr (W, C, E) Ks Kp - *MAP 1232*
*Calcareous rocky places, damp ground, weed
communities, cultivated & waste areas; 0-500m;
fl. 2-9.*
Crete (widespread); Kasos, Karpathos [almost
throughout Europe].
Plants are sometimes collected by the local
people as a wild vegetable.

6. Withania Pauquy

1. W. somnifera (L.) Dunal in DC., *Prodr.*
13(1): 453 (1852) - *FE* **3**: 195.
Cr (W, C) - *MAP 1233*

Near old walls and ruins; 0-200m; fl. 8.
W. & C. Crete [Mediterranean region].

STYRACACEAE

1. Styrax L.

1. S. officinalis L., *Sp. pl.*: 444 (1753) - *FE* **3**:
52.
Cr (W, C, E) Kp - *MAP 1234*
*Scrub, stream-banks, roadside banks; 50-600m;
fl. 4-5.*
Mainly W. & C. Crete; Karpathos [mainly E.
Mediterranean region].

TAMARICACEAE

1. Tamarix L.

T. dalmatica Baum is given for the Cretan area
in *FE* **2**: 293, although there are no records as a
basis for this (Greuter, 1974: 139).

1. T. parviflora DC., *Prodr.* **3**: 97 (1828) - *FE*
2: 293.
Cr (W, C) - *MAP 1235*
River-banks & marshes near sea; fl. 3-4.
W. & C. Crete [mainly Balkan peninsula].

2. T. smyrnensis Bunge, *Tent. gen. Tamaric.*:
53 (1852) - *FE* **2**: 293.
Cr (W, C, E) Kp - *MAP 1236*
*River-banks, maritime sands, frequently planted
for shade near sea; fl. 10.*
Crete (sporadic); Karpathos [S.E. Europe].
Doubtfully native (Barclay, 1986: 93).

THELIGONACEAE

1. Theligonum L.

1. T. cynocrambe L., *Sp. pl.*: 993 (1753) - *FE*
2: 312.
Cr (W, C, E) Ks Kp Sa - *MAP 1237*
*Platanus woodland, calcareous rock-crevices,
old walls; 0-1200m; fl. 4.*
Crete (widespread); Karpathos group [S.
Europe].

THYMELAEACEAE

1. Daphne L.

1. D. gnidioides Jaub. & Spach, *Ill. pl. orient.*
4: t.4 (1850) - *FE* **2**: 258.
Cr (W) - *MAP 1238*
*Olive groves, coastal scrub & garigue, crevices
of calcareous cliffs, maritime sands; 0-120m; fl.*

9-11.
W. Crete (S. coast) [?N. Sporades (Skiathos), ?Evvia, ?Kiklades (Astipalea); otherwise E. Aegean Islands & Turkey].
Recorded since *FE* (Turland, 1991; 1992*a*: 353).

2. D. jasminea Sm., *Fl. Graec. prodr.* **1**: 260 (1809) - *FE* **2**: 258.
Cr (W) - *MAP 1239*
Calcareous cliffs, phrygana; 50-550m; fl. 4, 8-10.
W. Crete (S. side) [S.E. Greece; otherwise N.E. Libya].
[Plate 7.] Recorded since *FE* (Turland, 1992*a*: 353).

3. D. oleoides Schreb., *Icon. descr. pl.*: 13 (1766) - *FE* **2**: 257.
a. subsp. **oleoides**
Cr (W, C, E) - *MAP 1240*
Calcareous open rocky places; (450-)1000-2300m; fl. 5-8.
Crete (Lefka Ori, Kedros & Dikti) [S. Europe].

4. S. sericea Vahl, *Symb. bot.* **1**: 28 (1790) - *FE* **2**: 258.
Cr (W, C, E) - *MAP 1241*
Calcareous open woodland, garigue, phrygana; 100-1200m; fl. 3-5.
Crete (sporadic) [C. & E. Mediterranean region].

2. Thymelaea Mill.

1. T. hirsuta (L.) Endl., *Gen. pl. Suppl.* **4**: 65 (1848) - *FE* **2**: 259.
Cr (W, C, E) Ks - *MAP 1242*
Calcareous rocky places, maritime sands, abandoned fields, waste areas; 0-300m; fl. 9-11, 3.
Mainly W. & C. Crete; Kasos [Mediterranean region].

2. T. tartonraira (L.) All., *Fl. pedem.* **1**: 133 (1785) - *FE* **2**: 259.
Cr (W, C) Kp - *MAP 1243*
Calcareous phrygana & rocky places, dry open stony ground; 0-1050m; fl. 3-4.
a. subsp. **argentea** (Sm.) Holmboe in *Bergens Mus. Skr.* ser.2, **1(2)**: 133 (1914) - *FE* **2**: 259.
W. & C. Crete [Aegean region; otherwise S.W. Asia].
Not endemic to Crete & Greece as given in *FE* (cf. Tan in Davis, 1982: 528).
b. subsp. **tartonraira**
W. & C. Crete [Mediterranean region].
Erroneously regarded as absent from the Cretan area in *FE* (Greuter, 1974: 140).

The species sensu lato occurs mainly in W. Crete and also in Karpathos.

ULMACEAE

1. Celtis L.

C. australis L. is erroneously given as native to the Cretan area in *FE* **1**: 66 (Greuter, 1974: 154); it is probably only planted.

1. C. tournefortii Lam., *Encycl.* **4**: 138 (1797) - *FE* **1**: 66.
Cr (W, E) - *MAP 1244*
Calcareous cliffs in gorges; 400-750m.
W. & E. Crete [mainly Sicily & Balkan peninsula].
Recorded since *FE* (Greuter, 1973*a*: 27; Turland, 1992*a*: 354).

2. Ulmus L.

U. canescens Melville (*FE* **1**: 65) = **1a**.

1. U. minor Mill., *Gard. Dict.* ed.8: no.6 (1768) - *FE* **1**: 65.
a. subsp. **canescens** (Melville) Browicz & Ziel. in *Fragm. flor. geobot.* **23**: 145 (1977) - *FE* **1**: 65 as *U. canescens* Melville.
Cr (W) - *MAP 1245*
Riverbanks, lake-shore, northern slopes of hill; 0-50m.
W. Crete [C. & E. Mediterranean region].
Grows in natural habitats and appears native in Crete, rather than introduced as given in *FE*. Old reports of *Ulmus* on the island, as well as a more recent record from C. Crete (Rechinger, 1943*b*: 63), are possibly referable to cultivated individuals of subsp. *minor* (Greuter, 1973*a*: 27).

3. Zelkova Spach

●**1. Z. abelicea** (Lam.) Boiss., *Fl. orient.* **4**: 1159 (1879) - *FE* **1**: 65.
Cr (W, C, E) - *MAP 1246*
Open calcareous woodland, scrub & garigue on rocky mountain slopes, often with Acer, Cupressus & Quercus coccifera; 1000-1700m; fl. 5.
Crete (Lefka Ori, Kedros, Psiloritis & Dikti) - Endemic.
[Plate 7.] Should be considered endemic to Crete. Historically collected from Cyprus, but no specimen could be traced by Meikle, who suspected a misidentification; never since recorded (Meikle, 1985: 1463). Vulnerable species, legally protected.

UMBELLIFERAE
(APIACEAE)

1. Ammi L.

1. A. majus L., *Sp. pl.*: 243 (1753) - *FE* 2: 353.
Cr (W, C) Kp - *MAP 1247*
Olive groves, fallow fields, waste areas; fl. 4-5.
W. & C. Crete; Karpathos [S. Europe].

2. Anethum L.

[1. A. graveolens] L., *Sp. pl.*: 263 (1753) - *FE* 2: 341.
Cr (C) - *MAP 1248*
Cultivated and possibly naturalized in fallow fields.
C. Crete (W. of Iraklio) [mainly C. & S. Europe; from S.W. Asia & India].

3. Anthriscus Pers.

1. A. nemorosa (M.Bieb.) Spreng., *Pl. umbell. Prodr.*: 27 (1813) - *FE* 2: 326.
Cr (W) - *MAP 1249*
Calcareous rocky slopes beneath trees; 650m; fl. 4-5.
W. Crete (Askifos plain in Lefka Ori) [mainly E. & S.E. Europe].

4. Apium L.

1. A. graveolens L., *Sp. pl.*: 264 (1753) - *FE* 2: 351.
Cr (W, C) Kp - *MAP 1250*
Brackish coastal marshes, streams; fl. 4-5.
W. & C. Crete; Karpathos [coasts of most of Europe].

2. A. nodiflorum (L.) Lag., *Amen. nat. Españ.* 1: 101 (1821) - *FE* 2: 351.
Cr (W, C, E) Kp - *MAP 1251*
Marshes, streams & other wet places; 0-600m; fl. 3-5.
Crete (widespread, rarer towards E.); Karpathos [most of Europe].
Erroneously given as doubtfully present in the Cretan area in *FE* (Greuter, 1974: 140).

A. repens (Jacq.) Lag. is given for the Cretan area in *FE* 2: 351, although there are no records as a basis for this (Greuter, 1974: 139).

5. Athamanta L.

1. A. macedonica (L.) Spreng. in Roem. & Schult., *Syst. veg.* 6: 491 (1820) - *FE* 2: 340 as

A. macedonica (L.) Spreng. subsp. *macedonica*.
Cr (W) - *MAP 1252*
Calcareous cliffs; 1450-1800m; fl. 6-7.
W. Crete (Lefka Ori) [S. Italy & S. Balkan peninsula].
Recorded since *FE* (Greuter et al., 1984b: 293).

6. Bifora Hoffm.

1. B. testiculata (L.) Spreng. ex Schult. in Roem. & Schult., *Syst. veg.* 6: xxxviii & 448 (1820) - *FE* 2: 328.
Cr (W, C) Kp - *MAP 1253*
Cultivated fields & terraces; 400-500m; fl. 4.
W. & C. Crete; Karpathos [S. Europe].

Bonannia graeca (L.) Halácsy (*FE* 2: 358) was almost certainly recorded in error (Greuter, 1974: 158).

7. Bunium L.

1. B. ferulaceum Sm., *Fl. Graec. prodr.* 1: 186 (1806) - *FE* 2: 329.
Cr (W, C, E) Kp - *MAP 1254*
Cultivated & abandoned land; 150-800m; fl. 4.
Crete (sporadic); Karpathos [mainly Balkan peninsula & Aegean region].

8. Bupleurum L.

●**1. B. gaudianum** Snogerup in *Willdenowia* 14: 309 (1984).
Cr (W) - *MAP 1255*
Low phrygana; fl. 4-5.
W. Crete (Gavdos island) - Endemic.
The taxonomic affinities of this recently described annual species are uncertain (Snogerup, op. cit.)

2. B. gracile d'Urv. in *Mém. Soc. linn. Paris* 1: 286 (1822) - *FE* 2: 347.
Cr (W, C, E) Ks Kp Sa - *MAP 1256*
Open woodland, calcareous garigue, phrygana & rocky places, abandoned fields; 0-1150m; fl. 4-5.
Crete (widespread); Karpathos group [S.E. Greece & Aegean region; otherwise S.W. Asia].

●**3. B. kakiskalae** Greuter in *Bauhinia* 3: 250 (1967) - not cited in *FE*.
Cr (W) - *MAP 1257*
S.E.-facing calcareous cliffs; 1450-1500m; fl. 8-9.
W. Crete (Lefka Ori) - Endemic.
[Plate 7.] A distinct, monocarpic species growing for several years before flowering. Known only from the type locality, where it is

endangered because of its small population size and reproductive biology; legally protected.

4. B. lancifolium Hornem., *Hort. bot. hafn.*: 267 (1813) - *FE* 2: 346.
Cr (W) Ks Kp - *MAP 1258*
W. Crete; Kasos, Karpathos [S. Europe].

5. B. semicompositum L., *Demonstr. pl.*: 7 (1753) - *FE* 2: 348.
Cr (W, E) Ks Kp - *MAP 1259*
Sparse low phrygana, calcareous rocky places, maritime sands; near s.l.; fl. 4.
W. & E. Crete; Kasos, Karpathos [S. Europe].

6. B. trichopodum Boiss. & Spruner in *Annls Sci. nat.* ser.3 (Bot.), **1**: 145 (1884) - *FE* 2: 348.
Kp - *MAP 1260*
Karpathos [E. & S. Greece & Aegean region; otherwise S.W. Asia].

9. Cachrys L.

1. C. cristata DC., *Prodr.* **4**: 238 (1830) - *FE* 2: 343.
Cr (C) Kp - *MAP 1261*
Open ground under Pinus pinea trees, phrygana, calcareous rocky places & crevices; 0-500m.
C. Crete; Karpathos [S. Italy, S. Balkan peninsula & Aegean region].

Carum multiflorum (Sm.) Boiss. subsp. *multiflorum* (*FE* 2: 354) = **Hellenocarum 1**.

10. Chaerophyllum L.

●**1. C. creticum** Boiss. & Heldr. in Boiss., *Diagn. pl. orient.* ser.1, **10**: 51 (1849) - *FE* 2: 325.
Cr (W) - *MAP 1262*
Among spiny shrubs on deep clayey soil; 1050m; fl. 4-6.
W. Crete (Omalos plain in Lefka Ori) - Endemic.
[Plate 7.]

Cnidium silaifolium (Jacq.) Simonk. (*FE* 2: 355) = **Selinum 1**.

11. Conium L.

C. divaricatum Boiss. & Orph. (Barclay, 1986: 95) is included in synonymy of **1**.

1. C. maculatum L., *Sp. pl.*: 243 (1753) - *FE* 2: 342. (Including *C. divaricatum* Boiss. & Orph., in agreement with *FE*.)
Cr (W, C, E) - *MAP 1263*

Hedges, among Berberis bushes & ruined buildings, roadsides; 300-1250m; fl. 4-5.
Crete (sporadic) [almost throughout Europe].

12. Coriandrum L.

[1. C. sativum] L., *Sp. pl.*: 256 (1753) - *FE* 2: 328.
Cr (W) - *MAP 1264*
Cultivated and naturalized, luxuriant herbaceous vegetation; 200m.
W. Crete (S. of Hania) [C. & S. Europe; from N. Africa & W. Asia].

13. Crithmum L.

1. C. maritimum L., *Sp. pl.*: 246 (1753) - *FE* 2: 333.
Cr (W, C, E) Ks Kp Sa - *MAP 1265*
Maritime rocks & sands; fl. 8-10.
Crete (widespread); Karpathos group [coasts of Atlantic, Mediterranean & Black Sea].

14. Daucus L.

? D. broteri Ten., *Fl. napol.* **4**, *Syll. app.* **3**: 4 (1830) - *FE* 2: 373.
Doubtfully present in Crete (Greuter, 1974: 158) [Italy & Balkan peninsula].

1. D. carota L., *Sp. pl.*: 242 (1753) - *FE* 2: 374.
Cr (W, C, E) Kp - *MAP 1266*
a. subsp. **drepanensis** (Arcang.) Heywood in *Feddes Reprium* **79**: 68 (1968) - *FE* 2: 374.
Cr (E) - *MAP 1267*
Hard soil between rocks near sea, maritime sands.
E. Crete (Sideros peninsula) [Mediterranean region].
b. subsp. **major** (Vis.) Arcang., *Comp. fl. ital.*: 299 (1882) - *FE* 2: 374.
Cr - *NOT MAPPED*
Crete [S. Europe].
c. subsp. **maximus** (Desf.) Ball in *J. Linn. Soc. (Bot.)* **16**: 476 (1878) - *FE* 2: 374.
Cr (W, C, E) Kp - *NOT MAPPED*
Margins of fields & terraces, roadsides, among ancient ruins; 0-500m; fl. 4-5.
Crete; Karpathos [Mediterranean region].
The species sensu lato is widespread in Crete.

2. D. guttatus Sm., *Fl. Graec. prodr.* **1**: 184 (1806) - *FE* 2: 373.
a. subsp. **guttatus**
Cr (W, C) Kp - *MAP 1268*
Pinus brutia woodland, olive groves, rocky places, gorge-beds, maritime sands, abandoned

terraces, roadsides; 0-400m; fl. 4-5.
Mainly W. Crete; Karpathos [Italy, Greece & Aegean region].

3. D. involucratus Sm., *Fl. Graec. prodr.* **1**: 184 (1806) - *FE* **2**: 374.
Cr (W, C, E) Ks Kp Sa - *MAP 1269*
Calcareous rocky places & crevices, rubble, screes, low phrygana, seashores, abandoned terraces; 0-1450m; fl. 4.
Mainly W. & E. Crete; Karpathos group [E. & S. Greece & Aegean region; otherwise S.W. Asia].

15. Echinophora L.

1. E. tenuifolia L., *Sp. pl.*: 239 (1753) - *FE* **2**: 324.
a. subsp. **sibthorpiana** (Guss.) Tutin in *Feddes Reprium* **74**: 31 (1967) - *FE* **2**: 324.
Cr (C, E) - *MAP 1270*
Abandoned fields & waste areas; 0-50m; fl. 6-7.
C. & E. Crete [Greece to Crimea; otherwise S.W. & C. Asia].

16. Elaeoselinum W.D.J.Koch ex DC.

1. E. asclepium (L.) Bertol., *Fl. ital.* **3**: 383 (1838) - *FE* **2**: 368.
a. subsp. **asclepium**
Kp - *MAP 1271*
Karpathos [W. Italy & Sicily to S.E. Greece; otherwise E. Aegean Islands (Rodos) & S.W. Turkey (Marmaris peninsula)].
Recorded since *FE* (Greuter, 1974: 148).

17. Eryngium L.

"*E. amethystinum*" (*FE* **2**: 323) = **4**.

1. E. amorginum Rech.f. in *Magy. bot. Lap.* **33**: 9 (1934) - *FE* **2**: 323.
Cr (E) - *MAP 1272*
Calcareous cliffs, rarely in Pinus brutia woodland; 150-600m.
E. Crete [Kiklades].
Recorded since *FE* (Greuter, 1973a: 45).

2. E. campestre L., *Sp. pl.*: 233 (1753) - *FE* **2**: 323.
Cr (W, C, E) Kp - *MAP 1273*
Garigue, phrygana, maritime sands, flat clayey areas, cultivated & abandoned land; 0-1500m; fl. 4-6.
Crete (widespread); Karpathos [mainly C. & S. Europe].

3. E. creticum Lam., *Encycl.* **4**: 754 (1798) - *FE* **2**: 322.
Cr (W) - *MAP 1274*
Olive groves, phrygana, alluvial rubble,

roadsides, bare ground; 0-200m; fl. 7.
W. Crete [Balkan peninsula & Aegean region].

4. E. glomeratum Lam., *Encycl.* **4**: 755 (1798) - *FE* **2**: 323, included in synonymy of *E. amethystinum* L.
?Cr Kp - *MAP 1275*
Garigue, phrygana, bare stony ground; 0-300m.
?Crete; Karpathos [S.W. Asia].

5. E. maritimum L., *Sp. pl.*: 233 (1753) - *FE* **2**: 322.
Cr (W, C, E) Ks Kp - *MAP 1276*
Maritime sands; fl. 3-7.
Crete (sporadic); Kasos, Karpathos [coasts of most of Europe].

●**6. E. ternatum** Poir. in Lam., *Encycl., Suppl.* **4**: 295 (1816) - *FE* **2**: 323.
Cr (W, C) - *MAP 1277*
Calcareous cliffs; 50-600m; fl. 5-6.
W. Crete, one record from C. Crete - Endemic.

18. Ferula L.

F. chiliantha Rech.f. (Greuter et al., 1983a: 69) is included in synonymy of **1b**.

1. F. communis L., *Sp. pl.*: 246 (1753) - *FE* **2**: 359.
Cr (W, C, E) Ks Kp - *MAP 1278*
a. subsp. **communis**
Cr (W, C) - *MAP 1279*
Ledges of calcareous cliffs, abandoned cultivated land, field-margins, roadsides, waste areas; 0-450m; fl. 3-5.
W. & C. Crete [Mediterranean region].
b. subsp. **glauca** (L.) Rouy & Camus, *Fl. France* **7**: 398 (1901) - *FE* **2**: 359.
Cr (W, C, E) Ks Kp - *MAP 1280*
Calcareous cliffs, rocky places; 0-300m.
Crete (sporadic); Kasos, Karpathos [Mediterranean region].
Recorded from Karpathos as *F. chiliantha* Rech.f. (Greuter et al., 1983a: 69), which is otherwise known from the E. Aegean islands of Samos & Rodos, but is here included in synonymy **b**, after Peşmen (in Davis, 1972: 444).

19. Ferulago W.D.J.Koch

"*F. asparagifolia*" (*FE* **2**: 359) = **Elaeoselinum 1** (Greuter, 1974: 148).

1. F. nodosa (L.) Boiss., *Diagn. pl. orient.* ser.1, **10**: 37 (1849) - *FE* **2**: 359.
Cr (W, C, E) - *MAP 1281*
Rocky places, shady roadsides; 0-600m; fl. 4-5.
Crete (sporadic) [Sicily, S. Balkan peninsula & Aegean region].

● **2. F. thyrsiflora** (Sm.) W.D.J.Koch in *Nova Acta Acad. Caesar. Leop. Carol.* **12(1)**: 98 (1824) - *FE* **2**: 359.
Cr (W, C, E) - *MAP 1282*
Calcareous cliffs & rock-crevices; 50-1200m; fl. 4-5.
Mainly W. & C. Crete - Endemic.

20. Foeniculum Mill.

1. F. vulgare Mill., *Gard. Dict.* ed.8: no.1 (1768) - *FE* **2**: 341.
a. subsp. piperitum (Ucria) Cout., *Fl. Portugal*: 450 (1913) - *FE* **2**: 341.
Cr (W, C, E) Kp - *MAP 1283*
Fallow & abandoned land, roadsides, waste areas; 0-450m; fl. 7-9.
Crete (widespread); Karpathos [Mediterranean region].

21. Geocaryum Coss. emend. Engstrand

● **1. G. creticum** (Boiss. & Heldr.) Engstrand, *Biosyst. Tax. Geocaryum*: 40 (1977) - *FE* **2**: 330 as *Huetia cretica* (Boiss. & Heldr.) P.W.Ball.
Cr (E) - *MAP 1284*
Calcareous open stony slopes & screes; 1300-1950m; fl. 5-7.
E. Crete (Dikti) - Endemic.

22. Hellenocarum H.Wolff

1. H. multiflorum (Sm.) H.Wolff in *Pflanzenreich* **90(IV.228)**: 168 (1927) - *FE* **2**: 354 as *Carum multiflorum* (Sm.) Boiss. subsp. *multiflorum*.
Cr (W, C, E) Ks Kp Sa - *MAP 1285*
Calcareous cliffs, rock-crevices; 0-1850m; fl. 4-5.
Crete (widespread); Karpathos group [S.E. Italy, W. & S. Greece; otherwise E. Aegean Islands (Rodos), W. Turkey & ?Cyprus].

23. Horstrissea Greuter, Gerstb. & Egli

● **1. H. dolinicola** Greuter, Gerstb. & Egli in *Willdenowia* **19**: 391 (1990).
Cr (C) - *MAP 1286*
Between rocks & dwarf shrubs in flat areas of deep soil in dolines; 1500m; fl. 7-9.
C. Crete (Psiloritis) - Endemic.
[Plate 7.] The closest relative of this recently described, monospecific genus is *Scaligeria* DC. (Greuter et al., op. cit.)

Huetia cretica (Boiss. & Heldr.) P.W.Ball (*FE* **2**: 330) = **Geocaryum 1**.

24. Hydrocotyle L.

1. H. vulgaris L., *Sp. pl.*: 234 (1753) - *FE* **2**: 319.
Cr (W) - *MAP 1287*
Marshes, streams, margins of Phragmites bed; fl. 4-5.
W. Crete [W., C. & S. Europe].
Erroneously regarded as absent from the Cretan area in *FE* (Greuter, 1974: 140).

25. Kundmannia Scop.

1. K. sicula (L.) DC., *Prodr.* **4**: 143 (1830) - *FE* **2**: 342.
Cr (W) - *MAP 1288*
Phrygana, calcareous screes, grassy roadside banks; 0-250m; fl. 3-6.
W. Crete (N. side) [Mediterranean region].

26. Lagoecia L.

1. L. cuminoides L., *Sp. pl.*: 203 (1753) - *FE* **2**: 324.
Cr (W, C, E) Ks Kp Sa - *MAP 1289*
Sparse low phrygana, rocky places, gorge-beds, bare soil, abandoned terraces; 0-1500m; fl. 4-5.
Crete (widespread); Karpathos group [Mediterranean region].

27. Lecokia DC.

1. L. cretica (Lam.) DC., *Coll. mém.* **5**: 75 (1829) - *FE* **2**: 343.
Cr (W, C, E) - *MAP 1290*
Woodland, rocky slopes, bases of cliffs, moist roadside banks; 0-1450m; fl. 3-4.
Mainly W. Crete [S.W. Asia].

28. Oenanthe L.

1. O. pimpinelloides L., *Sp. pl.*: 255 (1753) - *FE* **2**: 338.
Cr (W, C) Kp - *MAP 1291*
Moist woodland & rocky places, marshes, ditches, shallow fresh water, damp grassland; 0-600m; fl. 3-5.
W. & C. Crete; Karpathos [W. & S. Europe].

"*O. prolifera*" (*FE* **2**: 339) ? = **1** (Barclay, 1986: 97).

29. Opopanax W.D.J.Koch

1. O. hispidus (Friv.) Griseb., *Spic. fl. rumel.* **1**: 378 (1843) - *FE* **2**: 360.
Cr (W, C, E) Kp Sa - *MAP 1292*

Phrygana, open ground near sea; 0-450m.
Crete (sporadic); Karpathos, Saria [S. Italy,
Sicily, S. Balkan peninsula & Aegean Region].

30. Orlaya Hoffm.

1. O. daucoides (L.) Greuter in *Boissiera* **13**:
92 (1967) - *FE* **2**: 372 as *O. kochii* Heywood.
Cr (W, C, E) Ks Kp - *MAP 1293*
*Rocky & sandy places, calcareous screes, clayey
fields; 0-1500m; fl. 3-4.*
Crete (widespread, rarer towards E.); Kasos,
Karpathos [S. Europe].

2. O. grandiflora (L.) Hoffm., *Gen. pl.
umbell.*: 58 (1814) - *FE* **2**: 373.
Cr (W) - *MAP 1294*
Calcareous rubble of gorge-beds; 0-200m; fl. 5.
W. Crete [W., C. & S. Europe].

O. kochii Heywood (*FE* **2**: 372) = **1**.

Petroselinum crispum (Mill.) A.W.Hill (*FE* **2**:
352) was probably recorded in error. Rechinger
(1943a: 403) cites only old records by
Gandoger, who is now known to have been
unreliable (Greuter, 1974: 153).

31. Peucedanum L.

1. P. alpinum (Sieber ex Schult.) B.L.Burtt &
P.H.Davis in *Kew Bull.* **1949**: 227 (1949) - *FE*
2: 364.
Cr (W) - *MAP 1295*
*Calcareous rubble & mobile gravelly screes;
1900-2400m; fl. 6-8.*
W. Crete (Lefka Ori) [S.W. Turkey].
Given as endemic to Crete in *FE*, although the
S.W. Turkish *P. pisidicum* (Boiss. & Heldr.)
Boiss. is treated here as conspecific, after
Chamberlain (in Davis, 1972: 479).

32. Pimpinella L.

P. anisum L. (*FE* **2**: 331) was almost certainly
recorded in error (Greuter, 1974: 158).

1. P. cretica Poir. in Lam., *Encycl., Suppl.* **1**:
684 (1811) - *FE* **2**: 331.
Cr (W, C, E) Ks Kp Sa - *MAP 1296*
*Calcareous rocky places, screes, dry stream-
beds, seashores, bare ground; 0-1000m; fl. 4.*
Crete (sporadic); Karpathos group [S. Aegean
region].

2. P. peregrina L., *Sp. pl.*: 264 (1753) - *FE* **2**:
331.
Cr (W, C) - *MAP 1297*
Olive groves, scrub, phrygana; 0-550m; fl. 4-5.

W. & C. Crete [S. Europe].

3. P. pretenderis (Heldr.) Orph. ex Halácsy,
Consp. fl. graec. **1**: 683 (1901) - *FE* **2**: 332.
Kp - *MAP 1298*
Calcareous cliffs; 1100-1200m.
Karpathos (Kalilimni) [Kiklades].
Recorded since *FE* (Greuter, 1974: 148).

4. P. tragium Vill., *Prosp. Hist. pl. Dauphiné*:
24 (1779) - *FE* **2**: 331.
●**a.** subsp. **depressa** (DC.) Tutin in *Feddes
Reprium* **79**: 62 (1968) - *FE* **2**: 332.
Cr (W, C, E) - *MAP 1299*
*Calcareous slopes with open scrub, rocky &
gravelly places, crevices, screes, flat clayey
areas; 1200-2400m; fl. 6-8.*
Crete (Lefka Ori, Psiloritis & Dikti) -
?Endemic.
Possibly occurring elsewhere in Greece (cf.
MFG **1**: 679). Records from Karpathos are
referable to **3** (Greuter, 1974: 148).

33. Pseudorlaya (Murb.) Murb.

1. P. pumila (L.) Grande in *Nuovo G. bot. ital.*
nov. ser., **32**: 86 (1925) - *FE* **2**: 375.
Cr (W, C, E) Ks Kp - *MAP 1300*
Maritime sands; fl. 3-5.
Mainly W. & E. Crete; Kasos, Karpathos
[Mediterranean region].

34. Ridolfia Moris

1. R. segetum Moris, *Enum. sem. hort. taur.*:
43 (1841) - *FE* **2**: 352.
Kp - *MAP 1301*
Karpathos [Mediterranean region].
Recorded since *FE* (Greuter, 1974: 148).

35. Scaligeria DC.

S. cretica (Mill.) Boiss. (*FE* **2**: 328) = **2**.

S. cretica subsp. *halophila* Rech.f. (*FE* **2**: 328)
= **1**.

1. S. halophila (Rech.f.) Rech.f. in *Öst. bot. Z.*
112: 186 (1965) - *FE* **2**: 328 as *S. cretica* subsp.
halophila Rech.f.
Cr (C, E) - *MAP 1302*
Calcareous maritime rock-crevices.
C. & E. Crete (Paximadia & Dionisiades
islands) [Kiklades].

2. S. napiformis (Spreng.) Grande in *Boll.
Orto. bot., Napoli* **4**: 188 (1914) - *FE* **2**: 328 as
S. cretica (Mill.) Boiss.
Cr (W, C, E) Ks Kp Sa - *MAP 1303*
Pinus brutia woodland, scrub, garigue,

phrygana, rock-crevices, flat clayey areas; 0-1800m; fl. 4-5.
Mainly W. & C. Crete; Karpathos group [W. & S. Balkan peninsula & Aegean region].

36. Scandix L.

1. S. australis L., *Sp. pl.*: 257 (1753) - *FE 2*: 327.
Cr (W, C, E) - *MAP 1304.*
a. subsp. **australis**
Cr (W, C, E) - *MAP 1305*
Calcareous rocky places, maritime rubble; 0-1700m.
Crete (sporadic).
b. subsp. **balcanica** Vierh. in *Verh. zool.-bot. Ges. Wien* **69**: 232 (1919) - *FE 2*: 327, included in synonymy of subsp. **a.**
Cr (W, C, E) - *MAP 1306*
Mountain slopes, among stones; -1400m.
Crete (Lefka Ori, Akrotiri peninsula, Psiloritis & Dikti).
c. subsp. **curvirostris** (Murb.) Vierh. in *Verh. zool.-bot. Ges. Wien* **69**: 231 (1919) - *FE 2*: 327, included in synonymy of subsp. **a.**
Cr (W, C) - *MAP 1307*
Rocky places.
W. & C. Crete.
The species sensu lato occurs mainly in W. Crete, and is distributed in S. Europe.

2. S. brachycarpa Guss., *Index sem. hort. boccad.*: 10 (1825), ex *Fl. sicul. prodr.* **1**: 350 (1827) - *FE 2*: 327 as *S. pecten-veneris* subsp. *brachycarpa* (Guss.) Thell.
Cr (W) - *MAP 1308*
1900-2100m.
W. Crete (Lefka Ori) [mainly S. Italy & Sicily]. Recorded since *FE (MFG* **1**: 671).

3. S. macrorhyncha C.A.Mey., *Index sem. hort. petrop.* **9**: 86 (1843) - *FE 2*: 327 as *S. pecten-veneris* subsp. *macrorhyncha* (C.A.Mey.) Rouy & Camus.
Cr (C) - *MAP 1309*
Open stony ground; 1700m.
C. Crete (Psiloritis) [S. Europe].
Additionally recorded from the Lefka Ori in W. Crete in *MFG* **1**: 670.

4. S. pecten-veneris L., *Sp. pl.*: 256 (1753) - *FE 2*: 327 as *S. pecten-veneris* L. subsp. *pecten-veneris.*
Cr (W, C, E) Ks Kp - *MAP 1310*
Olive groves, rocky places, cultivated & fallow fields, bare & disturbed ground; 0-1100m; fl. 3-4.
Crete (widespread); Kasos, Karpathos [W., C. & S. Europe].
Subsp. *macrorhyncha* (C.A.Meyer) Rouy &

Camus (*FE* **2**: 327) = **3**.

37. Selinum L.

1. S. silaifolium (Jacq.) Beck, *Fl. Bosne* **3**: 449 (1927) - *FE 2*: 355 as *Cnidium silaifolium* (Jacq.) Simonk.
Cr (W, E) - *MAP 1311*
Rocky places; 1750-2000m.
W. & E. Crete (Lefka Ori & Dikti) [S. Europe].

38. Seseli L.

1. S. gummiferum Pall. ex Sm., *Exot. bot.* **2**: 121 (1807) - *FE 2*: 335.
a. subsp. **crithmifolium** (DC.) P.H.Davis in *Notes R. bot. Gdn Edinb.* **21**: 120 (1953) - *FE 2*: 335. (Including subsp. *aegaeum* P.H.Davis - *FE* **2**: 335.)
Cr (E) Kp Sa - *MAP 1312*
Calcareous cliffs; 0-1100m; fl. 8.
E. Crete (S.E. of Sitia & Sideros peninsula); Karpathos, Saria [Kiklades; otherwise E. Aegean Islands (Rodos)].

39. Smyrnium L.

S. apiifolium Willd. (*FE* **2**: 328) = **1**.

1. S. creticum Mill., *Gard. Dict.* ed.8: no.4 (1768) - *FE 2*: 328 as *S. apiifolium* Willd.
Cr (W, C, E) Kp - *MAP 1313*
Calcareous cliff-ledges, gorge-beds, rocky places, around old buildings; 0-1100m; fl. 4-5.
Crete (sporadic); Karpathos [Aegean region; otherwise E. Aegean Islands & Turkey].

2. S. olusatrum L., *Sp. pl.*: 262 (1753) - *FE 2*: 328.
Cr (W, C, E) Kp - *MAP 1314*
Olive groves, rocky places, old walls, roadsides, waste areas; 100-350m; fl. 3-4.
Crete (widespread); Karpathos [mainly S. Europe].

3. S. perfoliatum L., *Sp. pl.*: 262 (1753) - *FE* **2**: 328.
a. subsp. **rotundifolium** (Mill.) Hartvig in Strid, *Mount. Fl. Greece* **1**: 672 (1986) - *FE 2*: 328 as *S. rotundifolium* Mill.
Cr (W, C) - *MAP 1315*
Olive groves, rocky places, abandoned terraces; 0-800m; fl. 4-5.
W. & C. Crete [Mediterranean region].
All records of *S. perfoliatum* are referable to subsp. **a** (Barclay, 1986: 99).

S. rotundifolium Mill. (*FE* **2**: 328) = **3a**.

40. Thapsia L.

1. T. garganica L., *Mant. pl.*: 57 (1767) - *FE* 2: 370.
Cr (W, C, E) Kp Sa - *MAP 1316*
Calcareous rocky places, abandoned fields; 0-900m; fl. 4-5.
Mainly C. & E. Crete; Karpathos, Saria [Mediterranean region].

41. Tordylium L.

1. T. apulum L., *Sp. pl.*: 239 (1753) - *FE* 2: 367.
Cr (W, C, E) Ks Kp Sa - *MAP 1317*
Olive groves, phrygana, rocky places, gorge-beds, soil-filled hollows, fields, disturbed ground; 0-850m; fl. 3-4.
Crete (widespread, rarer towards E.); Karpathos group [Mediterranean region].

T. byzantinum (Azn.) Hayek (*FE* 2: 367) is included in synonymy of **T. trachycarpum**.

2. T. hirtocarpum P.Candargy in *Bull. Soc. bot. Fr.* **44**: 159 (1897) - not cited in *FE*.
Cr (E) Kp Sa - *MAP 1318*
Calcareous rocky debris below cliffs, phrygana; 50-300m; fl. 3.
E. Crete (S. side); Karpathos, Saria [Kiklades; otherwise E. Aegean Islands & W. Turkey].
Recorded by Runemark (1968: 256) and Greuter et al. (1984*b*: 294).

3. T. officinale L., *Sp. pl.*: 239 (1753) - *FE* 2: 367.
Cr (W) - *MAP 1319*
Rocky places, gorge-beds.
W. Crete [Italy, Balkan peninsula & Aegean region].

"*T. pestalozzae*" (*FE* 2: 367) = **2** (cf. Runemark, 1968: 252-255).

? T. trachycarpum (Boiss.) Al-Eisawi & Jury in *Bot. J. Linn. Soc.* **97**: 395 (1988) - *FE* 2: 367 as *Ainsworthia trachycarpa* Boiss. (Including *T. byzantinum* (Azn.) Hayek - *FE* 2: 367.)
Doubtfully present in Crete (Greuter, 1974: 158) [Turkey-in-Europe; otherwise S.W. Asia].

42. Torilis Adans.

1. T. arvensis (Huds.) Link, *Enum. hort. berol. alt.* **1**: 265 (1821) - *FE* 2: 371.
a. subsp. arvensis
Cr (W, E) - *MAP 1320*
Vineyards, shady stream-beds.
W. & E. Crete [W., C. & S. Europe].

b. subsp. **neglecta** (Spreng.) Thell. in Hegi, *Ill. Fl. Mitt.-Eur.* **5(2)**: 1055 (1926) - *FE* 2: 371.
?Cr Kp - *MAP 1321*
?Crete; Karpathos [C. & S. Europe].
c. subsp. **purpurea** (Ten.) Hayek in *Beih. Repert. nov. Spec. Regni veg.* **30(1)**: 1057 (1927) - *FE* 2: 371.
Cr (W, C, E) - *MAP 1322*
Platanus woodland, rocky places; 600m.
Crete (sporadic) [S. Europe].

2. T. leptophylla (L.) Rchb.f. in Rchb. & Rchb.f., *Icon. fl. germ. helv.* **21**: sub t.169 (1866) - *FE* 2: 371.
Cr (W, C) Kp - *MAP 1323*
Olive groves, rocky places; 0-500m; fl. 4.
W. & C. Crete; Kasos, Karpathos [mainly S. Europe].

3. T. nodosa (L.) Gaertn., *Fruct. sem. pl.* **1**: 82 (1788) - *FE* 2: 371.
Cr (W, C, E) Ks Kp Sa - *MAP 1324*
Platanus woodland, rocky places; 0-600m; fl. 3-4.
Mainly W. Crete; Karpathos group [W., C. & S. Europe].

T. webbii Jury in *Bot. J. Linn. Soc.* **95**: 297 (1987) differs from **3** in having all mericarps covered with spines. It has been recorded from various parts of the Mediterranean region, but apparently not yet from the Cretan area (Jury, op. cit.), although *T. nodosa* var. *bracteosa* (Bianca) Murb., cited as synonym of *T. webbii* by Jury (op. cit.), was recorded from Crete by Gandoger (Rechinger, 1943*a*: 419). These records require confirmation, however, because Gandoger is now known to have been unreliable (Greuter, 1974: 153).

43. Turgenia Hoffm.

1. T. latifolia (L.) Hoffm., *Gen. pl. umbell.*: 59 (1814) - *FE* 2: 372.
Cr - *NOT MAPPED*
Crete [mainly S.C. & S. Europe].

URTICACEAE

1. Parietaria L.

1. P. cretica L., *Sp. pl.*: 1052 (1753) - *FE* 1: 69.
Cr (W, C, E) Ks Kp Sa - *MAP 1325*
Cliffs, rocks, walls; 0-500m; fl. 4-5.
Crete (widespread); Karpathos group [Sicily, Greece & Aegean region].

P. diffusa Mert. & W.D.J.Koch (*FE* 1: 69) = **2**.

2. P. judaica L., *Diss. Fl. palaest.*: 32 (1756) -
FE 1: 69 as *P. diffusa* Mert. & W.D.J.Koch.
Cr (W, C, E) Kp Sa - *MAP 1326*
Scrub, rocks, walls, damp places; 0-600m; fl. 3-5.
Crete (widespread); Karpathos, Saria [mainly
W. & S. Europe].

3. P. lusitanica L., *Sp. pl.*: 1052 (1753) - *FE* 1:
69.
a. subsp. lusitanica
Cr (W, C, E) Ks Kp - *MAP 1327*
Platanus & Castanea woodland, shady gorge-beds, cliffs, rocky places; 50-600m.
Crete (sporadic); Kasos, Karpathos [S. Europe].

"*P. officinalis*" (*FE* 1: 69) = **2** (Barclay, 1986:
100).

2. Urtica L.

1. U. dubia Forssk., *Fl. aegypt.-arab.*: cxxi
(1775) - *FE* 1: 68.
Cr (W, C, E) Ks - *MAP 1328*
Caverns & ledges of cliffs, waste areas, villages, animal enclosures; 0-550m; fl. 3-5.
Crete (sporadic); Kasos [mainly Mediterranean
region].

2. U. pilulifera L., *Sp. pl.*: 983 (1753) - *FE* 1:
68.
Cr (W, C, E) Ks Kp Sa - *MAP 1329*
Caverns & ledges of cliffs, waste areas, villages, animal enclosures; 0-700m; fl. 3-5.
Crete (sporadic); Karpathos group [mainly C. &
S. Europe].

3. U. urens L., *Sp. pl.*: 984 (1753) - *FE* 1: 68.
Cr (W, C, E) Kp - *MAP 1330*
Cultivated ground, waste areas; fl. 3-5.
Crete (sporadic); Karpathos [almost throughout
Europe].

VALERIANACEAE

1. Centranthus DC.

1. C. calcitrapae (L.) Dufr., *Hist. nat. Valér.*:
39 (1811) - *FE* 4: 56.
a. subsp. calcitrapae
Cr (W, C, E) Ks Kp - *MAP 1331*
Calcareous rocky places, screes & stony ground beneath cliffs; 0-1500m; fl. 4-5.
Mainly W. & C. Crete; Kasos, Karpathos [S.
Europe].

C. nevadensis subsp. *sieberi* (Heldr.)
I.Richardson (*FE* 4: 56) = **3**.

[2. C. ruber] (L.) DC. in Lam. & DC., *Fl.
franç.* ed.3, **4**: 239 (1805) - *FE* 4: 55.

[a. subsp. ruber]
Cr (W, C) Kp - *MAP 1332*
Cultivated for ornament and possibly naturalized on old walls; 0-300m; fl. 4.
W. & C. Crete; Karpathos [W., C. & S.
Europe].

●**3. C. sieberi** Heldr. in *Verh. zool.-bot. Ges.
Wien* 15: 295 (1890) - *FE* 4: 56 as *C.
nevadensis* subsp. *sieberi* (Heldr.) I.Richardson.
Cr (W) - *MAP 1333*
Calcareous rock-crevices, open gravelly areas & screes; 1800-2300m; fl. 7-9.
W. Crete (Lefka Ori) - Endemic.
[Plate 8.]

2. Fedia Gaertn.

1. F. cornucopiae (L.) Gaertn., *Fruct. sem. pl.*
2: 37 (1790) - *FE* 4: 52.
Cr (C) - *MAP 1334*
Rocky places; 50-100m; fl. 2-3.
C. Crete [Mediterranean region].

3. Valeriana L.

●**1. V. asarifolia** Dufr., *Hist. nat. Valér.*: 44
(1811) - *FE* 4: 53.
Cr (W, C, E) Kp - *MAP 1335*
Calcareous cliffs, ledges & crevices, shady rocky places; 50-1300m; fl. 3-4.
Crete (widespread, rarer towards E.); Karpathos
- Endemic.

4. Valerianella Mill.

? **V. carinata** Loisel., *Not. fl. France*: 149
(1810) - *FE* 4: 50.
Doubtfully present in Crete [W., C. & S.
Europe].

1. V. coronata (L.) DC. in Lam. & DC., *Fl.
franç.* ed.3, **4**: 241 (1805) - *FE* 4: 49.
Cr (W) Ks Kp - *MAP 1336*
Coastal phrygana, gorges, calcareous screes; 0-450m.
W. Crete; Kasos, Karpathos [C. & S. Europe].

? **V. costata** (Steven) Betcke, *Animadv. bot.
Valer.*: 11 (1826) - *FE* 4: 51.
Doubtfully present in Crete [Balearic Islands,
Sicily & S.E. Europe].

2. V. discoidea (L.) Loisel., *Not. fl. France*:
148 (1810) - *FE* 4: 50.
Cr (W, C, E) Ks Kp - *MAP 1337*
Calcareous rocky places, fallow fields; fl. 4-5.
Mainly W. Crete; Kasos, Karpathos
[Mediterranean region].

3. V. echinata (L.) DC. in Lam. & DC., *Fl. franç.* ed.3, **4**: 242 (1805) - *FE* **4**: 51.
Cr (W, E) Ks Kp - *MAP 1338*
Rocky places; 300-1450m.
W. & E. Crete; Kasos, Karpathos [S. Europe].

4. V. eriocarpa Desv. in *J. Bot. Paris* **2**: 314 (1809) - *FE* **4**: 51.
Cr - *NOT MAPPED*
Crete [W. & S. Europe].

5. V. hirsutissima Link in *Linnaea* **9**: 580 (1835) - *FE* **4**: 50.
Cr - *NOT MAPPED*
Crete [E. Greece & Turkey-in-Europe; otherwise W. Turkey].

? V. locusta (L.) Laterr., *Fl. bordel.* ed.2: 93 (1821) - *FE* **4**: 50.
Doubtfully present in Crete [most of Europe].

6. V. microcarpa Loisel., *Not. fl. France*: 151 (1810) - *FE* **4**: 51.
Cr Kp - *NOT MAPPED*
Crete; Karpathos [Mediterranean region].

7. V. muricata (Steven ex M.Bieb.) Baxter in Loudon, *Suppl. Hort. brit.*: 654 (1850) - *FE* **4**: 51.
Cr (E) Kp - *MAP 1339*
Calcareous rocky places.
E. Crete; Karpathos [S. Europe].

8. V. obtusiloba Boiss., *Diagn. pl. orient.* ser.1, **3**: 59 (1843) - *FE* **4**: 50.
Cr (W, C) Kp - *MAP 1340*
Phrygana, gorge-beds, rocky places, open dry stony ground; 0-300m; fl. 4-5.
W. & C. Crete; Karpathos [S. Greece & Aegean region; otherwise S.W. Asia].

9. V. turgida (Steven) Betcke, *Animadv. bot. Valer.*: 14 (1826) - *FE* **4**: 51.
Cr (W, C) - *MAP 1341*
Fallow fields, field-margins; 900-1050m.
W. & C. Crete [S.E. Europe].

10. V. vesicaria (L.) Moench, *Methodus*: 493 (1794) - *FE* **4**: 50.
Cr (W, C, E) Ks Kp - *MAP 1342*
Calcareous rocky places, maritime sands; 0-600m; fl. 4-5.
Crete (sporadic); Kasos, Karpathos [C. & E. Mediterranean region].

VERBENACEAE

Lippia nodiflora (L.) Michx. (*FE* **3**: 123) = **Phyla 1**.

1. Phyla Lour.

1. P. nodiflora (L.) Greene in *Pittonia* **4**: 46 (1899) - *FE* **3**: 123 as *Lippia nodiflora* (L.) Michx.
Cr (W, C) - *MAP 1343*
Marshes, hollows of sand-dunes & other damp places near sea; fl. 7-10.
W. & C. Crete [Mediterranean region].

2. Verbena L.

1. V. officinalis L., *Sp. pl.*: 20 (1753) - *FE* **3**: 123.
Cr (W, C) Kp - *MAP 1344*
Scrub, damp ground, dry river-beds, waste areas; fl. 4-6.
W. & C. Crete; Karpathos [most of Europe].

2. V. supina L., *Sp. pl.*: 21 (1753) - *FE* **3**: 123.
Cr (W) - *MAP 1345*
Muddy gravel; 50-700m; fl. 11.
W. Crete [mainly S. Europe].

3. Vitex L.

1. V. agnus-castus L., *Sp. pl.*: 638 (1753) - *FE* **3**: 122.
Cr (W, C, E) Kp - *MAP 1346*
Riparian woodland, marshes & damp places, lake-shore, river-banks, gorge-beds, maritime sands; 0-600m; fl. 8-10.
Crete (widespread); Karpathos [S. Europe].

VIOLACEAE

1. Viola L.

V. alba Besser is given for the Cretan area in *FE* **2**: 272, although there are no records as a basis for this (Greuter, 1974: 139).

●**1. V. cretica** Boiss. & Heldr. in Boiss., *Diagn. pl. orient.* ser.1, **8**: 51 (1849) - *FE* **2**: 273.
Cr (C, E) - *MAP 1347*
Woodland, shady stream-banks, springs, stony mountain pastures; 100-1800m; fl. 3-5.
C. & E. Crete - Endemic.
Additionally recorded from the Lefka Ori in W. Crete in *MFG* **1**: 615.

●**2. V. fragrans** Sieber, *Reise Kreta* **2**: 320 (1823) - *FE* **2**: 277.
Cr (W, C, E) - *MAP 1348*
Calcareous rock-crevices, rubble & screes; (1400-)1600-2450m; fl. 4-7.
Crete (Lefka Ori, Psiloritis & Dikti) - Endemic.
Erroneously given as occurring in Greece in *FE*

(cf. *MFG* 1: 623).

3. V. heldreichiana Boiss., *Diagn. pl. orient.*
ser.1, **8**: 53 (1849) - *FE* 2: 281.
Kp - *MAP 1349*
Karpathos [S. Turkey].
Records from Crete (and Cyprus) are referable
to **5** (Erben, 1985: 372).

? V. hirta L., *Sp. pl.*: 934 (1753) - *FE* 2: 273.
Doubtfully present in Crete (Greuter, 1974: 156)
[most of Europe].

V. kitaibeliana Schult. is given for the Cretan
area in *FE* 2: 281, although there are no records
as a basis for this (Greuter, 1974: 139).

4. V. odorata L., *Sp. pl.*: 934 (1753) - *FE* 2:
272.
Cr - *NOT MAPPED*
Crete [most of Europe].

5. V. rauliniana Erben in *Mitt. bot. StSamml.
Münch.* **21**: 372 (1985).
Cr (W, C) - *MAP 1350*
*Calcareous rock-crevices, mobile screes, stony
& gravelly ground, flat clayey areas; 1400-
2300m; fl. 4-7.*
W. & C. Crete (Lefka Ori, Kedros & Psiloritis)
[Cyprus].

6. V. reichenbachiana Jord. ex Boreau, *Fl.
centre France* ed.3, **2**: 78 (1857) - *FE* 2: 274.
(Including *V. idaea* Gand. - not cited in *FE*.)
Cr (C) - *NOT MAPPED*
C. Crete (Psiloritis) [W., C. & S. Europe].
Regarded as absent from the Cretan area in *FE*,
although *V. idaea* Gand., *Fl. Cret.*: 14 (1916),
described from Psiloritis in C. Crete, is included
in synonymy here, after *MFG* 1: 617.

7. V. scorpiuroides Coss. in *Bull. Soc. bot. Fr.*
19: 80 (1872) - *FE* 2: 282.
Cr (W, E) - *MAP 1351*
*Rocky phrygana & steep banks, usually on
gypsum; 0-200m; fl. 3-4.*
W. & E. ends of Crete [Kithira & Andikithira;
otherwise N. Africa].

V. suavis M.Bieb. is given as doubtfully present
in the Cretan area in *FE* 2: 272, although there
are no records as a basis for this (Greuter, 1974:
139).

VITACEAE

1. Vitis L.

1. V. vinifera L., *Sp. pl.*: 202 (1753) - *FE* 2:
246.
a. subsp. **sylvestris** (C.C.Gmel.) Hegi, *Ill. Fl.
Mitt.-Eur.* **5**: 364 (1925) - *FE* 2: 246.
Cr (W) - *MAP 1352*

Tall maquis; 300m.
W. Crete (Fasas valley) [C. & S. Europe].
Recorded since *FE* (Greuter et al., 1984b: 295).
[b. subsp. **vinifera]**
Cr Ks Kp - *NOT MAPPED*
*Cultivated for its fruit, persisting in abandoned
vineyards and naturalized in woodland, olive
groves, scrub; 0-900m; fl. 5.*
Crete; Kasos, Karpathos [C. & S. Europe].

ZYGOPHYLLACEAE

1. Fagonia L.

1. F. cretica L., *Sp. pl.*: 386 (1753) - *FE* 2:
205.
Cr (C, E) - *MAP 1353*
*Olive groves, calcareous screes, among dwarf
shrubs on gravelly ground on offshore island,
roadsides; 0-125m; fl. 6.*
C. & E. Crete [Mediterranean region].

Peganum harmala L. (*FE* 2: 205) was almost
certainly recorded in error (Greuter, 1974: 156).

2. Tribulus L.

1. T. terrestris L., *Sp. pl.*: 387 (1753) - *FE* 2:
205.
Cr (W, C, E) - *MAP 1354*
*Cultivated & bare ground, town pavements,
maritime sands; 0-500m; fl. 4-9.*
Crete (sporadic) [mainly S. Europe].

3. Zygophyllum L.

1. Z. album L.f., *Dec. pl. Horti upsal.*: 11
(1762) - *FE* 2: 205.
Cr (E) Ks Kp - *MAP 1355*
*Superficially hardened flat sandy ground by sea;
fl. 6.*
E. Crete (Gaidouronisi & Koufonisi islands);
Kasos, Karpathos [N.E. Spain; otherwise N.
Africa & S.W. Asia].

MONOCOTYLEDONES

AGAVACEAE

1. Agave L.

[1. A. americana] L., *Sp. pl.*: 323 (1753) - *FE*
5: 74.
Cr (W, C, E) Kp - *MAP 1356*
*Cultivated and possibly naturalized on roadsides
& near villages; 0-400m.*
Mainly W. & C. Crete; Karpathos [mainly
Mediterranean region; from Mexico].

ALISMATACEAE

1. Alisma L.

1. A. lanceolatum With., *Arr. Brit. pl.* ed.3, **2**: 362 (1796) - *FE* **5**: 2.
Cr (W, C, E) - *MAP 1357*
Shallow fresh water, marshes, wet ditches.
Crete (sporadic) [most of Europe].

2. A. plantago-aquatica L., *Sp. pl.*: 342 (1753) - *FE* **5**: 2.
Cr - *NOT MAPPED*
Crete [almost throughout Europe].

AMARYLLIDACEAE

Leucojum autumnale L. (*FE* **5**: 76), given as "*L. aestivum*" by Barclay (1986: 103), was almost certainly recorded in error (Greuter et al., 1985: 23).

1. Narcissus L.

1. N. serotinus L., *Sp. pl.*: 290 (1753) - *FE* **5**: 79.
Cr (W, C, E) - *MAP 1358*
Sparse phrygana, open stony ground, calcareous screes, damp places; 0-750m; fl. 9-11.
Mainly W. & C. Crete [Mediterranean region].

2. N. tazetta L., *Sp. pl.*: 290 (1753) - *FE* **5**: 79.
a. subsp. tazetta
Cr (W, C, E) Ks Kp - *MAP 1359*
Marshes, damp places, field-margins; 0-750m; fl. 2-4.
Crete (sporadic); Kasos, Karpathos [Mediterranean region].

2. Pancratium L.

1. P. maritimum L., *Sp. pl.*: 291 (1753) - *FE* **5**: 84.
Cr (W, C, E) Kp - *MAP 1360*
Maritime sands; fl. 8-10.
Crete (sporadic); Karpathos [S. Europe].

3. Sternbergia Waldst. & Kit.

●**1. S. greuteriana** Kamari & R.Artelari in *Willdenowia* **19**: 371 (1990).
Cr (W, C, E) Ks Kp Sa - *MAP 1361*
Scrub, phrygana, calcareous rocks, flat clayey areas; 0-1200m; fl. 9-11.
Mainly E. Crete; Karpathos group - Endemic.
Morphologically closest to **2**, but with narrower leaves and smaller flowers.

2. S. lutea (L.) Ker-Gawl. ex Spreng., *Syst. veg.* **2**: 57 (1825) - *FE* **5**: 76 as *S. lutea* (L.) Ker-Gawl. ex Spreng. subsp. *lutea*.
Cr (W, C) - *MAP 1362*
Calcareous rocky slopes with scrub or phrygana; 350-600m; fl. 9-11.
W. & C. Crete [Mediterranean region].
Given as doubtfully present by Barclay (1986: 103), but occurrence since confirmed by Kamari & Artelari (1990).
Subsp. *sicula* (Tineo ex Guss.) D.A.Webb (*FE* **5**: 76) = **3**.

3. S. sicula Tineo ex Guss., *Fl. sicul. syn.* **2**: 811 (1845) - *FE* **5**: 76 as *S. lutea* subsp. *sicula* (Tineo ex Guss.) D.A.Webb.
Cr (W, C, E) - *MAP 1363*
Clearings in Pinus brutia woodland, rocky scrub, phrygana, calcareous rock-crevices; 100-1000m; fl. 9-11.
Crete (sporadic) [S. Italy, Sicily, S. Greece & Aegean region].
A record from Karpathos (Greuter et al., 1983a: 71) is almost certainly referable to **1** (cf. Kamari & Artelari, 1990).

ARACEAE

1. Arisarum Mill.

1. A. vulgare Targ.Tozz. in *Annali Mus. Stor. nat. Firenze* **2**(2): 67 (1810) - *FE* **5**: 272 as *A. vulgare* Targ.Tozz. subsp. *vulgare*.
Cr (W, C, E) Kp - *MAP 1364*
Woodland, olive groves, maquis, scrub, rocky places; 0-650m; fl. 10, 3-4.
Mainly W. & C. Crete; Karpathos [mainly Mediterranean region].

2. Arum L.

1. A. alpinum Schott & Kotschy in *Bot. Ztg* **9**: 285 (1851).
Cr (W, C) - *MAP 1365*
Flat clayey areas, bases of cliffs; 950-1400m; fl. 5.
W. & C. Crete (Lefka Ori, Kedros & Psiloritis) [mainly S. Europe].
Recorded since *FE*, where erroneously included in synonymy of *A. orientale* M.Bieb. subsp. *orientale* (Greuter, 1984: 20-21).

2. A. concinnatum Schott, *Prodr. syst. Aroid.*: 84 (1860) - not cited in *FE*.
Cr (W, C, E) - *MAP 1366*
Woodland, olive groves, rocky places, waste areas in & near villages; 0-650m; fl. 4-5.
Crete (widespread) [Greece & Aegean region; otherwise S.W. Asia].
This is the most frequent species in the *A.*

italicum complex in the Aegean region.

3. A. creticum Boiss. & Heldr. in Boiss., *Diagn. pl. orient.* ser.1, **13**: 9 (1853) - *FE* **5**: 270.
Cr (W, C, E) Ks Kp - *MAP 1367*
Calcareous woodland, beneath trees, rocky garigue, stone heaps in fields, other rocky places; 0-1500m; fl. 3-5.
Crete (sporadic); Kasos, Karpathos [E. Aegean Islands & S.W. Turkey].
Not endemic to the Cretan area as given in *FE* (cf. Mill in Davis, 1984: 54). Plants with white or pale green spathes and dark purple spadices (as included in the description in *FE*) belong to **5**.

4. A. cyrenaicum Hruby in *Bull. Soc. bot. Genève* **4**: 159 (1912).
Cr (W) - *MAP 1368*
Platanus woodland, in & among rocks & boulders; 100-550m; fl. 3-4.
W. Crete [N.E. Libya].
Recorded since *FE* (Briggs in Turland, 1992*b*: 162).

● **5. A. idaeum** Coustur. & Gand., *Fl. cret.*: 98 (1916).
Cr (W, C, E) - *MAP 1369*
Calcareous woodland, open stony slopes with Berberis bushes, flat clayey areas; 900-2400m; fl. 4-5.
Crete (Lefka Ori, Kedros, Psiloritis, Dikti & Afendis Kavousi) - Endemic.
Erroneously included in synonymy of *A. maculatum* L. in *FE* **5**: 270 (Greuter, 1984: 19).

"*A. italicum*", including "subsp. *byzantinum*" (*FE* **5**: 270) = **2** (Greuter, 1984: 20; Greuter et al., 1985: 24).

"*A. maculatum*" (*FE* **5**: 270) = **5** (Greuter, 1984: 19).

A. nickelii Schott (Barclay, 1986: 104) = **2**.

● **6. A. purpureospathum** P.C.Boyce in *Aroideana* **10(1)**: 8 (1987).
Cr (W) - *MAP 1370*
Shady hollows among calcareous boulders, beneath trees, bases of cliffs, short grass, maritime sands, among ruined buildings; 0-150m; fl. 2-4.
W. Crete (S. coast) - Endemic.
[Plate 8.] Vulnerable species, legally protected.

3. Biarum Schott

1. B. davisii Turrill in *Gdnr's Chron.* ser.3, **104**: 437 (1938) - *FE* **5**: 271.
● **a.** subsp. **davisii**
Cr (W, C, E) - *MAP 1371*

Open calcareous phrygana, bare stony ground, rock-crevices, soil-pockets in & among rocks; 50-800m; fl. 9-11.
Crete (sporadic) - Endemic.
The species occurs outside the Cretan area on the E. Aegean Island of Simi and in S.W. Turkey, as subsp. *marmarisense* P.C.Boyce (Boyce, 1989).

2. B. tenuifolium (L.) Schott in Schott & Endl., *Melet. bot.*: 17 (1832) - *FE* **5**: 271.
● **a.** subsp. **idomenaeum** P.C.Boyce & Athanasiou in *Flora medit.* **1**: 6 (1991).
Cr (C, E) - *MAP 1372*
Calcareous stony ground with Quercus coccifera trees, phrygana, soil-pockets in & beneath cliffs; 50-1500m; fl. 9-10(-11).
C. & E. Crete - Endemic.
b. subsp. **tenuifolium** var. **zelebori** (Schott) Engl. in A.& C.DC., *Monogr. phan.* **2**: 574 (1879) - *FE* **5**: 271 as *B. zelebori* Schott.
Cr (E) - *MAP 1373*
Step-crevices of rocks, among calcareous rubble of gorge-bed; 200-850m.
E. Crete [E. Aegean Islands & S.W. Turkey].
Most Cretan records of var. *zelebori* are referable to subsp. **a** (Boyce & Athanasiou, 1991: 5; Turland, 1992*b*: 162). Var. *tenuifolium* is not known to occur.

B. zelebori Schott (*FE* **5**: 271) = **2b** var. **zelebori**.

4. Dracunculus Mill.

1. D. vulgaris Schott in Schott & Endl., *Melet. bot.*: 17 (1832) - *FE* **5**: 272.
Cr (W, C, E) Ks Kp - *MAP 1374*
Olive groves, scrub, waste areas in & near villages; 0-1050m; fl. 4-5.
Mainly W. & C. Crete; Kasos, Karpathos [mainly C. & E. Mediterranean region].
Both spathes and spadices are normally dark purple, although some populations include variants with whitish spathes; intermediates, with marbled spathes and orange spadices, also occur.

CYPERACEAE

1. Bolboschoenus Asch. ex Palla

1. B. maritimus (L.) Palla in W.D.J.Koch, *Syn. deut. schweiz. Fl.* ed.3, **3**: 2532 (1905) - *FE* **5**: 278 as *Scirpus maritimus* L.
Cr (W, C, E) - *MAP 1375*
Coastal marshes & wet ditches; fl. 4-5.
Crete (sporadic) [almost throughout Europe].

2. Carex L.

1. C. caryophyllea Latourr., *Chlor. lugd.*: 27 (1785) - *FE* **5**: 312.
Cr (W) - *MAP 1376*
Hollows in calcareous rocks; 1400m.
W. Crete (Lefka Ori) [most of Europe].
Recorded since *FE* (Greuter et al., 1985: 25).

2. C. cretica Gradst. & J.Kern in *Acta bot. neerl.* **17**: 242 (1968) - *FE* **5**: 308.
Cr (W) - *MAP 1377*
Riparian Platanus woodland, stream-banks in maquis, other damp places; 250-350m.
W. Crete (S. of Kastelli Kissamou & Fasas valley) [E. Aegean Islands (Ikaria)].
Not endemic to Crete as given in *FE* (cf. Nilsson in Davis, 1985: 130).

3. C. distachya Desf., *Fl. atlant.* **2**: 336 (1799) - *FE* **5**: 296.
Cr (W, C, E) - *MAP 1378*
Woodland, especially Platanus; 100-750m; fl. 4.
Crete (sporadic) [S. Europe].

4. C. distans L., *Syst. nat.* ed.10, **2**: 1263 (1759) - *FE* **5**: 308.
Cr (W, E) Kp - *MAP 1379*
Marshes, seasonally wet places, damp grassland, damp shady rocks.
Mainly W. Crete; Karpathos [most of Europe].

5. C. divisa Huds., *Fl. angl.*: 348 (1762) - *FE* **5**: 299.
Cr (W, C, E) Kp - *MAP 1380*
Marshes, damp grassland, flat clayey areas, coastal saline ground; 0-1400m; fl. 4-5.
Crete (sporadic); Karpathos [W., S.C. & S. Europe].

6. C. divulsa Stokes in With., *Bot. arr. Brit. pl.* ed.2, **2**: 1035 (1787) - *FE* **5**: 298.
Cr (W) - *MAP 1381*
Marshes, stream-banks, ditches, damp, shady & rocky places; 0-1800m; fl. 4.
W. Crete [most of Europe].
Greuter et al. (1985: 26) observe that Cretan specimens show features sometimes regarded as diagnostic for other, related species, but without any clear correlation of characters.

7. C. extensa Gooden. in *Trans. Linn. Soc. Lond.* **2**: 175 (1794) - *FE* **5**: 309.
Cr (W, C) Kp - *MAP 1382*
Brackish coastal marshes; fl. 4.
W. & C. Crete; Karpathos [coasts of most of Europe].

8. C. flacca Schreb., *Spic. fl. lips.*, *App.*: 178 (1771) - *FE* **5**: 306.

a. subsp. **serrulata** (Biv.) Greuter in *Boissiera* **13**: 167 (1967) - *FE* **5**: 306.
Cr (W, C, E) Kp - *MAP 1383*
Marshes, streams, ditches, springs & other damp ground; 0-900m; fl. 4-5.
Mainly W. & C. Crete; Karpathos [S. Europe].

9. C. halleriana Asso, *Syn. Stirp. Aragon.*: 133 (1779) - *FE* **5**: 311.
Cr (W, C, E) - *MAP 1384*
Moist shaded calcareous rocks & crevices; 400-750m.
Crete (sporadic) [S.C. & S. Europe].

10. C. hispida Willd. in Schkuhr, *Beschr. Riedgräs.*: 63 (1801) - *FE* **5**: 306.
Cr (W, C, E) Kp - *MAP 1385*
Marshes, stream-banks, ditches, springs, damp ground, seasonally wet places; 0-400m; fl. 4.
Crete (sporadic); Karpathos [Mediterranean region].

●**11. C. idaea** Greuter, Matthäs & Risse in *Willdenowia* **15**: 25 (1985).
Cr (C) - *MAP 1386*
Small spring-fed marshes on calcareous rocky ground; 1250-1600m; fl. 4-5.
C. Crete (Psiloritis) - Endemic.
[Plate 8.] An old record from Dikti in E. Crete requires confirmation (Greuter et al., 1985: 26). Related to **4**.

12. C. illegitima Ces. in Friedr., *Reise*: 272 (1838) - *FE* **5**: 313.
Cr (E) Kp - *MAP 1387*
Pinus brutia woodland; 200-700m; fl. 3.
E. Crete (Afendis Kavousi); Karpathos [Sicily (Pantelleria) & W. coast of Balkan peninsula; otherwise S.W. Asia].
Regarded as absent from the Cretan area in *FE*, although doubtful records already existed; occurrence since confirmed by Turland (1992*b*: 163).
"*C. muricata*" (Zaffran, 1976: 199; 1990: 379)
? = **6** (cf. Greuter et al., 1985: 26).

13. C. otrubae Podp. in *Spisy vydáv. prír. Fak. Masaryk. Univ.* **12**: 15 (1922) - *FE* **5**: 297.
Cr (W, C) - *MAP 1388*
Marshes, ditches, springs, seasonally wet places; 0-400m; fl. 4.
W. & C. Crete [almost throughout Europe].

14. C. pendula Huds., *Fl. angl.*: 352 (1762) - *FE* **5**: 305.
Cr (W, C) - *MAP 1389*
Streams & ditches in shady places; 0-550m; fl. 4-5.
W. & C. Crete [W., C. & S. Europe].

15. C. punctata Gaudin, *Agrost. helv.* 2: 152 (1811) - *FE* **5**: 308.
Cr (W) - *MAP 1390*
Stream-banks in maquis; 200m.
W. Crete (Fasas valley) [mainly W. & S. Europe].

16. C. remota L., *Fl. angl.*: 24 (1754) - *FE* **5**: 300.
Cr (W) - *MAP 1391*
Stream-banks in Platanus woodland & maquis; 250-350m.
W. Crete (Fasas valley) [most of Europe].

"*C. spicata*" (*FE* **5**: 298) ? = **6** (Greuter et al., 1985: 26).

? **C. vulpina** L., *Sp. pl.*: 973 (1753) - *FE* **5**: 297.
Doubtfully present in Crete [most of Europe].

3. Cladium R.Br.

1. C. mariscus (L.) Pohl, *Tent. fl. bohem.* 1: 32 (1809) - *FE* **5**: 288.
Cr (W, C) - *MAP 1392*
Marshes, river-banks, springs & other damp places; 0-400m.
W. & C. Crete [almost throughout Europe].

4. Cyperus L.

1. C. capitatus Vand., *Fasc. pl.*: 5 (1771) - *FE* **5**: 287.
Cr (W, C, E) - *MAP 1393*
Maritime sands; fl. 3-4.
Crete (sporadic) [S. Europe].

[2. C. esculentus] L., *Sp. pl.*: 45 (1753) - *FE* **5**: 286.
Cr - *NOT MAPPED*
Introduced, exact status not known.
Crete [mainly Mediterranean region].

C. flavescens L. (*FE* **5**: 288) = **Pycreus 1**.

C. flavidus Retz. (*FE* **5**: 287) = **Pycreus 2**.

3. C. fuscus L., *Sp. pl.*: 46 (1753) - *FE* **5**: 286.
Cr (W, E) - *MAP 1394*
Dried mud at shore of lake, wet stony ground; 50-750m; fl. -10.
W. & E. Crete [most of Europe].

C. laevigatus L. (*FE* **5**: 287) = **Juncellus 1**.

4. C. longus L., *Sp. pl.*: 45 (1753) - *FE* **5**: 286. (Including subsp. *badius* (Desf.) Murb. - *FE* **5**: 286.)
Cr (W, E) - *MAP 1395*
Marshes, streams, springs, damp & seasonally wet places; 0-300m; fl. 4-5.

Mainly W. Crete [W., C. & S. Europe].

5. C. rotundus L., *Sp. pl.*: 45 (1753) - *FE* **5**: 286.
Cr (W, C) - *MAP 1396*
Marshy & damp places, grassy maritime sand, roadside; fl. 5-6.
W. & C. Crete [W.C. & S. Europe].

5. Eleocharis R.Br.

1. E. multicaulis (Sm.) Desv., *Observ. pl. Angers*: 74 (1818) - *FE* **5**: 283.
Cr (W) - *MAP 1397*
Marshy ground, wet rocks.
W. Crete (Agia lake & Fasas valley) [mainly W. Europe].

2. E. palustris (L.) Roem. & Schult., *Syst. veg.* 2: 151 (1817) - *FE* **5**: 283.
Cr (W, C) Kp - *MAP 1398*
Marshes, damp grassland, flat clayey areas periodically waterlogged; fl. 4-5.
W. & C. Crete; Karpathos [almost throughout Europe].

3. E. uniglumis (Link) Schult. in Schult. & Schult.f., *Mant.* 2: 88 (1824) - *FE* **5**: 283.
Cr (W) - *MAP 1399*
Moist ground, seasonally wet places.
W. Crete [most of Europe].

6. Fimbristylis Vahl

"*F. ferruginea*" (*FE* **5**: 284) = **1** (Tan in Davis, 1985: 46).

1. F. sieberiana Kunth, *Enum. pl.* 2: 237 (1837) - *FE* **5**: 284 as "*F. ferruginea*".
Cr (E) - *MAP 1400*
Roadside ditch or rivulet; 350m.
E. Crete (W. of Ierapetra) [S. Spain; otherwise S.W. Asia & warm temperate & tropical regions worldwide].

7. Fuirena Rottb.

1. F. pubescens (Poir.) Kunth, *Enum. pl.* 2: 182 (1837) - *FE* **5**: 284.
Cr (W) - *MAP 1401*
Damp stream-banks in maquis, seasonally wet places; fl. 4-5.
W. Crete (Agia lake & Fasas valley) [Mediterranean region].

8. Isolepis R.Br.

1. I. cernua (Vahl) Roem. & Schult., *Syst. veg.* 2: 106 (1817) - *FE* **5**: 279 as *Scirpus cernuus* Vahl.
Cr (W) Kp - *MAP 1402*

*Muddy puddles, damp bare ground, wet rocks;
0-550m; fl. 4-5.*
W. Crete; Karpathos [W. & S. Europe].

9. Juncellus C.B.Clarke

1. J. laevigatus (L.) C.B.Clarke in Hook.f., *Fl.
Brit. India* **6**: 596 (1893) - *FE* **5**: 287 as *Cyperus
laevigatus* L.
a. subsp. **distachyos** (All.) P.H.Davis, *Fl.
Turkey* **9**: 42 (1985) - *FE* **5**: 287 as *Cyperus
laevigatus* subsp. *distachyos* (All.) Maire &
Weiller.
Cr (W, C) Kp - *MAP 1403*
Brackish coastal marshes; fl. 4-5.
W. & C. Crete; Karpathos [Mediterranean
region].

10. Pycreus P.Beauv.

1. P. flavescens (L.) Rchb., *Fl. germ. excurs.*
1: 72 (1830) - *FE* **5**: 288 as *Cyperus flavescens*
L.
Cr (C) - *MAP 1404*
Damp place; 600m.
C. Crete [most of Europe].

2. P. flavidus (Retz.) T.Koyama in *J. Jap. Bot.*
51(10): 316 (1976) - *FE* **5**: 287 as *Cyperus
flavidus* Retz.
Cr (E) - *MAP 1405*
Roadside ditch or rivulet; 350m.
E. Crete (W. of Ierapetra) [S. Europe].

11. Schoenoplectus (Rchb.) Palla

1. S. lacustris (L.) Palla in *Bot. Jb.* **10**: 299
(1888) - *FE* **5**: 278 as *Scirpus lacustris* L.
a. subsp. **tabernaemontani** (C.C.Gmel.) A.&
D.Löve in *Folia geobot. phytotax.* **10**: 275
(1975) - *FE* **5**: 278 as *Scirpus lacustris* subsp.
tabernaemontani (C.C.Gmel.) Syme.
Cr (W) - *MAP 1406*
Fresh water.
W. Crete (Agia lake) [most of Europe].

2. S. litoralis (Schrad.) Palla in *Bot. Jb.* **10**:
299 (1888) - *FE* **5**: 278 as *Scirpus litoralis*
Schrad.
Cr Kp - *NOT MAPPED*
Crete; Karpathos [S. Europe].

12. Schoenus L.

1. S. nigricans L., *Sp. pl.*: 43 (1753) - *FE* **5**:
289.
Cr (W, C, E) Kp - *MAP 1407*
Damp ground, springs, moist rocks; 0-400m; fl.

4-5.
Mainly W. Crete; Karpathos [most of Europe].

13. Scirpoides Ség.

1. S. holoschoenus (L.) Sojak in *Cas. narod.
Mus.* **140**(3-4): 127 (1972) - *FE* **5**: 279 as
Scirpus holoschoenus L.
Cr (W, C, E) Kp - *MAP 1408*
*Marshes, streams, ditches, springs, damp &
rocky places, flat clayey areas, maritime sands;
0-1600m; fl. 4-5.*
Crete (widespread); Karpathos [most of
Europe].

Scirpus cernuus Vahl (*FE* **5**: 279) = **Isolepis 1**.

S. holoschoenus L. (*FE* **5**: 279) = **Scirpoides 1**.

S. lacustris L. (*FE* **5**: 278) = **Schoenoplectus 1**.

S. litoralis Schrad. (*FE* **5**: 278) =
Schoenoplectus 2.

S. maritimus L. (*FE* **5**: 278) = **Bolboschoenus
1**.

S. mucronatus L., given as doubtfully present in
Crete by Barclay (1986: 106), was almost
certainly recorded in error (Greuter, 1974: 162).

DIOSCOREACEAE

1. Tamus L.

1. T. communis L., *Sp. pl.*: 1028 (1753) - *FE*
5: 85. (Including *T. cretica* L. - *FE* **5**: 85.)
Cr (W, C, E) Kp - *MAP 1409*
*Woodland, olive groves, scrub & other shady
places; 0-600m; fl. 4.*
Mainly W. & C. Crete; Karpathos [W., S.C. &
S. Europe].

GRAMINEAE
(POACEAE)

Aegilops dichasians (Zhuk.) Humphries (*FE* **5**:
201) = **Triticum 3**.

A. geniculata Roth (*FE* **5**: 201) = **Triticum 7**.

A. lorentii Hochst. (*FE* **5**: 201) = **Triticum 2**.

A. neglecta Req. ex Bertol. (*FE* **5**: 202) =
Triticum 4.

A. umbellulata Zhuk. (*FE* **5**: 201) = **Triticum
5**.

A. uniaristata Vis. (*FE* **5**: 201) = **Triticum 6**.

1. Aeluropus Trin.

1. A. lagopoides (L.) Trin. ex Thwaites, *Enum. pl. zeyl.*: 374 (1864) - *FE* **5**: 256.
Cr (E) Ks Kp - *MAP 1410*
Hard sandy ground near sea.
E. Crete; Kasos, Karpathos [Sicily & Malta; otherwise N. & E. Africa & S.W. to C. Asia].

2. A. littoralis (Gouan) Parl., *Fl. ital.* **1**: 461 (1850) - *FE* **5**: 256.
Cr (W, C, E) - *MAP 1411*
Sandy coastal & saline ground.
Crete (sporadic) [S.E. Europe & Mediterranean region].

2. Agrostis L.

1. A. gigantea Roth, *Tent. fl. Germ.* **1**: 31 (1788) - *FE* **5**: 234.
a. subsp. gigantea
Cr (C) - *MAP 1412*
Flat clayey areas; 1400m.
C. Crete (Nida plain in Psiloritis) [most of Europe].
Given as doubtfully present in the Cretan area in *FE*, although previously recorded by Greuter (1973a: 76).

2. A. stolonifera L., *Sp. pl.*: 62 (1753) - *FE* **5**: 234.
Cr (E) - *MAP 1413*
Marshy ground by river.
E. Crete (near Sitia); Karpathos [almost throughout Europe].

3. Aira L.

1. A. cupaniana Guss., *Fl. sicul. syn.* **1**: 148 (1843) - *FE* **5**: 227.
Cr - *NOT MAPPED*
Crete [S. Europe].

2. A. elegantissima Schur in *Verh. Mitt. siebenb. Ver. Naturw.* **4** *(Sert. Fl. Transs.)*: 85 (1853) - *FE* **5**: 227.
Cr (W, C, E) Ks Kp - *MAP 1414*
Bare soil in phrygana, clayey pastures, abandoned fields & terraces; 0-800m; fl. 4-5.
Mainly W. Crete; Kasos, Karpathos [S.C. & S. Europe].

? A. provincialis Jord., *Pug. pl. nov.*: 142 (1852) - *FE* **5**: 228.
Doubtfully present in Crete [S.E. France & Corsica].

? A. tenorei Guss., *Fl. sicul. prodr.* **1**: 62 (1827) - *FE* **5**: 228.
Doubtfully present in Crete [Mediterranean region].

4. Alopecurus L.

1. A. creticus Trin. in Spreng., *Neue Entd.* **2**: 45 (1821) - *FE* **5**: 242.
Cr - *NOT MAPPED*
Crete [S. Balkan peninsula].

2. A. myosuroides Huds., *Fl. angl.* ed.1: 23 (1762) - *FE* **5**: 242.
Cr (W, E) - *MAP 1415*
Vineyards, roadsides; fl. 4.
W. & E. Crete [most of Europe].

3. A. rendlei Eig in *J. Bot., Lond.* **75**: 187 (1937) - *FE* **5**: 242.
Cr - *NOT MAPPED*
Crete [W. & S. Europe].

5. Ammophila Host

1. A. arenaria (L.) Link, *Hort. berol.* **1**: 105 (1827) - *FE* **5**: 236.
a. subsp. arundinacea H.Lindb. in *Acta Soc. Scient. fenn.* ser. nov., B, **1(2)**: 10 (1932) - *FE* **5**: 236.
Cr (W, C) - *MAP 1416*
Maritime sands; fl. 4-5.
W. & C. Crete [coasts of S. Europe].

6. Andropogon L.

1. A. distachyos L., *Sp. pl.*: 1046 (1753) - *FE* **5**: 266.
Cr (W, C, E) Ks Kp - *MAP 1417*
Phrygana, rocky places, roadsides; 0-300m; fl. 4-5.
Crete (sporadic); Kasos, Karpathos [Mediterranean region].

7. Anthoxanthum L.

1. A. gracile Biv., *Stirp. rar. Sicilia* **1**: t.1, fig.1 (1813) - *FE* **5**: 230.
Cr (W, C) - *MAP 1418*
Soil-pockets on calcareous rock-ledges; 100-750m; fl. 4-5.
W. & C. Crete [C. & E. Mediterranean region].

2. A. odoratum L., *Sp. pl.*: 28 (1753) - *FE* **5**: 230.
a. subsp. odoratum
Cr (W, C, E) Kp - *MAP 1419*
Woodland, damp & rocky places, fallow & abandoned fields; 0-1700m; fl. 4-5.
Mainly W. Crete; Karpathos [N., C. & S. Europe].

3. A. ovatum Lag., *Elench. pl.*: 2 (1816) - *FE* **5**: 230.
Cr (W) - *MAP 1420*

Maritime sands.
W. Crete (Georgioupoli) [Mediterranean region].
Recorded since *FE* (Greuter et al., 1985: 28).

8. Antinoria Parl.

1. A. insularis Parl., *Fl. palerm.* **1**: 94 (1845) - *FE* **5**: 228.
Cr - *NOT MAPPED*
Crete [W.C. Mediterranean region].

9. Aristida L.

"*A. adscensionis*" (*FE* **5**: 254) = **1** (Greuter et al., 1985: 28).

1. A. caerulescens Desf., *Fl. atlant.* **1**: 109 (1798) - *FE* **5**: 254.
Cr (C, E) - *MAP 1421*
Phrygana, rocky slopes near coast, gorge-beds, alluvial soil; 0-200m.
C. & E. Crete (mainly S. coast) [S. Europe].

10. Arrhenatherum P.Beauv.

1. A. palaestinum Boiss., *Diagn. pl. orient.* ser.1, **13**: 51 (1853) - *FE* **5**: 216.
Cr Ks Kp - *NOT MAPPED*
Crete; Kasos, Karpathos [S. Balkan peninsula & S. Aegean region].

11. Arundo L.

[1. A. donax] L., *Sp. pl.*: 81 (1753) - *FE* **5**: 253.
Cr (W, C, E) Kp - *MAP 1422*
Planted for wind shelter and widely naturalized along streams, ditches & field-margins, marshy places; 0-400m.
Crete (widespread); Karpathos [S. Europe; ?from C. & S. Asia].
The bamboo-like stems are cut and made into screens to provide shelter against wind and sun.

2. A. pliniana Turra, *Farsetia*: 11 (1765) - *FE* **5**: 253 as *A. plinii* Turra.
Cr (C) - *MAP 1423*
C. Crete [Mediterranean region].

A. plinii Turra (*FE* **5**: 253) = **2**.

12. Avellinia Parl.

1. A. michelii (Savi) Parl., *Pl. nov.*: 61 (1842) - *FE* **5**: 232.
Cr - *NOT MAPPED*
Crete [Mediterranean region].

13. Avena L.

1. A. barbata Pott ex Link in *J. Bot. Göttingen* **1799(2)**: 315 (1800) - *FE* **5**: 206.
Cr (W, C, E) Ks Kp - *MAP 1424*
Vineyards, calcareous rocky places, soil-filled hollows, roadsides, disturbed ground, waste areas; 0-300m; fl. 4-5.
Crete (widespread); Kasos, Karpathos [S. Europe].

A. fatua L. (*FE* **5**: 207) was recorded in error (Greuter et al., 1985: 29).

A. sativa L. (Greuter et al., 1983a: 71; Barclay, 1986: 108) is probably only cultivated.

2. A. sterilis L., *Sp. pl.* ed.2: 118 (1762) - *FE* **5**: 208.
Cr (W, C, E) Ks Kp - *MAP 1425*
Soil-filled hollows, cultivated & fallow land, maritime sands.
a. subsp. **ludoviciana** (Durieu) Gillet & Magne, *Nouv. fl. franç.* ed.3: 532 (1873) - *FE* **5**: 208.
Crete [S. Europe].
b. subsp. **sterilis**
Crete [S. Europe].
The species sensu lato is sporadic in Crete and occurs also in Kasos & Karpathos.

14. Avenula (Dumort.) Dumort.

1. A. cycladum (Rech.f. & J.Scheff.) Greuter in *Annls Mus. Goulandris* **1**: 75 (1973) - *FE* **5**: 215.
Cr (W, C, E) - *MAP 1426*
Phrygana, calcareous rocky places, alluvial soil, vineyards; 20-1750m.
Crete (sporadic) [Kiklades].

15. Brachiaria Griseb.

1. B. eruciformis (Sm.) Griseb. in Ledeb., *Fl. ross.* **4**: 469 (1853) - *FE* **5**: 262.
Kp - *MAP 1427*
Karpathos [Mediterranean region].

16. Brachypodium P.Beauv.

1. B. distachyon (L.) P.Beauv., *Ess. Agrostogr.*: 101, 155, 156 (1812) - *FE* **5**: 190.
Cr (W, C, E) Ks Kp - *MAP 1428*
Rocky & sandy places, seashores, fallow & abandoned land, roadsides, waste areas; 0-400m; fl. 4-5.
Crete (widespread); Kasos, Karpathos [S. Europe].

B. phoenicoides (L.) P.Beauv. ex Roem. & Schult. was recorded from Crete - without details of locality and date - by Damanakis (1983: 18); cf. Greuter et al. (1985: 29). However, this should be considered very doubtful, since the distribution given by Schippmann (1991) shows the species occurring mainly in S.W. Europe, E. only to C. Italy.

"B. pinnatum subsp. *pinnatum"* (*FE* 5: 189) ? = **3** (Greuter et al., 1985: 29-30).

B. pinnatum subsp. *rupestre* (Host) Schübl. & G.Martens (*FE* 5: 189) = **3**.

2. B. retusum (Pers.) P.Beauv., *Ess. Agrostogr.*: 101, 155, 156 (1812) - *FE* 5: 190.
Cr (W, C, E) Ks Kp - *MAP 1429*
Light woodland, maquis, scrub, garigue, phrygana, rocky places; 0-500m; fl. 4-6.
Crete (sporadic); Kasos, Karpathos [S.W. Europe & Mediterranean region].

3. B. rupestre (Host) Roem. & Schult., *Syst. veg.* ed. nov. (15), 2: 736 (1817) - *FE* 5: 189 as *B. pinnatum* subsp. *rupestre* (Host) Schübl. & G.Martens.
Cr (C, E) Kp - *MAP 1430*
Hillsides, rocky places, luxuriant grassy vegetation, roadside; 200-800m; fl. 5.
C. & E. Crete; Karpathos [W., C. & S. Europe].

4. B. sylvaticum (Huds.) P.Beauv., *Ess. Agrostogr.*: 101, 155, 156, 181 (1812) - *FE* 5: 189.
●**a.** subsp. **creticum** H.Scholz & Greuter in *Willdenowia* 15: 30 (1985).
Cr (W) - *MAP 1431*
Calcareous rocky places & crevices, mountain pastures; 1100-2100m; fl. 7-8.
W. Crete (Lefka Ori) - Endemic.
b. subsp. **sylvaticum** (including subsp. *glaucovirens* Murb.) - *FE* 5: 189).
Cr (W, C, E) Kp - *MAP 1432*
Woodland, banks of rivers & streams; 0-1100m.
Mainly W. & C. Crete; Karpathos [almost throughout Europe].

17. Briza L.

1. B. humilis M.Bieb., *Fl. taur.-caucas.* 1: 66 (1808) - *FE* 5: 173.
Kp - *MAP 1433*
Karpathos [S.E. Europe].

2. B. maxima L., *Sp. pl.*: 70 (1753) - *FE* 5: 173.
Cr (W, C, E) Ks Kp - *MAP 1434*
Olive groves, bare sandy places near sea, disturbed ground; 0-750m; fl. 4.
Mainly W. & C. Crete; Kasos, Karpathos [S. Europe].

3. B. minor L., *Sp. pl.*: 70 (1753) - *FE* 5: 173.
Cr (W, E) - *MAP 1435*
Marshes, ditches, moist ground, dry river-beds, vineyards; 0-300m; fl. 4-5.
W. & E. Crete [W. & S. Europe].

B. spicata Sm. (Greuter et al., 1983a: 72) = **1**.

18. Bromus L.

1. B. alopecuros Poir., *Voy. Barbarie* 2: 100 (1789) - *FE* 5: 188 as *B. alopecuros* Poir. subsp. *alopecuros.*
Cr (W, C, E) Ks Kp - *MAP 1436*
Calcareous rocky slopes, phrygana, grassy places, weed communities, cultivated and abandoned land; 70-700m.
Crete (sporadic); Kasos, Karpathos [C. & E. Mediterranean region].
Subsp. *caroli-henrici* (Greuter) P.M.Sm. (*FE* 5: 188) = **2**.

2. B. caroli-henrici Greuter in *Annln naturh. Mus. Wien* 75: 83 (1971) - *FE* 5: 188 as *B. alopecuros* subsp. *caroli-henrici* (Greuter) P.M.Sm.
Cr (W, C, E) Kp - *MAP 1437*
Coastal Tamarix groves, olive groves, phrygana, rocky places, abandoned fields, roadsides; 0-500m; fl. 4.
Crete (sporadic); Karpathos [Aegean region; otherwise S.W. Asia].

[3. B. catharticus] Vahl, *Symb. bot.* 2: 22 (1791) - *FE* 5: 189 as *B. willdenowii* Kunth.
Cr (W) - *MAP 1438*
Naturalized as a weed in Citrus groves.
W. Crete (W. of Hania) [S. Europe; from N. & S. America].
Recorded since *FE* (Greuter et al., 1985: 31).

4. B. diandrus Roth, *Bot. Abh. Beobacht.*: 44 (1787) - *FE* 5: 183.
Cr (W, C, E) Kp - *MAP 1439*
Rocky places, maritime sands, fallow fields, disturbed ground, roadsides, waste areas; 0-450m; fl. 4-5.
Crete (sporadic); Karpathos [S.W. Europe & Mediterranean region].

5. B. fasciculatus C.Presl, *Cyper. Gramin. sicul.*: 39 (1820) - *FE* 5: 184.
Cr (W, E) Ks Kp Sa - *MAP 1440*
Calcareous rocky places, open stony ground near sea; 0-200m; fl. 4-5.
W. & E. Crete; Karpathos group [Mediterranean region].

6. B. haussknechtii Boiss., *Fl. orient.* 5: 648 (1884).
Ks - *NOT MAPPED*

Kasos (Armathia island & small islet off S. coast) [Egypt, Azerbaijan, Iraq & Iran]. Recorded since *FE* (Raus, 1990: 32).

7. B. hordeaceus L., *Sp. pl.*: 77 (1753) - *FE* **5**: 187.
a. subsp. **divaricatus** (Bonnier & Layens) Kerguélen in *Bull. Soc. Éch. Pl. vascul. Europ. Bass. médit.* **18**: 27 (1981) - *FE* **5**: 187 as subsp. *molliformis* (Lloyd ex Godr.) Maire & Weiller.
Cr (W, E) Kp - *MAP 1441*
Marshes, damp grassland, sandy alluvial soil, fallow fields; fl. 4-5.
W. & E. Crete; Karpathos [S. Europe].
The occurrence of subsp. *hordeaceus* in Crete requires confirmation (Greuter et al., 1985: 32).

8. B. intermedius Guss., *Fl. sicul. prodr.* **1**: 114 (1827) - *FE* **5**: 188.
Cr (W, C, E) Ks Kp Sa - *MAP 1442*
Grazed open stony ground; 0-1750m.
Crete (sporadic); Karpathos group [Mediterranean region].

9. B. lanceolatus Roth, *Catal. bot.* **1**: 18 (1797) - *FE* **5**: 188.
Cr - *NOT MAPPED*
Crete [S. Europe].

10. B. madritensis L., *Cent. pl.* **1**: 5 (1755) - *FE* **5**: 184.
Cr (W, C, E) Ks Kp Sa - *MAP 1443*
Platanus woodland, vineyards, rocky places, Lygeum steppe, maritime sands; 0-1200m.
Mainly W. & E. Crete; Karpathos group [W. & S. Europe].

11. B. racemosus L., *Sp. pl.* ed.2: 114 (1762) - *FE* **5**: 187.
Cr (W) - *MAP 1444*
Brackish coastal marsh.
W. Crete (Georgioupoli) [most of Europe].

12. B. rigidus Roth in *Bot. Mag.* **4(10)**: 21 (1790) - *FE* **5**: 183.
Cr (W) Kp - *MAP 1445*
Grassy phrygana, maritime sands; 0-150m.
W. Crete; Karpathos [W. & S. Europe].

13. B. rubens L., *Cent. pl.* **1**: 5 (1755) - *FE* **5**: 184.
Cr (W, C, E) Ks Kp - *MAP 1446*
Calcareous rocky places, sandy places near sea; 0-200m; fl. 4-5.
Crete (sporadic); Kasos, Karpathos [S.W. Europe & Mediterranean region].

14. B. scoparius L., *Cent. pl.* **1**: 6 (1755) - *FE* **5**: 188.
Cr (W, C, E) Kp - *MAP 1447*
Open dry stony ground, maritime sands, fallow

fields; 0-1050m; fl. 4-5.
Crete (sporadic); Karpathos [S. Europe].

? B. secalinus L., *Sp. pl.*: 76 (1753) - *FE* **5**: 186.
Doubtfully present in Crete [most of Europe]. Possibly recorded in error for **11** (Greuter, 1973a: 72).

15. B. squarrosus L., *Sp. pl.*: 76 (1753) - *FE* **5**: 188.
Cr (W, C) - *MAP 1448*
Rocky places; (650-)1400-2100m; fl. 6.
W. & C. Crete (mainly Lefka Ori & Psiloritis) [C. & S. Europe].

16. B. sterilis L., *Sp. pl.*: 77 (1753) - *FE* **5**: 183.
Cr (W, E) Ks Kp - *MAP 1449*
Rocky places, fallow fields, disturbed ground, roadsides, waste areas; 0-1050m; fl. 4-5.
Mainly W. Crete; Kasos, Karpathos [W., C. & S. Europe].

17. B. tectorum L., *Sp. pl.*: 77 (1753) - *FE* **5**: 184.
Cr (W, C) Kp - *MAP 1450*
Rocky places; 600-2100m.
W. & C. Crete; Karpathos [most of Europe].

18. B. tomentellus Boiss., *Diagn. pl. orient.* ser.1, **7**: 126 (1846) - *FE* **5**: 185.
Cr (W, C, E) - *MAP 1451*
Calcareous rocky mountain slopes & crevices; 1000-2300m; fl. 5-7.
Crete (Lefka Ori, Psiloritis & Dikti) [S.W. Asia].

19. Castellia Tineo

1. C. tuberculosa (Moris) Bor in *Indian Forester* **74**: 90 (1948) - *FE* **5**: 157.
Cr (E) - *MAP 1452*
Maritime sands.
E. Crete (S. of Agios Nikolaos) [Mediterranean region].

20. Catapodium Link

1. C. marinum (L.) C.E.Hubb. in *Kew Bull.* **9**: 375 (1954) - *FE* **5**: 158 as *Desmazeria marina* (L.) Druce.
Cr (W, E) Ks Kp - *MAP 1453*
Maritime sands & rocky places, coastal saline ground, sandy vineyards; fl. 4-5.
W. & E. Crete; Kasos, Karpathos [coats of W. & S. Europe].

2. C. rigidum (L.) C.E.Hubb. ex Dony, *Fl. Bedfordshire*: 437 (1953) - *FE* **5**: 158 as

Desmazeria rigida (L.) Tutin.
Cr (W, C, E) Ks Kp Sa - *MAP 1454*
*Phrygana, calcareous rocky places & screes,
bare stony ground, maritime sands; 0-450m; fl.
4-5.*
Mainly W. & C. Crete; Karpathos group [W. &
S. Europe].

21. Coix L.

[1. C. lacryma-jobi] L., *Sp. pl.*: 972 (1753) -
FE **5**: 267.
Cr (W, C) - *MAP 1455*
Naturalized along ditch in Citrus grove.
W. & C. Crete [Mediterranean region; from
tropical Africa & Asia].
Recorded since *FE* (Damanakis, 1983: 22;
1985), though also historically recorded as being
cultivated (Greuter et al., 1985: 32). Indeed, the
species is still grown locally in Crete today, for
its large seeds, which are used to make beads.

22. Cornucopiae L.

1. C. cucullatum L., *Sp. pl.*: 54 (1753) - *FE* **5**:
243.
Cr (E) - *MAP 1456*
*Weed communities in roadside ditches; 150m; fl.
3-4.*
E. Crete (W. of Agios Nikolaos) [W.C. Italy &
Malta (Gozo); otherwise S.W. Asia].
Doubtfully native in Europe (Greuter et al.,
1985: 32).

23. Corynephorus P.Beauv.

1. C. articulatus (Desf.) P.Beauv., *Ess.
Agrostogr.*: 159 (1812) - *FE* **5**: 231, included in
synonymy of of *C. divaricatus* (Pourr.) Breistr.
Cr (W, C) - *MAP 1457*
Seashores and sandy ground.
W. & C. Crete [Aegean region].

"*C. divaricatus*" (*FE* **5**: 231) = **1** (Greuter et
al., 1985: 32-33).

"*C. fasciculatus*", said to be almost certainly
recorded in error from Crete in *FE* **5**: 232, is
referred to **1** by Greuter et al. (loc. cit.).

24. Crithopsis Jaub. & Spach

1. C. delileana (Schult.) Roshev., *Zlaki*: 319
(1937) - *FE* **5**: 200.
Cr (C, E) - *MAP 1458*
Calcareous sandy soil.

C. & E. Crete (N. coast) [N. Africa & S.W.
Asia].

25. Crypsis Aiton

1. C. aculeata (L.) Aiton, *Hort. kew.* **1**: 48
(1789) - *FE* **5**: 258.
Cr (C) - *MAP 1459*
C. Crete (W. of Iraklio) [C. & S. Europe].

2. C. schoenoides (L.) Lam., *Tabl. encycl.* **1**:
166 (1791) - *FE* **5**: 258.
Cr (W) - *MAP 1460*
Maritime sands; fl. 4-5.
W. Crete [C. & S. Europe].

26. Cutandia Willk.

1. C. maritima (L.) Barbey, *Fl. Sard. comp.*:
72 (1885) - *FE* **5**: 159.
Cr (W, E) Ks Kp - *MAP 1461*
Maritime sands & gravel; fl. 3-5.
W. & E. Crete; Kasos, Karpathos
[Mediterranean region].

2. C. stenostachya (Boiss.) Stace in *Bot. J.
Linn. Soc.* **76**: 352 (1978) - *FE* **5**: 159.
Kp - *MAP 1462*
Shady gorges.
Karpathos [N. Aegean region (Samothraki);
otherwise E. Aegean Islands (Rodos) & W.
Turkey].

27. Cynodon Rich.

1. C. dactylon (L.) Pers., *Syn. pl.* **1**: 85 (1805)
- *FE* **5**: 259.
Cr (W, C, E) Ks Kp Sa - *MAP 1463*
*Phrygana, rocky & grassy places, maritime
sands, tracks, bare ground; 0-450m; fl. 4-7.*
Crete (widespread); Karpathos group [W., C. &
S. Europe].

28. Cynosurus L.

C. callitrichus Barbey (*FE* **5**: 172) = **C.
coloratus**.

? C. coloratus Lehm. ex Steud., *Nomencl. bot.*
ed.2, **1**: 465 (1840) - *FE* **5**: 172 as *C.
callitrichus* Barbey.
Doubtfully present in Crete (Greuter, 1974: 162)
[N. Africa & W. Syria].

1. C. echinatus L., *Sp. pl.*: 72 (1753) - *FE* **5**:
171.
Cr (W, C, E) Kp - *MAP 1464*
*Woodland, olive groves, rocky places, mountain
pastures, marshy places, fallow fields; 0-1700m;
fl. 4-5.*

Mainly W. & C. Crete; Karpathos [C. & S. Europe].

2. C. effusus Link in *J. Bot. Göttingen* **1799(2)**: 315 (1800) - *FE* **5**: 172 as "*C. elegans*".
Cr (W, C, E) Kp - *MAP 1465*
Calcareous rocky places; -1700m.
Crete (sporadic); Karpathos [Mediterranean region].

"*C. elegans*" (*FE* **5**: 172) = **2** (Mill in Davis, 1985: 515).

29. Dactylis L.

1. D. glomerata L., *Sp. pl.*: 71 (1753) - *FE* **5**: 171.
a. subsp. **hackelii** (Asch. & Graebn.) Cif. & Giacom., *Nomencl. fl. Ital.* **1**: 36 (1950) - *FE* **5**: 171 as *D. marina* Borrill.
Cr (W) Ks Kp - *MAP 1466*
Sparse low calcareous phrygana & bare stony ground near sea.
W. Crete (Elafonisi island); Kasos, Karpathos [coasts of Mediterranean region].
b. subsp. **hispanica** (Roth) Nyman, *Consp. fl. eur.*: 819 (1882) - *FE* **5**: 171.
Cr (W, C, E) Ks Kp Sa - *MAP 1467*
Woodland, phrygana, rocky places, screes, soil-filled hollows, maritime sands, fallow fields; 0-1050m; fl. 5-6.
Crete (widespread); Karpathos group [mainly Mediterranean region].
c. subsp. **rigida** (Boiss. & Heldr.) Hayek in *Beih. Repert. nov. Spec. Regni veg.* **30(3)**: 255 (1933) - *FE* **5**: 171, included in synonymy of subsp. **b**.
Cr (C, E) - *MAP 1468*
Calcareous rocky places, flat clayey areas; 1700-2000m.
C. & E. Crete (Psiloritis & Dikti).

30. Dactyloctenium Willd.

[1. D. aegyptium] (L.) P.Beauv., *Ess. Agrostogr.*: 72, 160 *Expl. Pl.* 15 (1812) - *FE* **5**: 259.
Kp - *MAP 1469*
Naturalized weed.
Karpathos [Mediterranean region; from tropics and subtropics].

31. Dasypyrum (Coss. & Durieu) P.Candargy

1. D. villosum (L.) P.Candargy in *Arch. Biol. Végét. pure appliquée* **1**: 35, 65 (1901) - *FE* **5**: 203.
Cr (W, C, E) - *MAP 1470*

Fallow fields, disturbed ground, roadsides, waste areas; 0-450m; fl. 4-5.
Mainly W. & C. Crete [S.E. Europe & Mediterranean region].

Desmazeria marina (L.) Druce (*FE* **5**: 158) = **Catapodium 1**.

D. rigida (L.) Tutin (*FE* **5**: 158) = **Catapodium 2**.

32. Digitaria Heist. ex Haller

[1. D. ciliaris] (Retz.) Koeler, *Descr. Gram.*: 27 (1802) - *FE* **5**: 262.
Cr (W) - *MAP 1471*
Naturalized as a weed on roadside; 70m.
W. Crete [Italy; from tropics & subtropics]. Recorded since *FE* (Greuter et al., 1985: 33).

2. D. sanguinalis (L.) Scop., *Fl. carniol.* ed.2, **1**: 52 (1772) - *FE* **5**: 262.
Cr (W, C) Kp - *MAP 1472*
Sparsely vegetated grassy places, roadsides, tracks; fl. 8-9.
W. & C. Crete; Karpathos [mainly C. & S. Europe].

33. Echinaria Desf.

1. E. capitata (L.) Desf., *Fl. atlant.* **2**: 385 (1799) - *FE* **5**: 178.
Cr (W) Ks Kp - *MAP 1473*
Phrygana, open stony ground; 20-550m; fl. 4.
W. Crete (mainly Korikos, Rodopos & Akrotiri peninsulas); Kasos, Karpathos [S. Europe].

34. Echinochloa P.Beauv.

[1. E. colona] (L.) Link, *Hort. berol.* **2**: 209 (1833) - *FE* **5**: 262.
Cr (W, C) - *MAP 1474*
Naturalized along ditches, garden weed.
W. & C. Crete [Mediterranean region; from tropics & subtropics].

2. E. crus-galli (L.) P.Beauv., *Ess. Agrostogr.*: 53, 161 (1812) - *FE* **5**: 262.
Cr (W, C) - *MAP 1475*
Marshy river-mouth, damp ditches, grassy maritime sands; fl. 5-9.
W. & C. Crete [mainly C. & S. Europe].

35. Eleusine Gaertn.

[1. E. indica] (L.) Gaertn., *Fruct. sem. pl.* **1**: 8 (1788) - *FE* **5**: 258.
Cr (W) - *MAP 1476*

Naturalized as a weed on roadside.
W. Crete [S. Europe; from tropics &
subtropics].
Recorded since *FE* (Greuter et al., 1985: 34).

36. Elymus L.

E. diae nomen nudum (Heneen & Runemark,
1962: 550) is an as yet undescribed taxon from
Dia island in C. Crete. It is octoploid (2n =
56), related to the tetraploid **4** and diploid **5**
(Heneen & Runemark, 1972).

1. E. elongatus (Host) Runemark in *Hereditas*
70: 156 (1972) - *FE* **5**: 195.
a. subsp. **flaccidifolius** (Boiss. & Heldr.)
Runemark in *Hereditas* **70**: 156 (1972) - *FE* **5**:
195 as *E. flaccidifolius* (Boiss. & Heldr.)
Melderis.
Cr (W, C, E) - *MAP 1477*
Brackish marshes, damp coastal grassland,
maritime sands.
Crete (sporadic) [C. & E. Mediterranean
region].
All records of *E. elongatus* are referable to
subsp. **a** (Greuter et al., 1985: 34).

2. E. farctus (Viv.) Rumemark ex Melderis in
Bot. J. Linn. Soc. **76**: 382 (1978) - *FE* **5**: 197 as
E. farctus (Viv.) Runemark ex Melderis subsp.
farctus.
Cr (W, C, E) Kp - *MAP 1478*
Maritime sands, damp ground at base of sand-
dunes.
Crete (sporadic); Karpathos [S. Europe].
Subsp. *rechingeri* (Runemark) Melderis (*FE* **5**:
198) = **4**.

E. flaccidifolius (Boiss. & Heldr.) Melderis (*FE*
5: 195) = **1a**.

? E. hispidus (Opiz) Melderis in *Bot. J. Linn.*
Soc. **76**: 380 (1978) - *FE* **5**: 197.
Subsp. **varnensis** (Velen.) Melderis in *Bot. J.*
Linn. Soc. **76**: 382 (1978) - *FE* **5**: 197.
Doubtfully present in Crete [E. Balkan
peninsula].

3. E. panormitanus (Parl.) Tzvelev in *Spisok*
Rast. Gerb. Flory SSSR **18**: 27 (1970) - *FE* **5**:
193.
Cr (C, E) - *MAP 1479*
Quercus pubescens grove, field-margin; 600-
800m; fl. 6.
C. & E. Crete [S.E. Europe & Mediterranean
region].
Doubtful occurrence confirmed since *FE*
(Greuter et al., 1985: 34).

4. E. rechingeri (Runemark) Runemark in
Hereditas **48**: 548 (1962) - *FE* **5**: 198 as *E.*

farctus subsp. *rechingeri* (Runemark) Melderis.
Cr (W, E) Ks Kp - *MAP 1480*
Maritime rocks, step-crevices; near s.l.
W. & E. Crete; Kasos, Karpathos [Aegean
region].

5. E. striatulus Runemark in *Bot. Notiser* **125**:
419 (1972) - not cited in *FE*.
Cr (C, E) - *MAP 1481*
Mobile maritime sands and gravel, never in
closed communities.
C. & E. Crete [Aegean region].
Recorded by Heneen & Runemark (1972: 420).

37. Eragrostis Wolf

1. E. cilianensis (All.) Vignolo ex Janch. in
Mitt. naturw. Ver. Univ. Wien **5**(9): 110 (1907)
- *FE* **5**: 257.
Cr (E) Kp - *MAP 1482*
Luxuriant grassy vegetation, cultivated ground;
-200m; fl. 5.
E. Crete; Karpathos [mainly S. Europe].

E. minor Host, recorded from W. Crete by
Yannitsaros (1979: 104), has not been confirmed
by others (Greuter et al., 1985: 35). It is not
given for Crete by Barclay (1986), and has
never been recorded by the authors.

38. Festuca L.

1. F. arundinacea Schreb., *Spic. fl. lips.*: 57
(1771) - *FE* **5**: 132.
Cr (W, E) - *MAP 1483*
Marshes, streams, ditches, damp coastal
grassland; 0-800m; fl. 4-5.
W. & E. Crete [most of Europe].
Cretan plants are referred to subsp. *fenas* (Lag.)
Arcang. (*FE* **5**: 133) by Barclay (1986: 112),
while subsp. *atlantigena* (St.-Yves) Auquier (*FE*
5: 133) is given as possibly occurring at low
altitudes in E. Crete in *MFG* **2**: 752. There are
certainly morphological differences between
populations of the species in Crete (e.g. in awn
length), and further study is required to
ascertain the full extent of infraspecific
variation. The species is not divided here.

F. circummediterranea Patzke (*FE* **5**: 144) is
included in synonymy of **3**.

2. F. gigantea (L.) Vill., *Hist. pl. Dauphiné* **2**:
110 (1787) - *FE* **5**: 132.
Cr (W) - *MAP 1484*
W. Crete (Agia Lake) [most of Europe].
Regarded as absent from the Cretan area in *FE*,
although previously recorded by Gradstein &
Smittenberg (1968, in erratis). This record is
accepted by Greuter (1973a: 74), but is

considered by Markgraf-Dannenberg (1976: 146) to refer probably to an introduction, lying well to the south of its native range.

3. F. jeanpertii (St.-Yves) Markgr. in Hayek, *Beih. Repert. nov. Spec. Regni veg.* **30(3)**: 276 (1933) - *FE* 5: 144. (Including *F. circummediterranea* Patzke - *FE* 5: 144.)
Cr (W, C, E) Kp - *MAP 1485*
Among calcareous rocks, crevices, rubble, rocky & grassy slopes; 750-2400m.
Crete (Lefka Ori, Psiloritis, Dikti & Afendis Kavousi); Karpathos (Kalilimni) [C. & E. Mediterranean region].

4. F. polita (Halácsy) Tzvelev in *Bot. Zh. SSSR* **56**: 1255 (1971) - *FE* 5: 150.
Cr (W) - *MAP 1486*
Rocky calcareous grassland in open stands of Acer & Zelkova; 1750-1800m.
W. Crete (Lefka Ori) [Greece; otherwise W. Turkey].
Cretan plants belong to the endemic var. **cretica** Markgr.-Dann. in *Veröff. geobot. Inst. Zürich* **56**: 106 (1976).

5. F. sipylea (Hack.) Markgr.-Dann. in *Veröff. geobot. Inst. Zürich* **56**: 110 (1976) - *FE* 5: 145.
Cr (W, C, E) - *MAP 1487*
Calcareous rocky slopes & crevices, loose screes; 1400-2400m; fl. 6-8.
Crete (Lefka Ori, Psiloritis & Dikti) [S.W. Turkey].

39. Gastridium P.Beauv.

1. G. ventricosum (Gouan) Schinz & Thell. in *Vjschr. naturf. Ges. Zürich* **58**: 39 (1913) - *FE* 5: 235.
Cr (W, C, E) Kp - *MAP 1488*
Platanus woodland, open stony & sandy ground; 0-1050m.
Crete (sporadic); Karpathos [W. & S. Europe].

40. Gaudinia P.Beauv.

1. G. fragilis (L.) P.Beauv., *Ess. Agrostogr.*: 95, 164 (1812) - *FE* 5: 217.
Cr (W) - *MAP 1489*
Wet ditches, damp ground, rocky places; 0-200m; fl. 4-5.
W. Crete [mainly S. Europe].

41. Hainardia Greuter

1. H. cylindrica (Willd.) Greuter in *Boissiera* **13**: 177 (1967) - *FE* 5: 244.
Cr (W) Kp - *MAP 1490*
W. Crete; Karpathos [S. Europe].

42. Hemarthria R.Br.

1. H. altissima (Poir.) Stapf & C.E.Hubb. in *Kew Bull.* **1934**: 109 (1934) - *FE* 5: 266.
Cr (W) Kp - *MAP 1491*
Moist places, ditches, by irrigation channels; 0-60m; fl. 10.
W. Crete; Karpathos [Mediterranean region].
Recorded from Crete by Turland (1992a: 356).

43. Holcus L.

1. H. lanatus L., *Sp. pl.*: 1048 (1753) - *FE* 5: 230.
Cr - *NOT MAPPED*
Crete [almost throughout Europe].

44. Hordeum L.

1. H. bulbosum L., *Amoen. acad.* **4**: 304 (1759) - *FE* 5: 205.
Cr (W, C, E) Kp - *MAP 1492*
Olive groves, vineyards, roadsides, waste areas; 0-800m; fl. 4-5.
Mainly W. & C. Crete; Karpathos [S.E. Europe & Mediterranean region].

2. H. geniculatum All., *Fl. pedem.* **2**: 259 (1785) - *FE* 5: 205 as *H. hystrix* Roth.
Cr (W) - *MAP 1493*
Flat alluvial & clayey areas flooded in winter, sandy areas & fallow fields near sea; 0-1050m.
W. Crete [E.C., S.E. & S. Europe].
Recorded by Greuter et al. (1985: 35), who consider the only previous record (Rechinger, 1943a: 769, from Karpathos) to be doubtful.

H. hystrix Roth (*FE* 5: 205) = **2**.

3. H. leporinum Link in *Linnaea* **9**: 133 (1835).
? subsp. **glaucum** (Steud.) T.Booth & A.J.Richards in *Bot. J. Linn. Soc.* **72**: 150 (1976) - *FE* 5: 205 as *H. murinum* subsp. *glaucum* (Steud.) Tzvelev.
Doubtfully present in Crete [S.W. Europe & Mediterranean region].
a. subsp. **leporinum** - *FE* 5: 205 as *H. murinum* subsp. *leporinum* (Link) Arcang.
Cr (W, C, E) Ks Kp Sa - *MAP 1494*
Rocky & sandy places near sea, roadsides, waste areas; 0-500m; fl. 4-5.
Crete (widespread); Karpathos group [mainly S. Europe].

4. H. marinum Huds., *Fl. angl.* ed.2, **1**: 57 (1778) - *FE* 5: 205.
Cr (E) Kp - *MAP 1495*

Marshy ditches.
E. Crete; Karpathos [W. & S. Europe].

H. murinum subsp. *glaucum* (Steud.) Tzvelev
(*FE 5*: 205) = 3 subsp. **glaucum**.

H. murinum subsp. *leporinum* (Link) Arcang.
(*FE 5*: 205) = **3a**.

5. H. spontaneum K.Koch in *Linnaea* **21**: 430
(1848) - *FE 5*: 204.
Cr (W, C, E) Kp - *MAP 1496*
Roadsides, waste areas; 0-350m; fl. 4-5.
Crete (sporadic); Karpathos [Greece & Aegean
region; otherwise Libya, Egypt & S.W. & C.
Asia].
Considered by Greuter et al. (1985: 36) to be a
fairly recent introduction, now naturalized in
Crete.

45. Hyparrhenia Andersson ex E.Fourn.

1. H. hirta (L.) Stapf in Prain, *Fl. trop. Afr.* **9**:
315 (1919) - *FE 5*: 266.
Cr (W, C, E) Ks Kp Sa - *MAP 1497*
*Phrygana, grassy, rocky & sandy places, damp
ground, roadsides; 0-250m; fl. 4-5.*
Crete (widespread); Karpathos group
[Mediterranean region].

46. Imperata Cirillo

1. I. cylindrica (L.) Raeusch., *Nomencl. bot.*
ed.3: 10 (1797) - *FE 5*: 265.
Cr (W, C) Kp - *MAP 1498*
*Damp sandy ground, ditches & moist grassland
near sea; fl. 4-5.*
W. & C. Crete; Karpathos [S. Europe].

47. Lagurus L.

1. L. ovatus L., *Sp. pl.*: 81 (1753) - *FE 5*: 225.
Cr (W, C, E) Ks Kp Sa - *MAP 1499*
*Pinus brutia woodland, olive groves, coastal
phrygana, rocky places, soil-pockets among
rocks, bare ground, sandy places near sea; 0-
200m; fl. 4-5.*
Crete (widespread, rarer towards E.); Karpathos
group [S. Europe].
Two records from Kasos & Karpathos have been
referred to subsp. *nanus* (Guss.) Messeri
(Scholz, 1990: 406), and one from Saria to
subsp. *vestitus* (Messeri) H.Scholz (Scholz, op.
cit.: 407). The full extent of infraspecific
variation within the Cretan area is not known,
however, and the species is not divided here.

48. Lamarckia Moench

1. L. aurea (L.) Moench, *Methodus*: 201 (1794)
- *FE 5*: 172.
Cr (C) Kp Sa - *MAP 1500*
*Olive groves, abandoned terraces, grassy waste
areas; 20-150m; fl. 4-6.*
C. Crete; Karpathos, Saria [Mediterranean
region].

49. Lolium L.

1. L. multiflorum Lam., *Fl. franç.* **3**: 621
(1779) - *FE 5*: 154.
Cr - *NOT MAPPED*
Crete [most of Europe].

2. L. perenne L., *Sp. pl.*: 83 (1753) - *FE 5*:
154.
Cr (W, C, E) Kp - *MAP 1501*
*Vineyards, grassy, rocky & sandy places, flat
clayey areas, fallow fields, roadsides, waste
areas; 0-1400m; fl. 4-5.*
Crete (sporadic); Karpathos [almost throughout
Europe].

3. L. rigidum Gaudin, *Agrost. helv.* **1**: 334
(1811) - *FE 5*: 154.
Cr (W, C, E) Ks Kp - *MAP 1502*
*Olive groves, vineyards, hedges, rocky places,
river-beds, fallow fields, seashores; 0-1100m; fl.
4-5.*
Crete (widespread); Kasos, Karpathos [S.
Europe].
Both subsp. *rigidum* and subsp. *lepturoides*
(Boiss.) Sennen & Mauricio (*FE 5*: 154) have
been recorded from Crete and Karpathos
(Greuter et al., 1983a: 73; Barclay, 1986: 114);
the latter is treated at varietal rank by Mill (in
Davis, 1985: 450), as var. *rottbollioides* Heldr.
ex Boiss., and is not separated here.

4. L. temulentum L., *Sp. pl.*: 83 (1753) - *FE 5*:
154.
Cr (W, C) Kp - *MAP 1503*
Damp grassy places, cultivated land; fl. 4-5.
W. & C. Crete; Karpathos [mainly S. Europe].

Lophochloa cristata (L.) Hyl. (*FE 5*: 220) =
Rostraria 1.

L. pubescens (Lam.) H.Scholz (*FE 5*: 220) =
Rostraria litorea.

50. Lygeum Loefl. ex L.

1. L. spartum L., *Gen. pl.* ed.5: [522] (1754) -
FE 5: 255.
Cr (W, C, E) - *MAP 1504*
Phrygana, steppe, grassy places, open ground,

maritime sands, normally in dry areas; 0-200m.
Mainly E. Crete [Mediterranean region].

51. Melica L.

M. bornmuelleri (Papp) Hempel (Greuter,
1973*a*: 73) is included in synonymy of **1**.

1. M. ciliata L., *Sp. pl.*: 66 (1753) - *FE* **5**: 178.
(Including subsp. *magnolii* (Gren. & Godr.)
Husn. and *M. cretica* Boiss. & Heldr. - both *FE*
5: 179, and *M. bornmuelleri* (Papp) Hempel -
not cited in *FE*.)
Cr (W, C, E) - MAP 1505
*Rocky places & crevices, gorge-beds; 50-
2250m.*
Mainly W. & C. Crete [mainly C. & S.
Europe].

M. cretica Boiss. & Heldr. (*FE* **5**: 179) is
included in synonymy of **1**, after *MFG* **2**: 785.

"*M. minuta*" (*FE* **5**: 178) = **2** (Barclay, 1986:
115).

2. M. ramosa Vill., *Hist. pl. Dauphiné* **2**: 91
(1787) - *FE* **5**: 178, included in synonymy of *M.
minuta* L.
Cr (W, C, E) Ks Kp Sa - MAP 1506
*Platanus woodland, cliffs & rock-crevices; 0-
750m; fl. 4-5.*
Mainly W. & E. Crete; Karpathos group
[Mediterranean region].

3. M. rectiflora Boiss. & Heldr. in Boiss.,
Diagn. pl. orient. ser.1, **13**: 56 (1854) - *FE* **5**:
178.
Cr (W, C, E) Ks Kp - MAP 1507
*Platanus woodland, cliffs, rock-crevices &
ledges, stony slopes; 0-2100m; fl. 4-7.*
Mainly W. Crete; Kasos, Karpathos [S.
Peloponnisos & Kiklades (Amorgos)].

52. Milium L.

1. M. vernale M.Bieb., *Fl. taur.-caucas.* **1**: 53
(1808) - *FE* **5**: 246.
a. subsp. **montianum** (Parl.) Jahand. & Maire,
Cat. pl. Maroc **1**: 36 (1931) - *FE* **5**: 246.
Cr (C, E) - MAP 1508
*Among Pteridium on schistose substratum at foot
of calcareous cliffs; c. 1300m.*
C. & E. Crete (Kedros & Dikti) [Sicily &
Aegean region].

53. Panicum L.

1. P. repens L., *Sp. pl.* ed.2: 87 (1762) - *FE* **5**:
261.
Cr (W, C, E) - MAP 1509

Marshes, Phragmites beds.
Mainly W. Crete [mainly Mediterranean
region].

54. Parapholis C.E.Hubb.

? P. filiformis (Roth) C.E.Hubb. in *Blumea,
Suppl.* **3**: 14 (1946) - *FE* **5**: 243.
Doubtfully present in Crete (Barclay, 1986: 115)
[coasts of S. Europe].

1. P. incurva (L.) C.E.Hubb. in *Blumea,
Suppl.* **3**: 14 (1946) - *FE* **5**: 243.
Cr (W, C, E) Ks Kp Sa - MAP 1510
Maritime sands; fl. 4-5.
Mainly W. & C. Crete; Karpathos group [coasts
of W. & S. Europe].

2. P. marginata Runemark in *Bot. Notiser* **115**:
8 (1962) - *FE* **5**: 243.
Cr (W, C, E) Ks Kp - MAP 1511
Coastal saline ground.
Mainly E. Crete; Kasos, Karpathos
[Mediterranean region].

55. Paspalum L.

[1. P. dilatatum] Poir. in Lam., *Encycl.* **5**: 35
(1804) - *FE* **5**: 263.
Cr (W) - MAP 1512
*Locally naturalized in moist ditches & irrigation
channels.*
W. Crete [S.W. Europe & Italy; from S.
America].
Regarded as absent from the Cretan area in *FE*,
although previously recorded by Yannitsaros
(1977).

[2. P. distichum] L., *Amoen. acad.* **5**: 391
(1760) - *FE* **5**: 263 as *P. paspalodes* (Michx.)
Scribner.
Cr (W, C) - MAP 1513
*Naturalized as a weed in moist ditches,
irrigation channels, fields, gardens & roadsides;
fl. 7-9.*
Mainly W. Crete [S. Europe; from tropics].
Regarded as absent from the Cretan area in *FE*,
although previously recorded by Yannitsaros
(1977).

56. Phalaris L.

1. P. aquatica L., *Cent. pl.* **1**: 4 (1755) - *FE* **5**:
244.
Cr (W, E) Ks Kp Sa - MAP 1514
Marshes, ditches; fl. 4-5.
W. & E. Crete; Karpathos group [S. Europe].

? P. brachystachys Link in *Neues J. Bot.* **1(3)**: 134 (1806) - *FE* **5**: 245.
Doubtfully present in Crete [S.W. Europe & Mediterranean region].

[? P. canariensis] L., *Sp. pl.*: 54 (1753) - *FE* **5**: 244.
Doubtfully present in Crete [C. & S. Europe; from Canary Islands & N.W. Africa].

2. P. coerulescens Desf., *Fl. atlant.* **1**: 56 (1798) - *FE* **5**: 245.
Cr Kp Sa - *NOT MAPPED*
Crete; Karpathos, Saria [Mediterranean region].

3. P. minor Retz., *Observ. bot.* **3**: 8 (1783) - *FE* **5**: 244.
Cr (W, C, E) Ks Kp Sa - *MAP 1515*
Olive groves, weed communities in cultivated areas; fl. 4-5.
Crete (sporadic); Karpathos group [W. Europe & Mediterranean region].

4. P. paradoxa L., *Sp. pl.* ed.2: 1665 (1763) - *FE* **5**: 245.
Cr (W, C) Kp Sa - *MAP 1516*
Weed communities in cultivated areas; fl. 4-5.
W. & C. Crete; Karpathos, Saria [S.W. Europe & Mediterranean region].

? P. truncata Guss. ex Bertol., *Fl. ital.* **2**: 777 (1836) - *FE* **5**: 244.
Doubtfully present in Crete [Mediterranean region].

57. Phleum L.

1. P. crypsoides (d'Urv.) Hack. ex Franch. in *Bull. Soc. bot. Fr.* **39**: 274 (1892) - *FE* **5**: 241.
a. subsp. **crypsoides**
Cr (W, C, E) Ks Kp - *MAP 1517*
Maritime rocks, open stony sandy ground by sea; fl. 3-4.
Mainly E. Crete; Kasos, Karpathos [S. Aegean region].

? P. echinatum Host, *Icon. descr. gram. austriac.* **3**: 8 (1805) - *FE* **5**: 240.
Doubtfully present in Crete [C. & E. Mediterranean region].

2. P. exaratum Hochst. ex Griseb., *Spic. fl. rumel.* **2**: 463 (1845) - *FE* **5**: 241 as *P. graecum* Boiss. & Heldr.
a. subsp. **aegaeum** (Vierh.) Dogan in *Notes R. bot. Gdn Edinb.* **40**: 509 (1983) - *FE* **5**: 241 as *P. graecum* subsp. *aegaeum* (Vierh.) Greuter.
Cr (W) - *MAP 1518*
Waste areas.
W. Crete (near Kastelli Kissamou) [S. Peloponnisos, Kithira, Andikithira & Kiklades; otherwise S.W. Asia].

Recorded since *FE* by Greuter et al. (1985: 37), who state that previous records of the species are doubtful and probably referable to **3**. Erroneously given as "*P. graecum* subsp. *graecum*" by Barclay (1986: 116).

P. graecum Boiss. & Heldr. (*FE* **5**: 241) = **2**.

? P. paniculatum Huds., *Fl. angl.* ed.1: 23 (1762) - *FE* **5**: 240.
Doubtfully present in Crete [S.C. & S. Europe].

3. P. subulatum (Savi) Asch. & Graebn., *Syn. mitteleur. Fl.* **2(1)**: 154 (1899) - *FE* **5**: 241.
Cr (W, C) Kp Sa - *MAP 1519*
Fallow & abandoned fields; 0-1050m; fl. 4..
a. subsp. **ciliatum** (Boiss.) Humphries in *Bot. J. Linn. Soc.* **76**: 339 (1978) - *FE* **5**: 241.
Crete; Karpathos [Jugoslavia & Greece].
b. subsp. **subulatum**
Crete; Karpathos [mainly S. Europe].
The species sensu lato occurs mainly in W. Crete and also in Saria.

58. Phragmites L.

1. P. australis (Cav.) Trin. ex Steud., *Nomencl. bot.* ed.2, **2**: 324 (1841) - *FE* **5**: 253.
Cr (W, C, E) Kp - *MAP 1520*
Marshes & river-banks, usually on coast, often forming dense stands; 0-500m.
Crete (widespread); Karpathos [almost throughout Europe].

59. Piptatherum P.Beauv.

1. P. coerulescens (Desf.) P.Beauv., *Ess. Agrostogr.*: 18, 173 (1812) - *FE* **5**: 246.
Cr (W, C, E) Ks Kp - *MAP 1521*
Scrub, shady rocky places & crevices; 0-750m; fl. 4-5.
Crete (sporadic); Kasos, Karpathos [Mediterranean region].

2. P. miliaceum (L.) Coss., *Notes pl. crit.*: 129 (1851) - *FE* **5**: 246.
a. subsp. **miliaceum**
Cr (W, C, E) Ks Kp Sa - *MAP 1522*
Olive groves, river-beds, waste areas; 0-500m; fl. 5.
Crete (widespread); Karpathos group [S. Europe].
b. subsp. **thomasii** (Duby) Freitag in *Notes R. bot. Gdn Edinb.* **33**: 363 (1975) - *FE* **5**: 246 as *P. thomasii* (Duby) Kunth.
Cr (C) Kp - *MAP 1523*
C. Crete; Karpathos [S.W. & S. Europe].

60. Poa L.

1. P. annua L., *Sp. pl.*: 68 (1753) - *FE* **5**: 161.
Cr (W, C) - *MAP 1524*
Riparian Platanus woodland, sandy alluvial soil near river-mouth, wet mud near springs; 0-1050m; fl. 4-5.
W. & C. Crete [almost throughout Europe].

2. P. bulbosa L., *Sp. pl.*: 70 (1753) - *FE* **5**: 165.
a. subsp. **bulbosa**
Cr (W, C, E) Kp - *MAP 1525*
Rocky places, mountain pastures, soil-filled hollows, fallow fields & field-margins, roadsides; 0-2100m; fl. 4-5.
Crete (widespread, rarer towards E.); Karpathos [most of Europe].
Some records from high altitudes in Crete may be referable to subsp. *pseudoconcinna* (Schur) Domin, which occurs from the Balkan peninsula to Czechoslovakia (*MFG* **2**: 771).

3. P. cenisia All., *Auct. fl. pedem.*: 40 (1789) - *FE* **5**: 162. (Including subsp. *contracta* (Nyár.) Nyár. - *FE* **5**: 163.)
Cr (W, C) - *MAP 1526*
Calcareous rocky places, among spiny dwarf shrubs; 2000-2300m.
W. & C. Crete (Lefka Ori & Psiloritis) [mountains of C. & S. Europe].

4. P. infirma Kunth in Humb., Bonpl. & Kunth, *Nov. gen. sp.* **1**: 158 (1817) - *FE* **5**: 161.
Cr (W, C) Kp - *MAP 1527*
Tracks, bare & trodden ground; 0-700m; fl. 2-4.
W. & C. Crete; Karpathos [W. & S. Europe].

5. P. palustris L., *Syst. nat.* ed.10, **2**: 874 (1759) - *FE* **5**: 164.
Cr (W) - *MAP 1528*
Marshy ground.
W. Crete (Fasas valley) [most of Europe].

6. P. pelasgis H.Scholz in *Willdenowia* **15**: 94 (1985).
Cr (W, C, E) Ks Kp - *MAP 1529*
Phrygana, rock-crevices, gorge-beds, dolines, fields; 300-1350m.
Crete (sporadic); Kasos, Karpathos [S. Greece & Aegean region; otherwise S.W. Asia].
Related to **2**.

7. P. pratensis L., *Sp. pl.*: 67 (1753) - *FE* **5**: 162.
Cr - *NOT MAPPED*
Crete [almost throughout Europe].

8. P. timoleontis Heldr. ex Boiss., *Fl. orient.* **5**: 607 (1884) - *FE* **5**: 165.
Cr (W, C, E) - *MAP 1530*
Calcareous cliffs & screes, open rocky ground,

alluvial mountain plain; 1100-2000m.
Crete (Lefka Ori, Psiloritis & Dikti) [Italy, Balkan peninsula & Aegean region].

9. P. trivialis L., *Sp. pl.*: 67 (1753) - *FE* **5**: 161.
a. subsp. **sylvicola** (Guss.) H.Lindb. in *Ofvers. finska VetenskSoc. Förh.* **48(13)**: 9 (1906) - *FE* **5**: 161.
Cr (W, C, E) Kp - *MAP 1531*.
Platanus woodland, marshes, damp grassland, ditches, rocky places; 0-1600m; fl. 4-5.
Crete (sporadic); Karpathos [S. Europe].

61. Polypogon Desf.

1. P. maritimus Willd. in *Neue Schr. Ges. naturf. Fr. Berl.* **3**: 442 (1801) - *FE* **5**: 235.
Cr (W, C, E) Kp - *MAP 1532*
Marshes & damp ground near sea, calcareous rocky places, vineyards; fl. 4-5.
a. subsp. **maritimus**
Crete [mainly W. Europe & Mediterranean region].
b. subsp. **subspathaceus** (Req.) Asch. & Graebn., *Syn. mitteleur. Fl.* **2(1)**: 162 (1899) - *FE* **5**: 236.
Crete; Karpathos [Mediterranean region].
The species sensu lato occurs mainly in W. Crete.

2. P. monspeliensis (L.) Desf., *Fl. atlant.* **1**: 67 (1798) - *FE* **5**: 235.
Cr (W, E) Kp - *MAP 1533*
Alluvial rubble, marshy places; fl. 4, 9.
Mainly W. Crete; Karpathos [W. & S. Europe].

3. P. viridis (Gouan) Breistr. in *Bull. Soc. bot. Fr.* **110** *(Sess. Extr. 89)*: 56 (1966) - *FE* **5**: 236.
Cr (W, C, E) Kp - *MAP 1534*
Streams, ditches, damp rocks & other wet places; 0-300m; fl. 4-5.
Crete (sporadic); Karpathos [S. Europe].

Hybrid:

P. monspeliensis x **P. viridis** = **P.** x **adscendens** Guss. ex Bertol., *Fl. ital.* **2**: 777 (1836) - *FE* **5**: 236.
W. Crete (Georgioupoli).
Recorded by Gradstein & Smittenberg (1968).

62. Psilurus Trin.

1. P. incurvus (Gouan) Schinz & Thell. in *Vjschr. naturf. Ges. Zürich* **58**: 40 (1913) - *FE* **5**: 173.
Cr (W, C) Ks Kp - *MAP 1535*
Sandy places near sea, open ground; 0-400m; fl. 4-5.

W. & C. Crete; Kasos, Karpathos [S. Europe].

63. Rostraria Trin.

1. R. cristata (L.) Tzvelev in *Nov. Sist.*
Vysshikh Rast. **7**: 47 (1971) - *FE* **5**: 220 as
Lophochloa cristata (L.) Hyl.
Cr (W, C, E) Ks Kp Sa - *MAP 1536*
Maritime rocks, river-beds, fallow fields, bare,
disturbed & saline ground; 0-1050m; fl. 4-5.
Crete (widespread); Karpathos group [S.W.
Europe & Mediterranean region].

? R. litorea (All.) Holub in *Folia geobot.*
phytotax. **9**: 271 (1974) - *FE* **5**: 220 as
Lophochloa pubescens (Lam.) H.Scholz.
Doubtfully present in Crete [Mediterranean
region].

64. Saccharum L.

1. S. ravennae (L.) L., *Syst. veg.* ed.13: 88
(1774) - *FE* **5**: 265.
Cr (C, E) Kp - *MAP 1537*
Ditches & damp places; 0-300m.
C. & E. Crete; Karpathos [mainly
Mediterranean region].

2. S. spontaneum L., *Mant. pl. alt.*: 183 (1771)
- *FE* **5**: 265.
Cr (W) - *NOT MAPPED*
W. Crete [Sicily; otherwise N. & E. Africa &
S. Asia].
Recorded since *FE* (Damanakis & Scholz, 1990:
422).

Schismus P.Beauv.

? S. arabicus Nees, *Fl. Afr. austral. ill.*: 422
(1841) - *FE* **5**: 254.
Doubtfully present in Crete [mainly S. Greece &
C. Aegean region; otherwise Egypt & S.W. &
C. Asia].

65. Sesleria Scop.

●**1. S. doerfleri** Hayek in *Öst. bot. Z.* **64**: 360
(1914) - *FE* **5**: 175.
Cr (W, C) - *MAP 1538*
Calcareous cliffs; 100-1300m; fl. 3-5.
W. & C. Crete - Endemic.
[Plate 9.]

66. Setaria P.Beauv.

1. S. adhaerens (Forssk.) Chiov. in *Nuovo G.*
bot. ital. nov. ser., **26**: 77 (1919) - *FE* **5**: 263.
Cr (W, C, E) Kp - *MAP 1539*

Irrigated fields & waste areas near coast; fl. 7-
9.
Crete (sporadic); Karpathos [Mediterranean
region].
Recorded by Greuter et al. (1985: 38).

S. italica (L.) P.Beauv. is given for the Cretan
area in *FE* **5**: 264, although there are no records
as a basis for this (Greuter et al., 1985: 39).

2. S. pumila (Poir.) Roem. & Schult., *Syst.*
veg. ed. nov. (15), **2**: 891 (1817) - *FE* **5**: 263.
Cr (W, E) Kp - *MAP 1540*
Moist ditches & irrigation channels, wet
roadsides.
W. & E. Crete; Karpathos [mainly C. & S.
Europe].
Probably recently introduced into the S. Aegean
region (Greuter et al., 1985: 39).

3. S. verticillata (L.) P.Beauv., *Ess.*
Agrostogr.: 51, 178 (1812) - *FE* **5**: 263.
Cr (C) - *MAP 1541*
Gorge; 25m.
C. Crete (E. of Iraklio) [mainly C. & S.
Europe].
Given as doubtfully present in Crete by Barclay
(1986: 118), although previously recorded by
Greuter et al. (1985: 38), who also state that a
record from Karpathos (Greuter et al., 1983a:
73) is referable to **1**.

4. S. viridis (L.) P.Beauv., *Ess. Agrostogr.*: 51,
178 (1812) - *FE* **5**: 263.
Cr - *NOT MAPPED*
Crete [most of Europe].

67. Sorghum Moench

1. S. halepense (L.) Pers., *Syn. pl.* **1**: 101
(1805) - *FE* **5**: 265.
Cr (W, C, E) Kp - *MAP 1542*
Fields, roadsides, grassy waste areas; 0-100m;
fl. 5-10.
Mainly W. & C. Crete; Karpathos [S.C. & S.
Europe].

68. Sporobolus R.Br.

1. S. pungens (Schreb.) Kunth, *Révis. gramin.*
1: 68 (1829) - *FE* **5**: 258.
Cr (W, C, E) Kp - *MAP 1543*
Maritime sands, calcareous rocks near sea.
Crete (sporadic); Karpathos [S. Europe].

69. Stipa L.

1. S. bromoides (L.) Dörfl. in *Herbm norm.*
34: 129 (1897) - *FE* **5**: 252.
Cr (W, C, E) Kp - *MAP 1544*

Calcareous rocky places, open stony ground;
200-2000m.
Mainly W. & E. Crete; Karpathos [S. Europe].

2. S. capensis Thunb., *Prodr. fl. cap.*: 19
(1794) - *FE* **5**: 250.
Cr (W, C, E) Ks Kp Sa - *MAP 1545*
Open phrygana, Lygeum steppe, calcareous
rocky places, fallow & abandoned fields; 0-
150m; fl. 3-4.
Mainly W. & E. Crete (mainly coastal);
Karpathos group [Mediterranean region].

S. capillata L. is given for the Cretan area in *FE*
5: 251, although there are no records as a basis
for this (Greuter et al., 1985: 39).

S. fontanesii Parl. (*FE* **5**: 251) = **3**.

3. S. holosericea Trin. in *Mém. Acad. Sci. St.*
Petersb. ser.6, Sci.Nat. **1**: 81 (1830), emend.
Tzvelev in *Nov. Sist. Vysshikh Rast.* **1966**: 18
(1966) - *FE* **5**: 251 as *S. fontanesii* Parl.
Cr (E) - *MAP 1546*
Mountain slopes & summit; 450-1150m.
E. Crete [S. Italy, Sicily & Aegean region].
Doubtful occurrence confirmed since *FE*
(Greuter et al., 1985: 39).

4. S. parviflora Desf., *Fl. atlant.* **1**: 98 (1798) -
FE **5**: 251.
Cr (E) - *MAP 1547*
Lygeum steppe, roadside; 80m.
E. Crete (near Ierapetra) [Spain & S. France;
otherwise N. Africa & adjacent S.W. Asia].
Doubtful occurrence confirmed since *FE*
(Greuter et al., 1985: 39).

70. Taeniatherum Nevski

1. T. caput-medusae (L.) Nevski in *Acta Univ.*
Asiae mediae ser.8b (Bot.), **17**: 38 (1934) - *FE*
5: 206.
a. subsp. **crinitum** (Schreb.) Melderis in *Notes*
R. bot. Gdn Edinb. **42**: 81 (1984) - *FE* **5**: 206 as
T. crinitum (Schreb.) Nevski.
Cr (E) - *MAP 1548*
Calcareous phrygana, grassland on schistose
hills, alluvial mountain plain; 1100-1200m.
E. Crete (Katharo plain in Dikti) [mainly Balkan
peninsula; otherwise N. Africa & S.W. & C.
Asia].
Recorded since *FE* (Greuter et al., 1985: 40).
Subsp. *caput-medusae* is given for Crete by
Barclay, in addition to subsp. **a** (1986: 119, both
taxa at specific rank); however, there appear to
be no records as a basis for its inclusion, and it
should be regarded as very doubtful until its
presence can be confirmed.

71. Triplachne Link

1. T. nitens (Guss.) Link, *Hort. berol.* **2**: 241
(1833) - *FE* **5**: 232.
Cr (W, C, E) Ks Kp - *MAP 1549*
Maritime sands, bare ground; fl. 4-5.
Crete (sporadic); Kasos, Karpathos
[Mediterranean region].

Trisetum flavescens (L.) P.Beauv. is given for
the Cretan area in *FE* **5**: 223, although there are
no records as a basis for this (Greuter et al.,
1985: 40).

72. Triticum L.

1. T. comosum (Sm.) K.Richt., *Pl. eur.* **1**: 128
(1890) - *FE* **5**: 201 as *Aegilops comosa* Sm.
a. subsp. **heldreichii** (Boiss.) Greuter in
Boissiera **13**: 171 (1967) - *FE* **5**: 201 as
Aegilops comosa subsp. *heldreichii* (Boiss.) Eig.
Cr (W) - *MAP 1550*
Phrygana on calcareous slopes; 250m.
W. Crete (W. of Kastelli Kissamou) [S.E.
Greece & Kithira].
Recorded since *FE* by Greuter et al. (1985: 40),
according to whom the respective distributions
given in *FE* for subsp. *comosum* ("S. & S.E.
Greece") and subsp. *heldreichii* ("N.E. Greece")
should be transposed.

2. T. lorentii (Hochst.) Zeven in *Taxon* **22**: 321
(1973) - *FE* **5**: 201 as *Aegilops lorentii* Hochst.
Cr (W, C, E) Ks Kp - *MAP 1551*
Olive groves, calcareous rocky places, maritime
rubble, fallow fields; 0-1500m.
Crete (sporadic); Kasos, Karpathos [S. Europe].

3. T. markgrafii Greuter in *Boissiera* **13**: 172
(1967) - *FE* **5**: 201 as *Aegilops dichasians*
(Zhuk.) Humphries.
Cr (W, C, E) Kp - *MAP 1552*
Rocky places, Lygeum steppe, open stony
ground; 0-400m; fl. 5.
Crete (widespread); Karpathos [S. Balkan
peninsula & Aegean region].

4. T. neglectum (Req. ex Bertol.) Greuter in
Boissiera **13**: 171 (1967) - *FE* **5**: 202 as
Aegilops neglecta Req. ex Bertol.
Cr (W) - *MAP 1553*
Hedges, calcareous rocky places, abandoned
terraces, maritime sands; 0-400m; fl. 4.
W. Crete [S. Europe].

? T. triunciale (L.) Raspail in *Annls Sci. nat.* **5**:
435 (1825) - *FE* **5**: 201 as *Aegilops triuncialis* L.
Doubtfully present in Crete (Greuter, 1974: 162)
[S. Europe].

5. T. umbellulatum (Zhuk.) Bowden in *Can. J. Bot.* **37**: 666 (1959) - *FE* **5**: 201 as *Aegilops umbellulata* Zhuk.
Cr (E) - *MAP 1554*
E. Crete [S.W. Asia].

6. T. uniaristatum (Vis.) K.Richt., *Pl. eur.* **1**: 128 (1890) - *FE* **5**: 201 as *Aegilops uniaristata* Vis.
Cr (C) - *MAP 1555*
C. Crete [Italy & Balkan peninsula].

7. T. vagans (Jord. & Fourr.) Greuter in *Boissiera* **13**: 170 (1967) - *FE* **5**: 201 as *Aegilops geniculata* Roth.
Cr (W, E) - *MAP 1556*
Scrub, coastal phrygana, calcareous rocky places, open stony ground near sea; 0-450m.
W. & E. Crete [S. Europe].

73. Ventenata Koeler

V. dubia (Leers) Coss. is given for Crete by Barclay (1986: 119), together with **1**; however, there appear to be no records as a basis for its inclusion, and it should be regarded as very doubtful until its presence can be confirmed.

1. V. subenervis Boiss. & Balansa in *Bull. Soc. bot. Fr.* **4**: 305 (1857).
Cr (E) - *MAP 1557*
Grassland on schistose hills; 1100m.
E. Crete (Katharo plain in Dikti) [E. Aegean Islands (Lesvos) & Turkey].
Recorded since *FE* (Greuter et al., 1985: 41).

74. Vulpia C.C.Gmel.

1. V. ciliata Dumort., *Observ. Gramin. belg.*: 100 (1824) - *FE* **5**: 156.
a. subsp. **ciliata**
Cr (W, C, E) Ks Kp - *MAP 1558*
Platanus woodland, calcareous rocky places, fallow fields, bare stony ground; 0-1050m; fl. 3-4.
Mainly W. & C. Crete; Kasos, Karpathos [S. Europe].

2. V. fasciculata (Forssk.) Fritsch, *Excursionsfl. Oesterreich* ed.2: 74 & 692 (1909) - *FE* **5**: 155.
Cr (W, C, E) Ks Kp - *MAP 1559*
Maritime sands, sandy vineyard; fl. 3-4.
Mainly W. Crete; Kasos, Karpathos [coasts of W. & S. Europe].

3. V. ligustica (All.) Link, *Hort. berol.* **1**: 148 (1827) - *FE* **5**: 155.
Cr - *NOT MAPPED*
Crete [Mediterranean region].
4. V. muralis (Kunth) Nees in *Linnaea* **19**: 694

(1847) - *FE* **5**: 156.
Cr (W, C) - *MAP 1560*
Low maquis on schistose substratum, flat clayey area with Pteridium, rocky places; 350-600m.
W. & C. Crete [S. Europe].
Recorded since *FE* (Greuter et al., 1985: 41).

5. V. myuros (L.) C.C.Gmel., *Fl. bad.* **1**: 8 (1805) - *FE* **5**: 156.
Cr (W, C) Kp - *MAP 1561*
Gorge; 50-500m.
W. & C. Crete; Karpathos [W., C. & S. Europe].

Zea mays L. (*FE* **5**: 267) is cultivated only.

HYDROCHARITACEAE

1. Halophila Thouars

[1. H. stipulacea] (Forssk.) Asch. in *Sber. Ges. naturf. Freunde Berl.* **1867**: 3 (1867) - *FE* **5**: 5.
Cr (W, C) - *MAP 1562*
Marine coves.
W. & C. Crete [C. & E. Mediterranean region; from Red Sea & W. Indian Ocean].
Entered the Mediterranean Sea after the opening of the Suez Canal. The first collections from Cretan coasts were made in 1955 (Greuter et al., 1985: 42).

IRIDACEAE

1. Crocus L.

1. C. biflorus Mill., *Gard. Dict.* ed.8: no.4 (1768) - *FE* **5**: 96.
a. subsp. **nubigena** (Herb.) B.Mathew, *The Crocus*: 82 (1982).
Kp - *MAP 1563*
Low phrygana, flat clayey areas; 1200m; fl. 3(-4).
Karpathos (Kalilimni) [E. Aegean Islands & W. Turkey].
Recorded since *FE* (Raus, 1983).

2. C. boryi Gay in *Bull. Sci. nat. Géol.* **25**: 320 (1831) - *FE* **5**: 98.
Cr (E) - *MAP 1564*
Scrub, banks of abandoned terraces; 150-550m; fl. 11.
E. Crete [W. & S. Greece].

3. C. cartwrightianus Herb. in *Bot. Reg.* **29**, Misc: 82 (1843) - *FE* **5**: 97.
Cr (W) - *MAP 1565*
30-60m; fl. 10-12.
W. Crete (N.E. of Hania) [S.E. Greece (Attiki) & Kiklades].

4. C. laevigatus Bory & Chaub. in Bory, *Exp. sci. Morée, Bot.*: t.3, fig.2 (1832) - *FE* **5**: 98.
Cr (W, C, E) - MAP 1566
Sparse open phrygana, rocky places, bare stony ground, flat clayey areas; 0-2350m; fl. 9-11.
Crete (sporadic) [E. & S. Greece (Evvia, Attiki & Peloponnisos) & Kiklades].

C. olivieri Gay (*FE* **5**: 96) was almost certainly recorded in error (Greuter, 1974: 161).

●**5. C. oreocreticus** B.L.Burtt in *Phyton, Horn* **1**: 224 (1949) - *FE* **5**: 97.
Cr (C, E) - MAP 1567
Sparse phrygana, open rocky slopes, flat clayey areas; 750-2000m; fl. 10-12.
C. & E. Crete (mainly Psiloritis, Kofinas, Dikti & Afendis Kavousi) - Endemic.

6. C. sieberi Gay in *Bull. Sci. nat. Géol.* **25**: 320 (1831) - *FE* **5**: 95.
●**a.** subsp. **sieberi**
Cr (W, C) - MAP 1568
Calcareous open woodland, among Berberis bushes, stony ground beneath cliffs, open slopes, flat clayey areas; 1050-2400m; fl. 3-4(-6).
W. & C. Crete (Lefka Ori, Kedros & Psiloritis) - Endemic.
Additionally recorded from Dikti in E. Crete in *MFG* **2**: 725.

7. C. tournefortii Gay in *Bull. Sci. nat. Géol.* **25**: 320 (1831) - *FE* **5**: 98.
Cr (E) Ks Kp - MAP 1569
Phoenix theophrasti grove, coastal scrub, soil at base of conglomerate cliffs, phrygana; 0-200m; fl. 10-11.
E. Crete (N. coast); Kasos, Karpathos [E. Peloponnisos (Idra island) & Kiklades; otherwise E. Aegean Islands].
Recorded from Crete since *FE* (Mathew, 1982: 115).

2. Gladiolus L.

1. G. italicus Mill., *Gard. Dict.* ed.8: no.2 (1768) - *FE* **5**: 102.
Cr (W, C, E) Ks Kp - MAP 1570
Olive groves, cultivated, fallow & abandoned land; 0-650m; fl. 4-5.
Crete (widespread, rarer towards E.); Kasos, Karpathos [S. Europe].

3. Gynandriris Parl.

1. G. monophylla Boiss. & Heldr. ex Klatt in *Linnaea* **34**: 578 (1865-1866) - not cited in *FE*.
Cr (W) - MAP 1571
W. Crete (Gavdos island) [Greece; otherwise Libya & Egypt].

Recorded by Rechinger (1943a: 742). Can be confused with dwarfed individuals of **2** (cf. Mill in Davis, 1984: 412).

2. G. sisyrinchium (L.) Parl., *Nuov. gen. sp. monocot.*: 52 (1854) - *FE* **5**: 92.
Cr (W, C, E) Ks Kp - MAP 1572
Phrygana, open stony ground, soil-filled hollows, flat clayey areas, fallow & abandoned fields, maritime sands & rocks, coastal saline ground; 0-700m; fl. 3-5.
Crete (widespread); Kasos, Karpathos [Mediterranean region].

4. Hermodactylus Mill.

1. H. tuberosus (L.) Mill., *Gard. Dict.* ed.8 (1768) - *FE* **5**: 87.
Cr (W, C, E) - MAP 1573
Platanus woodland, scrub, rocky hillsides, fallow fields & field-margins; 50-900m; fl. 2-4.
Crete (sporadic) [Mediterranean region].

5. Iris L.

I. albicans Lange (*FE* **5**: 91) is planted for ornament in cemeteries and areas of cultivation, where it persists but appears never to become naturalized.

I. cretensis Janka (*FE* **5**: 88) = **3a**.

I. germanica L. (*FE* **5**: 90) most probably has the same status as *I. albicans*; it has low fertility and is mainly dispersed vegetatively by man (*MFG* **2**: 721).

I. lutescens Lam. is given as doubtfully present in the Cretan area in *FE* **5**: 90, presumably based on an old record from Crete cited by Rechinger (1943a: 741). The species is W. Mediterranean and highly unlikely to occur in the Cretan area as a native, although it might once have been cultivated.

1. I. planifolia (Mill.) Fiori & Paol., *Fl. Italia* **1**: 227 (1896) - *FE* **5**: 91.
Cr (W) - MAP 1574
Phrygana; 150-600m; fl. 3(-4).
W. Crete (S.W. part) [Mediterranean region].

2. I. pseudacorus L., *Sp. pl.*: 38 (1753) - *FE* **5**: 88.
Cr (W) - MAP 1575
River-banks & marshes near sea; fl. 3-4.
W. Crete (N. coast) [almost throughout Europe].

3. I. unguicularis Poir., *Voy. Barbarie* **2**: 86 (1789) - *FE* **5**: 88.
●**a.** subsp. **cretensis** (Janka) A.P.Davis & Jury in *Bot. J. Linn. Soc.* **103**: 294 (1990) - *FE* **5**: 88

as *I. cretensis* Janka.
Cr (W, C, E) Ks Kp Sa - *MAP 1576*
Open woodland & scrub, phrygana, cliffs, banks
& rocky places; 0-1450m; fl. 2-5.
Crete (widespread); Karpathos group - Endemic.

6. Romulea Maratti

1. R. bulbocodium (L.) Sebast. & Mauri, *Fl.*
roman. prodr.: 17 (1818) - *FE* 5: 99.
Cr (W, C, E) Ks Kp - *MAP 1577*
Garigue, phrygana, soil-pockets among rocks,
flat clayey areas, abandoned fields; 50-1200m;
fl. 3-4.
Crete (sporadic); Kasos, Karpathos
[Mediterranean region].

2. R. columnae Sebast. & Mauri, *Fl. roman.*
prodr.: 18 (1818) - *FE* 5: 100.
Cr - *NOT MAPPED*
Crete [W. Europe & Mediterranean region].

? R. linaresii Parl., *Fl. panorm.* 1: 38 (1839) -
FE 5: 100.
Subsp. **graeca** Bég. in *Bot. Jb.* 38: 325 (1907) -
FE 5: 100.
Doubtfully present in Crete [Greece & Aegean
region; otherwise E. Aegean Islands (Hios) &
W. Turkey].

3. R. ramiflora Ten., *App. ind. sem.* 1827: 3
(1827) - *FE* 5: 100.
a. subsp. ramiflora
Cr (C) Ks Kp - *MAP 1578*
Abandoned fields; 700-750m; fl. 3-4.
C. Crete; Kasos, Karpathos [Mediterranean
region].

JUNCACEAE

1. Juncus L.

1. J. acutus L., *Sp. pl.*: 325 (1753) - *FE* 5:
104.
a. subsp. acutus
Cr (W) - *MAP 1579*
Maritime sands, damp ground near sea.
W. Crete (N. coast) [W. Europe &
Mediterranean region].

2. J. articulatus L., *Sp. pl.*: 327 (1753) - *FE* 5:
111.
Cr (W, C, E) Kp - *MAP 1580*
Marshy places, streams, ditches, springs, wet
bare ground; 0-400m; fl. 4-5.
Crete (sporadic); Karpathos [almost throughout
Europe].

3. J. bufonius L., *Sp. pl.*: 328 (1753) - *FE* 5:
107.
Cr (W, C, E) - *MAP 1581*

Streams, ditches, wet bare ground & sandy
places; 0-100m; fl. 4-5.
Crete (sporadic) [almost throughout Europe].

4. J. capitatus Weigel, *Observ. bot.*: 28 (1772)
- *FE* 5: 108.
Cr (W) - *MAP 1582*
Damp ground.
W. Crete [most of Europe].

5. J. effusus L., *Sp. pl.*: 326 (1753) - *FE* 5:
105.
Cr (W) - *MAP 1583*
Marshes, seasonally wet places, damp river-
banks in maquis, damp rocks; 0-500m.
W. Crete [almost throughout Europe].

6. J. heldreichianus T.Marsson ex Parl., *Fl.*
ital. 2: 315 (1852) - *FE* 5: 104.
a. subsp. heldreichianus
Cr (W, C, E) Kp Sa - *MAP 1584*
Brackish coastal marshes, maritime sands, other
damp places inland; 0-650m; fl. 4-5.
Crete (widespread); Karpathos, Saria [Greece &
Aegean region; otherwise S.W. Asia].

7. J. hybridus Brot., *Fl. lusit.* 1: 513 (1804) -
FE 5: 108.
Cr (W) Kp - *MAP 1585*
Coastal saline & damp ground.
W. Crete; Karpathos [Mediterranean region].

8. J. inflexus L., *Sp. pl.*: 326 (1753) - *FE* 5:
105.
Cr (W, C) - *MAP 1586*
Seasonally wet places, ditches; 0-550m; fl. 5.
W. & C. Crete [most of Europe].

9. J. littoralis C.A.Mey., *Verz. Pfl. Casp.*
Meer.: 34 (1831) - *FE* 5: 104.
Cr (W) - *MAP 1587*
Maritime sands.
W. Crete (Elafonisi island) [S.E. Europe &
Mediterranean region].

10. J. maritimus Lam., *Encycl.* 3: 264 (1789) -
FE 5: 104.
Cr (W) - *MAP 1588*
Brackish coastal marshes.
W. Crete [most of Europe].

11. J. minutulus V.I.Krecz. & Gontsch., *Fl.*
URSS 3: 625 (1935) - *FE* 5: 107.
Cr (C) - *MAP 1589*
Flat clayey area, apparently flooded in winter;
620m.
C. Crete [most of Europe].
Recorded since *FE* (Greuter et al., 1985: 43).

12. J. subulatus Forssk., *Fl. aegypt.-arab.*: 75
(1775) - *FE* 5: 105.
Cr (W) - *MAP 1590*
Brackish coastal marshes.

W. Crete [Mediterranean region].

2. Luzula DC.

? L. campestris (L.) DC. in Lam. & DC., *Fl. franç.* ed.3, **3**: 161 (1805) - *FE* **5**: 112.
Doubtfully present in Crete [most of Europe].

1. L. forsteri (Sm.) DC. in Lam. & DC., *Syn. pl. Fl. gall.*: 150 (1806) - *FE* **5**: 115.
Cr (W, E) - *MAP 1591*
Woodland, stream-banks & other moist shady places; 300-850m; fl. 4.
W. & E. Crete [W. S.C. & S. Europe].

2. L. nodulosa (Bory & Chaub.) E.Mey. in *Linnaea* **22**: 410 (1849) - *FE* **5**: 114.
Cr (W, C, E) Kp - *MAP 1592*
Light woodland, calcareous rocky places; 350-1200m; fl. 4.
Mainly W. & C. Crete; Karpathos [S. Greece & S. Aegean region; otherwise N.W. Africa, E. Aegean Islands & W. Turkey].

JUNCAGINACEAE

1. Triglochin L.

1. T. bulbosa L., *Mant. pl. alt.*: 226 (1771) - *FE* **5**: 7.
a. subsp. barrelieri (Loisel.) Rouy, *Fl. France* **13**: 271 (1912) - *FE* **5**: 7.
Cr (W) - *MAP 1593*
Coastal saline ground.
W. Crete (E. of Hania) [W. Europe & Mediterranean region].

LEMNACEAE

1. Lemna L.

1. L. minor L., *Sp. pl.*: 970 (1753) - *FE* **5**: 273.
Cr (W) - *MAP 1594*
Brackish swamps near sea.
W. Crete (Georgioupoli) [almost throughout Europe].

LILIACEAE

1. Allium L.

1. A. amethystinum Tausch in *Syll. Pl. nov. ratisbon. (Königl.-baier. bot. Ges.)* **2**: 256 (1828) - *FE* **5**: 67.
Cr Sa - *NOT MAPPED*
Crete; Saria [C. & E. Mediterranean region].

2. A. ampeloprasum L., *Sp. pl.*: 294 (1753) - *FE* **5**: 63.
Cr (W, C, E) Ks Kp - *MAP 1595*
Cultivated or abandoned fields, sometimes in more natural habitats; 0-600m; fl. 4-7.
Crete (widespread); Kasos, Karpathos [W. & S. Europe].

3. A. bourgeaui Rech.f. in *Annln naturh. Mus. Wien* **47**: 150 (1936) - *FE* **5**: 64.
a. subsp. bourgeaui
Ks Kp Sa - *MAP 1596*
Calcareous cliffs, ledges & crevices, offshore islets; 0-650m; fl. 6-7.
Karpathos group [E. Aegean Islands (Halki & Rodos) & S.W. Turkey].
●**b. subsp. creticum** Bothmer in *Mitt. bot. StSamml. Münch.* **12**: 272 (1975) - *FE* **5**: 64.
Cr (W, C, E) - *MAP 1597*
Calcareous cliffs; 0-600m; fl. 6-7.
Crete (widespread) - Endemic.

4. A. callimischon Link in *Linnaea* **9**: 140 (1835) - *FE* **5**: 59.
a. subsp. haemostictum Stearn in *Annls Mus. Goulandris* **4**: 151 (1978) - *FE* **5**: 60.
Cr (W, C) - *MAP 1598*
Calcareous cliffs, slopes, rocks & crevices; 300-2000m; fl. 10.
Mainly W. Crete [S.W. Turkey].
Not endemic to Crete as given in *FE* (cf. Kollmann in Davis, 1984: 130).

5. A. chamaespathum Boiss., *Diagn. pl. orient.* ser.1, **7**: 113 (1846) - *FE* **5**: 68.
Cr (W, C, E) - *MAP 1599*
Calcareous rocky slopes; 0-200m; fl. 9-10.
Crete (sporadic) [S. Balkan peninsula].

6. A. circinnatum Sieber, *Reise Kreta* **2**: 316 (1823) - *FE* **5**: 57.
●**a. subsp. circinnatum**
Cr (W, C, E) - *MAP 1600*
Phrygana, calcareous cliffs & crevices, soil-pockets in rocks; 50-250m; fl. 4.
Crete (sporadic, N. side) - Endemic.
A. circinnatum occurs outside the Cretan area in S. Greece, as subsp. *peloponnesiacum* Tzanoud. (Tzanoudakis, 1983).

7. A. commutatum Guss., *Enum. pl. Inarim.*: 339 (1854) - *FE* **5**: 64.
Cr (C, E) Ks Kp - *MAP 1601*
Frequently on offshore islets; 0-100m; fl. 5-7.
C. & E. Crete; Kasos, Karpathos [C. & E. Mediterranean region].

"*A. cupanii*" (Greuter, 1973a: 67) = **10** (Greuter et al., 1985: 45).

A. cupanii subsp. *hirtovaginatum* (Kunth) Stearn (*FE* **5**: 59) = **10**.

? **A. cyrilli** Ten., *Fl. napol.* **3**: 364 (1828-1829) - *FE* **5**: 69.
Doubtfully present in Crete (Greuter, 1974: 161) [S. Italy & S. & E. Greece; otherwise E. Aegean Islands (Hios) & W. Turkey].

●**8. A. dilatatum** Zahar. in *Annls Mus. Goulandris* **3**: 88 (1977) - *FE* **5**: 67.
Cr (W, C) - *MAP 1602*
Pinus brutia woodland, calcareous cliffs & rocky places; 0-800m; fl. 7-8.
W. & C. Crete - Endemic.
[Plate 10.]

9. A. guttatum Steven in *Mém. Soc. Nat. Moscou* **2**: 173 (1809) - *FE* **5**: 67.
a. subsp. **sardoum** (Moris) Stearn in *Annls Mus. Goulandris* **4**: 184 (1978) - *FE* **5**: 67.
Kp - *MAP 1603*
Growing through Sarcopoterium spinosum; 1000m; fl. 7.
Karpathos (Kalilimni) [Mediterranean region].
Regarded as absent from the Cretan area in *FE*, although previously recorded by Davis (1953: 142 as *A. margaritaceum* Sm. var. *margaritaceum*).

10. A. hirtovaginatum Kunth, *Enum. pl.* **4**: 412 (1843) - *FE* **5**: 59 as *A. cupanii* subsp. *hirtovaginatum* (Kunth) Stearn.
Cr (E) - *MAP 1604*
E. Crete (Sideros peninsula) [Balearic Islands, S. & E. Greece & Aegean region; otherwise N. Africa & S.W. Asia].

11. A. longanum Pamp. in *Boll. Soc. bot. ital.* **1912**: 116 (1912) - *FE* **5**: 57.
Cr (E) - *MAP 1605*
Among bushes on stony ground near sea; 10m.
E. Crete (Sideros peninsula) [S.E. Kiklades (Koutsomiti island off Astipalea, Sirna); otherwise N.E. Libya & Egypt].

12. A. neapolitanum Cirillo, *Pl. rar. neapol.* **1**: 13 (1788) - *FE* **5**: 57.
Cr (W) Ks Kp - *MAP 1606*
Olive groves, garigue, cultivated terraces; 50-450m; fl. 4.
W. Crete (Akrotiri peninsula); Kasos, Karpathos [Mediterranean region].

13. A. nigrum L., *Sp. pl.* ed.2: 430 (1762) - *FE* **5**: 68.
Cr (W, C, E) - *MAP 1607*
Cultivated & abandoned land; 0-500m; fl. 4-5.
Crete (sporadic) [S. Europe].

14. A. paniculatum L., *Syst. nat.* ed.10, **2**: 978 (1759) - *FE* **5**: 60.
Cr (C) - *MAP 1608*
Vineyards.
C. Crete [C. & S. Europe].

A record from Karpathos (Davis, 1953: 142) is referable to **19** (Greuter et al., 1983: 74).

15. A. roseum L., *Sp. pl.*: 296 (1753) - *FE* **5**: 56.
Cr (W, C) Kp - *MAP 1609*
Olive groves, moist grassy places, coastal saline ground, ditches; 0-550m; fl. 4.
W. & C. Crete; Karpathos [S. Europe].

●**16. A. rubrovittatum** Boiss. & Heldr. in Boiss., *Diagn. pl. orient.* ser.1, **13**: 29 (1853) - *FE* **5**: 68.
Cr (W, C, E) Ks Kp Sa - *MAP 1610*
Rocky places, open dry stony ground near sea; 0-2000m.
Crete (widespread); Karpathos group - Endemic.

17. A. scorodoprasum L., *Sp. pl.*: 297 (1753) - *FE* **5**: 65.
a. subsp. **rotundum** (L.) Stearn in *Annls Mus. Goulandris* **4**: 178 (1978) - *FE* **5**: 65.
Cr (E) - *MAP 1611*
Calcareous slopes, partly cultivated mountain plain; 850-1100m.
E. Crete (Dikti) [C. & S. Europe].
Regarded as absent from the Cretan area in *FE*, although doubtful records already existed; occurrence since confirmed by Greuter et al. (1985: 46).

A. staticiforme Sm. (*FE* **5**: 62) was recorded in error; most or all records may be referable to **19** (Greuter et al., 1985: 46).

18. A. subhirsutum L., *Sp. pl.*: 295 (1753) - *FE* **5**: 57.
Cr (W, C, E) Ks Kp Sa - *MAP 1612*
Calcareous rocky places, flat clayey areas; 0-1050m; fl. 4.
Mainly W. Crete; Karpathos group [Mediterranean region].

●**19. A. tardans** Greuter & Zahar. in *Biologia gallo-hellen.* **6**: 51 (1975) - *FE* **5**: 62.
Cr (W, C, E) Ks Kp - *MAP 1613*
Calcareous cliffs & crevices, among rocks of gorge-beds, phrygana, fallow fields; 100-1900m.
Crete (widespread); Kasos, Karpathos - Endemic.
Recorded from Kasos by Raus (1990: 33), and from Karpathos by Greuter et al. (1983a: 74).

20. A. trifoliatum Cirillo, *Pl. rar. neapol.* **2**: 11 (1792) - *FE* **5**: 57.
Cr (W, C, E) - *MAP 1614*
Cultivated fields; 400-800m; fl. 4.
Crete (sporadic) [Mediterranean region].

Aloë vera (L.) Burm.f. (*FE* **5**: 20) is cultivated for ornament in both Crete and Karpathos and also occurs as a casual escape.

2. Androcymbium Willd.

●1. **A. rechingeri** Greuter in *Candollea* 22: 248 (1967) - *FE* 5: 21.
Cr (W) - *MAP 1615*
Sandy soil-pockets in calcareous rocky phrygana, maritime sands; 0-25m; fl. before 3.
W. Crete (Elafonisi island & W. coast of Crete) - ?Endemic.
Endangered species, legally protected. *A. gramineum* var. *punicum* (Maire) Maire, from N. Africa, is considered doubtfully synonymous by Greuter (1967b: 252).

3. Asparagus L.

"*A. acutifolius*" (*FE* 5: 72) = **1a** (Barclay, 1986: 123).

1. **A. aphyllus** L., *Sp. pl.*: 314 (1753) - *FE* 5: 72.
a. subsp. **orientalis** (Baker) P.H.Davis, *Fl. Turkey* 8: 77 (1984) - not cited in *FE*.
Cr (W, C, E) Ks Kp Sa - *MAP 1616*
Olive groves, hedges, scrub, garigue, phrygana, rocky places & crevices; 0-2000m; fl. 10.
Crete (widespread); Karpathos group [Aegean region; otherwise Egypt & S.W. Asia].
The young shoots are collected by the local people as a condiment.

2. **A. stipularis** Forssk., *Fl. aegypt.-arab.*: 72 (1775) - *FE* 5: 72.
Cr (E) Ks Kp - *MAP 1617*
Among shrubs in rocky places on offshore islets.
E. Crete (Gaidouronisi & Dionisiades islands); Kasos, Karpathos [Mediterranean region].

4. Asphodeline Rchb.

1. **A. liburnica** (Scop.) Rchb., *Fl. germ. excurs.*: 116 (1830) - *FE* 5: 18.
Cr (W, C, E) - *MAP 1618*
Sparse garigue, rocky places; 0-1550m; fl. 6.
Mainly W. Crete [S. Italy & Balkan peninsula].

2. **A. lutea** (L.) Rchb., *Fl. germ. excurs.*: 116 (1830) - *FE* 5: 17.
Cr (W, C, E) - *MAP 1619*
Garigue, phrygana, rocky places & crevices, flat clayey areas; 0-1050m; fl. 3-5.
Mainly W. & C. Crete [Italy, Sicily, Balkan peninsula & Aegean region].

5. Asphodelus L.

1. **A. aestivus** Brot., *Fl. lusit.* 1: 525 (1804) - *FE* 5: 17.
Cr (W, C, E) Ks Kp Sa - *MAP 1620*

Deciduous Quercus woodland, garigue, phrygana, soil-filled hollows, maritime sands, fallow & abandoned land, field-margins; 0-1050m; fl. 3-6.
Crete (widespread); Karpathos group [Mediterranean region].

2. **A. fistulosus** L., *Sp. pl.*: 309 (1753) - *FE* 5: 17.
Cr (W, E) Ks Kp - *MAP 1621*
Rubble, ditches & roadsides, usually near sea; 0-600m; fl. 3-4.
W. & E. Crete (S. coast); Kasos, Karpathos [S.W. Europe & Mediterranean region].

6. Bellevalia Lapeyr.

●1. **B. brevipedicellata** Turrill in *Kew Bull.* 1940: 264 (1941) - *FE* 5: 45.
Cr (W) - *MAP 1622*
Calcareous rock-crevices, open rocky hillsides; 0-150m; fl. 1-2.
W. Crete (S.W. part) - Endemic.

2. **B. dubia** (Guss.) Rchb., *Fl. germ. excurs.*: 105 (1830) - *FE* 5: 45.
Cr (W) ?Ks - *MAP 1623*
Cliff; 300m; fl. 4.
W. Crete (Korikos peninsula); ?Kasos [C. & E. Mediterranean region].
Occurrence in the Cretan area confirmed since *FE* (Strasser, 1988: 6, 22). The only previous records - from Kasos - are considered doubtful by Greuter (1974: 161), and are possibly referable to **3**.

3. **B. trifoliata** (Ten.) Kunth, *Enum. pl.* 4: 308 (1843) - *FE* 5: 45.
?Cr Kp - *MAP 1624*
Olive groves, scrub, abandoned fields & terraces; 350-700m; fl. 3-4.
?Crete; Karpathos [C. & E. Mediterranean region].
Doubtful occurrence in the Cretan area confirmed here.

Chionodoxa cretica Boiss. & Heldr. (*FE* 5: 44) is included in synonymy of **Scilla 3**.

C. nana (Schult. & Schult.f.) Boiss. & Heldr. (*FE* 5: 44) = **Scilla 3**.

7. Colchicum L.

●1. **C. cousturieri** Greuter in *Candollea* 22: 247 (1967) - *FE* 5: 22.
Cr (E) - *MAP 1625*
E. Crete (Gaidouronisi & Koufonisi islands) - Endemic.
Vulnerable species, legally protected.

●2. C. cretense Greuter in *Candollea* 22: 246
(1967) - *FE* 5: 22.
Cr (W, C, E) - *MAP 1626*
*Sparse phrygana, mountain pastures, open stony
slopes & screes, flat clayey areas; (1050-)1200-
2300m; fl. (9-)10-11, rarely 5.*
Crete (Lefka Ori, Psiloritis & Dikti) - Endemic.

3. C. cupanii Guss., *Fl. sicul. prodr.* 1: 452-3
(1827) - *FE* 5: 22.
Cr (E) - *MAP 1627*
*Olive groves, calcareous stony hillsides; 90-
320m; fl. 11-12.*
E. Crete (Hersonisos to Neapoli area)
[Mediterranean region].
Doubtful occurrence confirmed since *FE*
(Turland, 1992*b*: 163).

4. C. macrophyllum B.L.Burtt in *Kew Bull.* 5:
433 (1951) - *FE* 5: 24.
Cr (W, C, E) - *MAP 1628*
*Olive groves, phrygana, fallow & abandoned
fields; 200-750m; fl. 9-11.*
Crete (sporadic) [E. Aegean Islands (Simi, Halki
& Rodos) & S.W. Turkey].

5. C. pusillum Sieber in *Flora, Jena* 5: 248
(1822) - *FE* 5: 22.
Cr (W, C, E) Ks Kp - *MAP 1629*
*Calcareous stony hillsides, low phrygana, bare
stony ground, flat clayey areas; 0-1200m; fl. 10-
12.*
Crete (widespread); Kasos, Karpathos [C. & S.
Greece & Kiklades; otherwise E. Aegean Islands
(Tilos, Simi & Rodos) & Cyprus].

8. Drimia Jacq.

1. D. maritima (L.) Stearn in *Annls Mus.
Goulandris* 4: 204 (1978) - *FE* 5: 41 as *Urginea
maritima* (L.) Baker.
Cr (W, C, E) Ks Kp - *MAP 1630*
*Garigue, phrygana, rocky places, soil-filled
hollows; 0-1050m; fl. 8-10.*
Crete (widespread); Kasos, Karpathos
[Mediterranean region].

9. Fritillaria L.

1. F. graeca Boiss. & Spruner in Boiss., *Diagn.
pl. orient.* ser.1, 7: 104 (1846) - *FE* 5: 32 as *F.
graeca* Boiss. & Spruner subsp. *graeca*.
Cr (W) - *MAP 1631*
Calcareous rocky place; 300m.
W. Crete (Rodopos peninsula) [S. & E. Greece
& Aegean region].

2. F. messanensis Raf. in Desv. in *J. Bot.
Agric. Pharm. Med. Arts Paris* 4: 272 (1814) -
FE 5: 32.

a. subsp. messanensis
Cr (W, C, E) - *MAP 1632*
*Woodland, scrub, garigue, phrygana, rocky
places; 0-1350m; fl. 3-5.*
Mainly W. Crete [S. Italy, Sicily & S. Balkan
peninsula].

10. Gagea Salisb.

G. amblyopetala Boiss. & Heldr. (*FE* 5: 28) is
included in synonymy of **2**.

1. G. bohemica (Zauschn.) Schult. & Schult.f.,
Syst. veg. 7: 549 (1829) - *FE* 5: 28.
a. subsp. bohemica
Cr (W, C) - *MAP 1633*
*Stony slopes, flat clayey areas; 1000-1800m; fl.
4.*
W. & C. Crete (Lefka Ori & Psiloritis) [C. & S.
Europe].

2. G. chrysantha (Jan) Schult. & Schult.f.,
Syst. veg. 7: 545 (1829) - *FE* 5: 28. (Including
G. amblyopetala Boiss. & Heldr. - *FE* 5: 28.)
Cr (W, C) - *MAP 1634*
Stony ground; 1050-1800m.
W. & C. Crete (Lefka Ori & Psiloritis) [mainly
Italy, Sicily & Balkan peninsula].

3. G. commutata K.Koch in *Linnaea* 22: 227
(1849) - *FE* 5: 27.
Cr (C, E) - *MAP 1635*
Flat clayey areas, dry places; 100-1500m.
C. & E. Crete [S.W. Asia].

4. G. fibrosa (Desf.) Schult. & Schult.f., *Syst.
veg.* 7: 552 (1829) - *FE* 5: 27.
Cr (W) - *MAP 1636*
*Calcareous garigue, dry stony hillsides; 250-
600m; fl. 3-4.*
W. Crete [Aegean region; otherwise N. Africa
& S.W. Asia].
Recorded since *FE* (Foley in Turland, 1992*b*:
163).

5. G. graeca (L.) A.Terracc. in *Mém. Soc. bot.
Fr.* 2: 25 (1905) - *FE* 5: 27.
Cr (W, C, E) Ks Kp - *MAP 1637*
*Scrub, garigue, phrygana, calcareous cliffs,
crevices & rocky places, abandoned terraces,
bare ground; 0-400m; fl. 4.*
Mainly W. & C. Crete; Kasos, Karpathos [S.
Greece & Aegean region; otherwise E. Aegean
Islands & W. Turkey].

6. G. granatellii (Parl.) Parl., *Fl. palerm.* 1:
276 (1845) - *FE* 5: 27.
Cr (E) - *NOT MAPPED*
E. Crete [mainly C. & E. Mediterranean
region].
Recorded since *FE* (*MFG* 2: 667).

7. G. peduncularis (J.& C.Presl) Pascher in *Sber. dt. naturw.-med. Ver. Böhm "Lotos"* nov. ser., **14**: 112 (1904) - *FE* **5**: 27.
Cr (W, C, E) Kp - *MAP 1638*
Garigue, phrygana, rocky places, open stony ground; 250-1050m; fl. 3-4.
Crete (sporadic); Karpathos [Sicily & Greece; otherwise N. Africa & S.W. Asia].

? G. reticulata (Pall.) Schult. & Schult.f., *Syst. veg.* **7**: 542 (1829) - *FE* **5**: 26.
Doubtfully present in Crete [S.E. Europe].
Probably recorded in error for **3** (Greuter, 1973a: 66).

Lilium candidum L. (*FE* **5**: 34) has been recorded from the Akrotiri peninsula in W. Crete, as probably planted and more or less established (Greuter, 1973a: 67).

11. Muscari Mill.

"*M.* aff. *atlanticum*" (Greuter, 1973a: 68) = **5**.

1. M. commutatum Guss., *Fl. sicul. prodr.* **1**: 426 (1827) - *FE* **5**: 48.
Cr (E) - *MAP 1639*
Step-crevices & soil-pockets in calcareous rocks; 400m.
E. Crete (S.E. of Sitia) [C. & E. Mediterranean region].

2. M. comosum (L.) Mill., *Gard. Dict.* ed.8: no.2 (1768) - *FE* **5**: 47.
Cr (W, C, E) Ks Kp - *MAP 1640*
Cultivated, fallow & abandoned land, phrygana, rocky places; 0-800m; fl. 3-5.
Mainly W. Crete; Kasos, Karpathos [mainly C. & S. Europe].
The bulbs are dug up, pickled and eaten by the local people, and are known as *volvi*.

"*M. cycladicum*" (*FE* **5**: 47) ? = **7** (Greuter et al., 1985: 47).

3. M. dionysicum Rech.f. in *Denkschr. Akad. Wiss. Wien* **105(2,1)**: 167 (1943) - *FE* **5**: 47.
Cr (C, E) - *MAP 1641*
Coastal rocks & crevices.
C. & E. Crete (Dia & Dionisiades islands) [W. Aegean region & Kiklades].

4. M. macrocarpum Sweet, *Brit. fl. gard.* ser.1: t.210 (1827) - *FE* **5**: 47.
Cr (E) - *MAP 1642*
Calcareous cliffs & rock-crevices; 50-750m; fl. 2.
E. Crete [Kiklades (Amorgos); otherwise E. Aegean islands & S.W. Turkey].

5. M. neglectum Guss. ex Ten., *Syll. pl. fl. neapol., App. quinta*: 13 (1842) - *FE* **5**: 48.
Cr (W, C, E) Kp - *MAP 1643*
Light woodland, scrub, garigue, phrygana, soil-pockets among rocks, abandoned cultivated land; 300-2000m; fl. 3-5.
Crete (mainly in mountains); Karpathos [mainly C. & S. Europe].
Compared with plants from Karpathos, those from Crete have relatively few flowers per raceme, with patent pedicels and shorter, lighter blue corollas.

6. M. parviflorum Desf., *Fl. atlant.* **1**: 309 (1798) - *FE* **5**: 48.
Cr (W) - *MAP 1644*
Step-crevices in small gorge leading down to sea; 80m; fl. 10.
W. Crete (Akrotiri peninsula) [Mediterranean region].

●**7. M. spreitzenhoferi** (Heldr. ex Osterm.) Vierh. in *Öst. bot. Z.* **66**: 167 (1916) - *FE* **5**: 47.
Cr (W, C, E) - *MAP 1645*
Calcareous rock-crevices, phrygana, flat clayey areas, maritime sands; 0-2100m; fl. 3-7.
Crete (widespread) - ?Endemic [doubtfully also in Algeria].

8. M. weissii Freyn in *Öst. bot. Z.* **28**: 87 (1878) - *FE* **5**: 47.
Ks Kp Sa - *MAP 1646*
Cliffs & rocky places, sparse phrygana, open ground near sea; 0-400m; fl. 4.
Karpathos group [S.E. Greece & Aegean region; otherwise E. Aegean Islands & S.W. Turkey].
Records from Crete are probably referable to **7** (Greuter et al., 1985: 47).

12. Ornithogalum L.

[**1. O. arabicum**] L., *Sp. pl.*: 307 (1753) - *FE* **5**: 40.
Cr (C) - *MAP 1647*
Rarely cultivated for ornament and locally naturalized in olive groves; 300m; fl. 4.
C. Crete (S.E. of Rethimno) [Mediterranean region].
Regarded as absent from the Cretan area in *FE*, although previously recorded by Rechinger (1943a: 725); occurrence since confirmed (Barclay, 1986: 125; Akeroyd, pers. comm., 1992).

O. collinum Guss. (*FE* **5**: 38) see **4**.

2. O. creticum Zahar. in *Annls Mus. Goulandris* **3**: 52 (1977) - *FE* **5**: 37.
Cr (W, C, E) Kp - *MAP 1648*
Calcareous cliffs, ledges, crevices & steep rocky slopes, phrygana, offshore islets; 0-1500m; fl. 4-

6.
Crete (widespread); Karpathos [S.E. Kiklades].
Recorded from Karpathos by Greuter et al.
(1985: 48), who state that records of *O.
visianicum* Tomm. from islets in the S.E.
Kiklades (Rechinger, 1943a: 726) presumably
belong here.

3. O. divergens Boreau, *Notes pl. franç.*: 15
(1847), réimpr. ex *Bull. Soc. industr. Angers* **18**
(1847) - *FE* **5**: 40.
Cr (W, C, E) - MAP 1649
*Cultivated, fallow & abandoned land; 0-850m;
fl. 4.*
Crete (sporadic) [mainly S. Europe].

4. O. exscapum Ten., *Fl. napol.* **1**: xxii, 175
(1811-1815) - *FE* **5**: 39.
Cr (W, C) ?Kp - MAP 1650
*Phrygana, rocky places, bare stony ground, flat
clayey areas; 0-500m.*
Mainly W. Crete; ?Karpathos [Mediterranean
region].
The Cretan collection cited in *MFG* 2: 690 is
here referred to **6** (see notes under *O. pumilum*).
O. collinum Guss. (*FE* 5: 38) is reduced to
varietal rank under **4** in *MFG* 2: 691, and is not
separated here.

5. O. narbonense L., *Cent. pl.* **2**: 15 (1756) -
FE **5**: 37.
Cr (W, C, E) Ks Kp - MAP 1651
*Olive groves, fallow fields, dry stony places; 0-
500m; fl. 4-5.*
Crete (sporadic); Kasos, Karpathos [S. Europe].

6. O. nivale Boiss., *Diagn. pl. orient.* ser.1, **5**:
65 (1844).
Cr (W, E) - MAP 1652
Calcareous rocks & slopes; 800-2100m.
W. & E. Crete (Lefka Ori & Dikti) [Turkey].
Recorded since *FE* (Raamsdonk, 1984: 121,
127, 135; Greuter et al., 1985: 49).

7. O. nutans L., *Sp. pl.*: 308 (1753) - *FE* **5**: 40.
Cr (C, E) Kp - MAP 1653
*Olive groves, grassy fields, cultivated ground;
450-1100m; fl. 4.*
C. & E. Crete; Karpathos [W., C. & S.
Europe].
Regarded as absent from the Cretan area in *FE*,
although previously recorded by Rechinger
(1943a: 727); occurrence since confirmed by
Greuter et al. (1983a: 75; 1985: 49). Always
found near human settlements, and may have
been originally introduced by man (Greuter et
al., 1985: 49).

O. pumilum Zahar. is given for Crete by
Barclay (1986: 125). It was described from the
E. Aegean island of Hios (Zahariadi et al.,
1982: 151), but was recorded from the Lefka

Ori in W. Crete (op. cit.) in error for **6** (Greuter
et al., 1985: 50). The same collection is referred
to **4** in *MFG* 2: 690, where **6** is not cited.

? O. sibthorpii Greuter in *Boissiera* **13**: 160
(1967) - *FE* **5**: 38.
Doubtfully present in Crete (Greuter et al.,
1985: 50) [Balkan peninsula & Aegean region].

"*O. visianicum*" (Greuter, 1973a: 68) = **2**
(Greuter et al., 1985: 48).

13. Ruscus L.

1. R. aculeatus L., *Sp. pl.*: 1041 (1753) - *FE* **5**:
73.
Cr (W, C) Kp - MAP 1654
*Calcareous woodland, scrub, shady rocky
places; 0-600m.*
W. & C. Crete; Karpathos [W., S.C. & S.
Europe].

[2. R. hypophyllum] L., *Sp. pl.*: 1041 (1753) -
FE **5**: 73.
Cr (C) - MAP 1655
*Naturalized in small ravine with scrub and
cultivated terraces; 450-500m.*
C. Crete (W. of Iraklio) [S. & E. Spain, S.E.
France & S.E. Sicily; otherwise N.W. Africa].
Recorded since *FE* (Greuter et al., 1985: 51).

14. Scilla L.

S. albescens Speta (Speta, 1976: 19; Barclay,
1986: 126) is included in synonymy of **3**, after
MFG 2: 696.

1. S. autumnalis L., *Sp. pl.*: 309 (1753) - *FE* **5**:
43.
Cr (W, C, E) Ks Kp - MAP 1656
*Phrygana, rocky places & crevices, screes, bare
stony ground; 0-500m; fl. 8-11.*
Crete (sporadic); Kasos, Karpathos [W. & S.
Europe].

2. S. bifolia L., *Sp. pl.*: 309 (1753) - *FE* **5**: 41.
Kp - MAP 1657
*Sparse low Acer scrub, stony ground beneath
cliffs; 1100-1150m; fl. 3-4.*
Karpathos (Kalilimni) [C. & S. Europe].
Recorded here as new to Karpathos and the
Cretan area.

●**3. S. nana** (Schult. & Schult.f.) Speta in *Öst.
bot. Z.* **119**: 14 (1971) - *FE* **5**: 44 as *Chionodoxa
nana* (Schult. & Schult.f.) Boiss. & Heldr.
(Including *Chionodoxa cretica* Boiss. & Heldr. -
FE 5: 44, and *Scilla albescens* Speta - not cited
in *FE*.)
Cr (W, C, E) - MAP 1658

Calcareous open woodland, among Berberis bushes, screes, stony ground beneath cliffs, floors of caves, open slopes, flat clayey areas; 900-2400m; fl. 3-5.
Crete (Lefka Ori, Kedros, Psiloritis, Dikti & Afendis Kavousi) - Endemic.
An old record from the E. Aegean Island of Rodos has never been confirmed (Meikle in Davis, 1984: 226), and is considered erroneous by Carlström (1987: 119).

15. Smilax L.

1. S. aspera L., *Sp. pl.*: 1028 (1753) - *FE* **5**: 74.
Cr (W, C, E) - *MAP 1659*
Woodland, olive groves, scrub; 0-500m; fl. 9-10.
Mainly W. & C. Crete [S. Europe].

16. Tulipa L.

T. bakeri A.D.Hall (*FE* **5**: 30) is included in synonymy of **4**.
●**1. T. cretica** Boiss. & Heldr. in Boiss., *Diagn. pl. orient.* ser.1, **13**: 19 (1853) - *FE* **5**: 30.
Cr (W, C, E) - *MAP 1660*
Calcareous phrygana, open slopes, cliffs, crevices, rocky places, screes; 0-2000m; fl. 3-5.
Crete (sporadic) - Endemic.

●**2. T. doerfleri** Gand., *Fl. cret.*: 102 (1916) - *FE* **5**: 29, included in synonymy of *T. orphanidea* Boiss. ex Heldr.
Cr (W, C) - *MAP 1661*
Cultivated & fallow fields; 400-750m; fl. 4-5.
W. & C. Crete - Endemic.
Triploid (2n = 36), according to Sonderhousen (1977: 148), whereas *T. orphanidea* is tetraploid (*MFG* **2**: 670).

3. T. goulimyi Sealy & Turrill in *Kew Bull.* **10**: 59 (1955) - *FE* **5**: 29.
Cr (W) - *MAP 1662*
Calcareous phrygana near coast, especially in sparse areas with bare soil, also banks of terraces; fl. 3-4.
W. Crete (W. coast) [S. Peloponnisos & Kithira].
[Plate 10.] Recorded since *FE* (Briggs, 1989; 1990). Vulnerable species, legally protected.

"*T. orphanidea*" (*FE* **5**: 29) = **2** (Barclay, 1986: 126).

4. T. saxatilis Sieber ex Spreng., *Syst. veg.* **2**: 63 (1825) - *FE* **5**: 29. (Including *T. bakeri*

A.D.Hall - *FE* **5**: 30.)
Cr (W, C, E) Kp - *MAP 1663*
Ledges & crevices of calcareous cliffs, rocky slopes & screes, stream banks in scrub, flat clayey areas, cultivated, fallow & abandoned fields, often on mountain plains; 0-2200m; fl. 3-5.
Crete (sporadic); Karpathos [E. Aegean Islands (Rodos) & S.W. Turkey].
The variant *T. bakeri* is treated as a separate species in *MFG* **2**: 671-672, where it is said to differ in a number of morphological characters, to be diploid (2n = 24), to occur mainly in more open habitats at higher altitudes (650-2200m compared with 0-*c*. 900m), and to be probably a more or less stabilized hybrid of fairly recent origin between *T. saxatilis* sensu stricto (diploid and triploid) and **1** (diploid). Introgressive populations of **1** with some traits of *T. saxatilis* apparently occur at low to moderate altitudes in Crete, while others, at higher altitudes, show signs of introgression from *T. bakeri* (*MFG* **2**: 671).

Urginea maritima (L.) Baker (*FE* **5**: 41) = **Drimia 1**.

MUSACEAE

Musa cavendishii Lamb. ex Paxton (*FE* **5**: 324) is cultivated only; either as occasional plants, or on a field scale in polythene greenhouses.

ORCHIDACEAE

1. Aceras R.Br.

1. A. anthropophorum (L.) W.T.Aiton, *Epitome ed.2 Hort. kew.*: 281 (1814) - *FE* **5**: 342.
Cr (W, C, E) Kp - *MAP 1664*
Woodland, garigue, phrygana, grassy places, soil-pockets among rocks; 0-1200m; fl. 3-5.
Crete (widespread); Karpathos [W. Europe & Mediterranean region].

2. Anacamptis (L.) Rich.

1. A. pyramidalis (L.) Rich., *De orchid. eur.*: 33 (1817) - *FE* **5**: 343.
Cr (W, C, E) Ks Kp Sa - *MAP 1665*
Woodland, olive groves, scrub, garigue, phrygana, grassy places, abandoned terraces; 0-1000m; fl. 4-5.
Crete (widespread); Karpathos group [mainly W., C. & S. Europe].

3. Barlia Parl.

1. B. robertiana (Loisel.) Greuter in *Boissiera*
13: 192 (1967) - *FE 5*: 342.
Cr (W, C, E) Kp - *MAP 1666*
Woodland, olive groves, scrub, garigue,
phrygana, rocky & grassy places, abandoned
terraces; 0-1200m; fl. 1-4.
Crete (widespread); Karpathos [Mediterranean
region].

4. Cephalanthera Rich.

●**1. C. cucullata** Boiss. & Heldr. in Boiss.,
Diagn. pl. orient. ser.1, **13**: 12 (1853) - *FE 5*:
328.
Cr (W, C, E) - *MAP 1667*
Calcareous woodland; 700-1500m; fl. 5-6.
Crete (Lefka Ori, Psiloritis & Dikti) - Endemic.
[Plate 10.] Endemic status not noted in *FE*.
Endangered species, legally protected.

2. C. damasonium (Mill.) Druce in *Ann. Scot.*
nat. Hist. **1906**: 225 (1906) - *FE 5*: 328.
Cr (C) - *MAP 1668*
Woodland of Acer & Quercus coccifera on N.E.-
facing slope; 1150-1250m; fl. 5.
C. Crete (Psiloritis) [W., C. & S. Europe].
Regarded as absent from the Cretan area in *FE*,
although previously recorded by Robatsch
(1978); cf. Greuter et al. (1985: 51).

3. C. longifolia (L.) Fritsch in *Öst. bot. Z.* **38**:
81 (1888) - *FE 5*: 328.
Cr (W) - *MAP 1669*
Castanea & Pinus brutia woodland, scrub; 700-
1000m; fl. 4-5.
W. Crete [most of Europe].
Regarded as absent from the Cretan area in *FE*,
although previously recorded by Künkele (1979:
297, 303); cf. Greuter et al. (1985: 51).

? C. rubra (L.) Rich., *De orchid. eur.*: 38
(1817) - *FE 5*: 329.
Doubtfully present in Crete [most of Europe].
Recorded from the Lefka Ori in W. Crete by
Teschner (1975a: 169) but never since
confirmed. A population of **1** occurs at the same
locality, where Alibertis & Alibertis (1989a: 33)
have observed plants with flowers a deeper than
usual shade of pink; this may be the basis of
Teschner's record.

5. Dactylorhiza Neck. ex Nevski

1. D. romana (Sebast. & Mauri) Soó, *Nom.*
nov. Gen. Dactylorhiza: 3 (1962) - *FE 5*: 334 as
D. sulphurea subsp. *pseudosambucina* (Ten.)
Franco.
Cr (W, C, E) - *MAP 1670*

Woodland, maquis, scrub; 150-900m; fl. 3-5.
Mainly W. & C. Crete [S. Europe].

D. sulphurea subsp. *pseudosambucina* (Ten.)
Franco (*FE 5*: 334) = **1**.

6. Epipactis Zinn

●**1. E. cretica** Kalop. & Robatsch in *Orchidee*
31: 142 (1980).
Cr (C, E) - *MAP 1671*
Calcareous woodland; 1150-1400m; fl. 6-7.
C. & E. Crete (Psiloritis & Dikti) - Endemic.
Closely related to *E. persica* (Soó) Renz (from
N. Greece to Iran) and *E. troodii* H.Lindb.
(endemic to Cyprus).

"*E. helleborine*" (*FE 5*: 327) ?= **1** (Greuter et
al., 1985: 52).

2. E. microphylla (Ehrh.) Sw. in *K. svenska*
VetenskAkad. Handl. nov.ser., **21**: 232 (1800) -
FE 5: 328.
Cr (W) - *MAP 1672*
Woodland, scrub; 750-1100m; fl. 5-6.
W. Crete [C. & S. Europe].

A putative hybrid between **1** and **2**, recorded by
Alibertis & Alibertis (1989a: 36, 161) from
Psiloritis in C. Crete, should be considered
doubtful; the only confirmed records for the
latter species are from W. Crete.

7. Himantoglossum W.D.J.Koch

1. H. caprinum (M.Bieb.) Spreng., *Syst. veg.*
3: 694 (1826) - *FE 5*: 342 as *H. hircinum* subsp.
caprinum (M.Bieb.) K.Richt.
Cr (W, C, E) - *MAP 1673*
Calcareous slopes; 1000-1300m; fl. 5-6.
Crete (Lefka Ori, Psiloritis & Dikti) [E.C. &
S.E. Europe].
Erroneously given as endemic to Crimea in *FE*
(cf. map in Baumann & Künkele, 1982: 154).
Recorded from Crete by Goulandris et al.
(1968); cf. Greuter (1973a: 77).

Rückbrodt & Rückbrodt (1987) suggested that a
population of *Himantoglossum* in the Lefka Ori
could be referable to *H. affine* (Boiss.) Schltr.,
which otherwise occurs in S.W. Asia. The
presence of this species was confirmed - but
without firm evidence - by Alibertis & Alibertis
(1989a: 16, 39), who also recorded its putative
hybrid with **1**, which they described as a new
"species", *H. samariensis* C.& A.Alibertis (op.
cit.: 15-16, 40; 1989c: 110, as "ssp. nov.").
Furthermore, an unidentified *Himantoglossum*
was recorded by Blaich (1991). After examining
the published data, it is evident that some plants

in the Lefka Ori appear closer to *H. affine* than *H. caprinum* (but not close enough for the former to be regarded as unquestionably present in Crete), while others are intermediate between the two species. If the occurrence of *H. affine* can be definitely confirmed, it might be appropriate to treat all these plants as hybrids; meanwhile, only *H. caprinum* should be regarded as present.

8. Limodorum Boehm.

1. L. abortivum (L.) Sw. in *Nova Acta R. Soc. Scient. upsal.* **6**: 80 (1799) - *FE* **5**: 329.
a. subsp. abortivum
Cr (W, C, E) Kp - *MAP 1674*
Woodland & clearings, maquis, scrub; 0-1000m; fl. 4-5.
Crete (sporadic); Karpathos [mainly C. & S. Europe].

9. Listera R.Br.

1. L. ovata (L.) R.Br. in W.T.Aiton, *Hortus kew.* **5**: 201 (1813) - *FE* **5**: 329.
Cr (W) - *MAP 1675*
Damp Castanea & Platanus woodland, damp rocks; 250-750m; fl. 4-5.
W. Crete [almost throughout Europe].

10. Neotinea Rchb.f.

1. N. maculata (Desf.) Stearn in *Annls Mus. Goulandris* **2**: 79 (1974) - *FE* **5**: 337.
Cr (W, C, E) Kp - *MAP 1676*
Woodland, scrub, phrygana, grassy places; 0-1000m; fl. 3-4.
Crete (widespread); Karpathos [W. Europe & Mediterranean region].

11. Ophrys L.

1. O. aegaea Kalteisen & H.R.Reinhard in *MittBl. ArbKreis heim. Orch. Baden-Württ.* **19**: 918 (1987).
●**a. subsp. aegaea**
?Ks Kp - *MAP 1677*
Pinus brutia woodland, olive & carob groves, garigue, phrygana, grassy & rocky places, abandoned terraces; 150-850m; fl. 3-4.
?Kasos, Karpathos - ?Endemic [possibly also in E. Aegean Islands (Lesvos)].
[Plate 10.] *O. aegaea* is related to *O. argolica*, and occurs outside the Cretan area on the E. Aegean island of Rodos, as subsp. *lucis* Kalteisen & H.R.Reinhard (op. cit.)

2. O. apifera Huds., *Fl. angl.*: 340 (1762) - *FE* **5**: 349.
Cr (W, C, E) - *MAP 1678*
Woodland, scrub, phrygana, grassy places, usually on moist ground; 0-800m; fl. 4-5.
Crete (sporadic) [W., C. & S. Europe].

"*O. araneola*" (Barclay, 1986: 127) = **19a** (Paulus, 1988).

? O. argolica H.Fleischm. in *Verh. zool.-bot. Ges. Wien* **69**: 295 (1919) - *FE* **5**: 347.
Doubtfully present in Crete [C. & S. Greece]. All Cretan records are considered erroneous, except for one which requires confirmation (Greuter et al., 1985: 52). Records from Karpathos are referable to **1a** (Hiller & Kalteisen, 1988: 459); presumably those from Kasos are too. Rare species, legally protected.

●**3. O. basilissa** C.& A.Alibertis & H.R.Reinhard in *MittBl. ArbKreis heim. Orch. Baden-Württ.* **22**: 201 (1990).
Cr (W, C, E) - *MAP 1679*
Pinus brutia woodland, olive groves, scrub, phrygana; 0-500m; fl. 12-3.
Mainly C. & E. Crete - Endemic.
Closely related to **17**.

4. O. bombyliflora Link in *J. Bot. Göttingen* **1799**(2): 325 (1800) - *FE* **5**: 349.
Cr (W, C, E) Ks Kp - *MAP 1680*
Woodland, olive groves, scrub, garigue, phrygana, grassy places; 0-1000m; fl. 2-4.
Crete (widespread); Kasos, Karpathos [Mediterranean region].

5. O. candica (E.Nelson ex Soó) H.Baumann & Künkele in *MittBl. ArbKreis heim. Orch. Baden-Württ.* **13**: 349 (1981) - *FE* **5**: 348 as *O. fuciflora* subsp. *candica* E.Nelson ex Soó.
Cr (W, C) - *MAP 1681*
Woodland, clearings in maquis, scrub, garigue, phrygana, grassy places, field-margins; 0-800m; fl. 4-5.
W. & C. Crete [S.E. Italy & S. Peloponnisos; otherwise E. Aegean Islands (Samos & Rodos) & S.W. Turkey].
A variant from W. Crete (S. of Kastelli Kissamou), with long basal protruberances on the labellum, has been described as subsp. *minoa* C.& A.Alibertis (Alibertis & Alibertis, 1989c: 111). It does not seem worthy of more than varietal rank, and is not separated here.

6. O. ciliata Biv., *Sicul. pl.* **1**: 60 (1806) - *FE* **5**: 345 as *O. speculum* Link subsp. *speculum*.
Cr (W, E) Kp - *MAP 1682*
Coastal rocky slope with scrub, abandoned terraces; 50-400m; fl. 3-4.
W. & E. Crete; Karpathos [Mediterranean region].

Doubtful occurrence confirmed since *FE* (Ackermann & Ackermann, 1986; Hiller & Kalteisen, 1988: 453, 469, 503, both as *O. vernixia* Brot.)

O. cretica (Vierh.) E.Nelson (*FE* 5: 348) is included in synonymy of **7**.

7. O. doerfleri H.Fleischm. in *Öst. bot. Z.* **74**: 185 (1925) - *FE* 5: 347. (Including *O. cretica* (Vierh.) E.Nelson - *FE* 5: 348.)
Cr (W, C, E) Kp - MAP 1683
Woodland, olive groves, scrub, garigue, phrygana, grassy places, abandoned terraces; 0-1200m; fl. 2-5.
Crete (widespread); Karpathos [S.E. Greece (Attiki & Egina) & Kiklades; otherwise E. Aegean Islands (Samos & Rodos)].

8. O. ferrum-equinum Desf. in *Annls Mus. Hist. nat. Paris* **10**: 226 (1807) - *FE* 5: 347 as *O. ferrum-equinum* Desf. subsp. *ferrum-equinum*.
Kp - MAP 1684
Pinus brutia woodland, olive groves, garigue, phrygana, grassy places, abandoned terraces; 30-900m; fl. 3-4.
Karpathos [S. Albania & Greece; otherwise E. Aegean Islands & Turkey].
Regarded as absent from the Cretan area in *FE*, although previously recorded by Nelson (1962: 200); cf. Greuter et al. (1983*a*: 65).
"Subsp. *gottfriediana*" (Greuter et al., 1983*a*: 65) = **8** (Hiller & Kalteisen, 1988: 454).

9. O. fleischmannii Hayek in *Reprium Spec. nov. Regni veg.* **22**: 388 (1926) - *FE* 5: 346, included in synonymy of *O. fusca* subsp. *omegaifera* (H.Fleischm.) E.Nelson.
Cr (W, C, E) - MAP 1685
Pinus brutia woodland, olive groves, scrub, phrygana; 100-600m; fl. 2-4.
Crete (sporadic) [S. Aegean region].
Closely related to **17**.

O. fuciflora subsp. *candica* E.Nelson ex Soó (*FE* 5: 348) = **5**.

O. fuciflora (F.W.Schmidt) Moench subsp. *fuciflora* (*FE* 5: 348) = **12**.

10. O. fusca Link in *J. Bot. Göttingen* **1799**(2): 324 (1800) - *FE* 5: 346 as *O. fusca* Link subsp. *fusca*.
Cr (W, C, E) Ks Kp - MAP 1686
Woodland, scrub, garigue, phrygana, grassy places, abandoned terraces; 0-850m; fl. 1-5.
Crete (widespread); Kasos, Karpathos [Mediterranean region].
Apparently four distinct variants occur in Crete (Paulus, 1988), but these have yet to receive formal taxonomic recognition.

Subsp. *iricolor* (Desf.) O.Schwarz (*FE* 5: 346) = **13**.
Subsp. *omegaifera* (H.Fleischm.) E.Nelson (*FE* 5: 346) = **17**.

11. O. heldreichii Schltr. in *Reprium Spec. nov. Regni veg.* **19**: 46 (1923) - *FE* 5: 348 as *O. scolopax* subsp. *heldreichii* (Schltr.) E.Nelson.
Cr (W, C, E) Kp - MAP 1687
Woodland, olive groves, scrub, garigue, phrygana, grassy places, abandoned terraces; 0-1200m; fl. 3-5.
Crete (widespread); Karpathos [?S.E. Italy, Greece & Aegean region].

12. O. holoserica (Burm.f.) Greuter in *Boissiera* **13**: 185 (1967) - *FE* 5: 348 as *O. fuciflora* (F.W.Schmidt) Moench subsp. *fuciflora*.
Cr (W, C, E) Ks Kp - MAP 1688.
a. subsp. holoserica
Cr (W, C, E) Kp - MAP 1689
Woodland, olive groves, scrub, garigue, phrygana, grassy places; 0-1200m; fl. 4-5.
Crete (widespread); Karpathos [W., C. & S. Europe].
Given as doubtfully present in Crete by Barclay (1986: 128), although recorded by several authors (Vöth, 1981; Hölzinger & Hölzinger, 1986; Hiller & Kalteisen, 1988; Wellinghausen & Koch, 1989; Kreutz, 1990).
b. subsp. maxima (H.Fleischm.) Greuter in *Boissiera* **13**: 185 (1967) - not cited in *FE*.
Cr (W, C, E) Ks Kp - MAP 1690
Pinus brutia woodland, olive groves, phrygana, grassy places, abandoned terraces; 0-1200m; fl. 3-5.
Crete (widespread); Kasos, Karpathos [S. Aegean region].

13. O. iricolor Desf. in *Annls Mus. Hist. nat. Paris* **10**: 224 (1807) - *FE* 5: 346 as *O. fusca* subsp. *iricolor* (Desf.) O.Schwarz.
Cr (W, C, E) Ks Kp - MAP 1691
Woodland, scrub, garigue, phrygana, grassy places, abandoned terraces; 0-900m; fl. 3-4.
Crete (widespread); Kasos, Karpathos [C. & E. Mediterranean region].

14. O. lutea Cav., *Icon.* **2**: 46 (1793) - *FE* 5: 345.
a. subsp. lutea
Cr (W, C, E) - MAP 1692
Pinus brutia woodland, phrygana, grassy places; -900m; fl. 3-4.
Mainly C. & E. Crete [C. & E. Mediterranean region].
b. subsp. minor (Tod.) O.& E.Danesch in *Pl. Syst. Evol.* **124**: 82 (1975) - *FE* 5: 345, included

in synonymy of *O. lutea* subsp. *murbeckii*
(H.Fleischm.) Soó.
Cr (W, C, E) Kp - *MAP 1693*
Woodland, olive groves, scrub, garigue,
phrygana, grassy places, abandoned terraces; 0-
900m; fl. 1-4.
Crete (widespread); Karpathos [Mediterranean
region].

15. O. mammosa Desf. in *Annls Mus. Hist.*
nat. Paris **10**: 222 (1807) - *FE* **5**: 347 as *O.*
sphegodes subsp. *mammosa* (Desf.) Soó ex
E.Nelson.
Cr (W, C, E) - *MAP 1694*
Pinus brutia woodland, olive groves, scrub,
phrygana, grassy places, abandoned terraces; 0-
1000m; fl. 3-5.
Crete (widespread) [S.E. Europe].

16. O. oestrifera M.Bieb., *Fl. taur.-caucas.* **2**:
369 (1808) - *FE* **5**: 348 as *O. scolopax* subsp.
oestrifera (M.Bieb.) Soó.
a. subsp. **bremifera** (Steven) K.Richt., *Pl. eur.*
1: 264 (1890) - not cited in *FE*.
Kp - *MAP 1695*
Phrygana, grassy places; 25-450m; fl. 3-4.
Karpathos [recorded from Greece & Aegean
region].
Recorded by Hiller & Kalteisen (1988: 453,
470, 471, 475, 499).

17. O. omegaifera H.Fleischm. in *Öst. bot. Z.*
74: 184 (1925) - *FE* **5**: 346 as *O. fusca* subsp.
omegaifera (H.Fleischm.) E.Nelson.
Cr (W, C, E) Kp - *MAP 1696*
Pinus brutia woodland, olive groves, scrub,
phrygana, grassy places, abandoned terraces; 0-
900m; fl. 2-5.
Mainly C. & E. Crete; Karpathos [E. Aegean
Islands & S.W. Anatolia].

O. scolopax subsp. *heldreichii* (Schltr.)
E.Nelson (*FE* **5**: 348) = **11**.

●**18. O. sitiaca** Paulus & C.& A.Alibertis in
MittBl. ArbKreis heim. Orch. Baden-Württ. **20**:
839 (1988).
Cr (C, E) - *MAP 1697*
Pinus brutia woodland, olive groves, scrub,
phrygana; 100-600m; fl. 1-4.
C. & E. Crete - Endemic.
Closely related to **17**.

O. speculum Link subsp. *speculum* (*FE* **5**: 345)
= **6**.

19. O. sphegodes Mill., *Gard. Dict.* ed.8: no.8
(1768) - *FE* **5**: 346 as *O. sphegodes* Mill. subsp.
sphegodes.
Cr (W, C, E) - *MAP 1698*
●**a.** subsp. **cretensis** H.Baumann & Künkele in

MittBl. ArbKreis heim. Orch. Baden-Württ. **18**:
375 (1986).
Cr (W, C, E) - *MAP 1699*
Woodland, olive groves, scrub, phrygana,
grassy places; 50-900m; fl. 2-4.
Crete (sporadic) - Endemic.
●**b.** subsp. **gortynia** H.Baumann & Künkele in
MittBl. ArbKreis heim. Orch. Baden-Württ. **18**:
377 (1986).
Cr (W, C, E) - *MAP 1700*
Pinus brutia woodland, olive groves, garigue,
phrygana, grassy places; 0-650m; fl. 4-5.
Crete (sporadic) - Endemic.
Subsp. *mammosa* (Desf.) Soó ex E.Nelson (*FE*
5: 347) = **15**.
The species sensu lato is widespread in Crete,
and it is possible that most or all plants are
referable to either subsp. **a** or subsp. **b**.
However, further study is required to ascertain
the full extent of infraspecific variation.

20. O. spruneri Nyman, *Consp. fl. eur.*: 698
(1882) - *FE* **5**: 347 as *O. spruneri* Nyman subsp.
spruneri.
Cr (W, C, E) - *MAP 1701*
Pinus brutia woodland, phrygana, rocky &
grassy places; 0-700m; fl. 2-4.
Mainly W. & C. Crete [Greece & Aegean
region].

21. O. tenthredinifera Willd., *Sp. pl.*: **4**: 67
(1805) - *FE* **5**: 349.
Cr (W, C, E) Ks Kp - *MAP 1702*
Woodland, olive groves, maquis, garigue,
phrygana, grassy places; 0-1000m; fl. 1-4.
Crete (widespread); Kasos, Karpathos
[Mediterranean region].

22. O. umbilicata Desf. in *Annls Mus. Hist.*
nat. Paris **10**: 227 (1807) - *FE* **5**: 348 as *O.*
carmeli H.Fleischm. & Bornm.
a. subsp. **rhodia** H.Baumann & Künkele in
MittBl. ArbKreis heim. Orch. Baden-Württ. **18**:
388 (1986).
Kp - *MAP 1703*
Open phrygana, waste area; 30-50m; fl. 4.
Karpathos [E. Aegean Islands (Rodos)].
Described from Rodos; recorded from
Karpathos by Hiller & Kalteisen (1988: 453,
467, 502).

Hybrids:

Distributions, habitats, altitudes & flowering
times are not given.

O. aegaea x O. heldreichii
Recorded from Karpathos by Kalteisen &
Reinhard (1987) and Hiller & Kalteisen (1988:
473).

O. bombyliflora x **O. doerfleri**
Recorded from Crete by Klein (1978*b*).

O. bombyliflora x **O. heldreichii**
Recorded from Crete by Klein (1978*a*).

O. bombyliflora x **O. spruneri** = **O. x
selinensis** H.Blatt & Hertel in *MittBl. ArbKreis
heim. Orch. Hessen* **4**: 8 (1982).
Described from Crete.

O. bombyliflora x **O. tenthredinifera**
Recorded from Crete by Kreutz (1990: 374).

O. candica x **O. heldreichii** = **O. x
warwarensis** H.Baumann & Künkele in *MittBl.
ArbKreis heim. Orch. Baden-Württ.* **18**: 445
(1986).
Described from Crete.

O. candica x **O. holoserica** subsp. **maxima** =
O. x sivana H.Baumann & Künkele in *MittBl.
ArbKreis heim. Orch. Baden-Württ.* **18**: 446
(1986).
Described from Crete.

O. doerfleri x **O. fusca** = **O. x varvarae**
Faller & K.Kreutz in *MittBl. ArbKreis heim.
Orch. Baden-Württ.* **22**: 363 (1990).
Described from Crete.

O. doerfleri x **O. heldreichii**
Recorded from Crete by Halx (1972).

O. doerfleri x **O. mammosa** = **O. x sieberi**
H.Baumann & Künkele in *MittBl. ArbKreis
heim. Orch. Baden-Württ.* **18**: 453 (1986).
Described from Crete; also recorded by Halx
(1972).

O. doerfleri x **O. sphegodes** subsp. **cretensis** =
O. x baumanniana nothosubsp. **hierapetrae**
H.Baumann & Künkele in *MittBl. ArbKreis
heim. Orch. Baden-Württ.* **18**: 454 (1986).
Described from Crete.

O. doerfleri x **O. sphegodes** subsp. **gortynia** =
O. x baumanniana nothosubsp. **baumanniana**
Soó in *Acta bot. hung.* **25**: 363 (1980).
Described from Crete.

O. doerfleri x **O. spruneri** = **O. x plorae** C.
& A.Alibertis in *Orchidophile* **86**: 81 (1989).
Described from Crete; also recorded by Halx
(1972).

O. ferrum-equinum x **O. heldreichii**
Recorded from Karpathos by Hiller & Kalteisen
(1988: 465).

O. ferrum-equinum x **O. holoserica**
Recorded from Karpathos by Hiller & Kalteisen
(1988: 478).

O. fleischmannii x **O. omegaifera** = **O. x
asterusica** C.& A.Alibertis in *Orchidophile* **86**:

81 (1989).
Described from Crete.

O. fleischmannii x **O. sitiaca** = **O. x pauliana**
C.& A.Alibertis in *Orchidophile* **86**: 81 (1989).
Described from Crete.

O. heldreichii x **O. holoserica** subsp. **maxima**
= **O. x anomala** Renz in *Reprium Spec. nov.
Regni veg.* **30**: 109 (1932).
Described from Crete; also recorded by Kreutz
(1990: 375).

O. heldreichii x **O. tenthredinifera**
Recorded from Crete by Klein (1978*a*).

O. holoserica x **O. tenthredinifera**
Recorded from Crete by Alibertis & Alibertis
(1989*a*: 163).

O. mammosa x **O. sphegodes** subsp. **cretensis**
Recorded from Crete by Alibertis & Alibertis
(1989*a*: 163).

O. mammosa x **O. spruneri** = **O. x
pseudospruneri** Renz ex Soó in *Reprium Spec.
nov. Regni veg.* **26**: 280 (1929).
Recorded from Crete by Alibertis & Alibertis
(1989*a*: 163) and Kreutz (1990: 377, 378).

O. omegaifera x **O. sitiaca** = **O. x lithinensis**
C.& A.Alibertis in *Orchidophile* **86**: 81 (1989).
Described from Crete.

O. sphegodes subsp. **cretensis** x **O. spruneri** =
O. x burneriana C.& A.Alibertis in
Orchidophile **86**: 83 (1989).
Described from Crete.

O. sphegodes subsp. **gortynia** x **O. spruneri**
Recorded from Crete by Kreutz (1990: 375).

O. spruneri x **O. tenthredinifera** = **O. x
alibertiana** C.& A.Alibertis in *Orchidophile* **86**:
83 (1989).
Described from Crete.

12. Orchis L.

1. O. anatolica Boiss., *Diagn. pl. orient.* ser.1,
5: 56 (1844) - *FE* 5: 341.
Cr (W, C, E) Ks Kp - *MAP 1704.*
a. subsp. anatolica
Cr Ks Kp - *NOT MAPPED*
Pinus brutia woodland, garigue, phrygana,
abandoned terraces; 100-1400m; fl. 3-5.
Crete; Kasos, Karpathos [S. Aegean region;
otherwise S.W. Asia].
●**b. subsp. sitiaca** Renz in *Reprium Spec. nov.
Regni veg.* **30**: 100 (1932) - *FE* 5: 341.
Cr (C, E) - *MAP 1705*
*Woodland, scrub, phrygana, grassy places; 0-
1000m; fl. 3-5.*

C. & E. Crete - Endemic.
The species sensu lato is widespread in Crete.

2. O. boryi Rchb.f., *Icon. fl. germ. helv.* **13**: 19 (1851) - *FE* **5**: 338.
Cr (W, C, E) - *MAP 1706*
Scrub, phrygana, grassy places, abandoned fields; 150-1200m; fl. 3-5.
Mainly C. Crete [Greece & Aegean region].

3. O. collina Banks & Sol. in Russell, *Nat. hist. Aleppo* ed.2, **2**: 264 (1794) - *FE* **5**: 340 as *O. saccata* Ten.
Cr (W, C, E) Kp - *MAP 1707*
Woodland, maquis, scrub, garigue, phrygana, grassy places, abandoned terraces; 0-1200m; fl. 12-4.
Crete (widespread); Karpathos [Mediterranean region].

4. O. coriophora L., *Sp. pl.*: 940 (1753) - *FE* **5**: 339.
a. subsp. fragrans (Pollini) Sudre, *Fl. toulous.*: 187 (1907) - *FE* **5**: 339.
Cr (W, C, E) Kp - *MAP 1708*
Woodland, olive groves, scrub, phrygana, grassy & sandy places, abandoned terraces; 0-750m; fl. 4-6.
Crete (widespread); Karpathos [mainly S. Europe].

5. O. italica Poir. in Lam., *Encycl.* **4**: 600 (1798) - *FE* **5**: 339.
Cr (W, C, E) Kp - *MAP 1709*
Woodland, olive groves, scrub, garigue, phrygana, grassy places, abandoned terraces; 0-1200m; fl. 2-4.
Crete (widespread); Karpathos [Mediterranean region].

6. O. lactea Poir. in Lam., *Encycl.* **4**: 594 (1798) - *FE* **5**: 339.
Cr (W, C, E) Kp - *MAP 1710*
Quercus woodland, olive groves, phrygana, grassy places; 0-1200m; fl. 2-4.
Crete (widespread); Karpathos [Mediterranean region].

7. O. laxiflora Lam., *Fl. franç.* **3**: 504 (1779) - *FE* **5**: 341.
a. subsp. laxiflora
Cr (W, C, E) Kp - *MAP 1711*
Woodland, scrub, marshes, grassy places, ditches, damp ground; 0-1200m; fl. 3-5.
Crete (widespread, rarer towards E.); Karpathos [W. & S. Europe].
Subsp. *palustris* (Jacq.) Bonnier & Layens (*FE* **5**: 342) = **9**.

8. O. morio L., *Sp. pl.*: 940 (1753) - *FE* **5**: 338.

a. subsp. morio
Kp - *MAP 1712*
Phrygana, grassy places; 140-250m; fl. 3-4.
Karpathos [most of Europe].
Recorded since *FE* (Hiller & Kalteisen, 1988: 454, 464, 465, 472, 510).

9. O. palustris Jacq., *Collectanea* **1**: 75 (1786) - *FE* **5**: 342 as *O. laxiflora* subsp. *palustris* (Jacq.) Bonnier & Layens.
Cr (W, C, E) - *MAP 1713*
Coastal marshes; fl. 4-5.
Crete (sporadic) [W., C. & S. Europe].
The first records (Campbell, 1979) were doubted by Greuter et al. (1985: 54), but on further consideration appear reliable. Recorded since by Hölzinger & Hölzinger (1986) and Kreutz (1990).

10. O. papilionacea L., *Syst. nat.* ed.10, **2**: 1242 (1759) - *FE* **5**: 338.
Cr (W, C, E) Kp - *MAP 1714*
Woodland, olive groves, maquis, scrub, garigue, phrygana, grassy places, abandoned terraces; 0-1300m; fl. 1-5.
Crete (widespread); Karpathos [S. Europe].

11. O. pauciflora Ten., *Fl. napol.* **1**: lii (1811-1815) - *FE* **5**: 341 as *O. provincialis* subsp. *pauciflora* (Ten.) E.G.Camus.
Cr (W, C, E) - *MAP 1715*
Woodland, phrygana, grassy places, soil-pockets among rocks; 200-1400m; fl. 3-4.
Crete (widespread) [C. & E. Mediterranean region].

●**12. O. prisca** Hautz. in *Pl. Syst. Evol.* **124**: 311 (1976) - *FE* **5**: 340 as *O. spitzelii* subsp. *nitidifolia* (W.P.Teschner) Soó.
Cr (W, C, E) - *MAP 1716*
Calcareous woodland & clearings, phrygana; 600-1700m; fl. 3-5.
Crete (mainly Lefka Ori, Psiloritis & Afendis Kavousi) - Endemic.
Teschner (1975b) puts forward the somewhat implausible hypothesis that *O. prisca* is likely to be a product of hybridization between **1** and *O. spitzelii* Saut. ex W.Koch. which, although sporadic in the Mediterranean region, has never been recorded from Crete.

13. O. provincialis Balb. ex DC. in Lam. & DC., *Syn. pl. Fl. gall.*: 169 (1806) - *FE* **5**: 341 as *O. provincialis* Balb. ex DC. subsp. *provincialis*.
Cr (W) Kp - *MAP 1717*
Pinus brutia woodland, clearings in maquis, scrub, phrygana, on non-calcareous substrata; 25-750m; fl. 4-5.
W. Crete; Karpathos [S. Europe].
Subsp. *pauciflora* (Ten.) E.G.Camus (*FE* **5**:

341) = **11**.

14. O. quadripunctata Cirillo ex Ten., *Fl. napol.* **1**: liii (1811-1815) - *FE* **5**: 341.
Cr (W, C, E) - *MAP 1718*
Pinus brutia woodland, olive groves, scrub, garigue, phrygana, grassy places, soil-pockets among rocks, gorges; 0-1450m; fl. 3-5.
Crete (widespread) [Mediterranean region].

O. saccata Ten. (*FE* **5**: 340) = **3**.

15. O. sancta L., *Syst. nat.* ed.10, **2**: 1242 (1759) - *FE* **5**: 339.
Cr (W, E) Ks Sa - *MAP 1719*
Abandoned fields & terraces, often with O. coriophora; -100m; fl. 4-5.
W. & E. Crete; Kasos, Saria [Aegean region; otherwise S.W. Asia].
Recorded from Crete by Schneider (1987) and Turland (1992*a*: 356).

16. O. simia Lam., *Fl. franç.* **3**: 507 (1779) - *FE* **5**: 339.
Cr (W, C, E) Kp - *MAP 1720*
Woodland, olive groves, scrub, phrygana, grassy places; 0-1000m; fl. 3-5.
Crete (widespread); Karpathos [W. & S. Europe].
The occurrence in Karpathos (Renz in Rechinger, 1943*a*: 839), doubted by Greuter et al. (1983*a*: 75), has been confirmed by Hiller & Kalteisen (1988: 454, 464, 476, 513).

O. spitzelii subsp. *nitidifolia* (W.P.Teschner) Soó (*FE* **5**: 340) = **12**.

17. O. tridentata Scop., *Fl. carniol.* ed.2, **2**: 190 (1772) - *FE* **5**: 339. (Including subsp. *commutata* (Tod.) Nyman - *FE* **5**: 339.)
Cr (W, C, E) - *MAP 1721*
Phrygana, grassy places; 500-1200m; fl. 3-4.
Crete (sporadic) [C. & S. Europe].

Hybrids:

Distributions, habitats, altitudes & flowering times are not given.

O. anatolica x **O. pauciflora** = **O.** x **thriftiensis** Renz in *Reprium Spec. nov. Regni veg.* **30**: 103 (1932).
Described from Crete.

O. anatolica x **O. prisca**
Recorded from Crete by Kellenberger (1978) and Kreutz (1990: 378).

O. anatolica x **O. quadripunctata** = **O.** x **sezikiana** B.& H.Baumann in *MittBl. ArbKreis heim. Orch. Baden-Württ.* **23**: 215 (1991).
Recorded from Crete by Baumann & Baumann (1991).

O. anatolica x **O. tridentata** = **O.** x

hermaniana C.& A.Alibertis in *Orchidophile* **87**: 108 (1989).
Described from Crete.

O. anatolica subsp. **sitiaca** x **O. collina** = **O.** x **salkowskiana** C.& A.Alibertis in *Orchidophile* **87**: 108 (1989).
Described from Crete.

O. boryi x **O. laxiflora** = **O.** x **gerakarionis** Faller & K.Kreutz in *MittBl. ArbKreis heim. Orch. Baden-Württ.* **22**: 365 (1990).
Described from Crete.

O. boryi x **O. papilionacea** = **O.** x **lasithica** Renz in *Reprium Spec. nov. Regni veg.* **28**: 241 (1930).
Described from Crete.

O. coriophora subsp. **fragrans** x **O. sancta**
Recorded from Crete by Schneider (1989).

O. italica x **O. simia**
Recorded from Crete by Alibertis & Alibertis (1989*a*: 165).

O. pauciflora x **O. quadripunctata**
Recorded from Crete by Kreutz (1990: 376).

13. Serapias L.

1. S. bergonii E.G.Camus, *Monogr. orchid.*: 61 (1908) - *FE* **5**: 344 as *S. vomeracea* subsp. *laxiflora* (Soó) Gölz & H.R.Reinhard.
Cr (W, C, E) Kp - *MAP 1722*
Woodland, olive groves, scrub, garigue, phrygana, grassy places, abandoned terraces, waste areas; 0-750m; fl. 3-5.
Crete (widespread); Karpathos [E. Mediterranean region].

2. S. cordigera L., *Sp. pl.* ed.2: 1345 (1763) - *FE* **5**: 343.
Cr (W, C, E) - *MAP 1723*
Scrub, garigue, phrygana; 50-600m; fl. 4-5.
Crete (sporadic) [W. & S. Europe].
Considered doubtfully present by Greuter (1974: 162), and regarded as absent from the Cretan area in *FE*, although the species definitely occurs (cf. map in Baumann & Künkele, 1982: 374).

3. S. lingua L., *Sp. pl.*: 950 (1753) - *FE* **5**: 344.
Cr (W, C, E) - *MAP 1724*
Woodland, olive groves, garigue, phrygana, grassy places, usually on damp ground; 0-1200m; fl. 3-5.
Mainly W. & C. Crete [S.W. Europe & Mediterranean region].

4. S. orientalis (Greuter) H.Baumann & Künkele in *MittBl. ArbKreis heim. Orch. Baden-Württ.* **20**: 636 (1988) - *FE* **5**: 343 as *S.*

vomeracea subsp. *orientalis* Greuter.
a. subsp. **orientalis**
Cr (W, C, E) Kp - *MAP 1725*
Pinus brutia woodland, olive groves, scrub, garigue, phrygana, grassy places, dry river-beds, abandoned terraces; 0-800m; fl. 3-5.
Crete (widespread, rarer in W.); Karpathos [Greece & Aegean region].

5. S. parviflora Parl. in *G. Sci. Sic.* **59**: 66 (1837) - *FE* **5**: 344.
Cr (W, C, E) Kp - *MAP 1726*
Woodland, phrygana, grassy places, dry river-beds; 0-900m; fl. 3-5.
Mainly C. & E. Crete; Karpathos [W. Europe & Mediterranean region].

S. vomeracea subsp. *laxiflora* (Soó) Gölz & H.R.Reinhard (*FE* **5**: 344) = **1**.

S. vomeracea subsp. *orientalis* Greuter (*FE* **5**: 343) = **4**.

Hybrids:

Distributions, habitats, altitudes & flowering times are not given.

S. bergonii x **S. lingua** = **S.** x **demadesii** Renz in *Reprium Spec. nov. Regni veg.* **25**: 239 (1928), emend. Greuter in *Boissiera* **13**: 189 (1967).
Recorded from Crete by Renz (in Rechinger, 1943a: 826).

S. bergonii x **S. orientalis** = **S.** x **wettsteinii** H.Fleischm. in *Öst. bot. Z.* **74**: 190 (1925).
Described from Crete.

S. lingua x **S. orientalis** = **S.** x **sitiae** Renz in *Reprium Spec. nov. Regni veg.* **30**: 112 (1932).
Described from Crete.

14. Spiranthes Rich.

1. S. spiralis (L.) Chevall., *Fl. gén. env. Paris* 2: 330 (1827) - *FE* **5**: 330.
Cr (W, C, E) - *MAP 1727*
Clearings in woodland, scrub, dry grassy places; 0-750m; fl. 9-11.
Crete (sporadic) [W., C. & S. Europe].

Bigeneric hybrid:

Aceras anthropophorum x **Orchis simia** = x **Orchiaceras bergonii** (Nanteuil) Camus in *J. Bot. Paris* **6**: 107 (1892).
Pinus brutia woodland.
E. Crete (Afendis Kavousi).
Recorded by Alibertis & Alibertis (1989a: 161) and Kreutz (1990: 379).

PALMAE
(ARECACEAE)

1. Phoenix L.

1. P. theophrasti Greuter in *Bauhinia* **3**: 243 (1967) - *FE* **5**: 268.
Cr (W, C, E)
Moist valley-floors, stream-banks, by springs, phrygana, coastal rocks, cliffs, always near sea; 0-230m; fl. 4-5.
Crete (sporadic) [?E. Aegean Islands, S.W. Turkey].
[Plate 9.] Vulnerable species, legally protected. Not endemic to Crete as given in *FE* (cf. Tan in Davis, 1984: 39). Palms resembling *P. theophrasti* have been observed on the E. Aegean islands of Kalimnos and Nisiros by Chilton, and on Nisiros and nearby Simi by Akeroyd (pers. comm., 1992). These records require confirmation, however, because they might prove referable to the related *P. dactylifera* L., which is occasionally planted in the Aegean region (including the Cretan area). This species can resemble *P. theophrasti*, especially if the dead leaves are allowed to persist naturally, as they sometimes are, for example, in Karpathos.

POTAMOGETONACEAE

1. Posidonia C.Konig

1. P. oceanica (L.) Delile, *Descr. Égypte, Hist. nat.* **2**: 78 (1813) - *FE* **5**: 12.
Cr (W, C, E) Ks Kp - *MAP 1729*
Rocky areas on sea-bed.
Crete (sporadic); Kasos, Karpathos [coasts of S.W. Europe & Mediterranean region].

2. Potamogeton L.

1. P. lucens L., *Sp. pl.*: 126 (1753) - *FE* **5**: 9.
Cr (W) - *MAP 1730*
Fresh water.
W. Crete (Agia lake) [almost throughout Europe].

? P. natans L., *Sp. pl.*: 126 (1753) - *FE* **5**: 9.
Doubtfully present in Crete [almost throughout Europe].

2. P. nodosus Poir. in Lam., *Encycl., Suppl.* **4**: 535 (1816) - *FE* **5**: 9.
Cr (W, C) - *MAP 1731*
Rivers, ponds, marshes, springs & other fresh water; 0-400m.
W. & C. Crete [mainly W., C. & S. Europe].

3. P. pectinatus L., *Sp. pl.*: 127 (1753) - *FE* **5**: 11.
Cr (W, E) - *MAP 1732*
Fresh & brackish running water, brackish marshes.
W. & E. Crete [almost throughout Europe].

4. P. trichoides Cham. & Schltdl. in *Linnaea* **2**: 175 (1827) - *FE* **5**: 10.
Cr (W) - *MAP 1733*
Fresh water.
W. Crete (Agia lake) [most of Europe].

3. Ruppia L.

1. R. cirrhosa (Petagna) Grande in *Boll. Orto bot., Napoli* **5**: 58 (1918) - *FE* **5**: 11.
Cr (E) Ks - *MAP 1734*
Brackish pond near sea.
E. Crete (Sideros peninsula); Kasos [coasts of most of Europe].

2. R. maritima L., *Sp. pl.*: 127 (1753) - *FE* **5**: 11.
Cr Kp - *NOT MAPPED*
Crete; Karpathos [most of Europe].

4. Zostera L.

1. Z. marina L., *Sp. pl.*: 968 (1753) - *FE* **5**: 12.
Cr (W) - *MAP 1735*
Sandy & silty areas on sea-bed.
W. Crete [coasts of most of Europe].

SPARGANIACEAE

1. Sparganium L.

1. S. erectum L., *Sp. pl.*: 971 (1753) - *FE* **5**: 274.
a. subsp. **neglectum** (Beeby) K.Richt., *Pl. eur.* **1**: 10 (1890) - *FE* **5**: 274.
Cr (W, C, E) - *MAP 1736*
Fresh water, river-banks, marshes; 0-400m.
Crete (sporadic) [most of Europe].

TYPHACEAE

1. Typha L.

1. T. domingensis (Pers.) Steud., *Nomencl. bot.*: 860 (1824) - *FE* **5**: 276.
Cr (W, C, E) Kp - *MAP 1737*
Fresh water, streams, ditches, Phragmites beds, marshes; 0-400m.
Mainly W. Crete; Karpathos [S. Europe].

ZANNICHELLIACEAE

1. Cymodocea C.Konig

1. C. nodosa (Ucria) Asch. in *Sber. Ges. naturf. Freunde Berl.* **1869**: 4 (1869) - *FE* **5**: 13.
Cr Ks Kp - *NOT MAPPED*
Crete; Kasos, Karpathos [coasts of Mediterranean region].

2. Zannichellia L.

1. Z. palustris L., *Sp. pl.*: 969 (1753) - *FE* **5**: 13.
Cr (W, C) - *MAP 1738*
Fresh water.
W. & C. Crete [almost throughout Europe].

ATLAS

THE MAPPING GRID

The following distribution maps are based on a grid of 8.25km squares overlying Crete and the Karpathos island group. The latter area is shown in an artificial position off the eastern end of Crete (south-west of its actual geographical location) in order to conserve space within the page layout. The main island of Crete and its satellites comprise a total of 163 land squares, the three divisions of western, central and eastern Crete having 56, 57 and 50 squares respectively. The Karpathos island group has a total of 11 land squares, nine of them for Karpathos and one each for Kasos and Saria.

Where only a small amount of land exists within a coastal square (usually 10% of its area or less), it forms an extension of the adjacent square having the greatest land area. Islands and small islets close to the coast are incorporated into the nearest land square, sometimes necessitating further slight distortions of the grid. Islands more distant from the coast (including Kasos and Saria) have their own squares, the boundaries of which have been adjusted, where necessary, so that no island falls into more than one square.

Figures 1-4 (pp. vi-ix) show the grid and all deviations from the basic pattern of squares.

CRITERIA FOR INCLUSION OF RECORDS ON THE MAPS

The mapped plant records mostly fall into two categories: field observations and collections made by Chilton and Turland (nearly all material at BM), and literature records which unambiguously refer to a particular taxon and have not been doubted or shown to be erroneous (see references: p. 424 for full list of literature sources). Those which remain comprise unpublished records by other botanists, and are mapped only if accompanied by herbarium material, photographs or other sound evidence; in a few cases, these are collections at The Natural History Museum (BM). Details of records, including page references for literature sources, are not published here but have been lodged at the Museum.

Several of the first two authors' records, together with a few by other botanists, are new for Crete or significantly extend known distributions on the island. These have already been published (Turland, 1991; 1992a, b). The same authors have also recorded numerous taxa as new to Karpathos (see Appendix 2: p. 422), all of which will be published in more detail in the near future (Turland & Chilton, in prep.)

Where localities cited by literature records fall onto boundaries between squares, the authors have used their personal knowledge of the habitats in that area to allocate the most probable square. Some earlier records have been disregarded where the possible squares already have other, unambiguous literature records. No record is mapped if it could not not be assigned with reasonable confidence to a particular square.

Most records made before 1930 have been disregarded, for various reasons. Foremost among these is that it is unwise to assume that a plant still exists at a locality where it was recorded 60 or more years ago (unless, of course, there are more recent, confirming records). This date has been chosen in accordance with *Atlas Florae Europaeae*, which uses different mapping symbols for records made since and before 1930. Some old literature records have been rendered ambiguous by subsequent taxonomic work, or were made by botanists who have been shown to be unreliable, as for example Gandoger (Greuter, 1974). There are, however, exceptions to this mapping rule: old unconfirmed records from Kasos, Karpathos and Saria are mapped, unless rejected by Greuter et al. (1983a), and some old records from Crete are mapped if they were made by generally reliable botanists within the last 100 years and have not been doubted or shown to be erroneous. These are mainly the records of Baldacci and Dörfler cited by Rechinger (1943*a*), and those of Langeron (Rechinger, 1943*b*). Numerous taxa appear not to have been recorded at all since 1930 from Crete, the Karpathos island group or the Cretan area as a whole; these are listed in Appendix 1 (p. 417).

If a taxon is not mapped, it is usually because the records from Crete or the Cretan area as a whole fail to satisfy these criteria. In the remaining instances, mapping could give a misleading impression of distribution, e.g. subspecies which appear to be very rare, but are thought to be under-recorded because the species is frequent and widespread.

MAPPING SYMBOLS

The standard symbols ● and ○ indicate records made since 1930 and before 1930 respectively. No distinction is made between literature records and those of the authors or other botanists. However, when a taxon is mapped for Karpathos solely on the basis of literature records, then a single, larger symbol ● is placed on the island to indicate presence there only, i.e. not an occurrence within any particular square (the pre-1930 equivalent is ◯). All records for individual squares in Karpathos, mapped with the standard symbol, are based on the field observations and collections of the authors. Only literature records are mapped for Kasos and Saria, neither of which have been visited by the authors. The standard symbols can be used without ambiguity here, since each island comprises only one square.

ATLAS FLORAE EUROPAEAE

For numerous taxa, *Atlas Florae Europaeae* is an important source of distributional data within the Cretan area. The way in which the records are cited is, however, different to that of this checklist, necessitating a special mapping technique. *Atlas Florae Europaeae* divides Crete into 11 squares, Kasos has its own square, and Karpathos is split between two, the northern square also incorporating Saria. Fortunately, most of the Cretan squares correspond to the western, central and eastern divisions of the island defined in this checklist. Where *Atlas Florae Europaeae* shows a taxon as present within a division of Crete for which there are otherwise no accepted records (apart from those on offshore islands), then a single, larger symbol ● or ◯ is placed within the division to indicate presence there only (the same symbols that are used in mapping literature records from Karpathos.) Two squares in *Atlas Florae Europaeae* straddle the joint boundary of western and central Crete; their records cannot mapped, so notes are included in the text instead, if necessary. For example, *Ophioglossum lusitanicum* is mapped from the western and eastern ends of Crete in this checklist, but is also recorded from one of the two ambiguous squares in *Atlas Florae Europaeae*. The not would read thus:

> Additionally recorded from W./C. Crete in *Atlas FE* **1**: 42.

Taxa remain unmapped if their only records from Crete refer merely to divisions, rather than to particular squares. Basic distributional data such as these are adequately covered by the textual annotations.

MOUNTAIN FLORA OF GREECE

Mountain Flora of Greece cites its records mainly as the localities of collections seen. These are not always precise, however, and may be entire massifs, e.g. 'Psiloritis', or ambiguous mountain names of which there are more than one in Crete, e.g. 'Mavri'. An approach similar to that described above could be adopted, were it not for the fact that an indication of the date of the collections is hardly ever given. The records are, therefore, excluded from the maps, but distributional discrepancies are explained by means of textual notes. For example, *Anthemis abrotanifolia* is mapped from C. & E. Crete (Psiloritis, Dikti & the Afendis Kavousi area) in this checklist, but is additionally recorded from the Lefka Ori in *Mountain Flora of Greece*. The note would read thus:

> Additionally recorded from the Lefka Ori in W.
> Crete in *MFG* 2: 427.

The literature records cited in *Mountain Flora of Greece* are subect to the usual criteria for inclusion on the maps and may, therefore, be rejected.

DISTRIBUTIONAL TRENDS AND RECORDING BIAS

Some taxa appear to become less frequent towards the east of Crete. Two contributory factors are likely to be the diminishing rainfall from west to east and a recording bias (central and eastern Crete generally being less intensively botanized than the west). Almost certainly the former factor more than the latter underlies the distribution of species such as *Quercus ilex*, which prefers comparatively humid conditions.

In fact, it is very likely that most taxa are more frequent and widespread than is suggested by their mapped distributions. Although plant records exist from nearly all squares in the Cretan area, the number of records per square varies greatly, from those which have been intensively botanized for many years to others which have been barely touched. There is also the problem of widespread Mediterranean and Euro-Siberian taxa being under-recorded in the literature, owing to the tendency of some botanists to concentrate their efforts on Aegean endemics and other special elements within the flora. Another recording bias results from the majority of botanizing in our area taking place during the main flowering period from March to May. Those species which are not in flower or are unidentifiable during this period are likely to be under-recorded. The authors have endeavoured to diminish these factors of recording bias by visiting as many squares as possible during as many seasons as possible, and recording every taxon seen.

TIME SPENT IN THE CRETAN AREA BY THE AUTHORS

CRETE (C = Chilton, T = Turland)

> 1982 April (C)
> 1983 April (C)
> 1984 April (C,T); September (C)
> 1985 April-May (C); May (T)
> 1986 April-May (C); May (T); October (C,T)
> 1987 April-November (C); April-May, October (T)
> 1988 March-November (C); April-May, October (T)
> 1989 March-November (C); March-April, October (T)
> 1990 February-November (C); March-April (T)
> 1991 January-August (C); March-April, August (T)
> 1992 April-May (C); April (T)

KARPATHOS

> 1990 July (C)
> 1992 April (C,T)

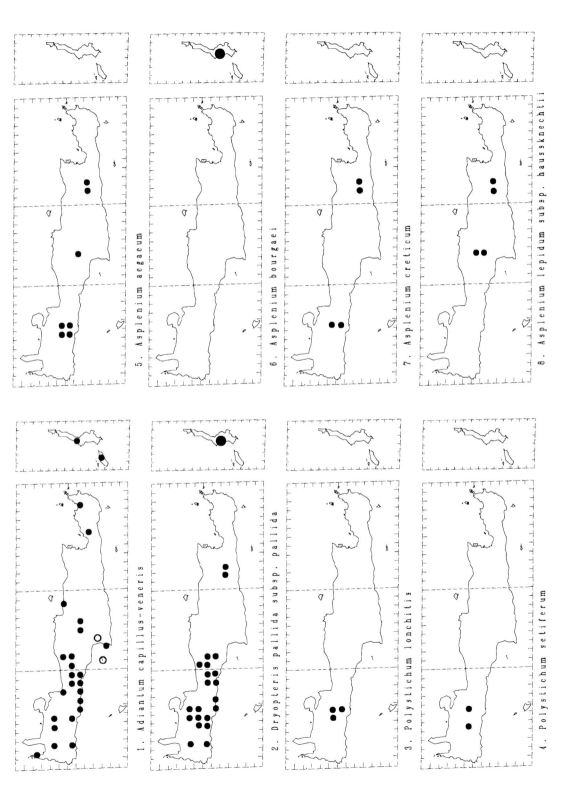

1. Adiantum capillus-veneris

2. Dryopteris pallida subsp. pallida

3. Polystichum lonchitis

4. Polystichum setiferum

5. Asplenium aegaeum

6. Asplenium bourgaei

7. Asplenium creticum

8. Asplenium lepidum subsp. haussknechtii

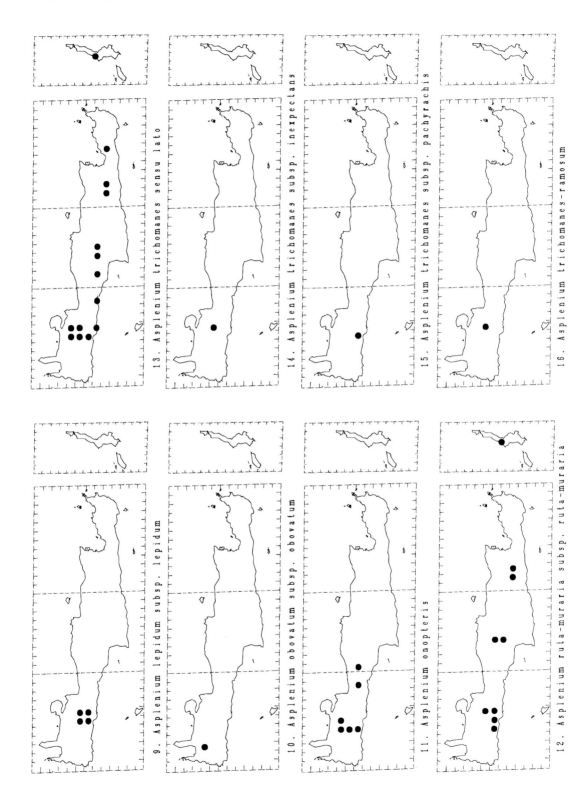

9. Asplenium lepidum subsp. lepidum

10. Asplenium obovatum subsp. obovatum

11. Asplenium onopteris

12. Asplenium ruta-muraria subsp. ruta-muraria

13. Asplenium trichomanes sensu lato

14. Asplenium trichomanes subsp. inexpectans

15. Asplenium trichomanes subsp. pachyrachis

16. Asplenium trichomanes-ramosum

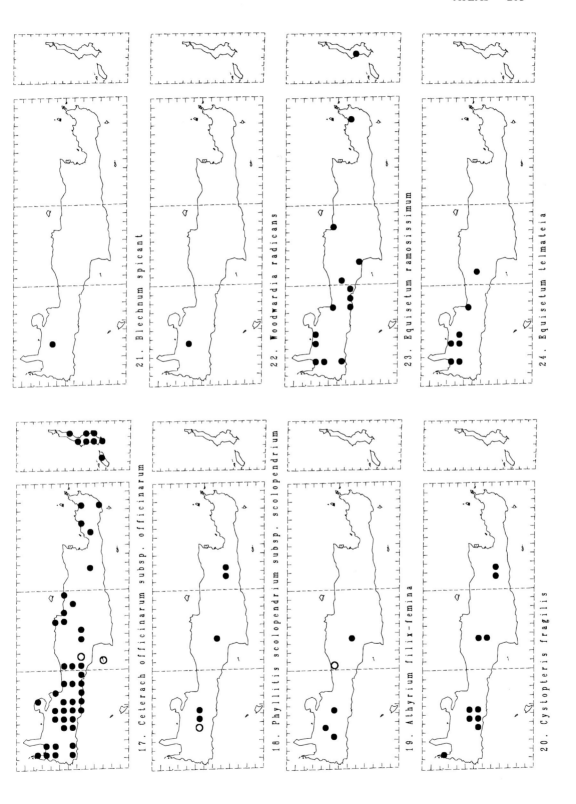

21. Blechnum spicant

22. Woodwardia radicans

23. Equisetum ramosissimum

24. Equisetum telmateia

17. Ceterach officinarum subsp. officinarum

18. Phyllitis scolopendrium subsp. scolopendrium

19. Athyrium filix-femina

20. Cystopteris fragilis

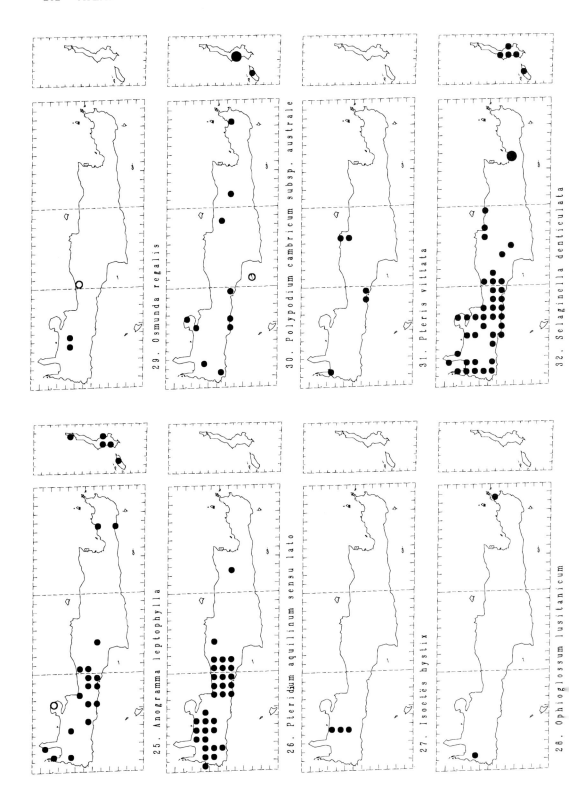

25. Anogramma leptophylla

26. Pteridium aquilinum sensu lato

27. Isoetës hystrix

28. Ophioglossum lusitanicum

29. Osmunda regalis

30. Polypodium cambricum subsp. australe

31. Pteris vittata

32. Selaginella denticulata

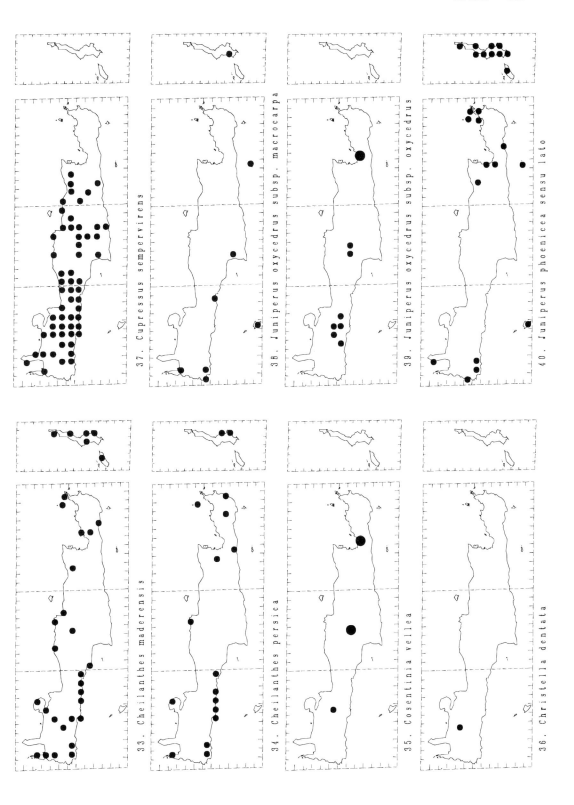

37. Cupressus sempervirens

38. Juniperus oxycedrus subsp. macrocarpa

39. Juniperus oxycedrus subsp. oxycedrus

40. Juniperus phoenicea sensu lato

33. Cheilanthes maderensis

34. Cheilanthes persica

35. Cosentinia vellea

36. Christella dentata

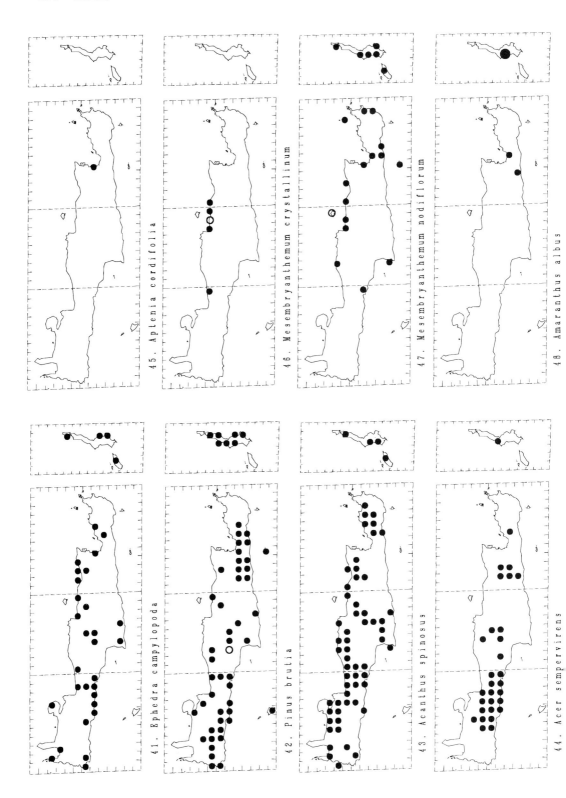

41. Ephedra campylopoda

42. Pinus brutia

43. Acanthus spinosus

44. Acer sempervirens

45. Aptenia cordifolia

46. Mesembryanthemum crystallinum

47. Mesembryanthemum nodiflorum

48. Amaranthus albus

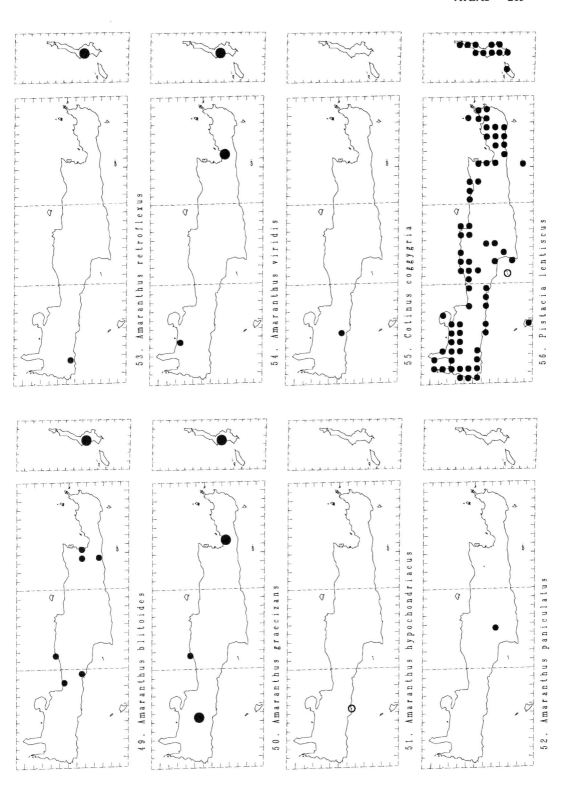

49. Amaranthus blitoides

50. Amaranthus graecizans

51. Amaranthus hypochondriacus

52. Amaranthus paniculatus

53. Amaranthus retroflexus

54. Amaranthus viridis

55. Cotinus coggygria

56. Pistacia lentiscus

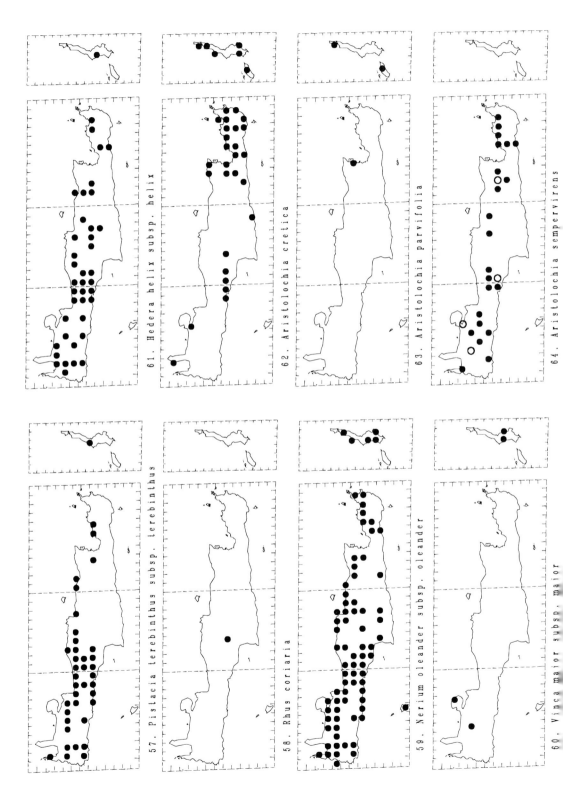

57. Pistacia terebinthus subsp. terebinthus

58. Rhus coriaria

59. Nerium oleander subsp. oleander

60. Vinca maior subsp. maior

61. Hedera helix subsp. helix

62. Aristolochia cretica

63. Aristolochia parvifolia

64. Aristolochia sempervirens

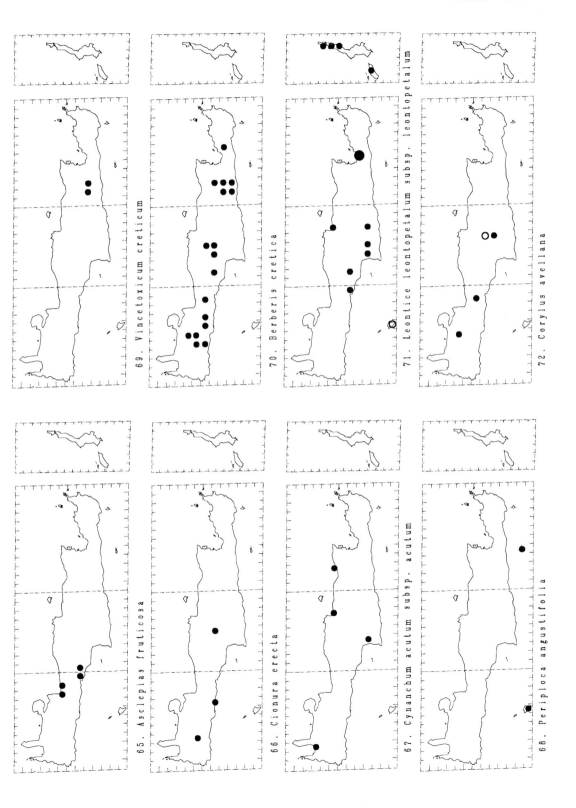

69. Vincetoxicum creticum

70. Berberis cretica

71. Leontice leontopetalum subsp. leontopetalum

72. Corylus avellana

65. Asclepias fruticosa

66. Cionura erecta

67. Cynanchum acutum subsp. acutum

68. Periploca angustifolia

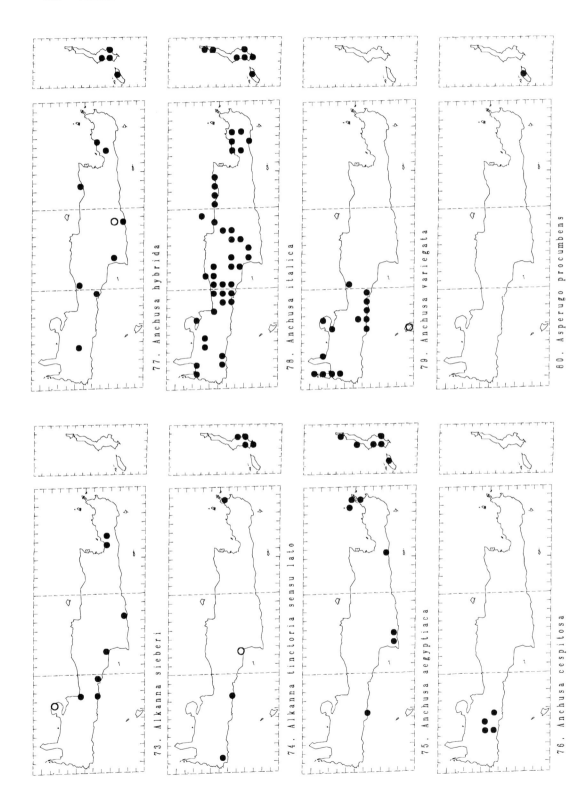

73. Alkanna sieberi

74. Alkanna tinctoria sensu lato

75. Anchusa aegyptiaca

76. Anchusa cespitosa

77. Anchusa hybrida

78. Anchusa italica

79. Anchusa variegata

80. Asperugo procumbens

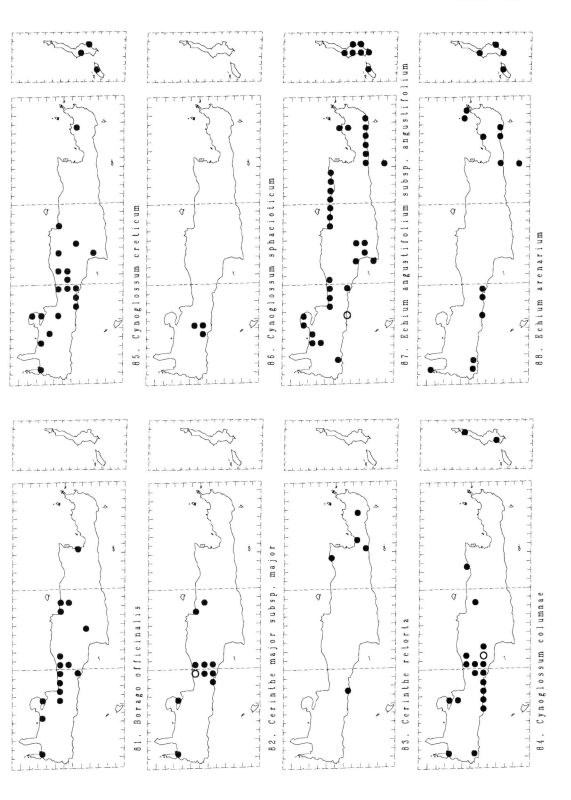

81. Borago officinalis

82. Cerinthe major subsp. major

83. Cerinthe retorta

84. Cynoglossum columnae

85. Cynoglossum creticum

86. Cynoglossum sphacioticum

87. Echium angustifolium subsp. angustifolium

88. Echium arenarium

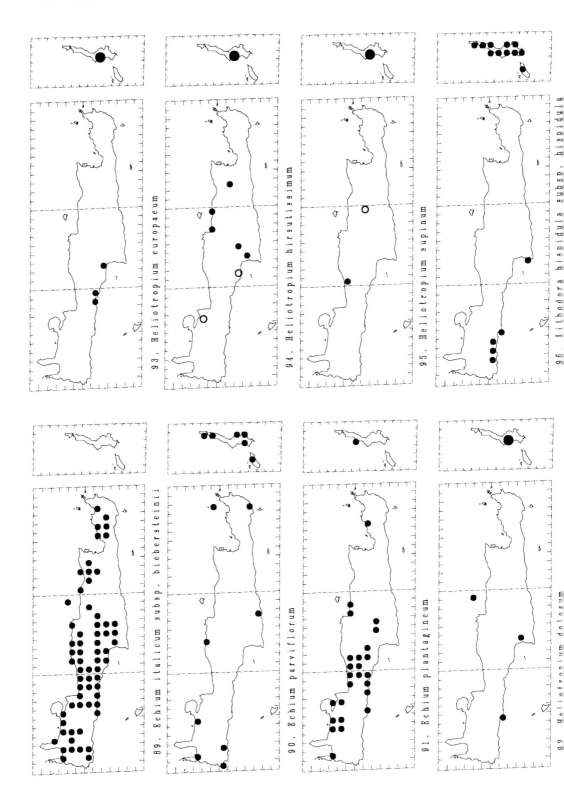

89. Echium italicum subsp. biebersteinii

90. Echium parviflorum

91. Echium plantagineum

93. Heliotropium europaeum

94. Heliotropium hirsutissimum

95. Heliotropium supinum

96. Lithodora hispidula subsp. hispidula

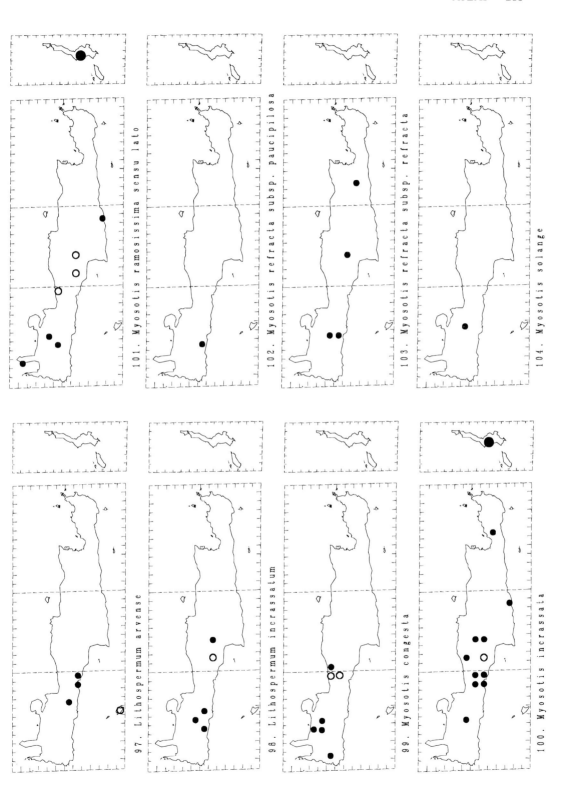

97. Lithospermum arvense

98. Lithospermum incrassatum

99. Myosotis congesta

100. Myosotis incrassata

101. Myosotis ramosissima sensu lato

102. Myosotis refracta subsp. paucipilosa

103. Myosotis refracta subsp. refracta

104. Myosotis solange

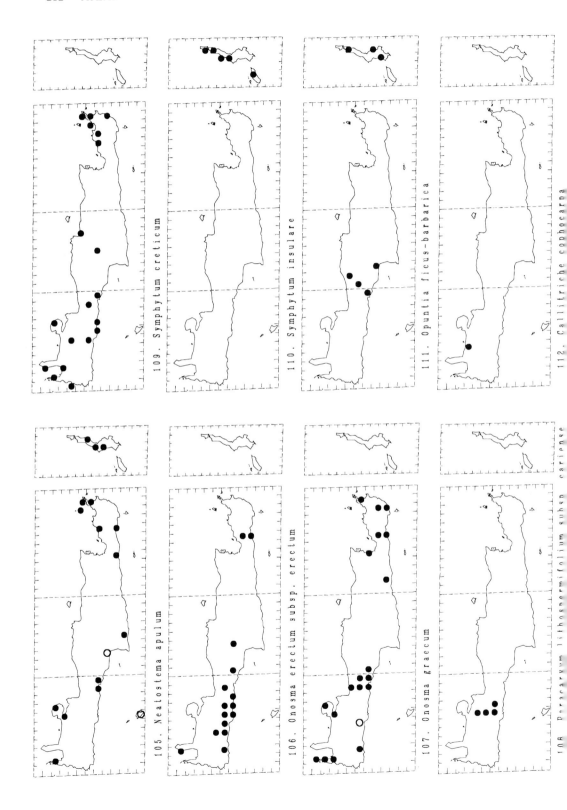

105. Neatostema apulum

106. Onosma erectum subsp. erectum

107. Onosma graecum

108. Paracaryum lithospermifolium subsp. cariense

109. Symphytum creticum

110. Symphytum insulare

111. Opuntia ficus-barbarica

112. Callitriche cophocarpa

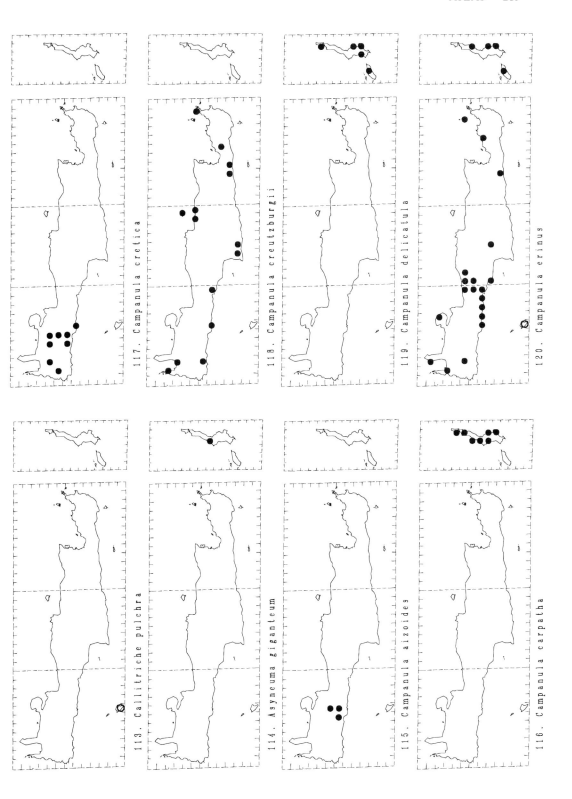

117. Campanula cretica

118. Campanula creutzburgii

119. Campanula delicatula

120. Campanula erinus

113. Callitriche pulchra

114. Asyneuma giganteum

115. Campanula aizoides

116. Campanula carpatha

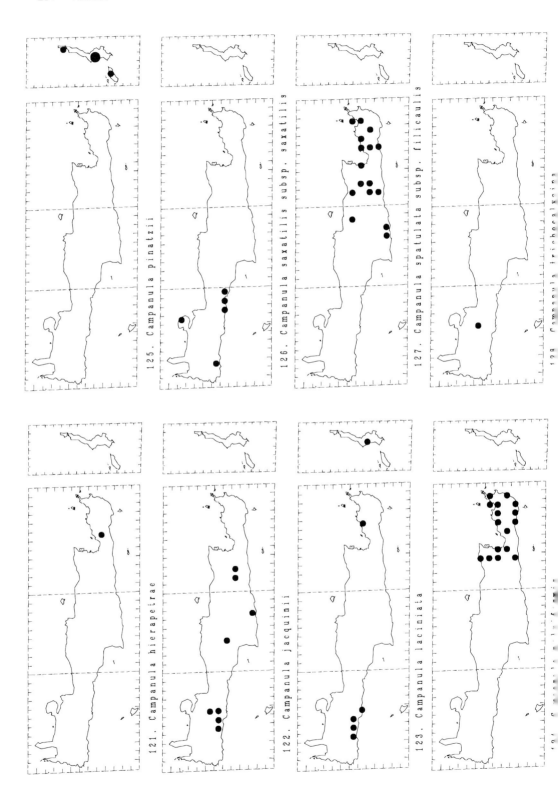

125. Campanula pinatzii

126. Campanula saxatilis subsp. saxatilis

127. Campanula spatulata subsp. filicaulis

128. Campanula trichocalycina

121. Campanula hierapetrae

122. Campanula jacquinii

123. Campanula laciniata

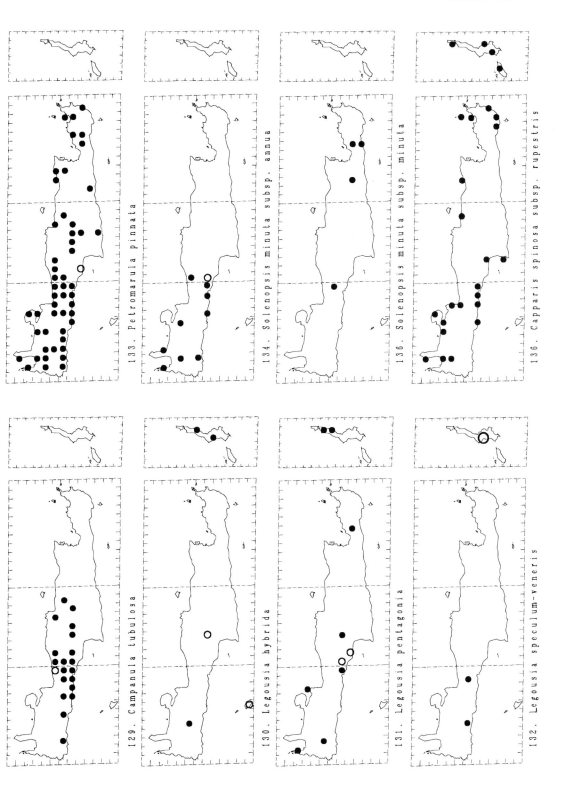

129. Campanula tubulosa

130. Legousia hybrida

131. Legousia pentagonia

132. Legousia speculum-veneris

133. Petromarula pinnata

134. Solenopsis minuta subsp. annua

136. Solenopsis minuta subsp. minuta

136. Capparis spinosa subsp. rupestris

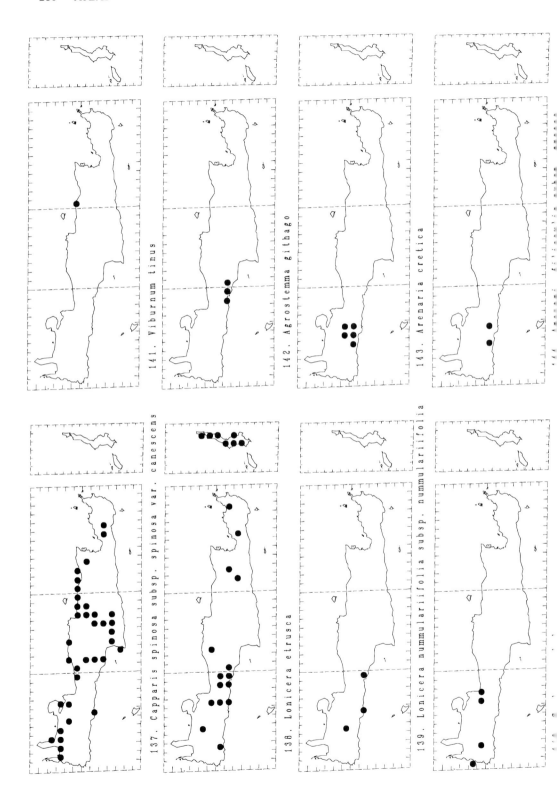

141. Viburnum tinus

142. Agrostemma githago

143. Arenaria cretica

137. Capparis spinosa subsp. spinosa var. canescens

138. Lonicera etrusca

139. Lonicera nummulariifolia subsp. nummulariifolia

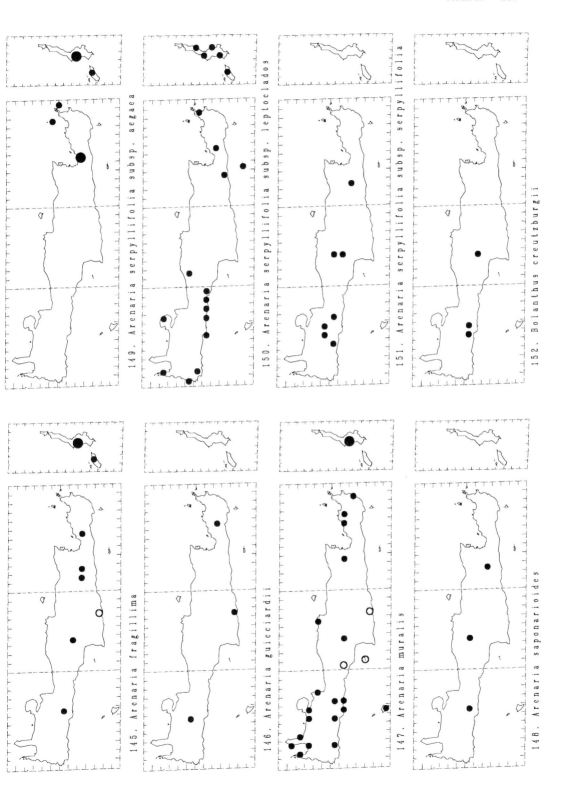

149. Arenaria serpyllifolia subsp. aegaea

150. Arenaria serpyllifolia subsp. leptoclados

151. Arenaria serpyllifolia subsp. serpyllifolia

152. Bolanthus creutzburgii

145. Arenaria fragillima

146. Arenaria guicciardii

147. Arenaria muralis

148. Arenaria saponarioides

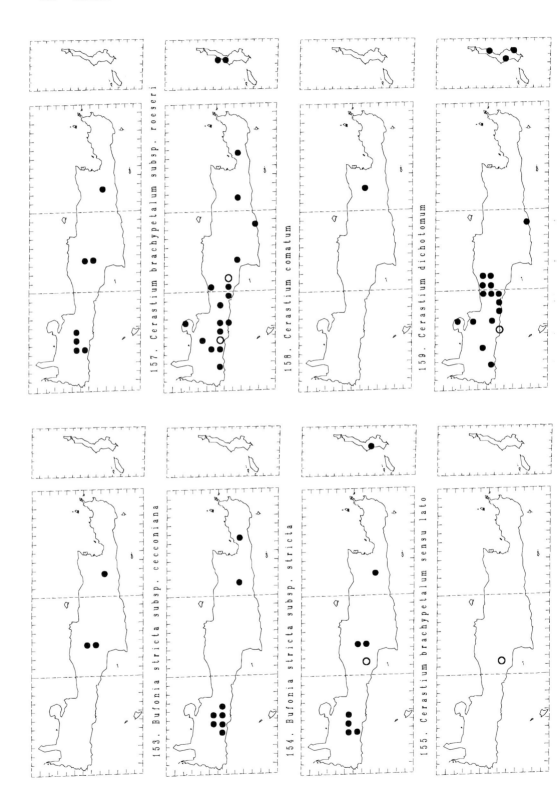

153. Bufonia stricta subsp. cecconiana

154. Bufonia stricta subsp. stricta

155. Cerastium brachypetalum sensu lato

157. Cerastium brachypetalum subsp. roeseri

158. Cerastium comatum

159. Cerastium dichotomum

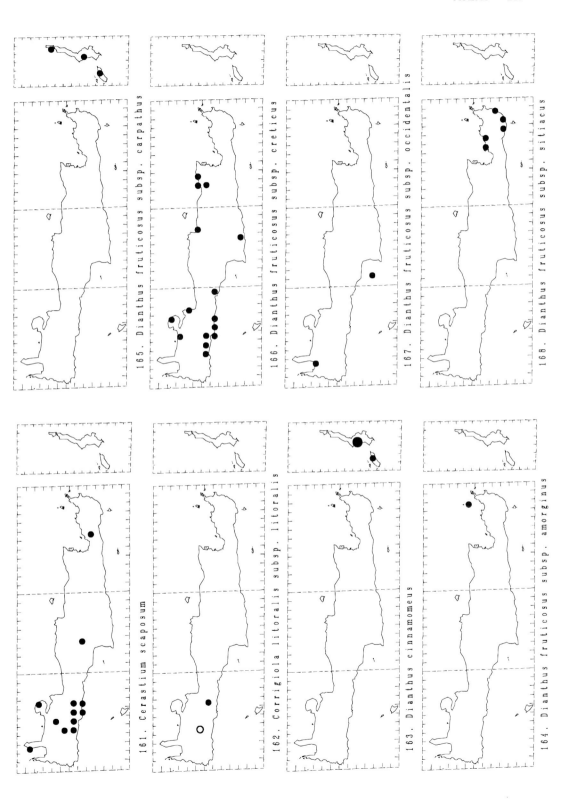

161. Cerastium scaposum

162. Corrigiola litoralis subsp. litoralis

163. Dianthus cinnamomeus

164. Dianthus fruticosus subsp. amorginus

165. Dianthus fruticosus subsp. carpathus

166. Dianthus fruticosus subsp. creticus

167. Dianthus fruticosus subsp. occidentalis

168. Dianthus fruticosus subsp. sitiacus

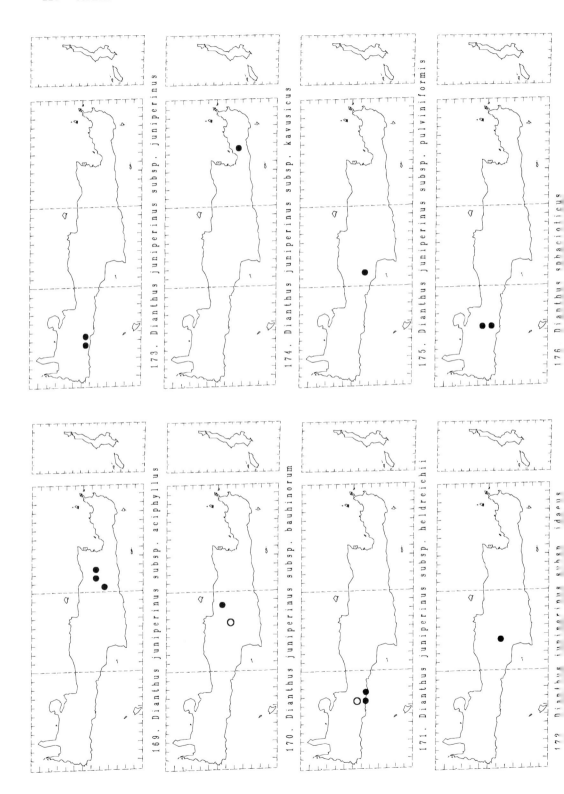

169. Dianthus juniperinus subsp. aciphyllus

170. Dianthus juniperinus subsp. bauhinorum

171. Dianthus juniperinus subsp. heldreichii

172. Dianthus juniperinus subsp. idaeus

173. Dianthus juniperinus subsp. juniperinus

174. Dianthus juniperinus subsp. kavusicus

175. Dianthus juniperinus subsp. pulviniformis

176. Dianthus sphacioticus

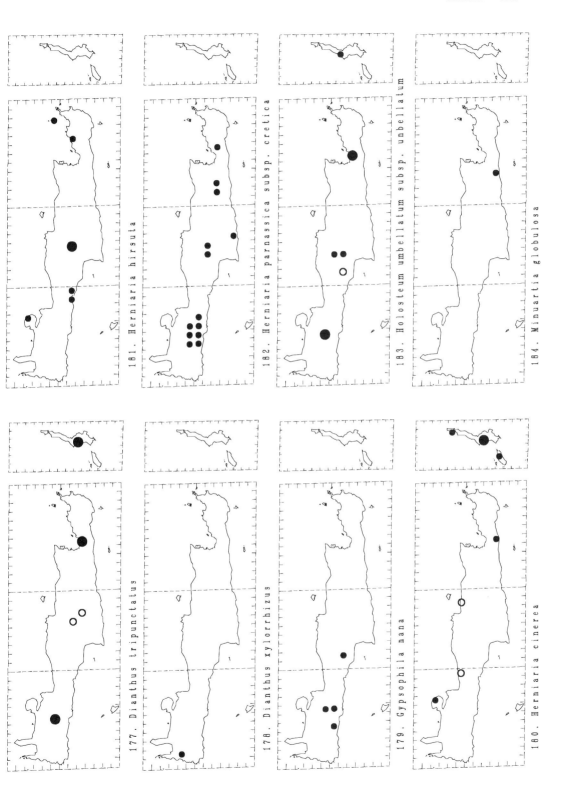

177. Dianthus tripunctatus

178. Dianthus xylorrhizus

179. Gypsophila nana

180. Herniaria cinerea

181. Herniaria hirsuta

182. Herniaria parnassica subsp. cretica

183. Holosteum umbellatum subsp. umbellatum

184. Minuartia globulosa

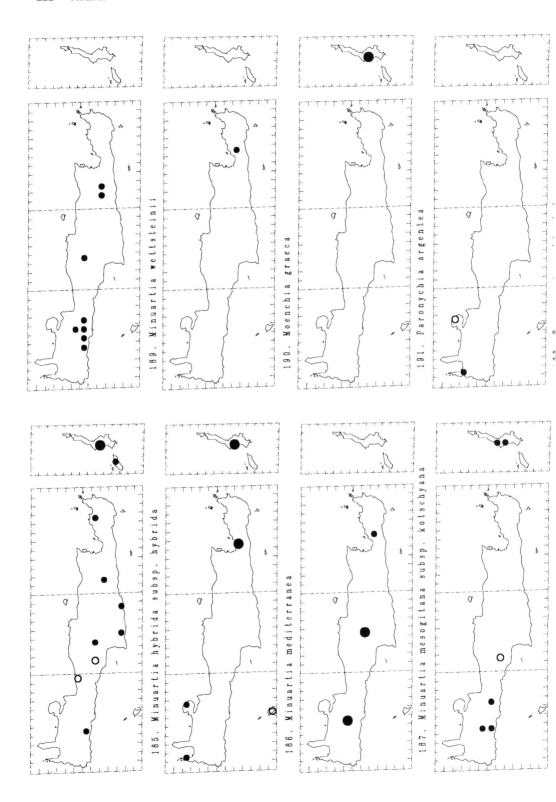

185. Minuartia hybrida subsp. hybrida

186. Minuartia mediterranea

187. Minuartia mesogitana subsp. kotschyana

189. Minuartia wettsteinii

190. Moenchia graeca

191. Paronychia argentea

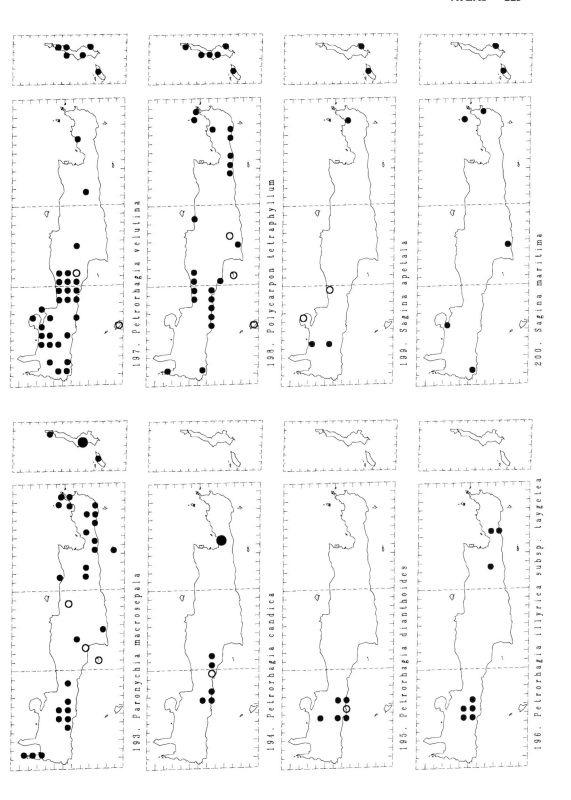

193. Paronychia macrosepala

194. Petrorhagia candica

195. Petrorhagia dianthoides

196. Petrorhagia illyrica subsp. taygetea

197. Petrorhagia velutina

198. Polycarpon tetraphyllum

199. Sagina apetala

200. Sagina maritima

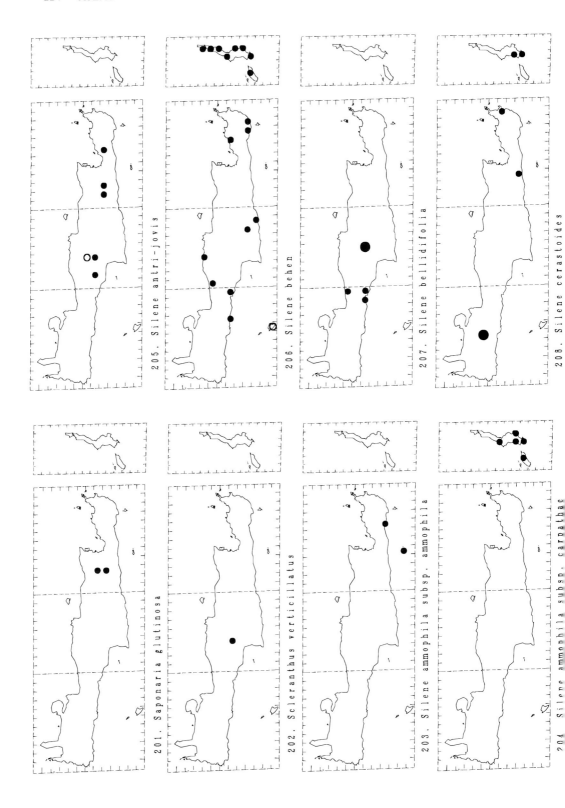

201. Saponaria glutinosa

202. Scleranthus verticillatus

203. Silene ammophila subsp. ammophila

204. Silene ammophila subsp. carpathae

205. Silene antri-jovis

206. Silene behen

207. Silene bellidifolia

208. Silene cerastoides

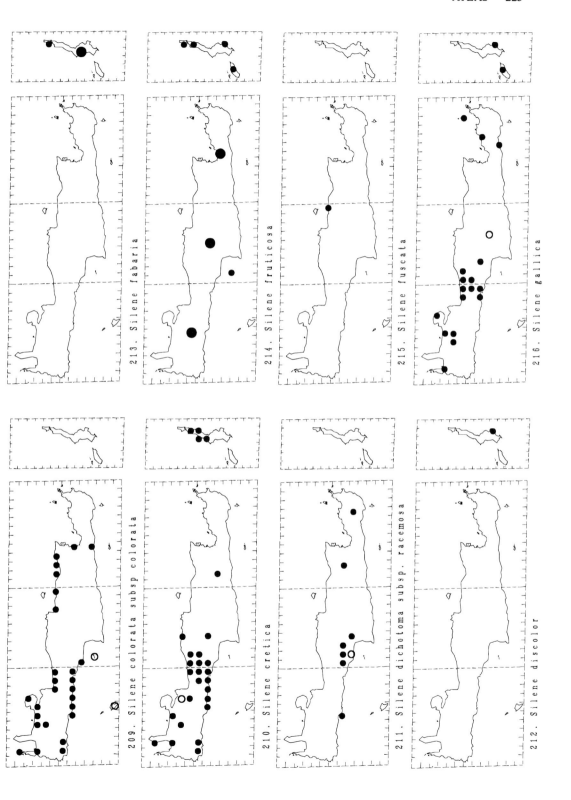

209. Silene colorata subsp colorata

210. Silene cretica

211. Silene dichotoma subsp. racemosa

212. Silene discolor

213. Silene fabaria

214. Silene fruticosa

215. Silene fuscata

216. Silene gallica

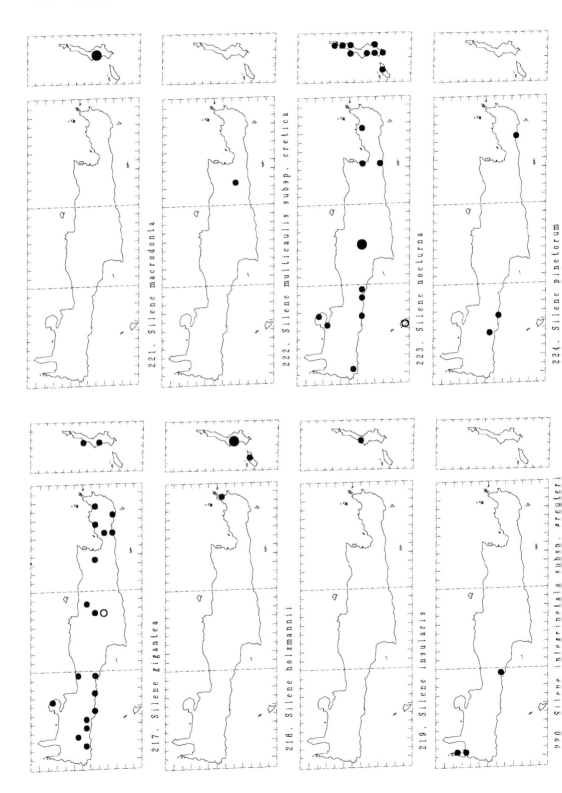

221. Silene macrodonta

222. Silene multicaulis subsp. cretica

223. Silene nocturna

224. Silene pinetorum

217. Silene gigantea

218. Silene holzmannii

219. Silene insularis

220. Silene integripetala subsp. greuteri

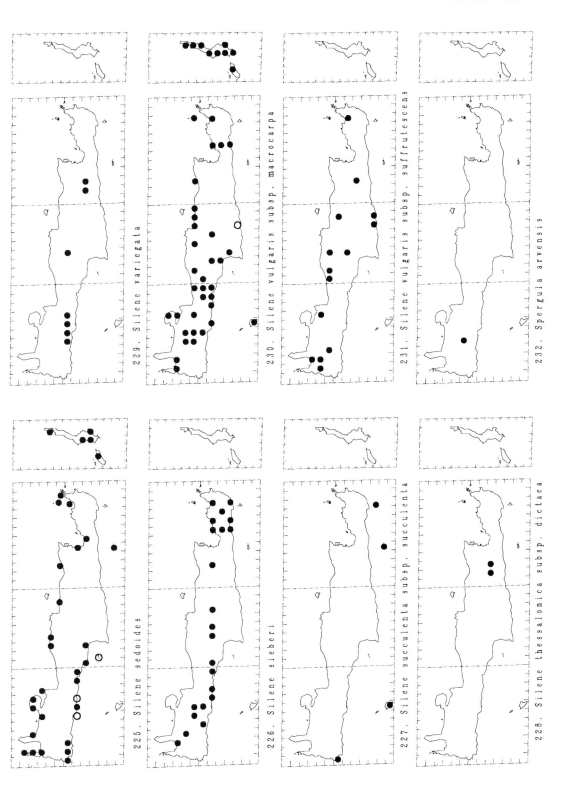

229. Silene variegata

230. Silene vulgaris subsp. macrocarpa

231. Silene vulgaris subsp. suffrutescens

232. Spergula arvensis

225. Silene sedoides

226. Silene sieberi

227. Silene succulenta subsp. succulenta

228. Silene thessalonica subsp. dictaea

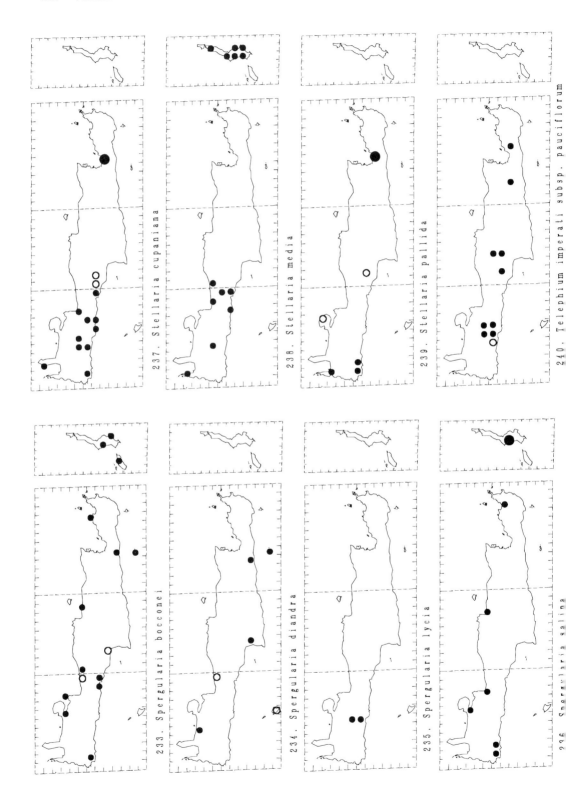

233. Spergularia bocconei

234. Spergularia diandra

235. Spergularia lycia

236. Spergularia salina

237. Stellaria cupaniana

238. Stellaria media

239. Stellaria pallida

240. Telephium imperati subsp. pauciflorum

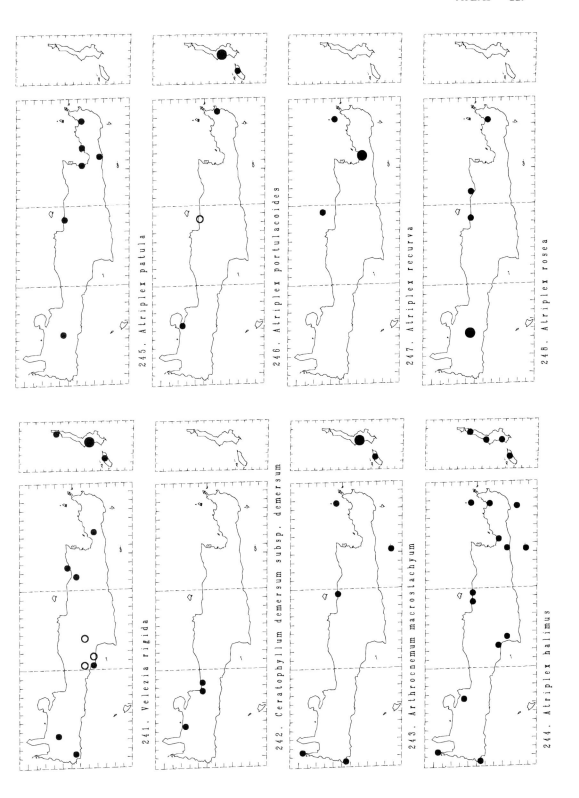

241. Velezia rigida

242. Ceratophyllum demersum subsp. demersum

243. Arthrocnemum macrostachyum

244. Atriplex halimus

245. Atriplex patula

246. Atriplex portulacoides

247. Atriplex recurva

248. Atriplex rosea

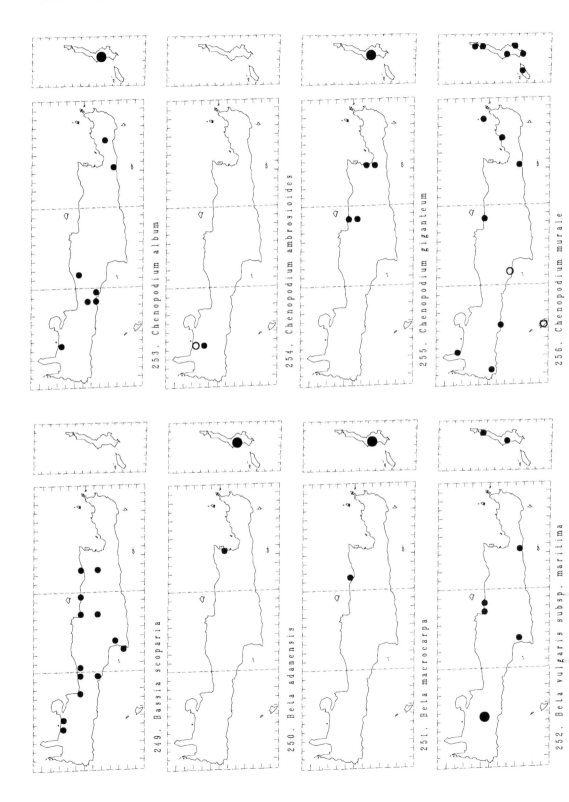

249. Bassia scoparia

250. Beta adanensis

251. Beta macrocarpa

252. Beta vulgaris subsp. maritima

253. Chenopodium album

254. Chenopodium ambrosioides

255. Chenopodium giganteum

256. Chenopodium murale

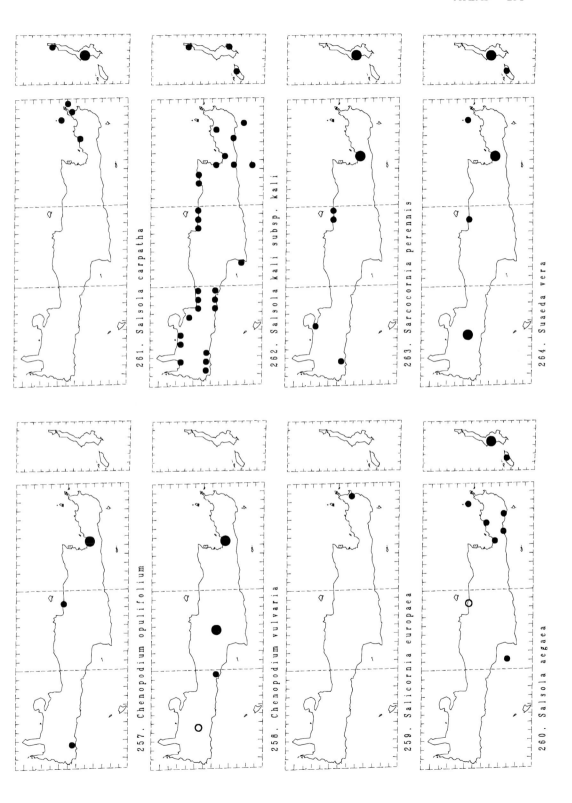

257. Chenopodium opulifolium

258. Chenopodium vulvaria

259. Salicornia europaea

260. Salsola aegaea

261. Salsola carpatha

262. Salsola kali subsp. kali

263. Sarcocornia perennis

264. Suaeda vera

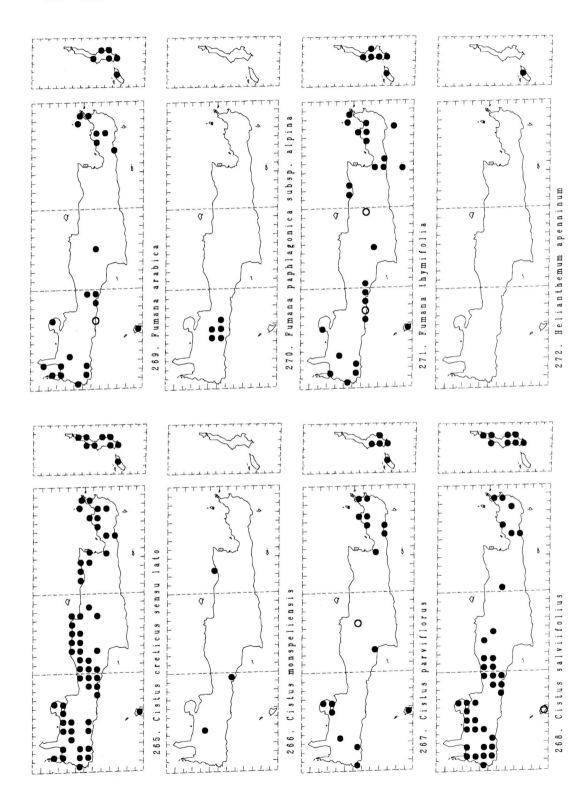

265. Cistus creticus sensu lato

266. Cistus monspeliensis

267. Cistus parviflorus

268. Cistus salviifolius

269. Fumana arabica

270. Fumana paphlagonica subsp. alpina

271. Fumana thymifolia

272. Helianthemum apenninum

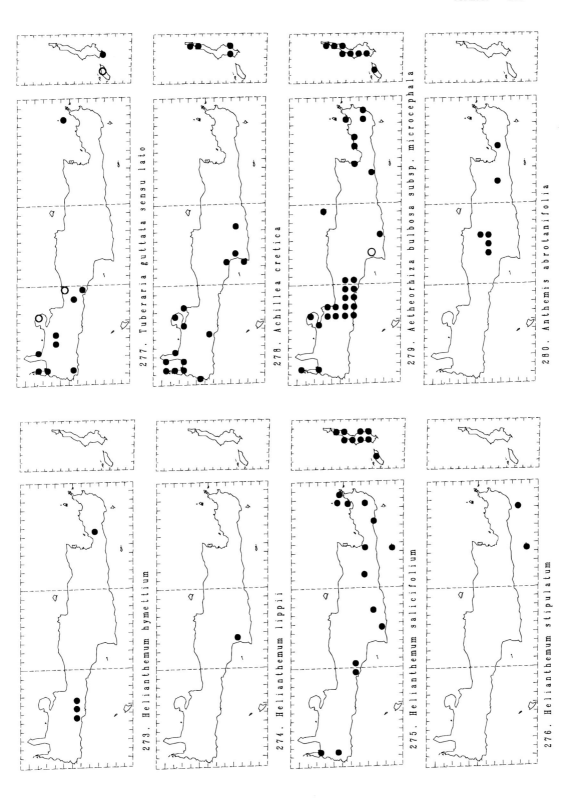

277. Tuberaria guttata sensu lato

278. Achillea cretica

279. Aetheorhiza bulbosa subsp. microcephala

280. Anthemis abrotanifolia

273. Helianthemum hymettium

274. Helianthemum lippii

275. Helianthemum salicifolium

276. Helianthemum stipulatum

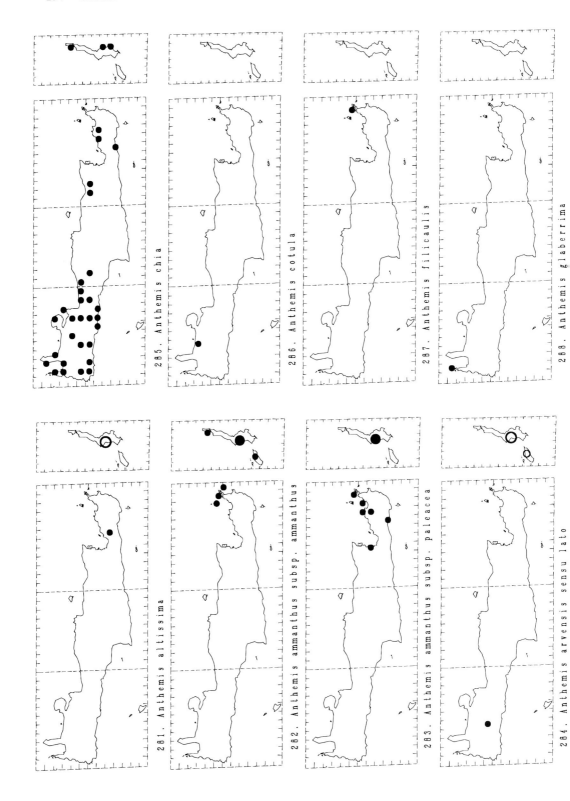

281. Anthemis altissima

282. Anthemis ammanthus subsp. ammanthus

283. Anthemis ammanthus subsp. paleacea

284. Anthemis arvensis sensu lato

285. Anthemis chia

286. Anthemis cotula

287. Anthemis filicaulis

288. Anthemis glaberrima

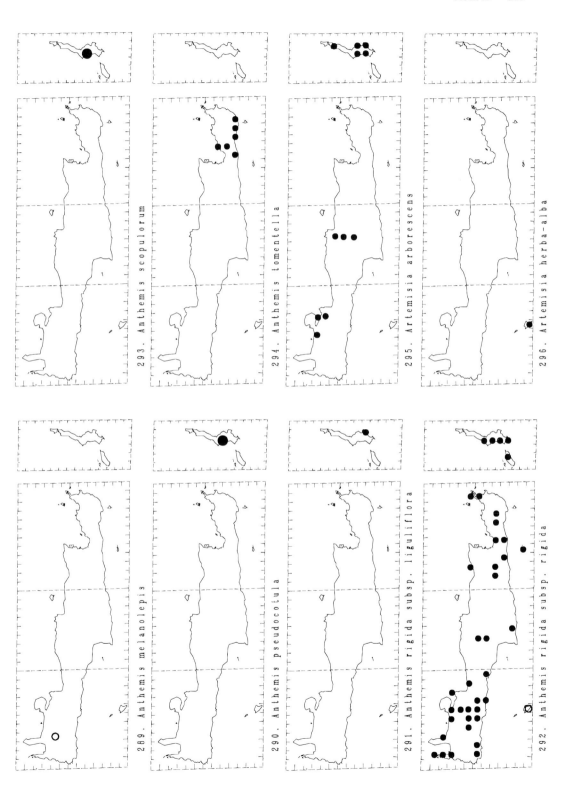

289. Anthemis melanolepis

290. Anthemis pseudocotula

291. Anthemis rigida subsp. liguliflora

292. Anthemis rigida subsp. rigida

293. Anthemis scopulorum

294. Anthemis tomentella

295. Artemisia arborescens

296. Artemisia herba-alba

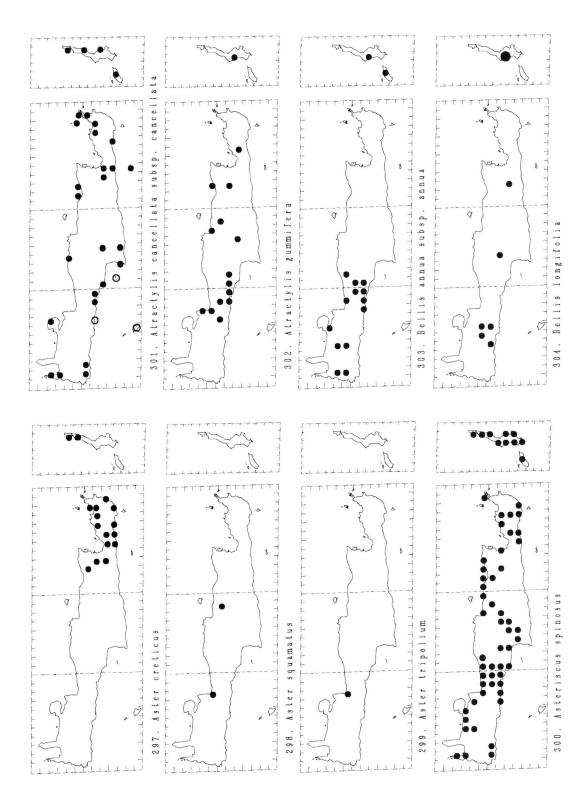

297. Aster creticus

298. Aster squamatus

299. Aster tripolium

300. Asteriscus spinosus

301. Atractylis cancellata subsp. cancellata

302. Atractylis gummifera

303. Bellis annua subsp. annua

304. Bellis longifolia

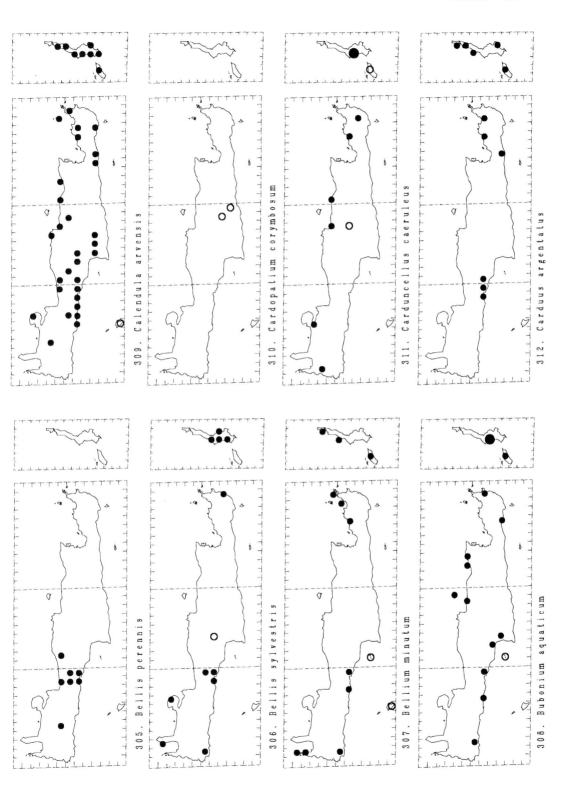

305. Bellis perennis

306. Bellis sylvestris

307. Bellium minutum

308. Bubonium aquaticum

309. Calendula arvensis

310. Cardopatium corymbosum

311. Carduncellus caeruleus

312. Carduus argentatus

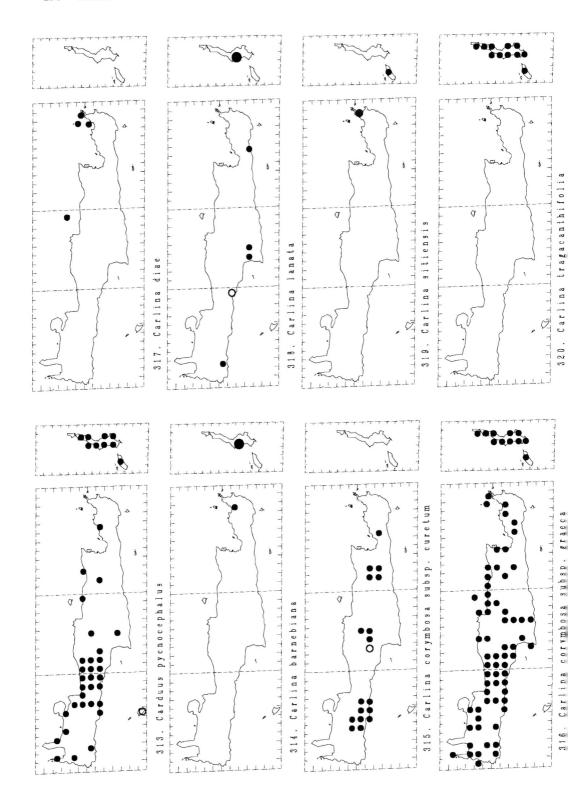

317. Carlina diae

318. Carlina lanata

319. Carlina sitiensis

320. Carlina tragacanthifolia

313. Carduus pycnocephalus

314. Carlina barnebiana

315. Carlina corymbosa subsp. curetum

316. Carlina corymbosa subsp. graeca

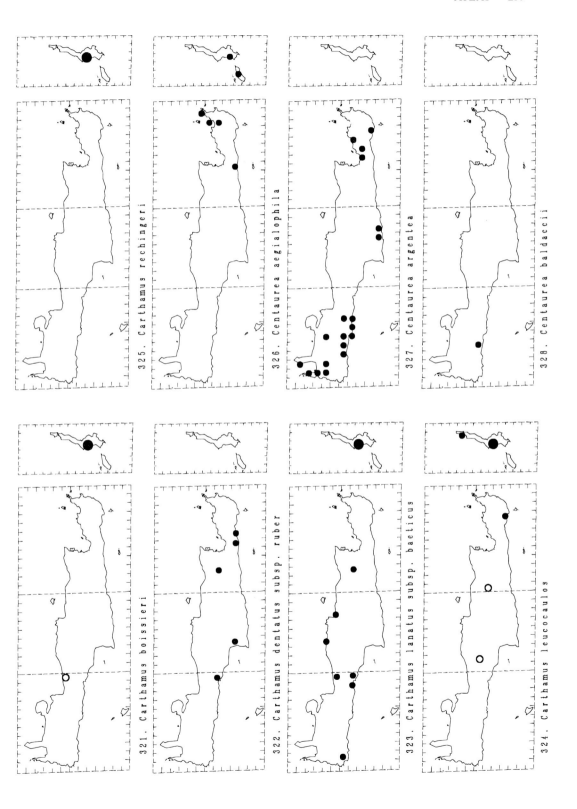

321. Carthamus boissieri

322. Carthamus dentatus subsp. ruber

323. Carthamus lanatus subsp. baeticus

324. Carthamus leucocaulos

325. Carthamus rechingeri

326. Centaurea aegialophila

327. Centaurea argentea

328. Centaurea baldaccii

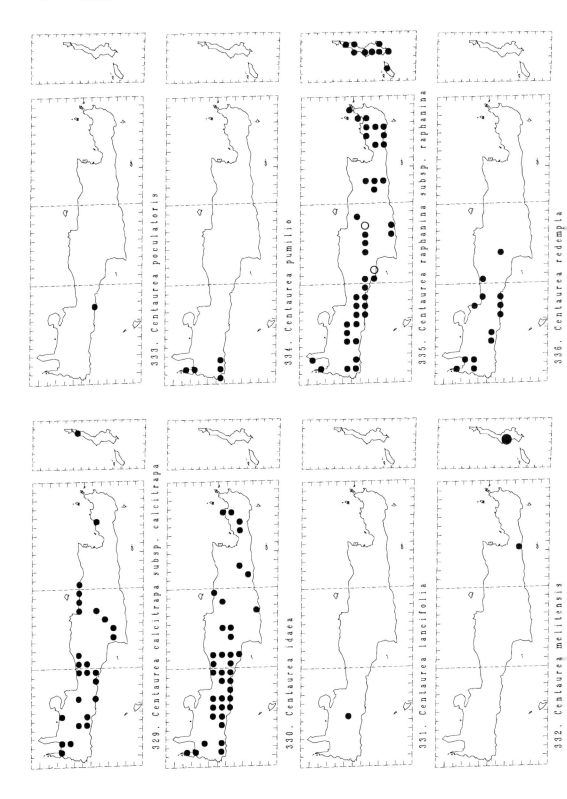

329 . Centaurea calcitrapa subsp. calcitrapa

330 . Centaurea idaea

331 . Centaurea lancifolia

332 . Centaurea melitensis

333 . Centaurea poculatoris

334 . Centaurea pumilio

335 . Centaurea raphanina subsp. raphanina

336 . Centaurea redempta

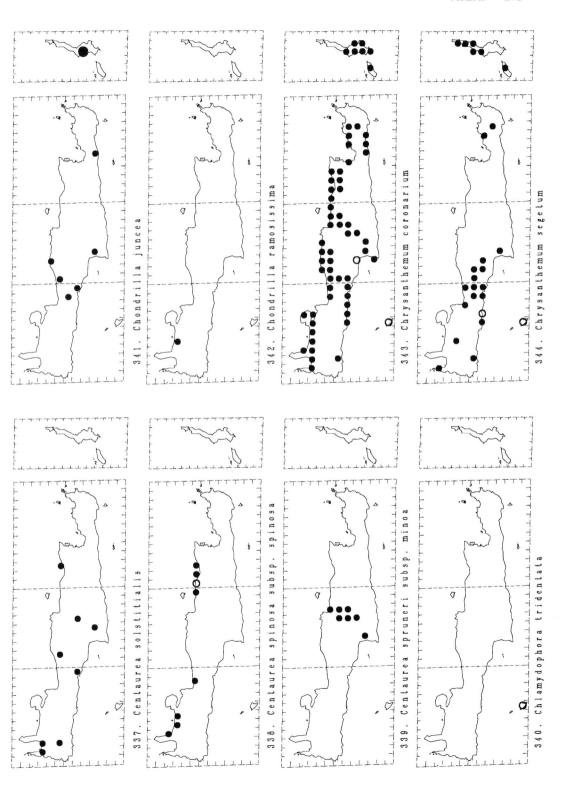

341. Chondrilla juncea

342. Chondrilla ramosissima

343. Chrysanthemum coronarium

344. Chrysanthemum segetum

337. Centaurea solstitialis

338. Centaurea spinosa subsp. spinosa

339. Centaurea spruneri subsp. minoa

340. Chlamydophora tridentata

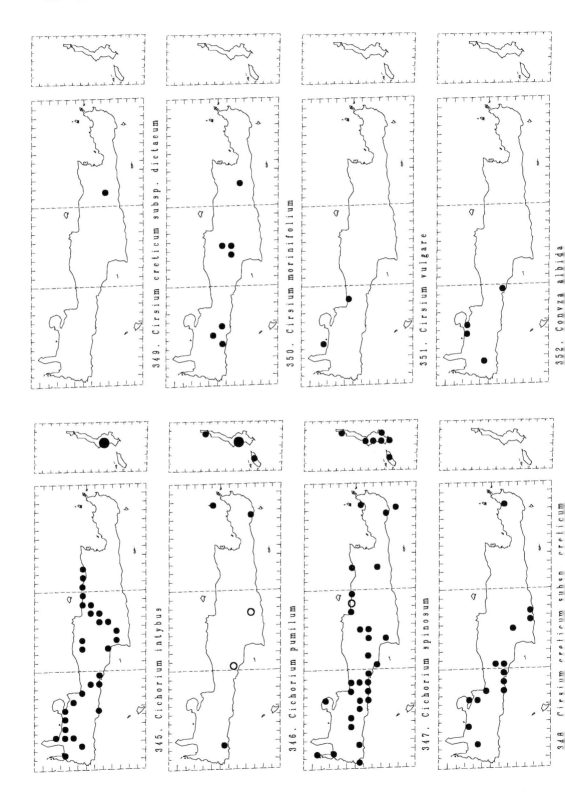

349. Cirsium creticum subsp. dictaeum

350. Cirsium morinifolium

351. Cirsium vulgare

352. Conyza albida

345. Cichorium intybus

346. Cichorium pumilum

347. Cichorium spinosum

348. Cirsium creticum subsp. creticum

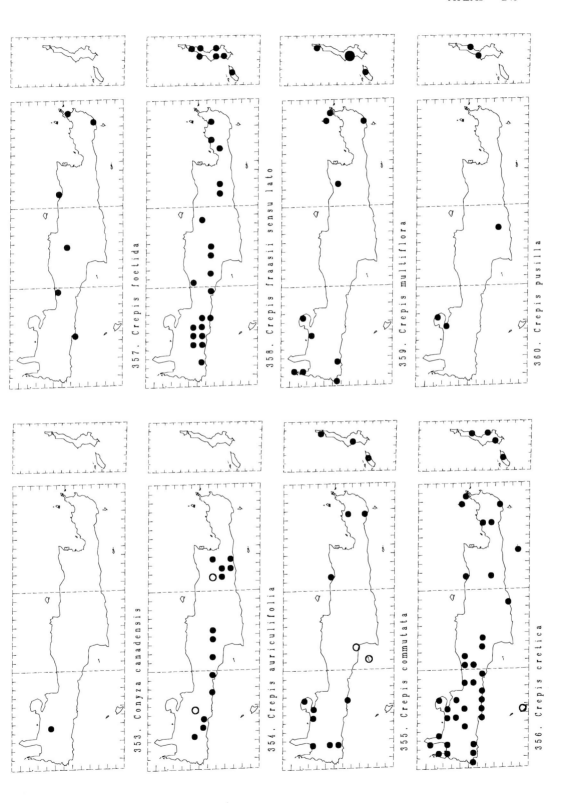

353. Conyza canadensis

354. Crepis auriculifolia

355. Crepis commutata

356. Crepis cretica

357. Crepis foetida

358. Crepis fraasii sensu lato

359. Crepis multiflora

360. Crepis pusilla

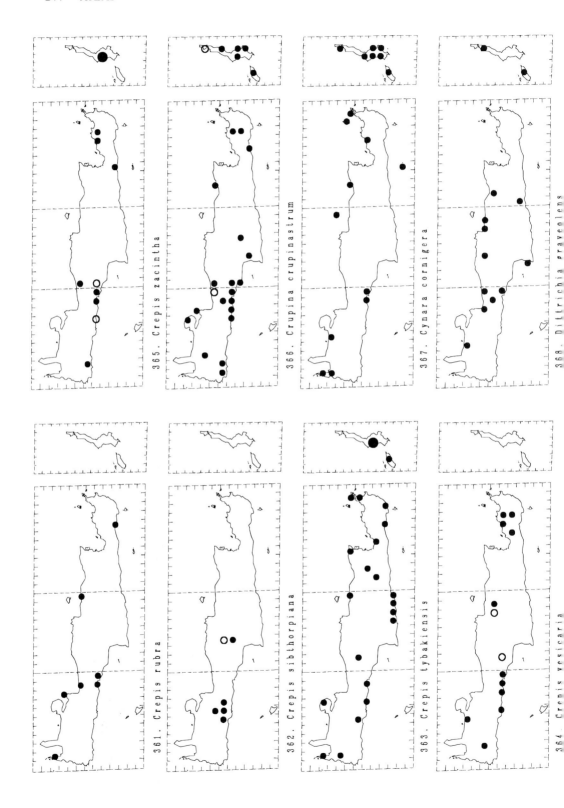

361. Crepis rubra

362. Crepis sibthorpiana

363. Crepis tybakiensis

364. Crepis vesicaria

365. Crepis zacintha

366. Crupina crupinastrum

367. Cynara cornigera

368. Dittrichia graveolens

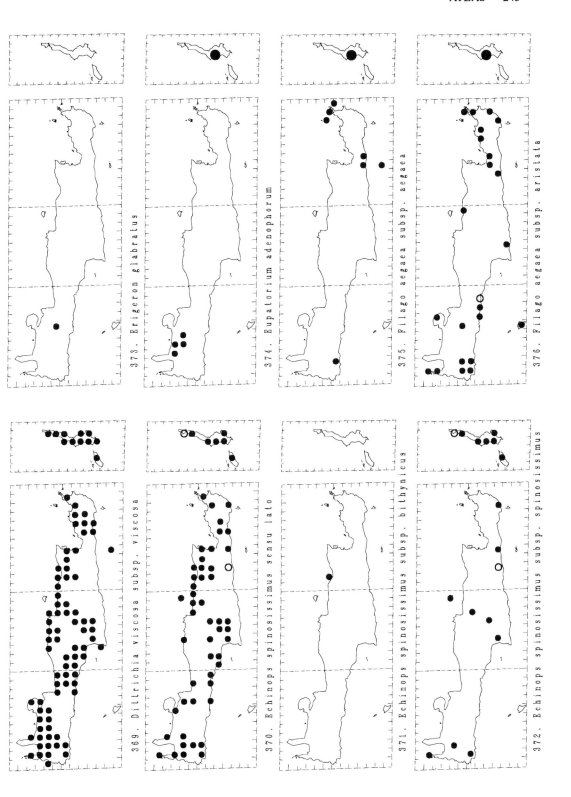

369. Dittrichia viscosa subsp. viscosa

370. Echinops spinosissimus sensu lato

371. Echinops spinosissimus subsp. bithynicus

372. Echinops spinosissimus subsp. spinosissimus

373. Erigeron glabratus

374. Eupatorium adenophorum

375. Filago aegaea subsp. aegaea

376. Filago aegaea subsp. aristata

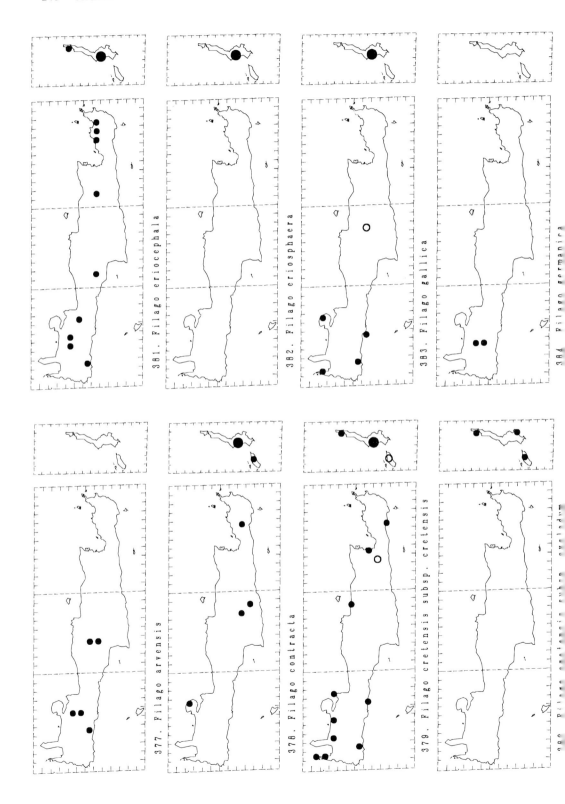

381. Filago eriocephala

382. Filago eriosphaera

383. Filago gallica

384. Filago germanica

377. Filago arvensis

378. Filago contracta

379. Filago cretensis subsp. cretensis

380. Filago cretensis subsp. sveladum

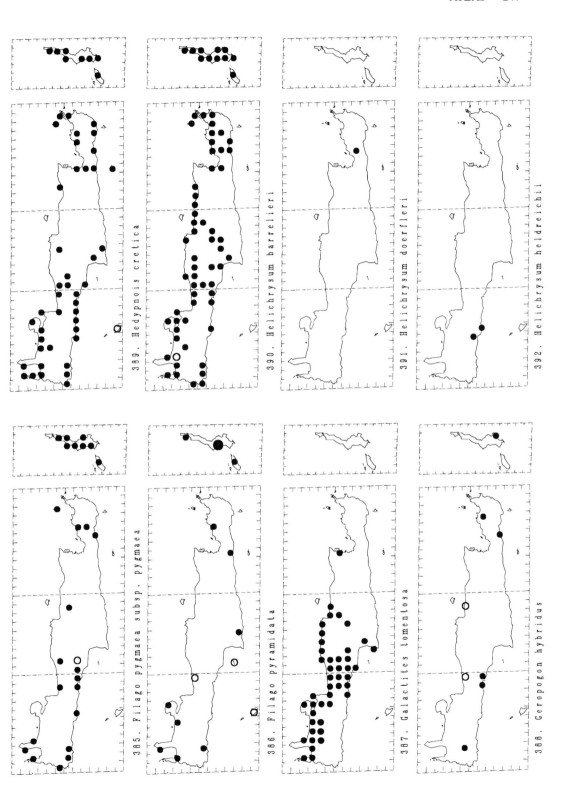

385. Filago pygmaea subsp. pygmaea

386. Filago pyramidata

387. Galactites tomentosa

388. Geropogon hybridus

389. Hedypnois cretica

390. Helichrysum barrelieri

391. Helichrysum doerfleri

392. Helichrysum heldreichii

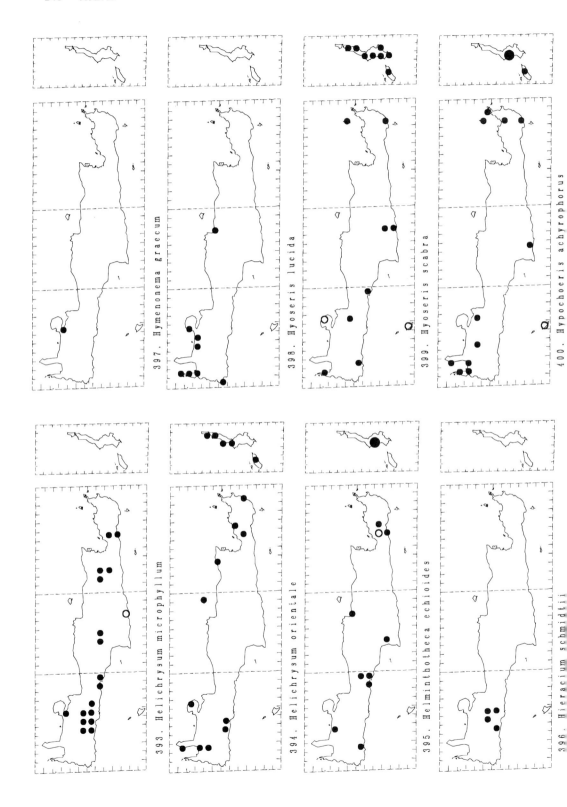

393. Helichrysum microphyllum

394. Helichrysum orientale

395. Helminthotheca echioides

396. Hieracium schmidtii

397. Hymenonema graecum

398. Hyoseris lucida

399. Hyoseris scabra

400. Hypochoeris achyrophorus

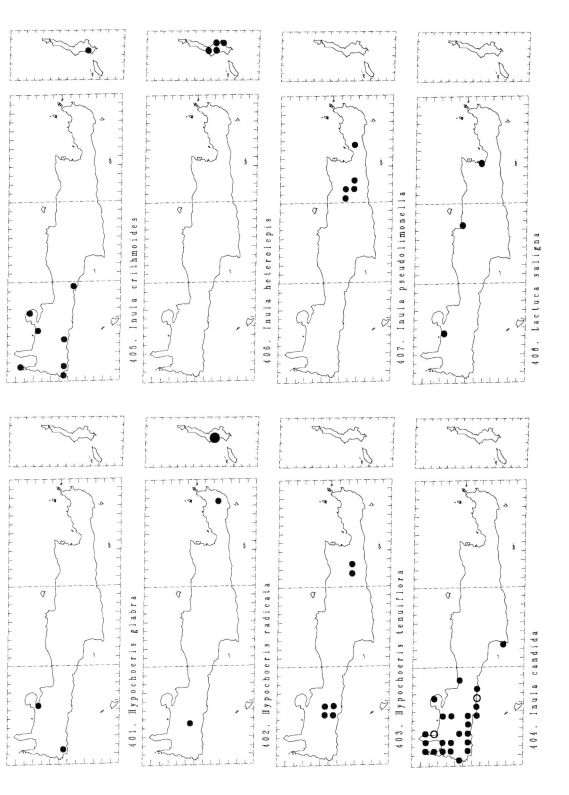

405. Inula crithmoides

406. Inula heterolepis

407. Inula pseudolimonella

408. Lactuca saligna

401. Hypochoeris glabra

402. Hypochoeris radicata

403. Hypochoeris tenuiflora

404. Inula candida

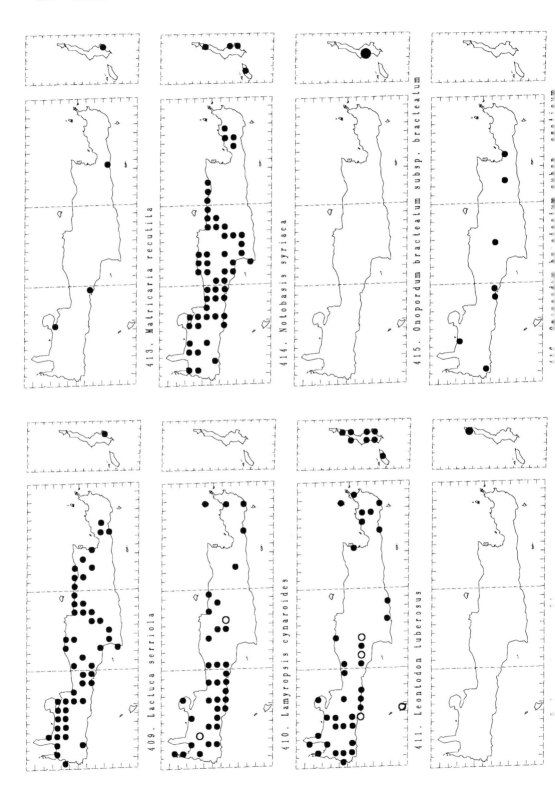

409. Lactuca serriola

410. Lamyropsis cynaroides

411. Leontodon tuberosus

413. Matricaria recutita

414. Notobasis syriaca

415. Onopordum bracteatum subsp. bracteatum

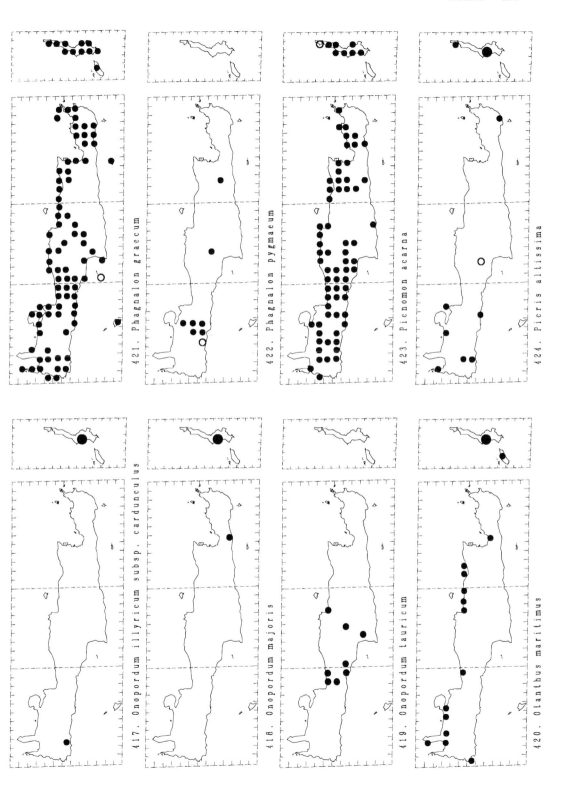

417. Onopordum illyricum subsp. cardunculus

418. Onopordum majoris

419. Onopordum tauricum

420. Otanthus maritimus

421. Phagnalon graecum

422. Phagnalon pygmaeum

423. Picnomon acarna

424. Picris altissima

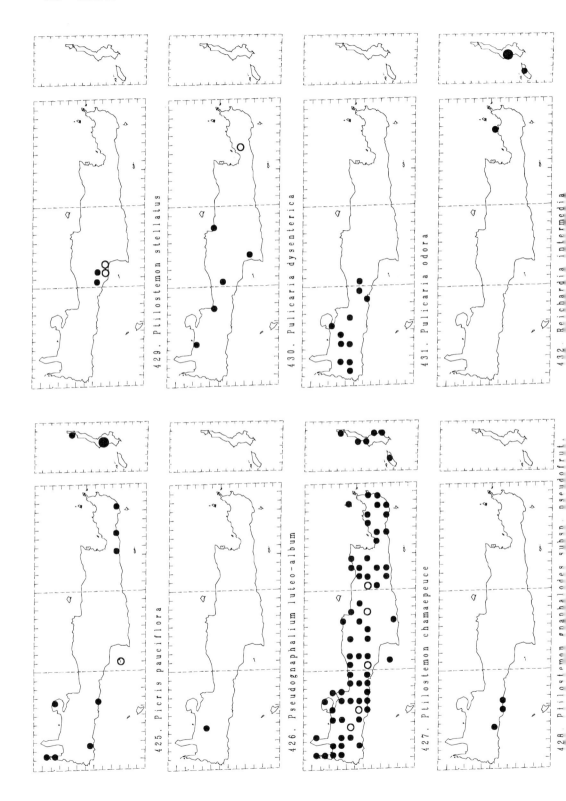

425. Picris pauciflora

426. Pseudognaphalium luteo-album

427. Ptilostemon chamaepeuce

428. Ptilostemon gnaphalodes subsp. pseudofrut.

429. Ptilostemon stellatus

430. Pulicaria dysenterica

431. Pulicaria odora

432. Reichardia intermedia

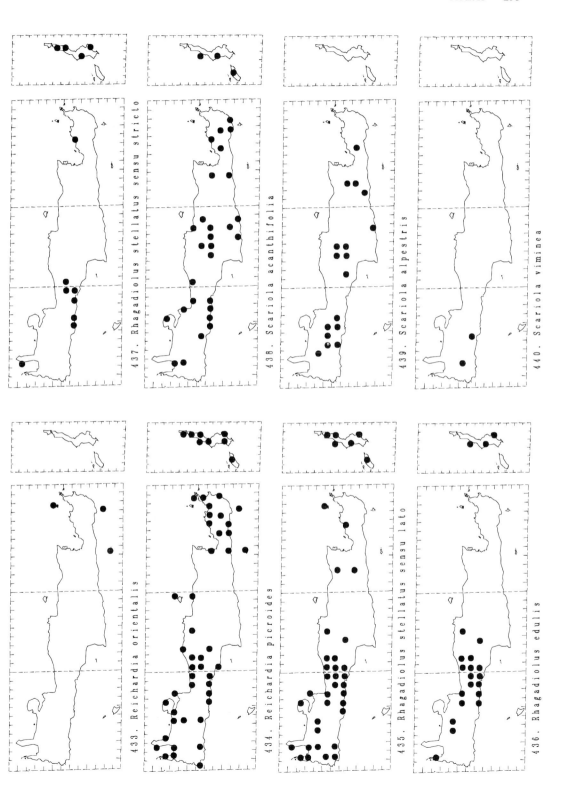

433. Reichardia orientalis

434. Reichardia picroides

435. Rhagadiolus stellatus sensu lato

436. Rhagadiolus edulis

437. Rhagadiolus stellatus sensu stricto

438. Scariola acanthifolia

439. Scariola alpestris

440. Scariola viminea

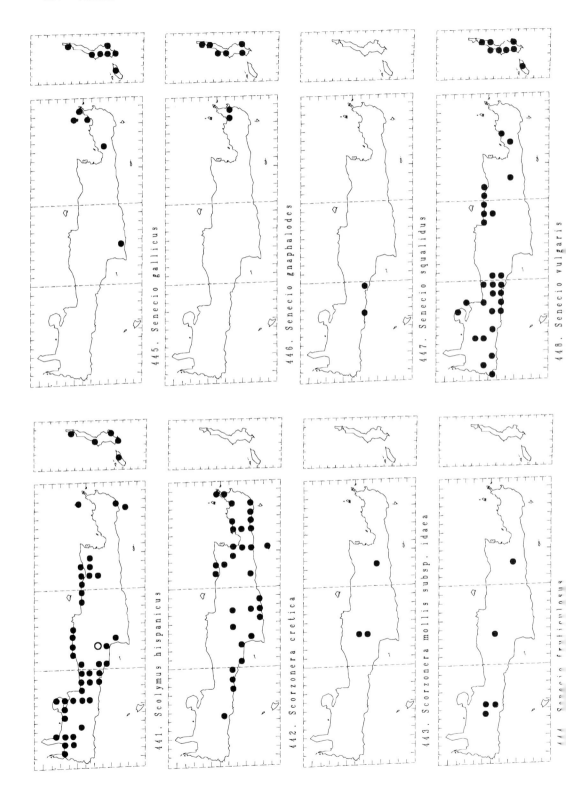

441. Scolymus hispanicus

442. Scorzonera cretica

443. Scorzonera mollis subsp. idaea

444. Senecio fruticulosus

445. Senecio gallicus

446. Senecio gnaphalodes

447. Senecio squalidus

448. Senecio vulgaris

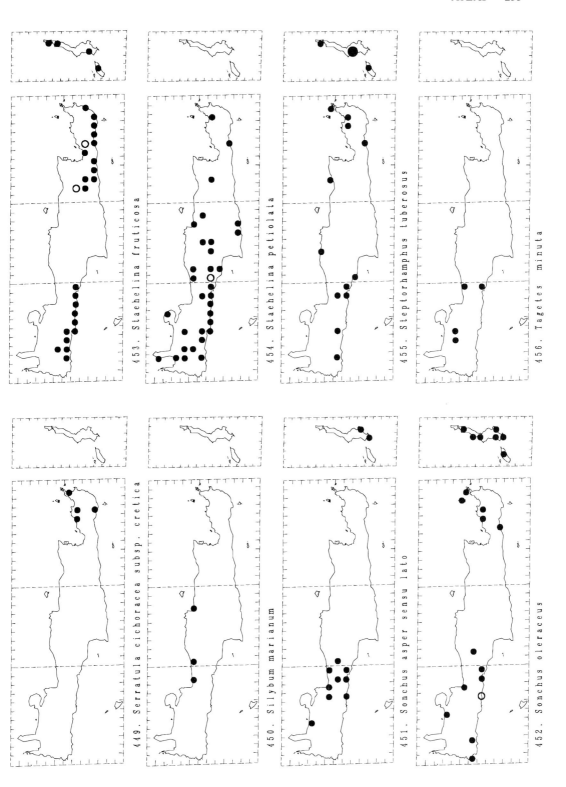

449. Serratula cichoracea subsp. cretica

450. Silybum marianum

451. Sonchus asper sensu lato

452. Sonchus oleraceus

453. Staehelina fruticosa

454. Staehelina petiolata

455. Steptorhamphus tuberosus

456. Tagetes minuta

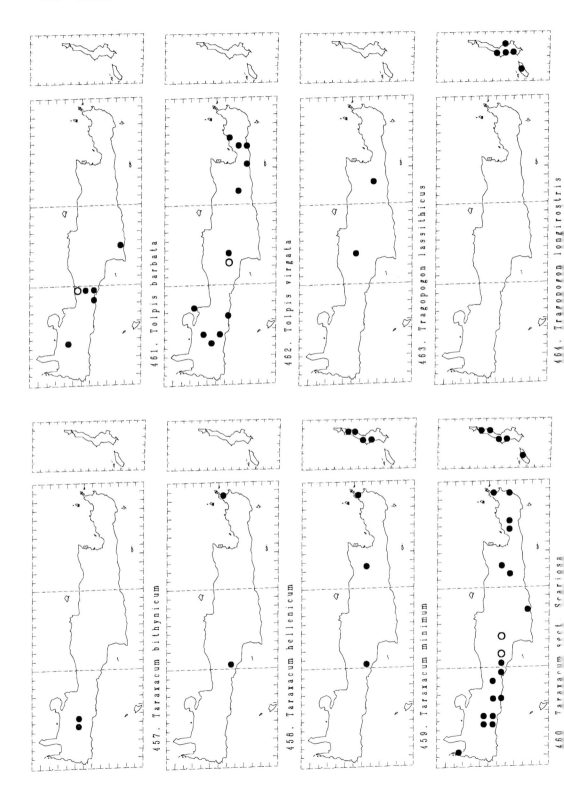

461. Tolpis barbata

462. Tolpis virgata

463. Tragopogon lassithicus

464. Tragopogon longirostris

457. Taraxacum bithynicum

458. Taraxacum hellenicum

459. Taraxacum minimum

460. Taraxacum sect. Scariosa

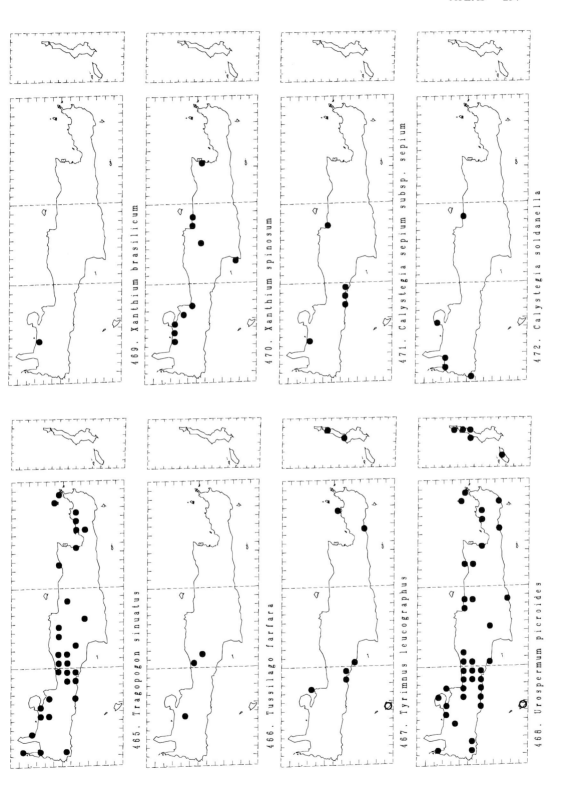

465. Tragopogon sinuatus

466. Tussilago farfara

467. Tyrimnus leucographus

468. Urospermum picroides

469. Xanthium brasilicum

470. Xanthium spinosum

471. Calystegia sepium subsp. sepium

472. Calystegia soldanella

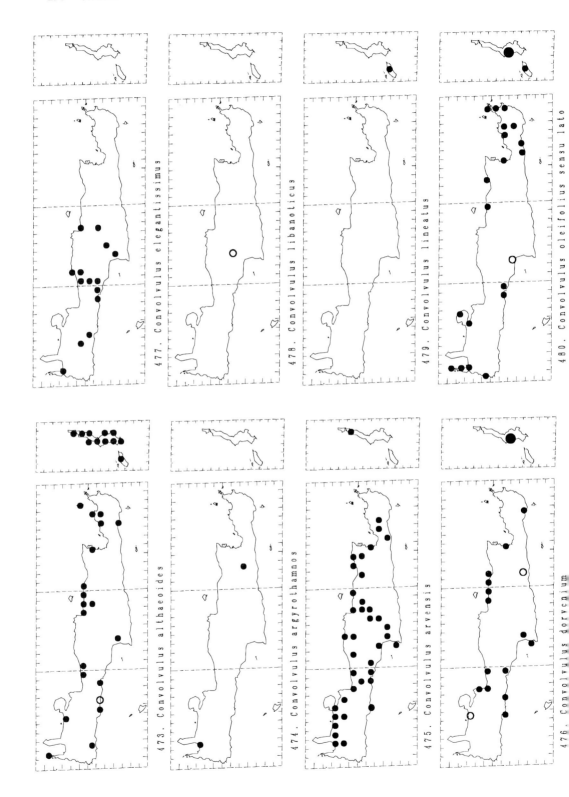

473. Convolvulus althaeoides

474. Convolvulus argyrothamnos

475. Convolvulus arvensis

476. Convolvulus dorycnium

477. Convolvulus elegantissimus

478. Convolvulus libanoticus

479. Convolvulus lineatus

480. Convolvulus oleifolius sensu lato

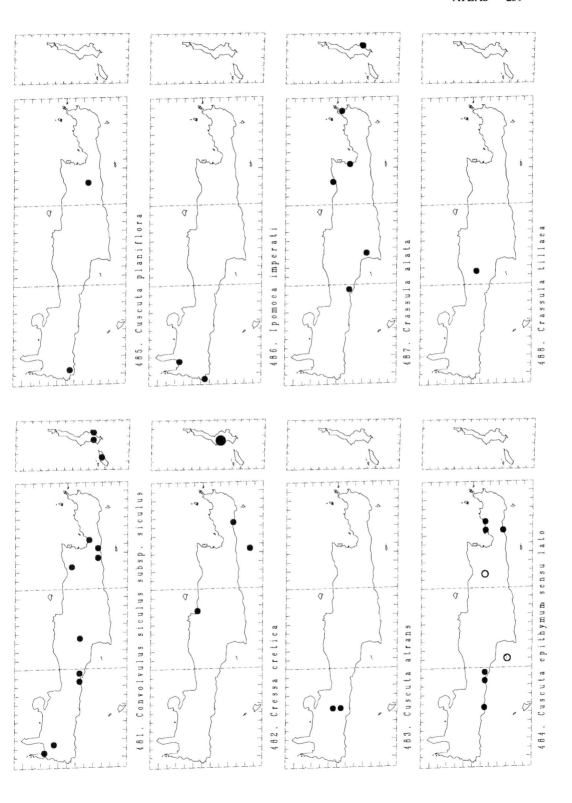

481. Convolvulus siculus subsp. siculus

482. Cressa cretica

483. Cuscuta atrans

484. Cuscuta epithymum sensu lato

485. Cuscuta planiflora

486. Ipomoea imperati

487. Crassula alata

488. Crassula tillaea

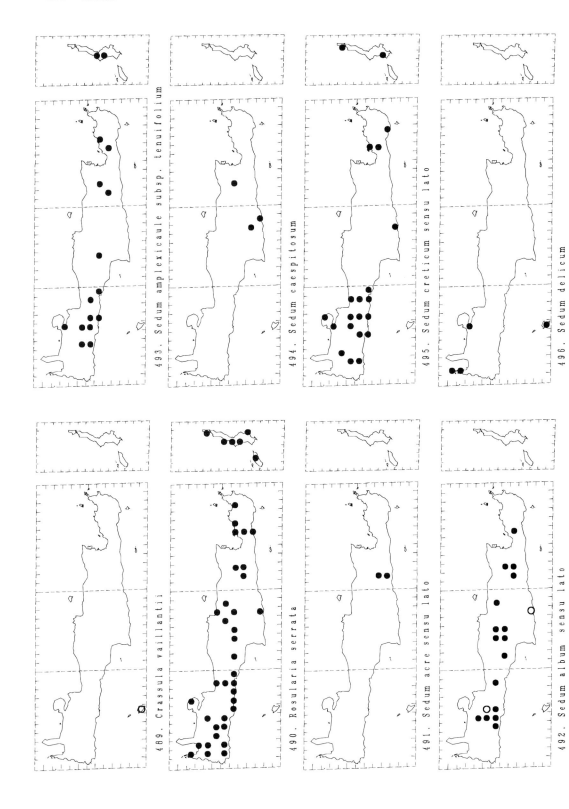

489. Crassula vaillantii

490. Rosularia serrata

491. Sedum acre sensu lato

492. Sedum album sensu lato

493. Sedum amplexicaule subsp. tenuifolium

494. Sedum caespitosum

495. Sedum creticum sensu lato

496. Sedum delicum

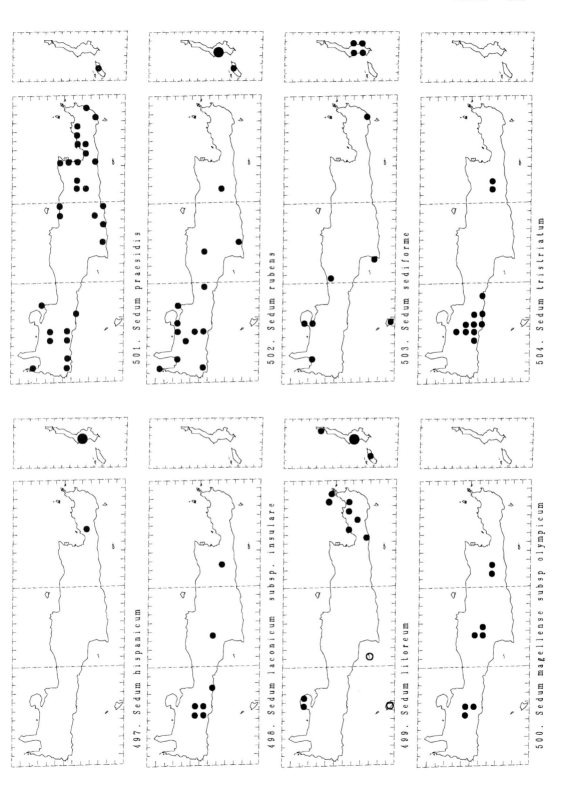

497. Sedum hispanicum

498. Sedum laconicum subsp. insulare

499. Sedum litoreum

500. Sedum magellense subsp olympicum

501. Sedum praesidis

502. Sedum rubens

503. Sedum sediforme

504. Sedum tristriatum

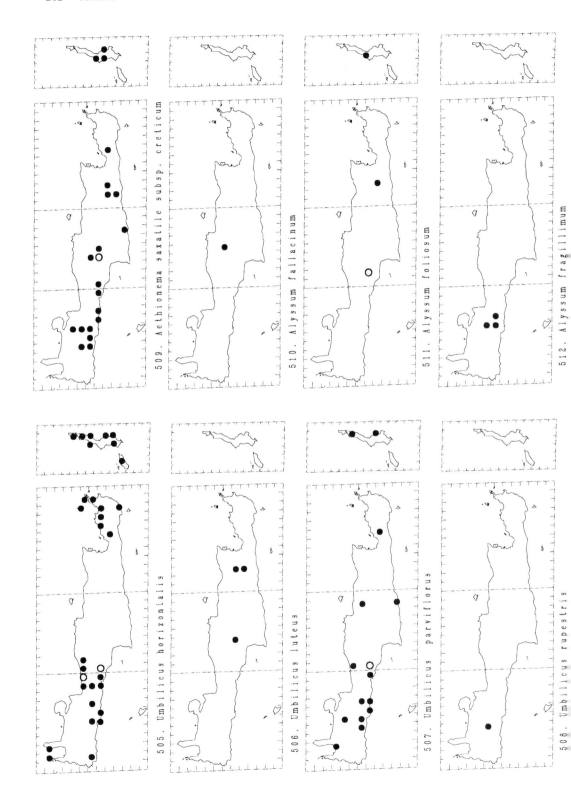

509. Aethionema saxatile subsp. creticum

510. Alyssum fallacinum

511. Alyssum foliosum

512. Alyssum fragillimum

505. Umbilicus horizontalis

506. Umbilicus luteus

507. Umbilicus parviflorus

508. Umbilicus rupestris

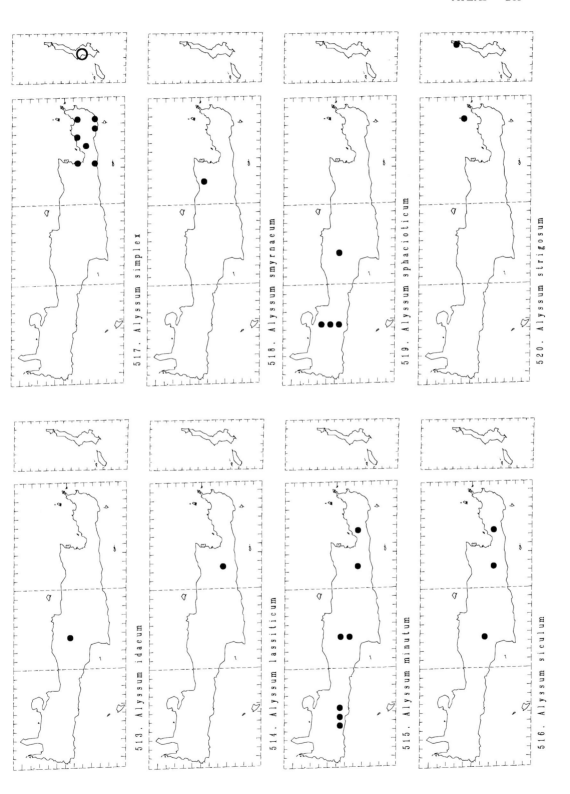

517. Alyssum simplex

518. Alyssum smyrnaeum

519. Alyssum sphaciolicum

520. Alyssum strigosum

513. Alyssum idaeum

514. Alyssum lassiticum

515. Alyssum minutum

516. Alyssum siculum

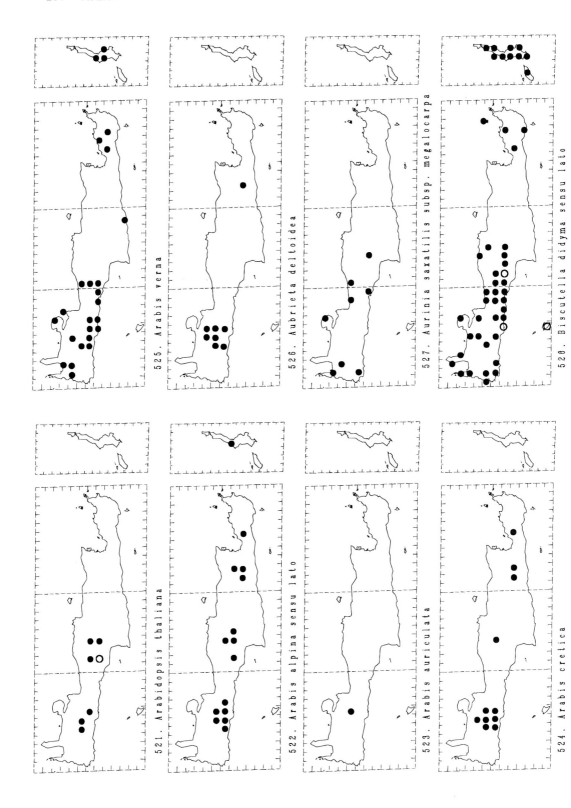

521. *Arabidopsis thaliana*

522. *Arabis alpina sensu lato*

523. *Arabis auriculata*

524. *Arabis cretica*

525. *Arabis verna*

526. *Aubrieta deltoidea*

527. *Aurinia saxatilis subsp. megalocarpa*

528. *Biscutella didyma sensu lato*

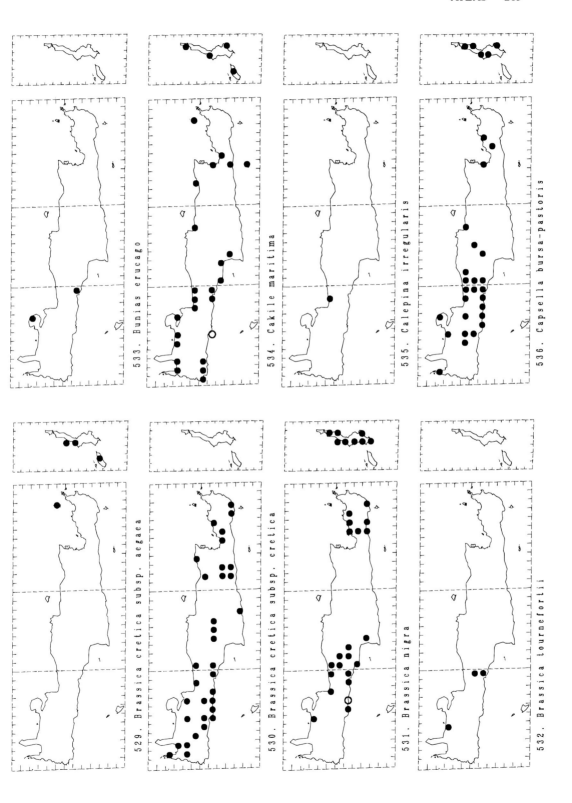

529. Brassica cretica subsp. aegaea

530. Brassica cretica subsp. cretica

531. Brassica nigra

532. Brassica tournefortii

533. Bunias erucago

534. Cakile maritima

535. Calepina irregularis

536. Capsella bursa-pastoris

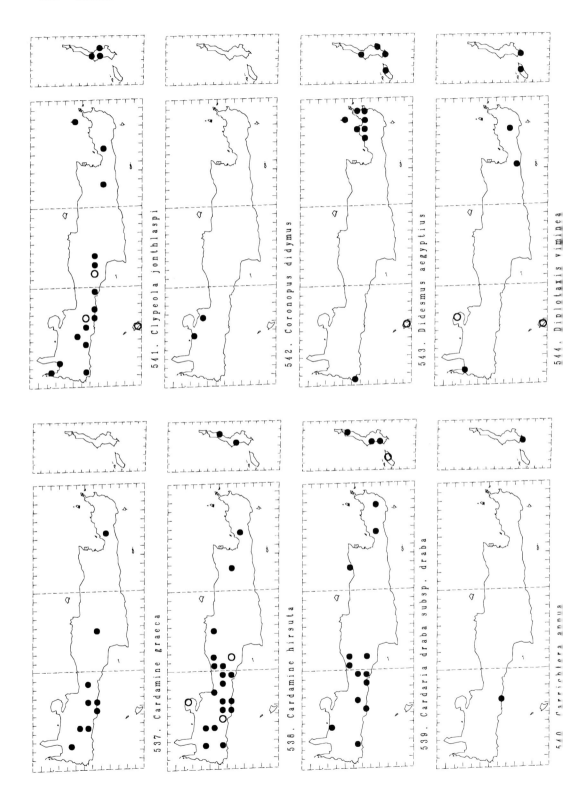

541. Clypeola jonthlaspi

542. Coronopus didymus

543. Didesmus aegyptius

544. Diplotaxis viminea

537. Cardamine graeca

538. Cardamine hirsuta

539. Cardaria draba subsp. draba

540. Carrichtera annua

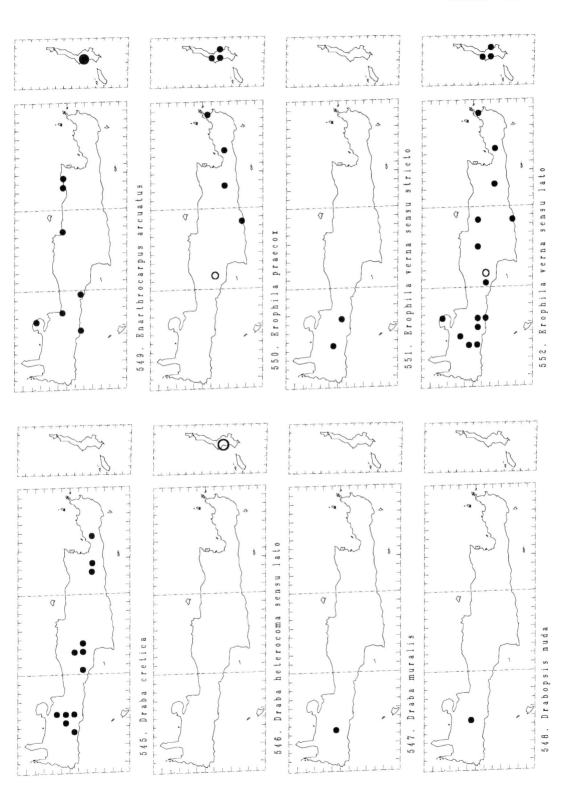

549. Enarthrocarpus arcuatus

550. Erophila praecox

551. Erophila verna sensu stricto

552. Erophila verna sensu lato

545. Draba cretica

546. Draba heterocoma sensu lato

547. Draba muralis

548. Drabopsis nuda

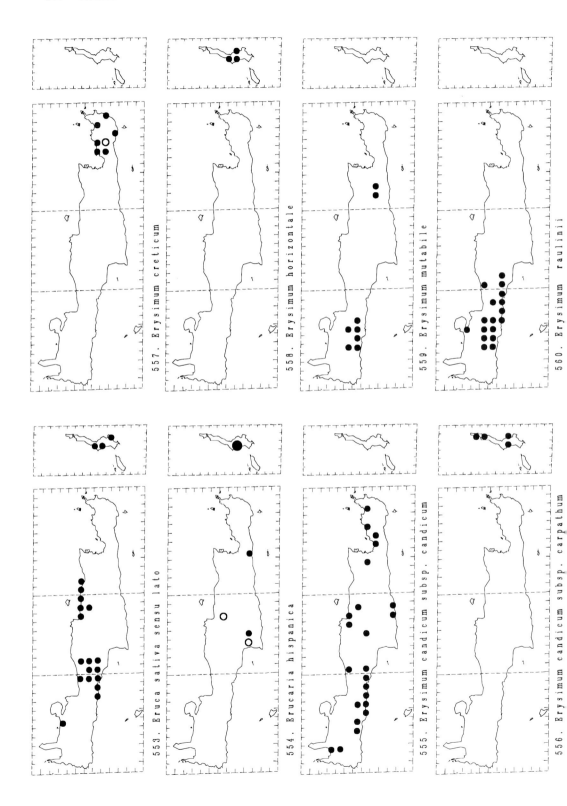

553. Eruca sativa sensu lato

554. Erucaria hispanica

555. Erysimum candicum subsp. candicum

556. Erysimum candicum subsp. carpathum

557. Erysimum creticum

558. Erysimum horizontale

559. Erysimum mutabile

560. Erysimum raulinii

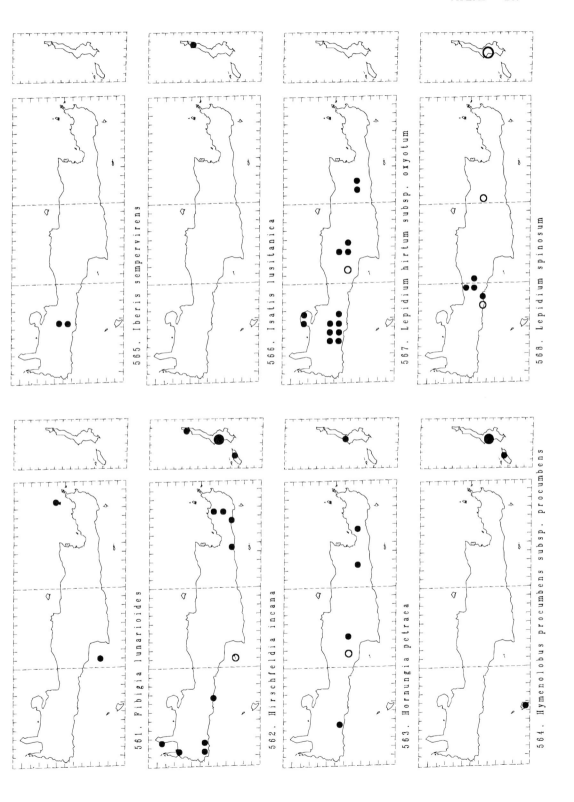

565. Iberis sempervirens

566. Isatis lusitanica

567. Lepidium hirtum subsp. oxyotum

568. Lepidium spinosum

561. Fibigia lunarioides

562. Hirschfeldia incana

563. Hornungia petraea

564. Hymenolobus procumbens subsp. procumbens

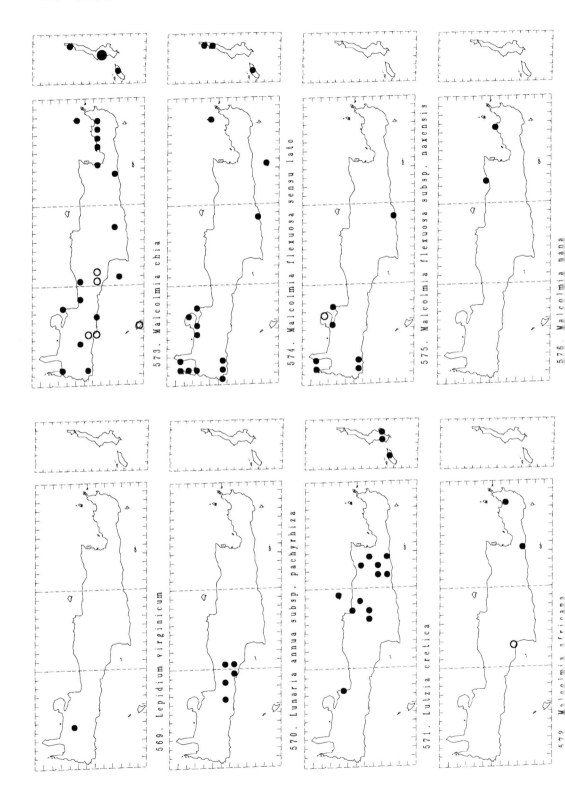

569. Lepidium virginicum

570. Lunaria annua subsp. pachyrhiza

571. Lutzia cretica

572. Malcolmia africana

573. Malcolmia chia

574. Malcolmia flexuosa sensu lato

575. Malcolmia flexuosa subsp. naxensis

576. Malcolmia nana

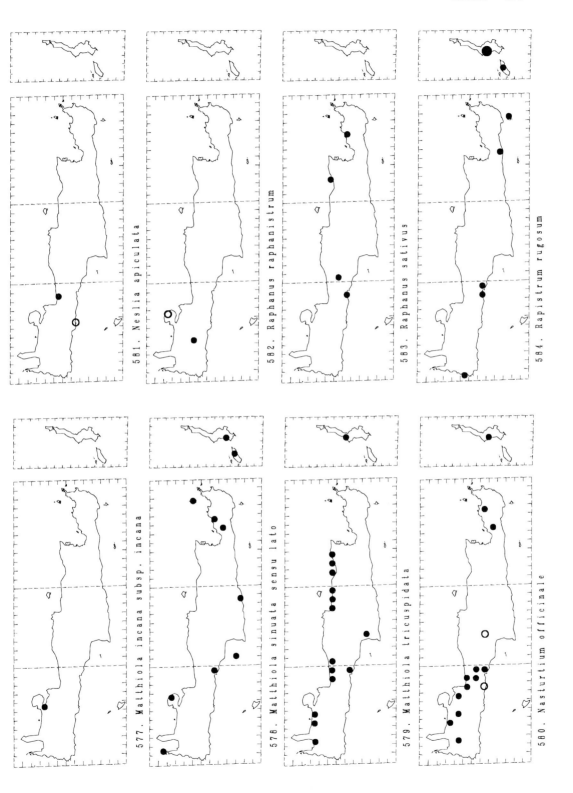

581. Neslia apiculata

582. Raphanus raphanistrum

583. Raphanus sativus

584. Rapistrum rugosum

577. Matthiola incana subsp. incana

578. Matthiola sinuata sensu lato

579. Matthiola tricuspidata

580. Nasturtium officinale

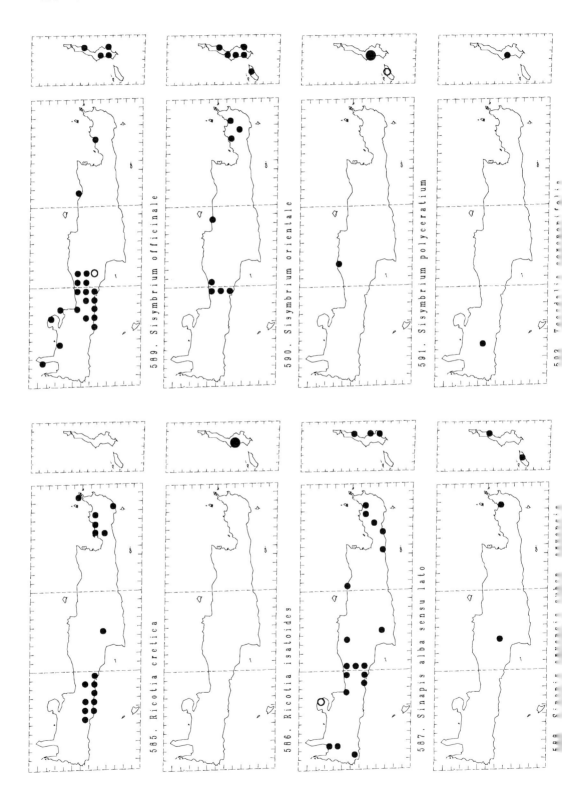

585. Ricotia cretica

586. Ricotia isatoides

587. Sinapis alba sensu lato

589. Sisymbrium officinale

590. Sisymbrium orientale

591. Sisymbrium polyceratium

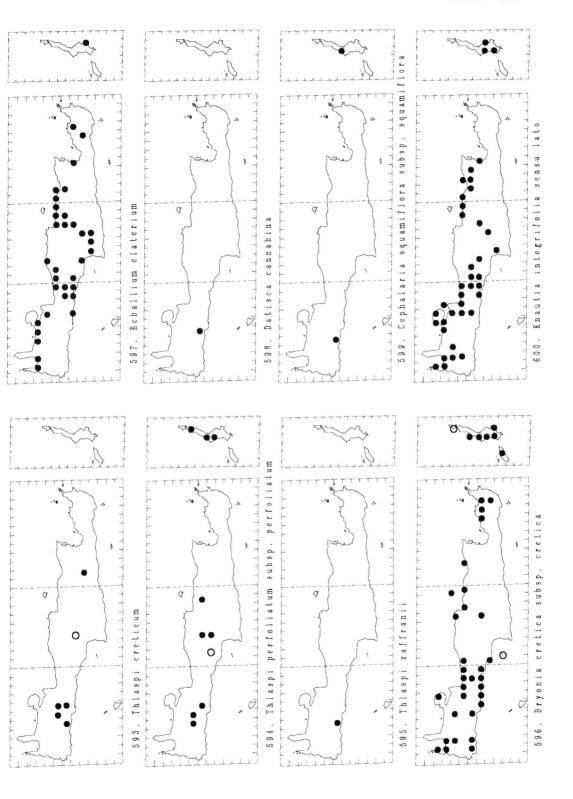

593. Thlaspi creticum

594. Thlaspi perfoliatum subsp. perfoliatum

595. Thlaspi zaffranii

596. Bryonia cretica subsp. cretica

597. Ecballium elaterium

598. Datisca cannabina

599. Cephalaria squamiflora subsp. squamiflora

600. Knautia integrifolia sensu lato

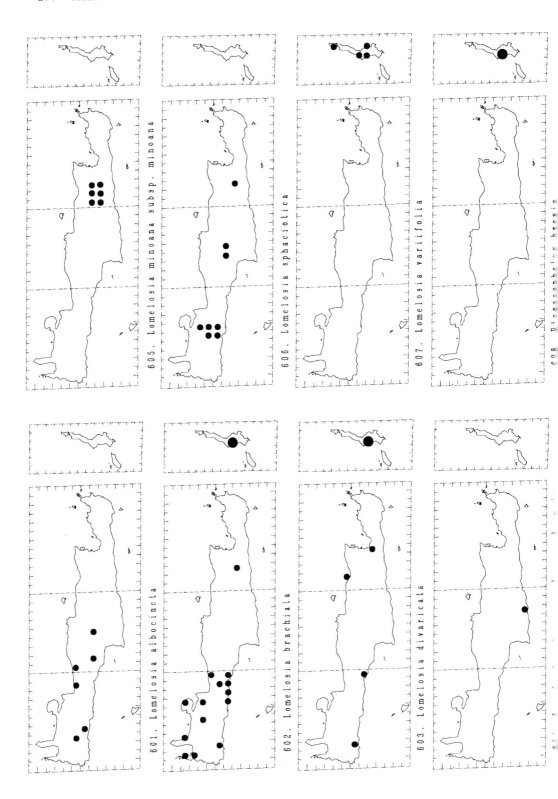

601. Lomelosia albocincta

602. Lomelosia brachiata

603. Lomelosia divaricata

605. Lomelosia minoana subsp. minoana

606. Lomelosia sphaciotica

607. Lomelosia variifolia

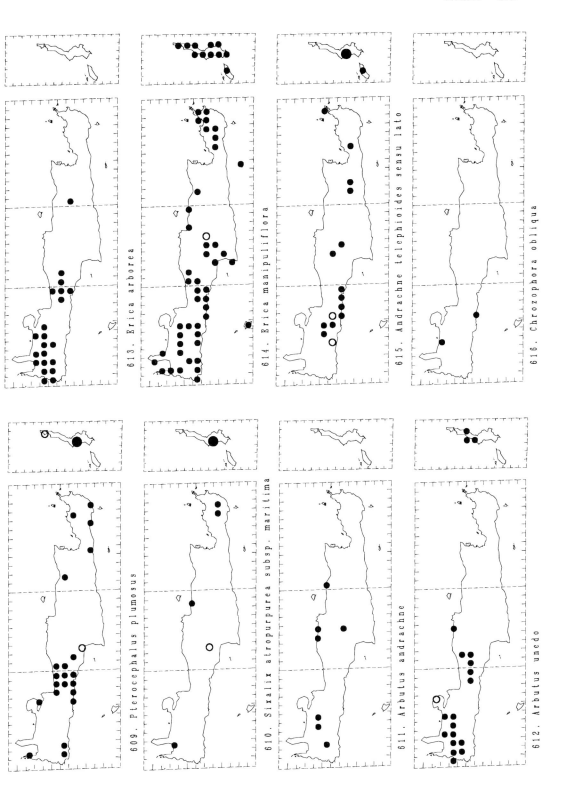

609. Pterocephalus plumosus

610. Sixalix atropurpurea subsp. maritima

611. Arbutus andrachne

612. Arbutus unedo

613. Erica arborea

614. Erica manipuliflora

615. Andrachne telephioides sensu lato

616. Chrozophora obliqua

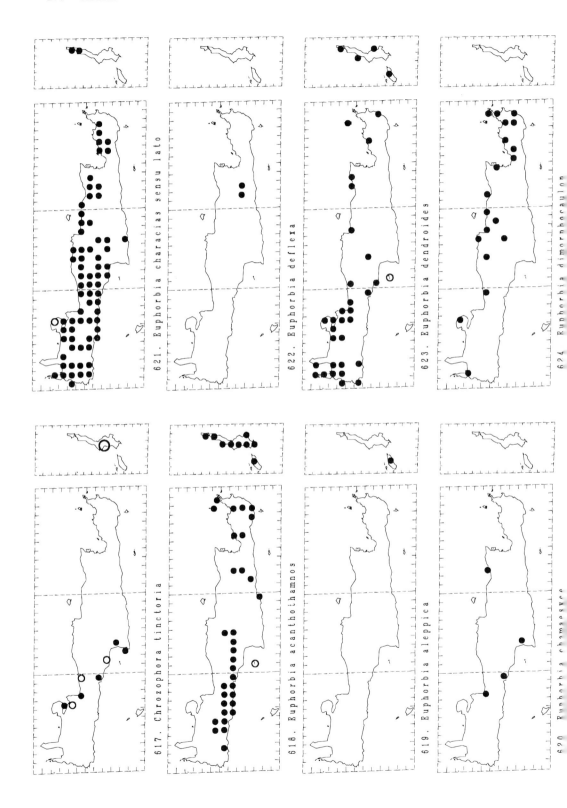

621. Euphorbia characias sensu lato

622. Euphorbia deflexa

623. Euphorbia dendroides

624. Euphorbia dimorphocaulon

617. Chrozophora tinctoria

618. Euphorbia acanthothamnos

619. Euphorbia aleppica

620. Euphorbia chamaesyce

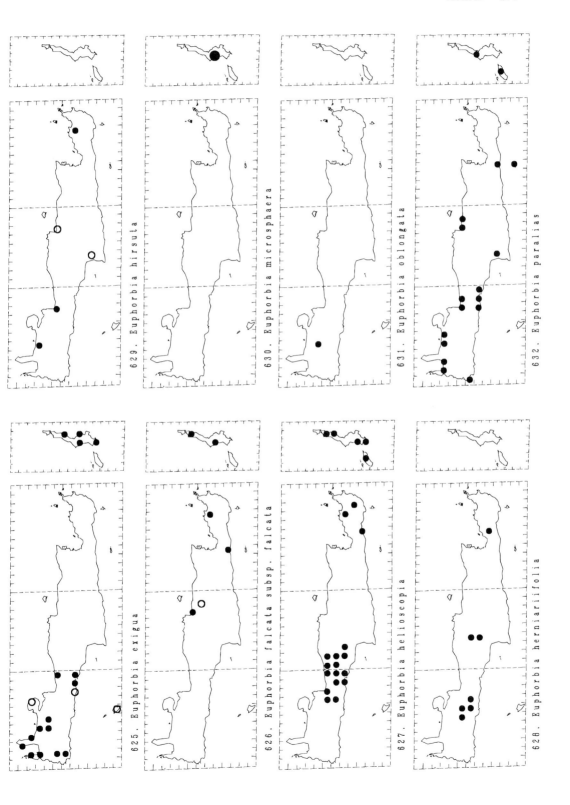

625. Euphorbia exigua

626. Euphorbia falcata subsp. falcata

627. Euphorbia helioscopia

628. Euphorbia herniariifolia

629. Euphorbia hirsuta

630. Euphorbia microsphaera

631. Euphorbia oblongata

632. Euphorbia paralias

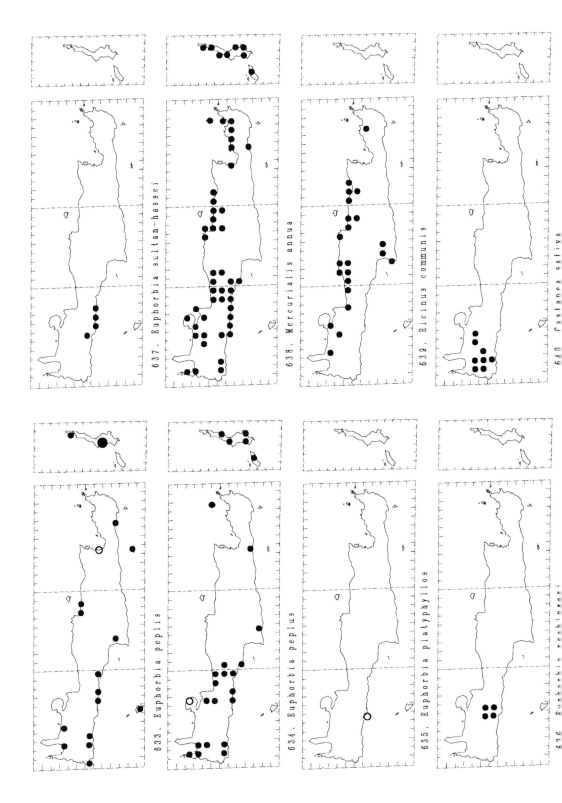

637. Euphorbia sultan-hassei

638. Mercurialis annua

639. Ricinus communis

640. Castanea sativa

633. Euphorbia peplis

634. Euphorbia peplus

635. Euphorbia platyphyllos

636. Euphorbia reshingeri

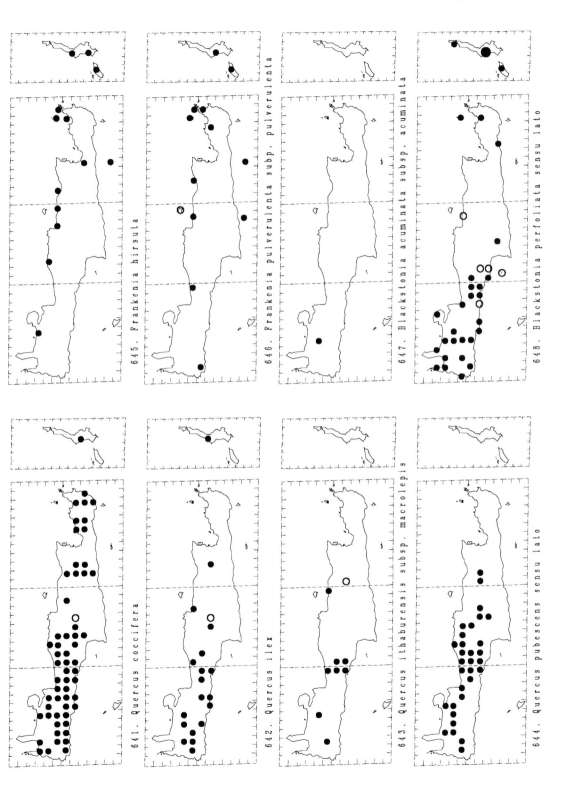

641. Quercus coccifera

642. Quercus ilex

643. Quercus ithaburensis subsp. macrolepis

644. Quercus pubescens sensu lato

645. Frankenia hirsuta

646. Frankenia pulverulenta subsp. pulverulenta

647. Blackstonia acuminata subsp. acuminata

648. Blackstonia perfoliata sensu lato

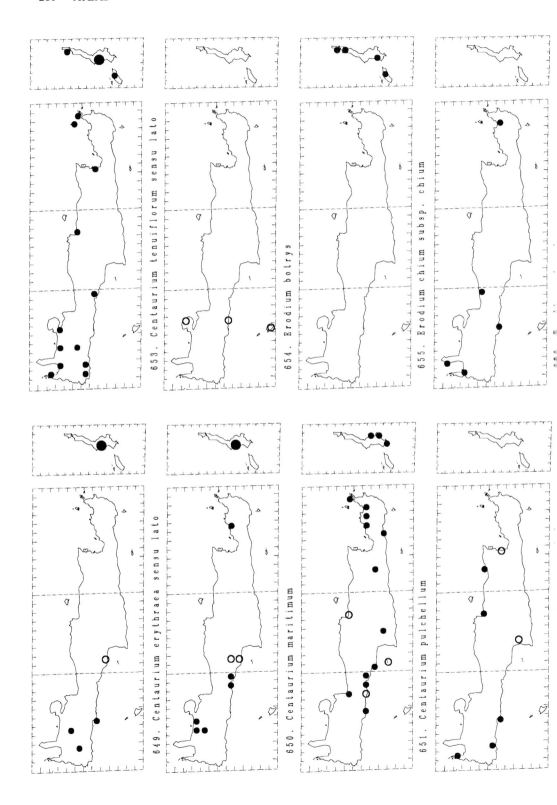

649. Centaurium erythraea sensu lato

650. Centaurium maritimum

651. Centaurium pulchellum

653. Centaurium tenuiflorum sensu lato

654. Erodium botrys

655. Erodium chium subsp. chium

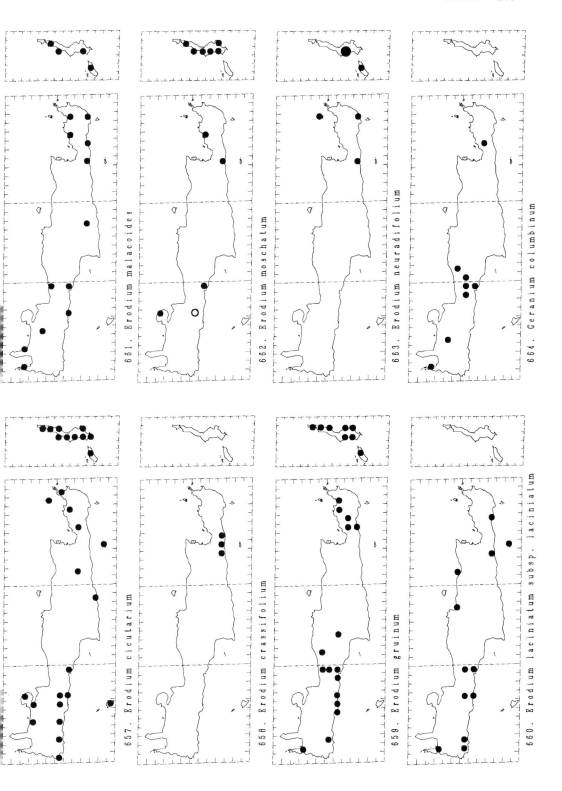

661. Erodium malacoides

662. Erodium moschatum

663. Erodium neuradifolium

664. Geranium columbinum

657. Erodium cicutarium

658. Erodium crassifolium

659. Erodium gruinum

660. Erodium laciniatum subsp. laciniatum

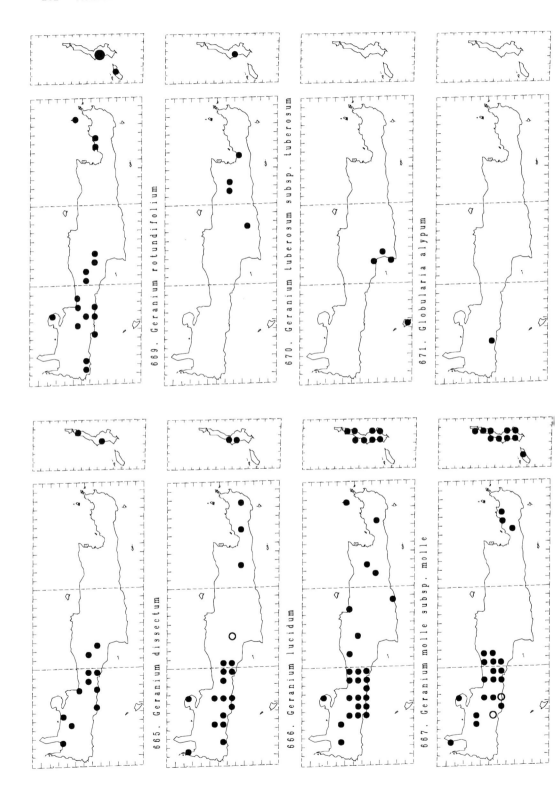

665. Geranium dissectum

666. Geranium lucidum

667. Geranium molle subsp. molle

669. Geranium rotundifolium

670. Geranium tuberosum subsp. tuberosum

671. Globularia alypum

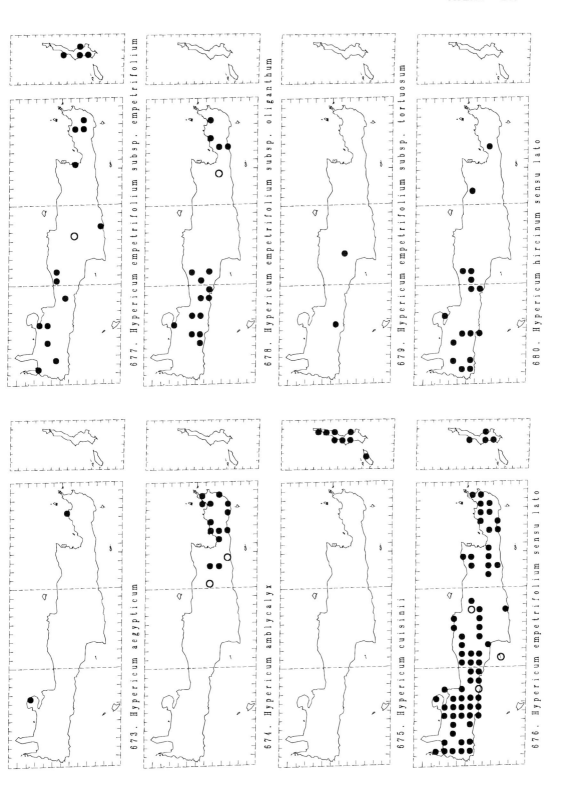

673. *Hypericum aegypticum*

674. *Hypericum amblycalyx*

675. *Hypericum cuisinii*

676. *Hypericum empetrifolium sensu lato*

677. *Hypericum empetrifolium subsp. empetrifolium*

678. *Hypericum empetrifolium subsp. oliganthum*

679. *Hypericum empetrifolium subsp. tortuosum*

680. *Hypericum hircinum sensu lato*

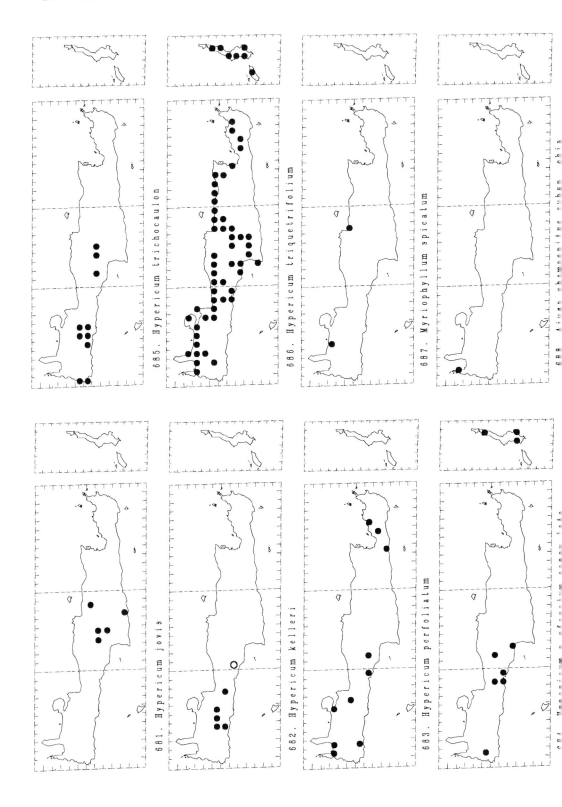

685. Hypericum trichocaulon

686. Hypericum triquetrifolium

687. Myriophyllum spicatum

681. Hypericum jovis

682. Hypericum kelleri

683. Hypericum perfoliatum

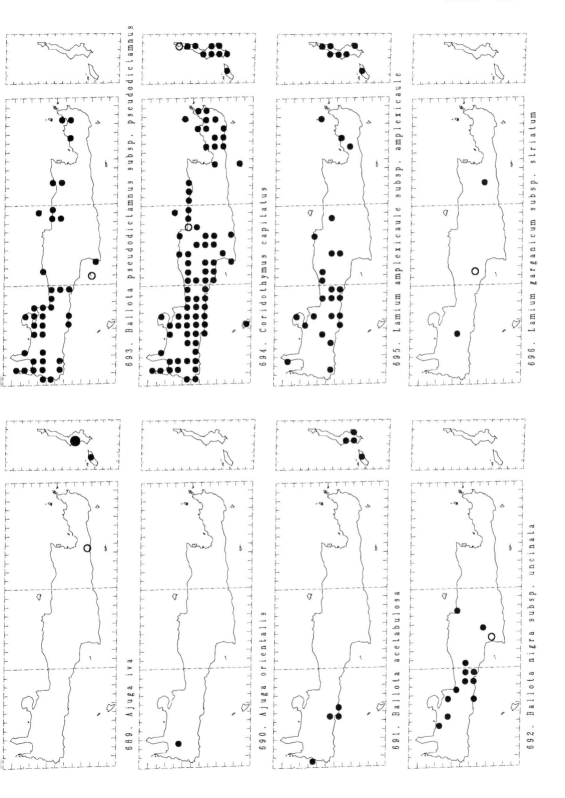

689. Ajuga iva

690. Ajuga orientalis

691. Ballota acetabulosa

692. Ballota nigra subsp. uncinata

693. Ballota pseudodictamnus subsp. pseudodictamnus

694. Coridothymus capitatus

695. Lamium amplexicaule subsp. amplexicaule

696. Lamium garganicum subsp. striatum

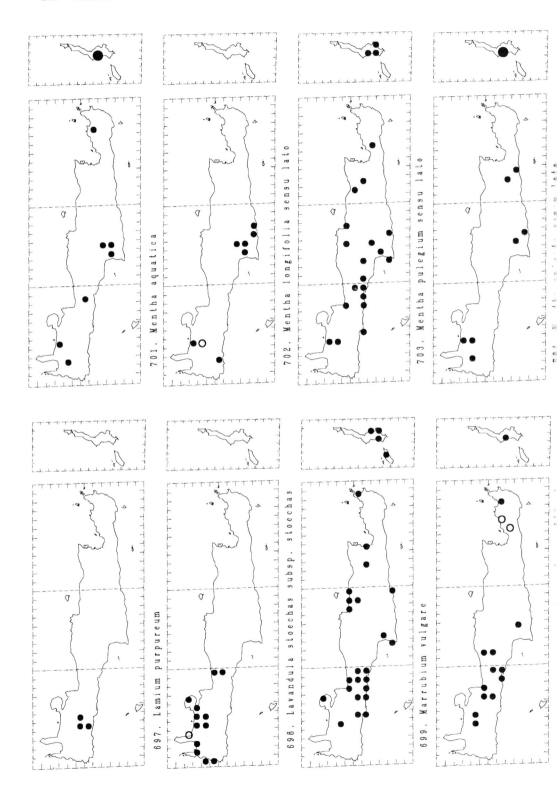

697. Lamium purpureum

698. Lavandula stoechas subsp. stoechas

699. Marrubium vulgare

701. Mentha aquatica

702. Mentha longifolia sensu lato

703. Mentha pulegium sensu lato

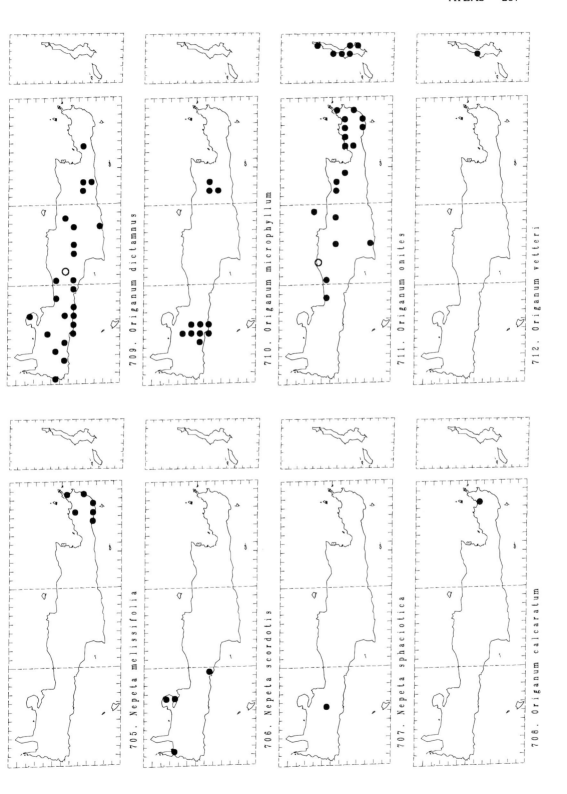

705. Nepeta melissifolia

706. Nepeta scordotis

707. Nepeta sphaciotica

708. Origanum calcaratum

709. Origanum dictamnus

710. Origanum microphyllum

711. Origanum onites

712. Origanum vetteri

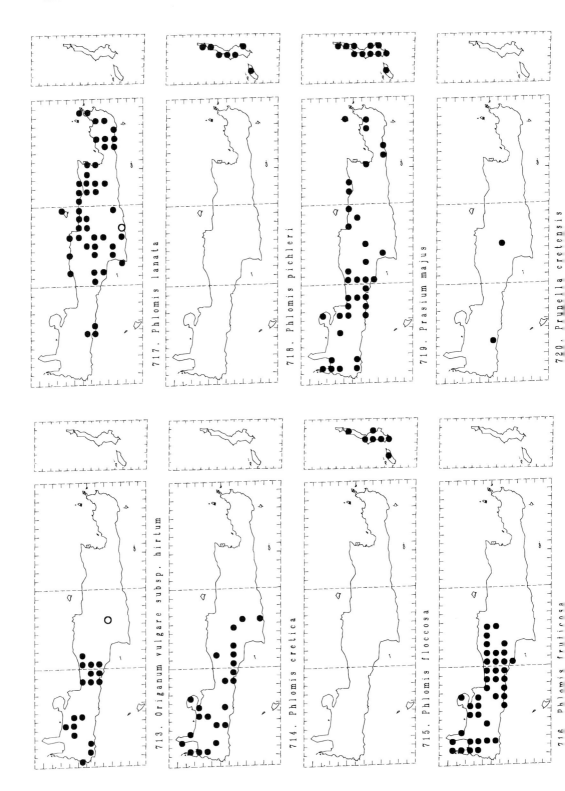

717. Phlomis lanata

718. Phlomis pichleri

719. Prasium majus

720. Prunella cretensis

713. Origanum vulgare subsp. hirtum

714. Phlomis cretica

715. Phlomis floccosa

716. Phlomis fruticosa

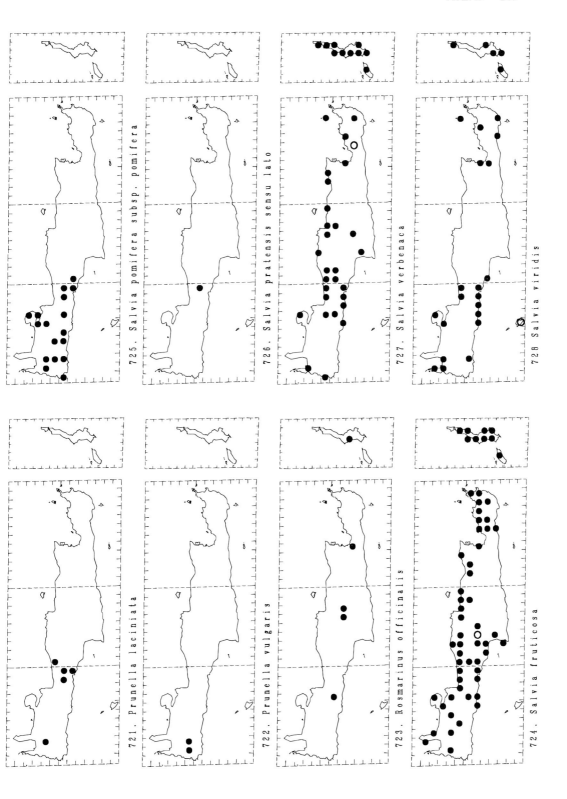

721. Prunella laciniata

722. Prunella vulgaris

723. Rosmarinus officinalis

724. Salvia fruticosa

725. Salvia pomifera subsp. pomifera

726. Salvia pratensis sensu lato

727. Salvia verbenaca

728. Salvia viridis

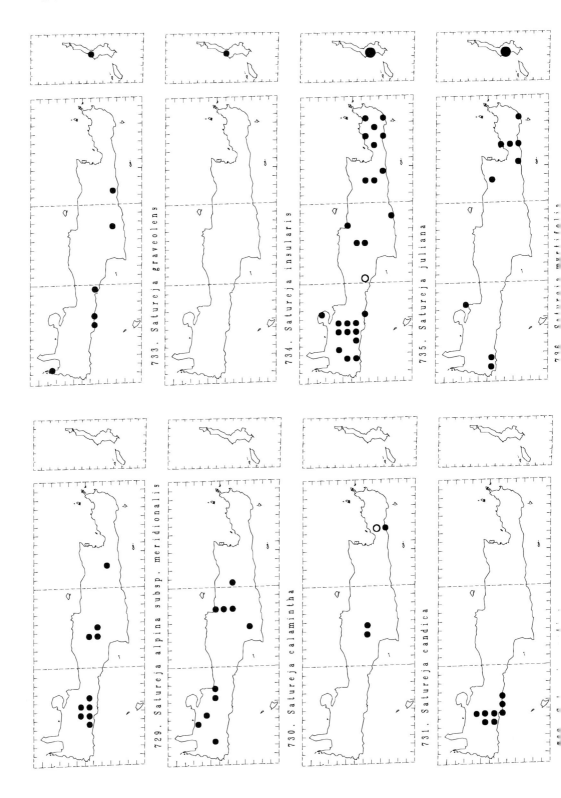

729. Satureja alpina subsp. meridionalis

730. Satureja calamintha

731. Satureja candica

733. Satureja graveolens

734. Satureja insularis

735. Satureja juliana

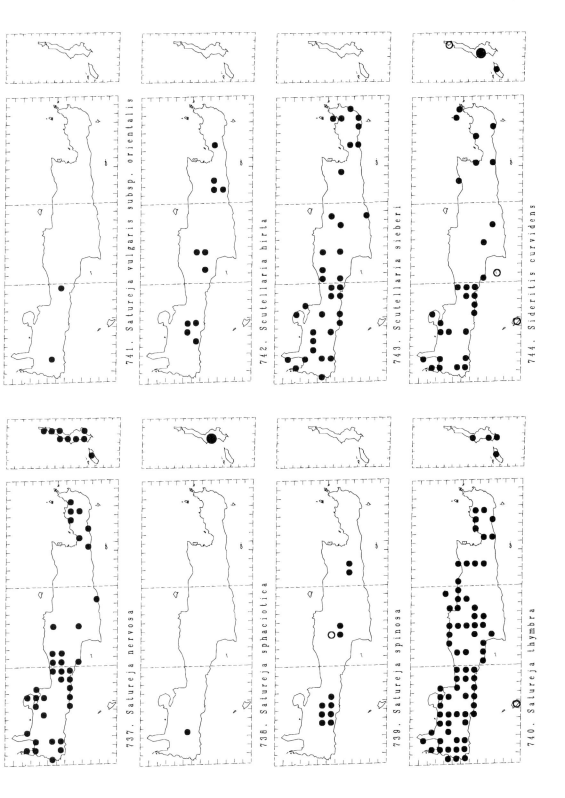

737. Satureja nervosa

738. Satureja sphaciotica

739. Satureja spinosa

740. Satureja thymbra

741. Satureja vulgaris subsp. orientalis

742. Scutellaria hirta

743. Scutellaria sieberi

744. Sideritis curvidens

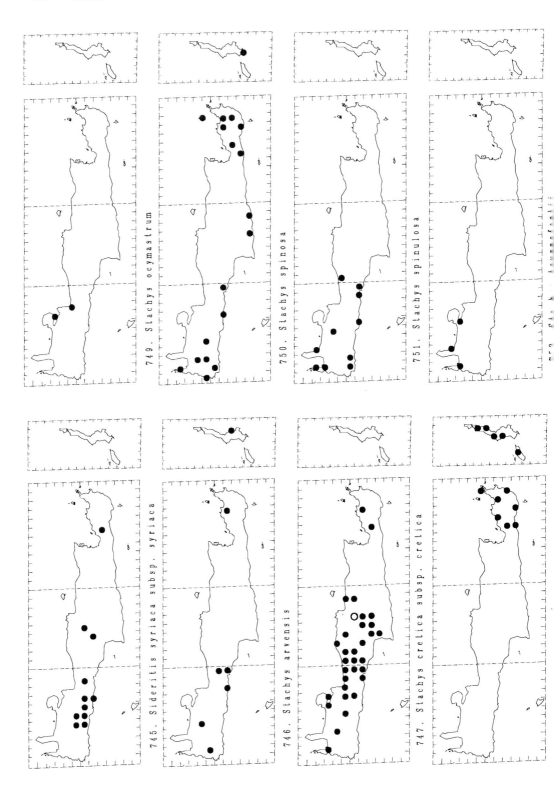

749. Stachys ocymastrum

750. Stachys spinosa

751. Stachys spinulosa

745. Sideritis syriaca subsp. syriaca

746. Stachys arvensis

747. Stachys cretica subsp. cretica

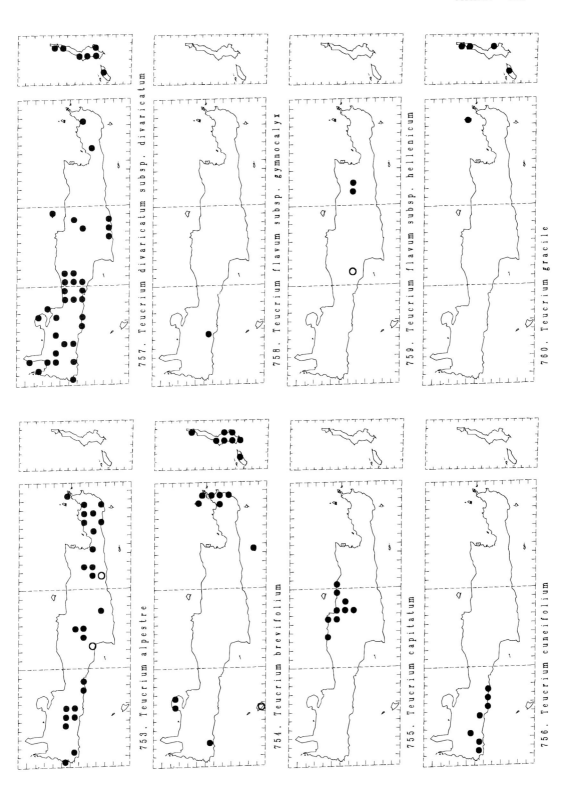

757. Teucrium divaricatum subsp. divaricatum

758. Teucrium flavum subsp. gymnocalyx

759. Teucrium flavum subsp. hellenicum

760. Teucrium gracile

753. Teucrium alpestre

754. Teucrium brevifolium

755. Teucrium capitatum

756. Teucrium cuneifolium

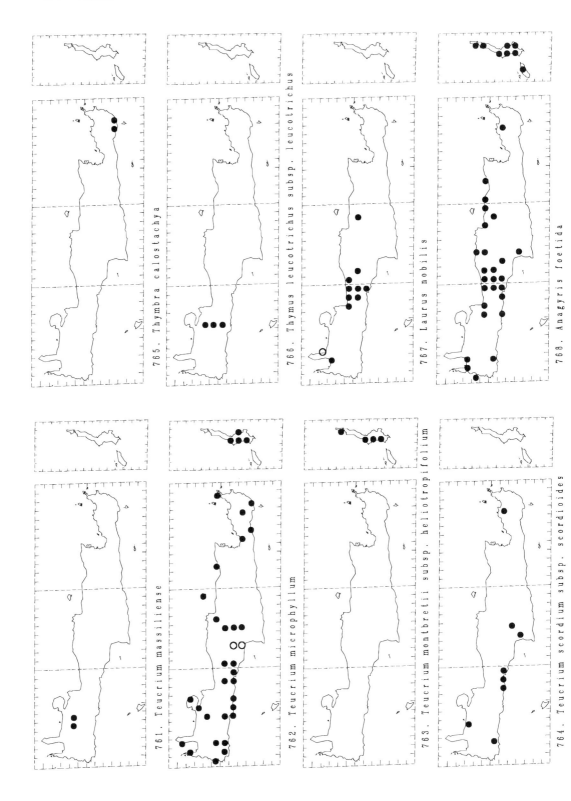

761. Teucrium massiliense

762. Teucrium microphyllum

763. Teucrium montbretii subsp. heliotropifolium

764. Teucrium scordium subsp. scordioides

765. Thymbra calostachya

766. Thymus leucotrichus subsp. leucotrichus

767. Laurus nobilis

768. Anagyris foetida

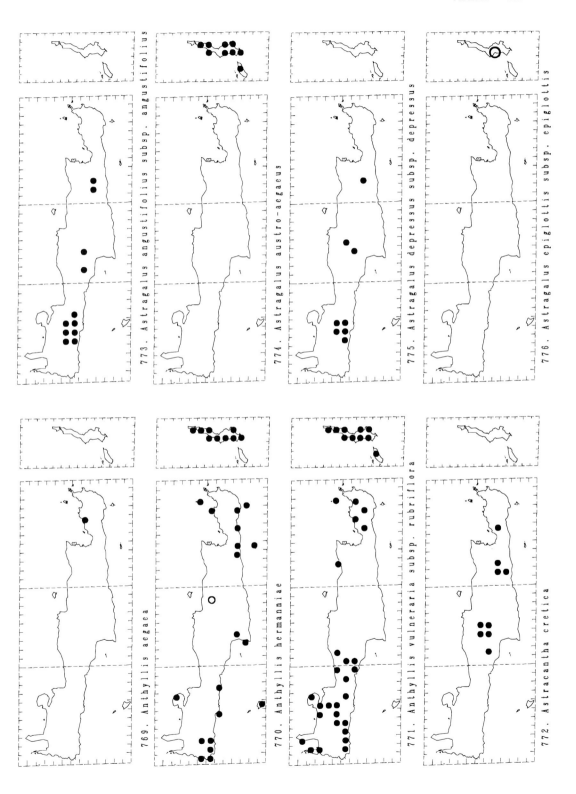

769. Anthyllis aegaea

770. Anthyllis hermanniae

771. Anthyllis vulneraria subsp. rubriflora

772. Astracantha cretica

773. Astragalus angustifolius subsp. angustifolius

774. Astragalus austro-aegaeus

775. Astragalus depressus subsp. depressus

776. Astragalus epiglottis subsp. epiglottis

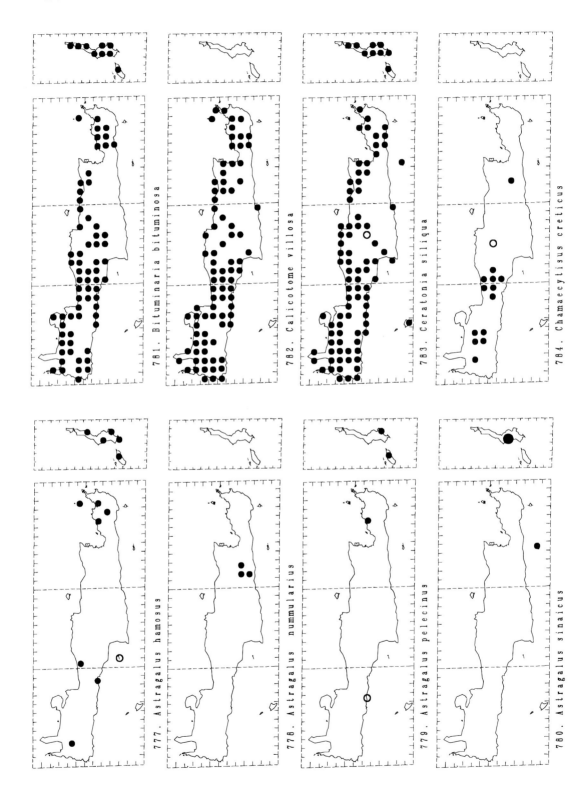

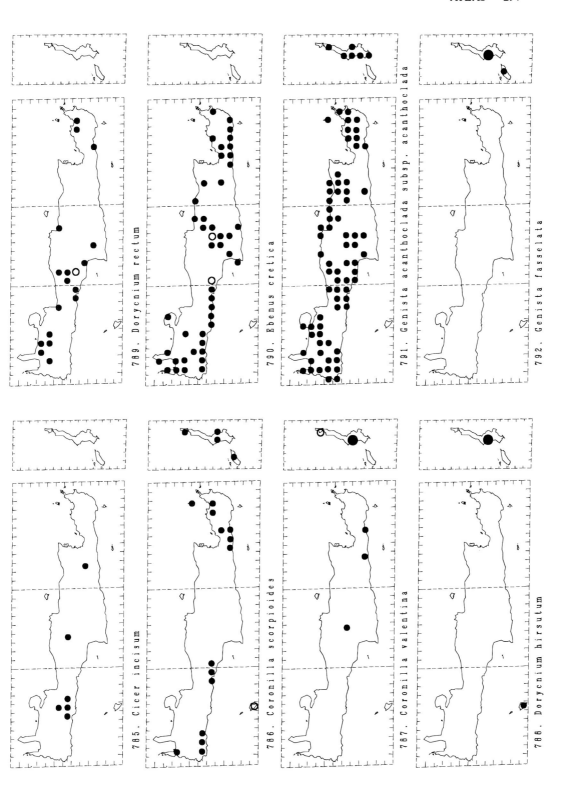

789 . Dorycnium rectum

790 . Ebenus cretica

791 . Genista acanthoclada subsp. acanthoclada

792 . Genista fasselata

785 . Cicer incisum

786 . Coronilla scorpioides

787 . Coronilla valentina

788 . Dorycnium hirsutum

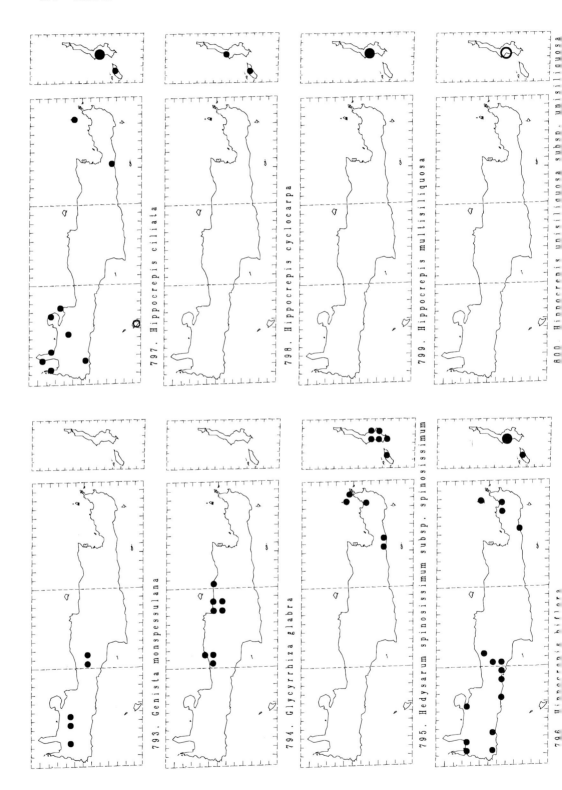

793. Genista monspessulana

794. Glycyrrhiza glabra

795. Hedysarum spinosissimum subsp. spinosissimum

796. Hippocrepis biflora

797. Hippocrepis ciliata

798. Hippocrepis cyclocarpa

799. Hippocrepis multisiliquosa

800. Hippocrepis unisiliquosa subsp. unisiliquosa

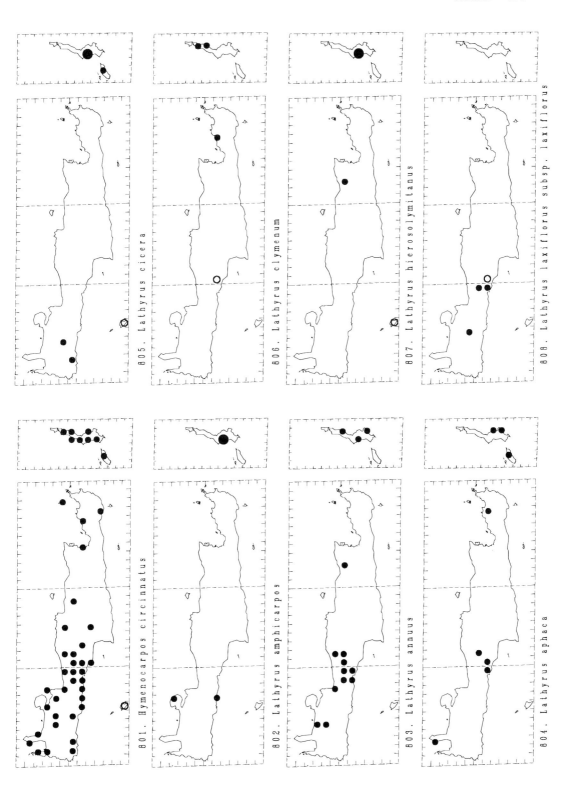

801. Hymenocarpos circinnatus

802. Lathyrus amphicarpos

803. Lathyrus annuus

804. Lathyrus aphaca

805. Lathyrus cicera

806. Lathyrus clymenum

807. Lathyrus hierosolymitanus

808. Lathyrus laxiflorus subsp. laxiflorus

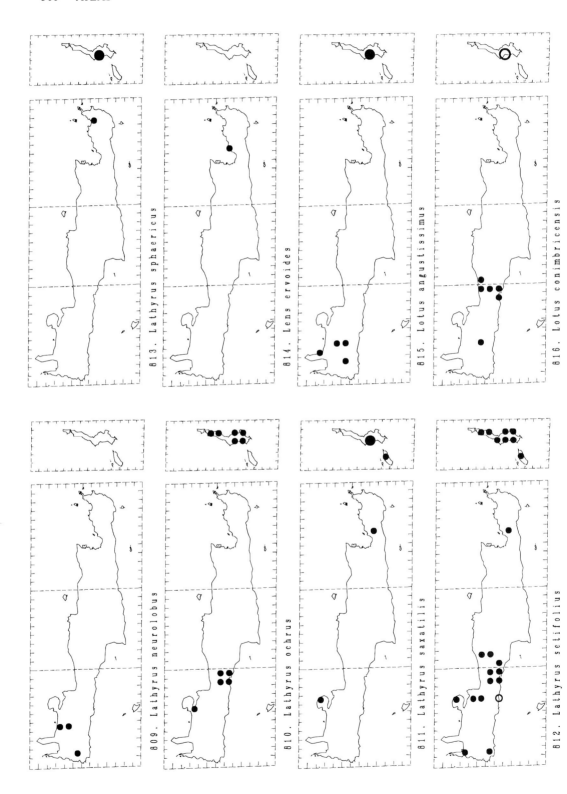

809. Lathyrus neurolobus

810. Lathyrus ochrus

811. Lathyrus saxatilis

812. Lathyrus setifolius

813. Lathyrus sphaericus

814. Lens ervoides

815. Lotus angustissimus

816. Lotus conimbricensis

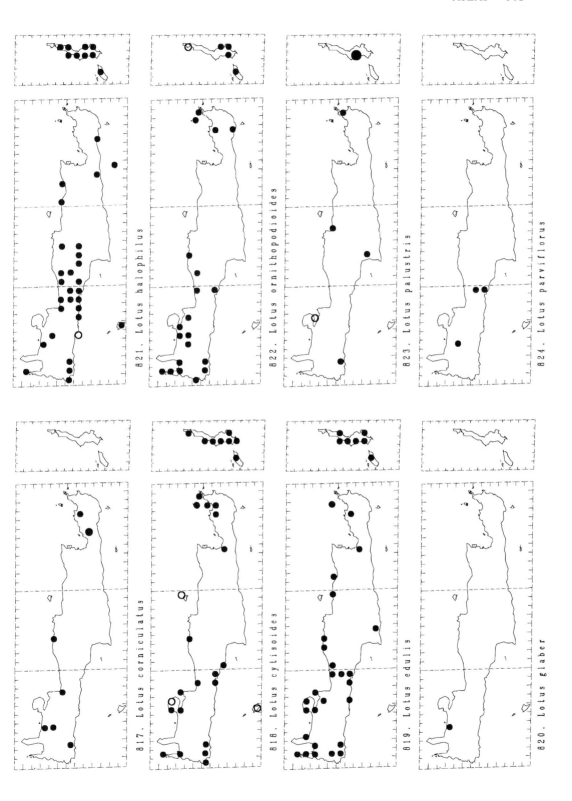

817. Lotus corniculatus

818. Lotus cytisoides

819. Lotus edulis

820. Lotus glaber

821. Lotus halophilus

822. Lotus ornithopodioides

823. Lotus palustris

824. Lotus parviflorus

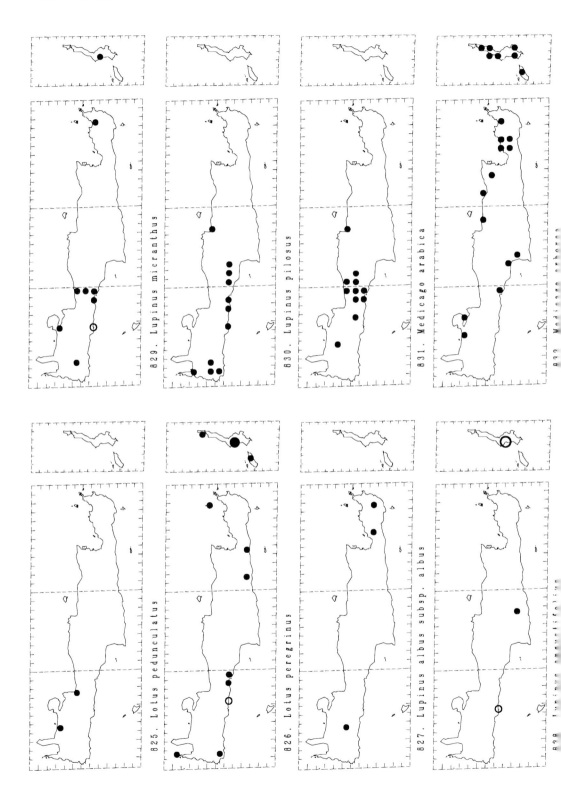

825. Lotus pedunculatus

826. Lotus peregrinus

827. Lupinus albus subsp. albus

829. Lupinus micranthus

830. Lupinus pilosus

831. Medicago arabica

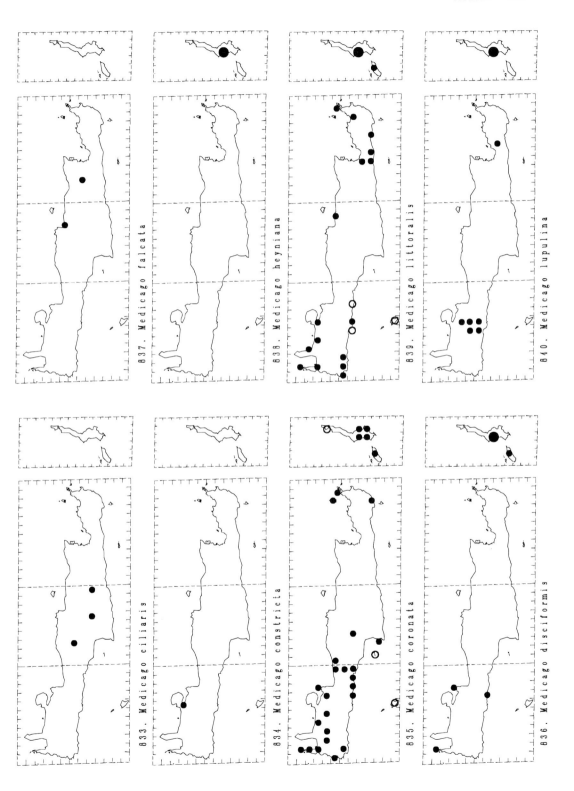

833. Medicago ciliaris

834. Medicago constricta

835. Medicago coronata

836. Medicago disciformis

837. Medicago falcata

838. Medicago heyniana

839. Medicago littoralis

840. Medicago lupulina

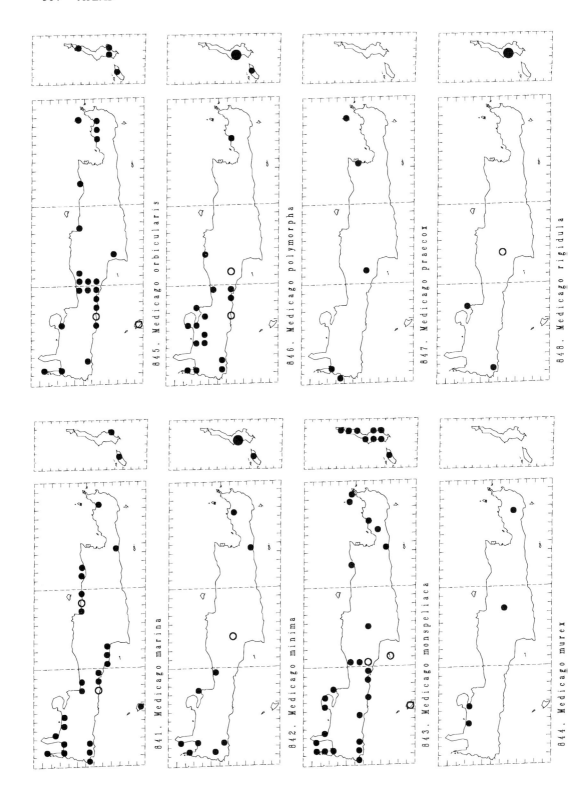

845. Medicago orbicularis

846. Medicago polymorpha

847. Medicago praecox

848. Medicago rigidula

841. Medicago marina

842. Medicago minima

843. Medicago monspeliaca

844. Medicago murex

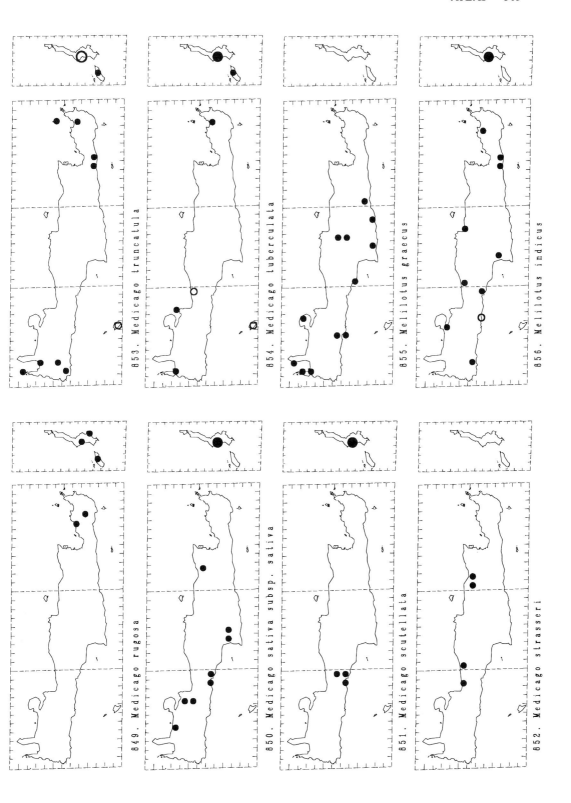

849. Medicago rugosa

850. Medicago sativa subsp. sativa

851. Medicago scutellata

852. Medicago strasseri

853. Medicago truncatula

854. Medicago tuberculata

855. Melilotus graecus

856. Melilotus indicus

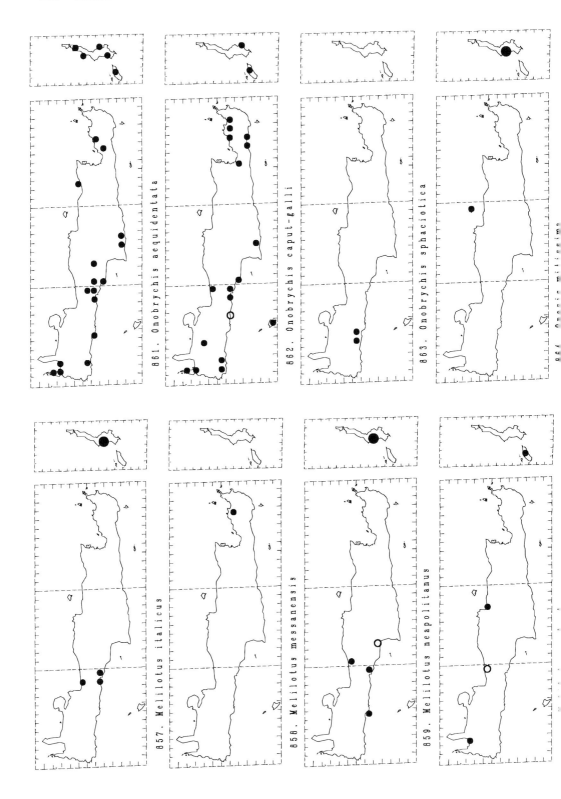

861. Onobrychis aequidentata

862. Onobrychis caput-galli

863. Onobrychis sphaciotica

857. Melilotus italicus

858. Melilotus messanensis

859. Melilotus neapolitanus

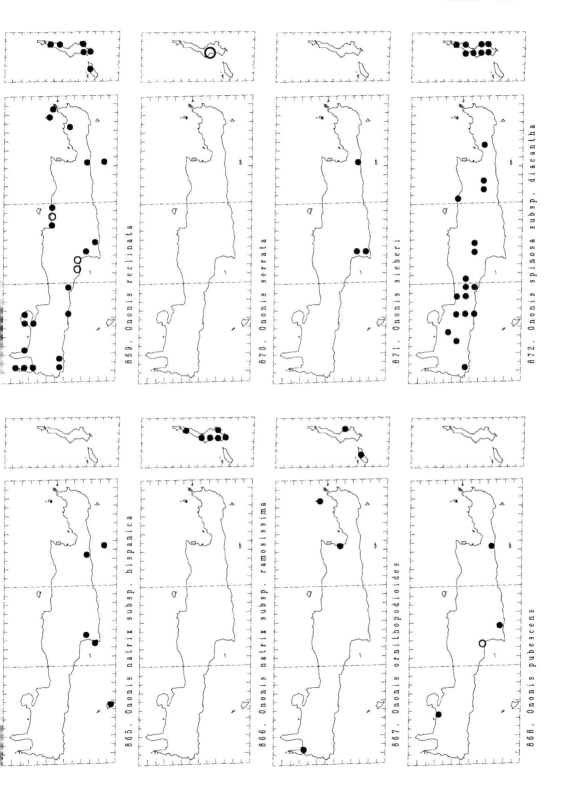

865. Ononis natrix subsp. hispanica

866. Ononis natrix subsp. ramosissima

867. Ononis ornithopodioides

868. Ononis pubescens

869. Ononis reclinata

870. Ononis serrata

871. Ononis sieberi

872. Ononis spinosa subsp. diacantha

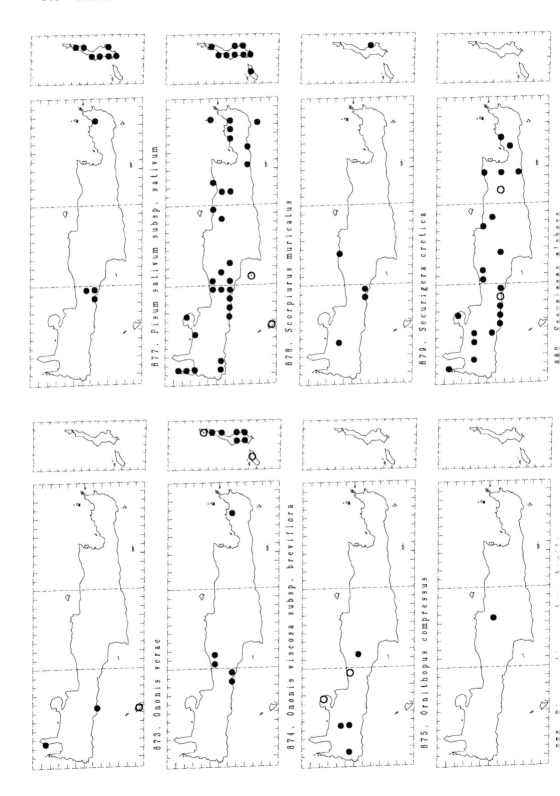

873. Ononis verae

874. Ononis viscosa subsp. breviflora

875. Ornithopus compressus

877. Pisum sativum subsp. sativum

878. Scorpiurus muricatus

879. Securigera cretica

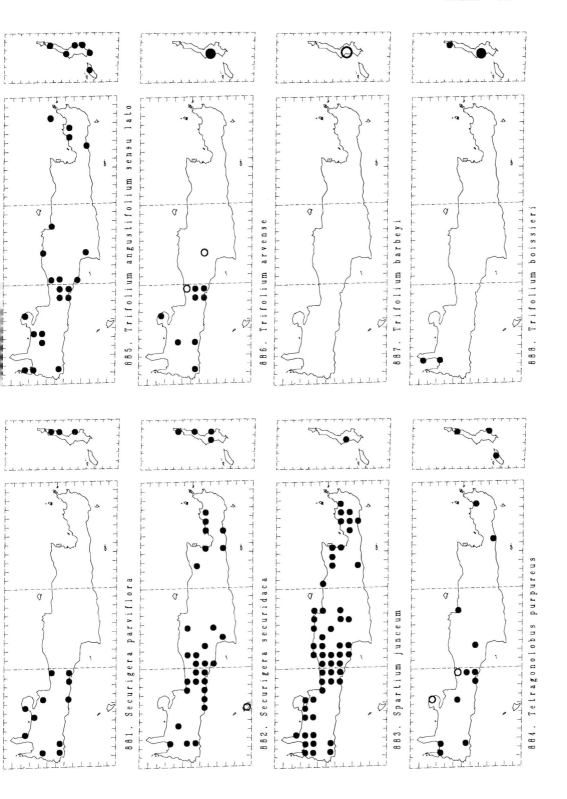

881. Securigera parviflora

882. Securigera securidaca

883. Spartium junceum

884. Tetragonolobus purpureus

885. Trifolium angustifolium sensu lato

886. Trifolium arvense

887. Trifolium barbeyi

888. Trifolium boissieri

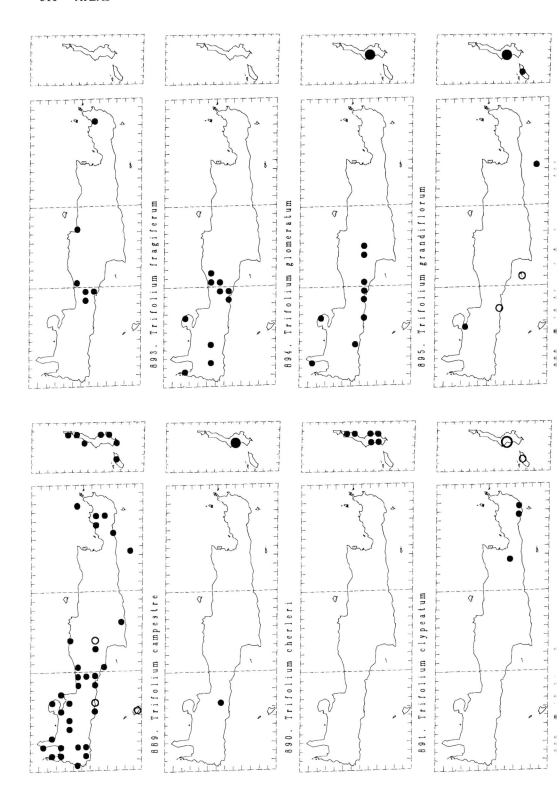

893. Trifolium fragiferum

894. Trifolium glomeratum

895. Trifolium grandiflorum

889. Trifolium campestre

890. Trifolium cherleri

891. Trifolium clypeatum

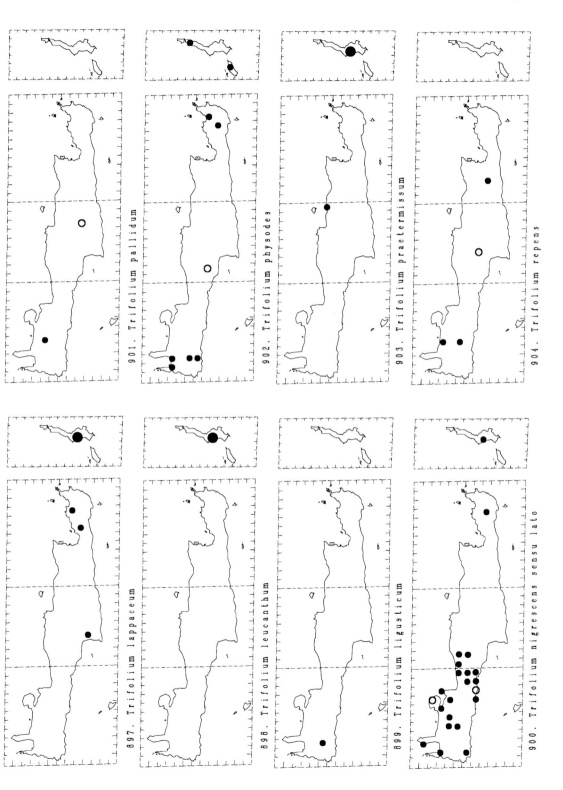

897. Trifolium lappaceum

898. Trifolium leucanthum

899. Trifolium ligusticum

900. Trifolium nigrescens sensu lato

901. Trifolium pallidum

902. Trifolium physodes

903. Trifolium praetermissum

904. Trifolium repens

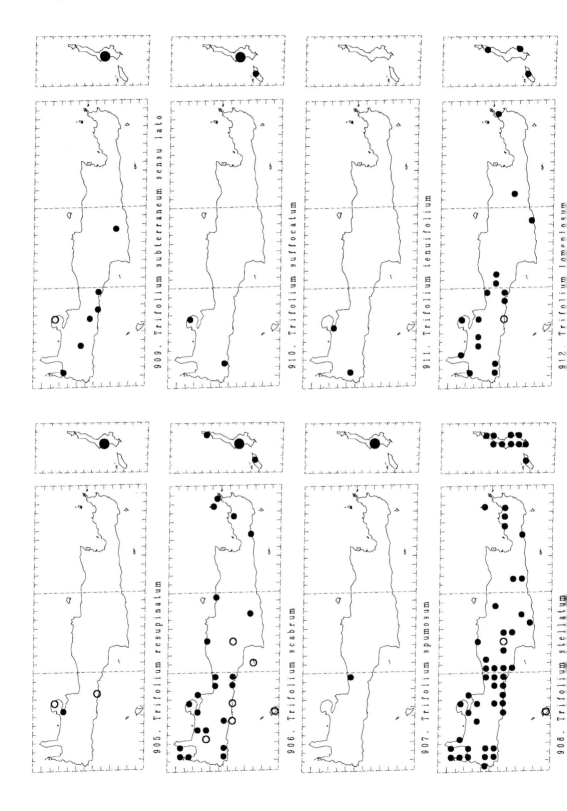

909. Trifolium subterraneum sensu lato

910. Trifolium suffocatum

911. Trifolium tenuifolium

912. Trifolium tomentosum

905. Trifolium resupinatum

906. Trifolium scabrum

907. Trifolium spumosum

908. Trifolium stellatum

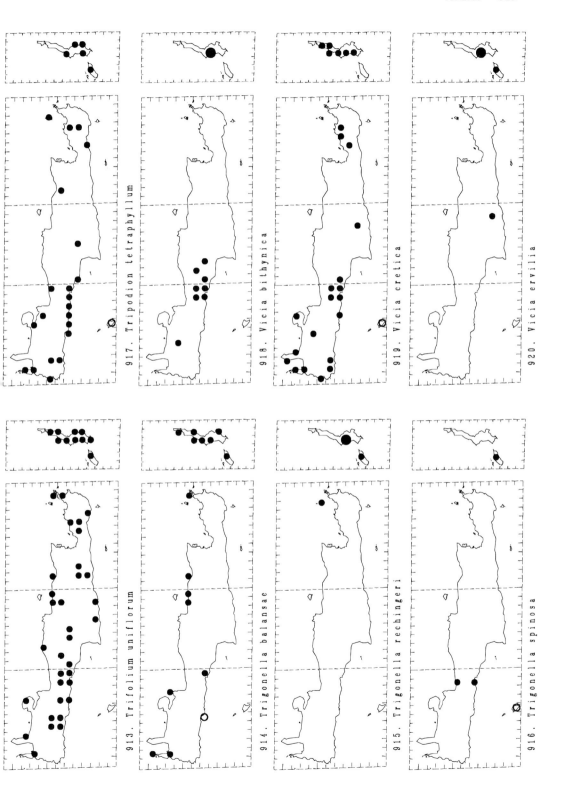

913. Trifolium uniflorum

914. Trigonella balansae

915. Trigonella rechingeri

916. Trigonella spinosa

917. Tripodion tetraphyllum

918. Vicia bithynica

919. Vicia cretica

920. Vicia ervilia

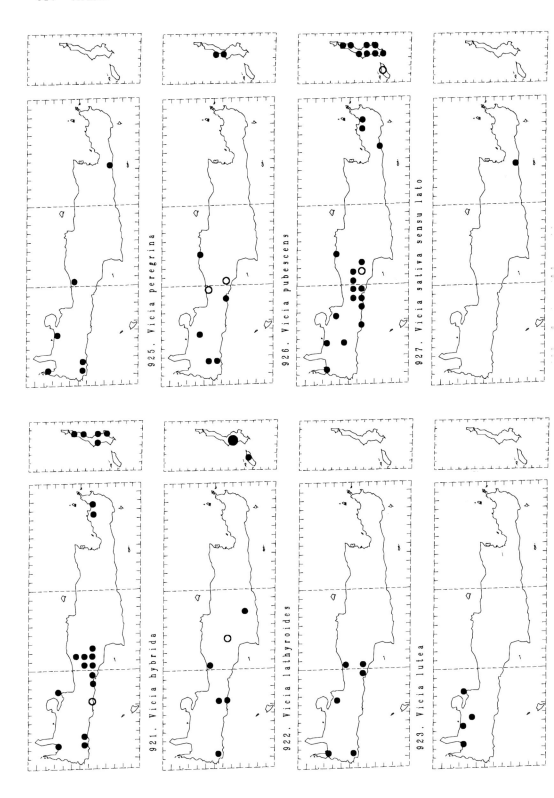

921. Vicia hybrida

922. Vicia lathyroides

923. Vicia lutea

925. Vicia peregrina

926. Vicia pubescens

927. Vicia sativa sensu lato

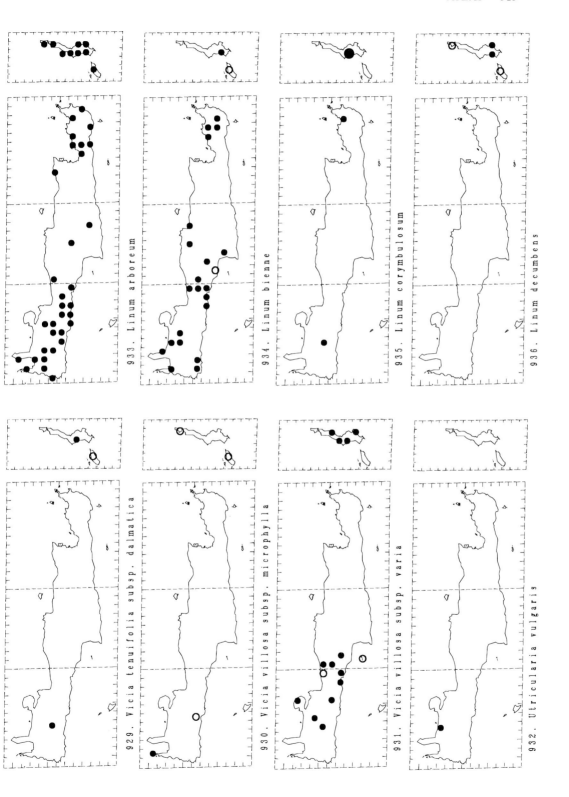

929. Vicia tenuifolia subsp. dalmatica

930. Vicia villosa subsp. microphylla

931. Vicia villosa subsp. varia

932. Utricularia vulgaris

933. Linum arboreum

934. Linum bienne

935. Linum corymbulosum

936. Linum decumbens

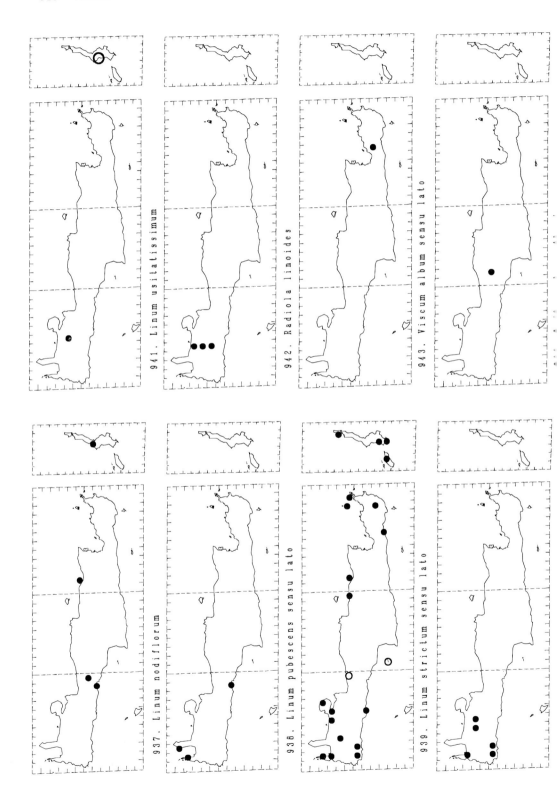

937. Linum nodiflorum

938. Linum pubescens sensu lato

939. Linum strictum sensu lato

941. Linum usitatissimum

942. Radiola linoides

943. Viscum album sensu lato

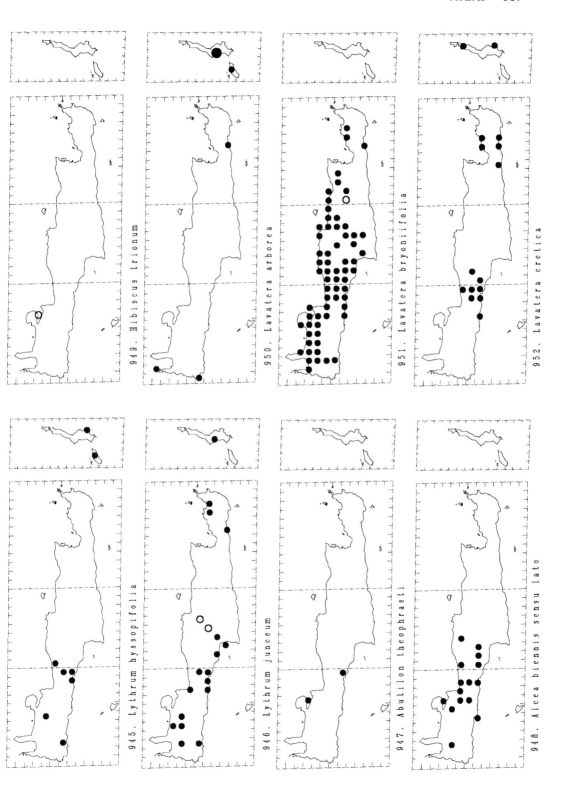

945. Lythrum hyssopifolia

946. Lythrum junceum

947. Abutilon theophrasti

948. Alcea biennis sensu lato

949. Hibiscus trionum

950. Lavatera arborea

951. Lavatera bryoniifolia

952. Lavatera cretica

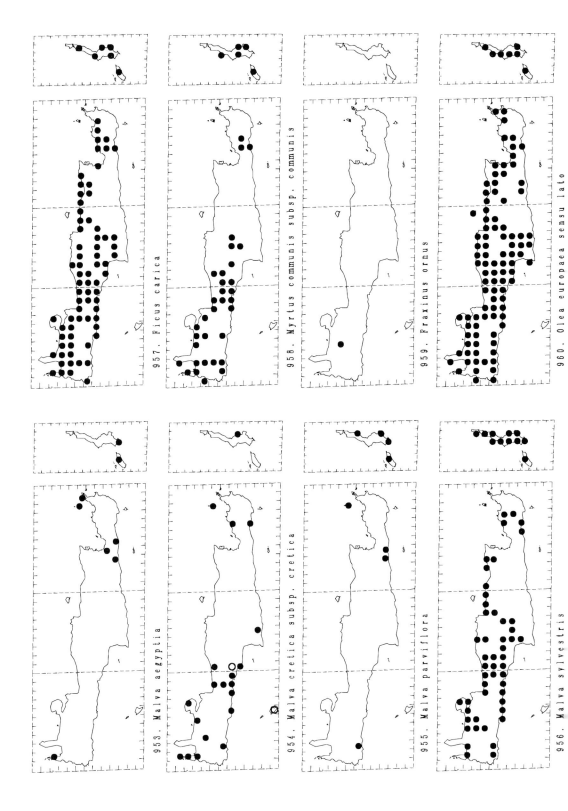

953. Malva aegyptia

954. Malva cretica subsp. cretica

955. Malva parviflora

956. Malva sylvestris

957. Ficus carica

958. Myrtus communis subsp. communis

959. Fraxinus ornus

960. Olea europaea sensu lato

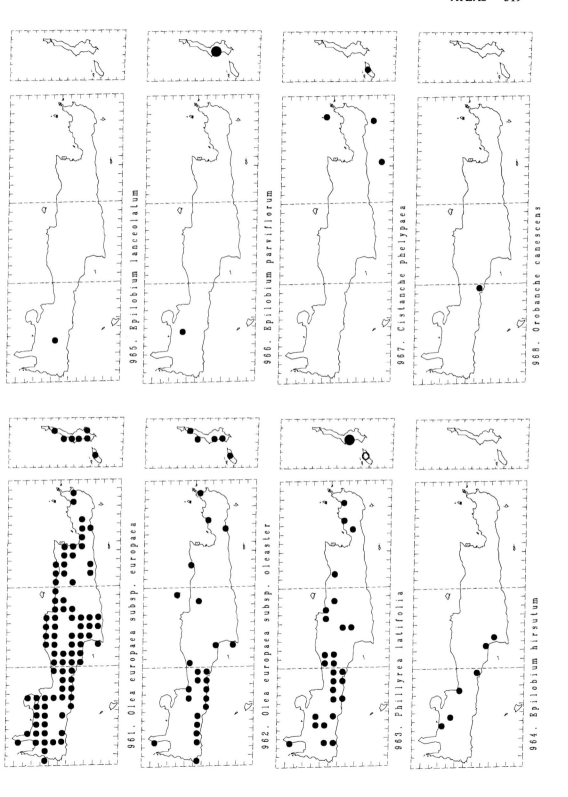

961. Olea europaea subsp. europaea

962. Olea europaea subsp. oleaster

963. Phillyrea latifolia

964. Epilobium hirsutum

965. Epilobium lanceolatum

966. Epilobium parviflorum

967. Cistanche phelypaea

968. Orobanche canescens

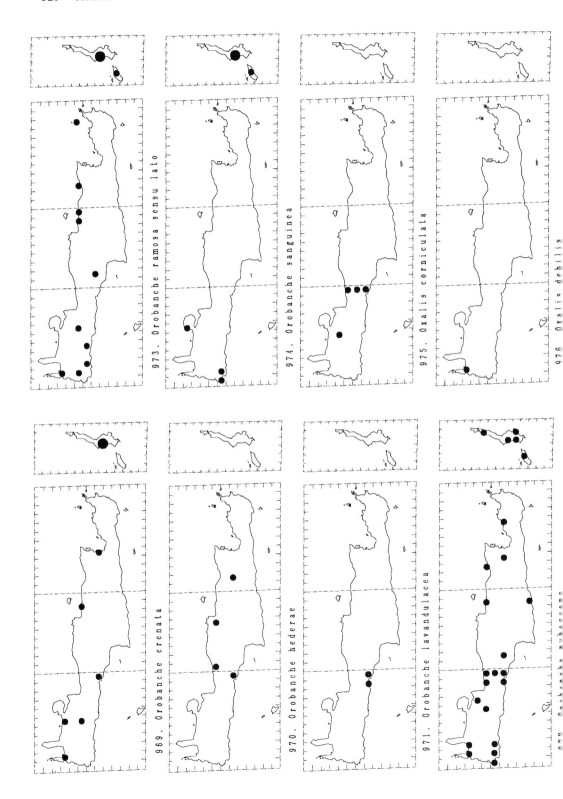

969. Orobanche crenata

970. Orobanche hederae

971. Orobanche lavandulacea

973. Orobanche ramosa sensu lato

974. Orobanche sanguinea

975. Oxalis corniculata

976. Oxalis debilis

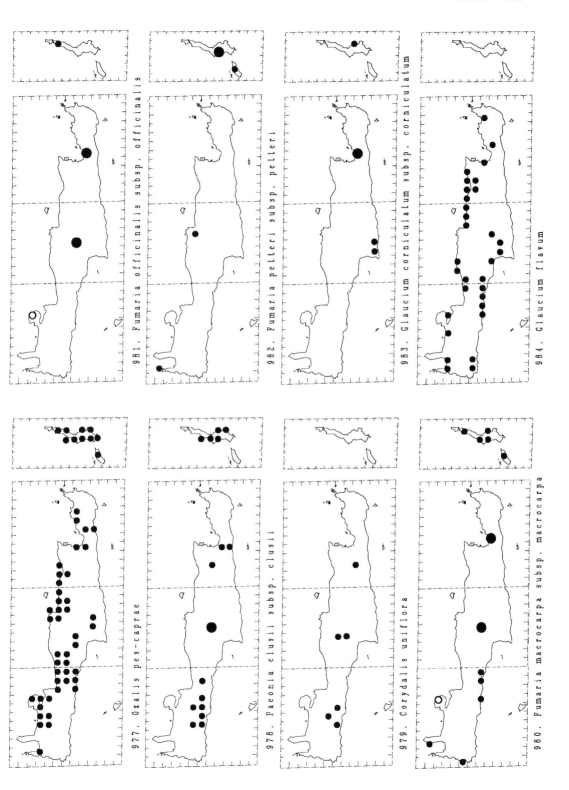

977. Oxalis pes-caprae

978. Paeonia clusii subsp. clusii

979. Corydalis uniflora

980. Fumaria macrocarpa subsp. macrocarpa

981. Fumaria officinalis subsp. officinalis

982. Fumaria petteri subsp. petteri

983. Glaucium corniculatum subsp. corniculatum

984. Glaucium flavum

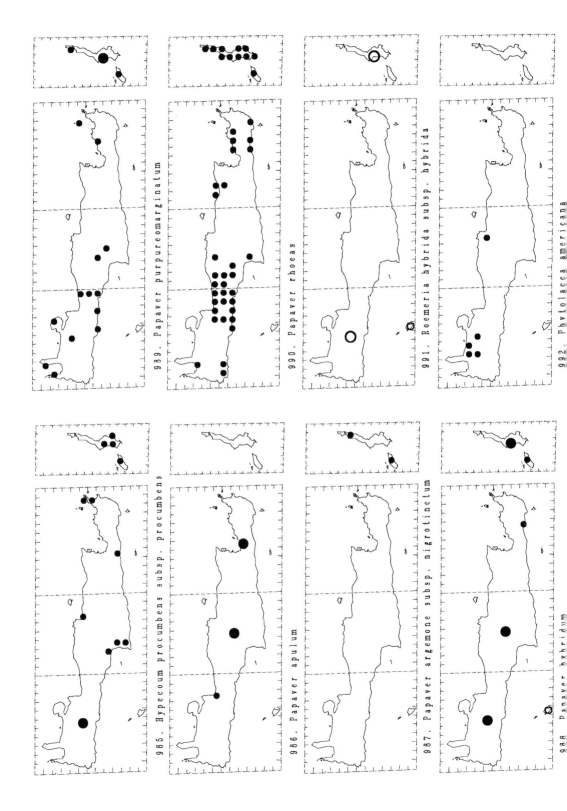

989. Papaver purpureomarginatum

990. Papaver rhoeas

991. Roemeria hybrida subsp. hybrida

992. Phytolacca americana

985. Hypecoum procumbens subsp. procumbens

986. Papaver apulum

987. Papaver argemone subsp. nigrotinctum

988. Papaver hybridum

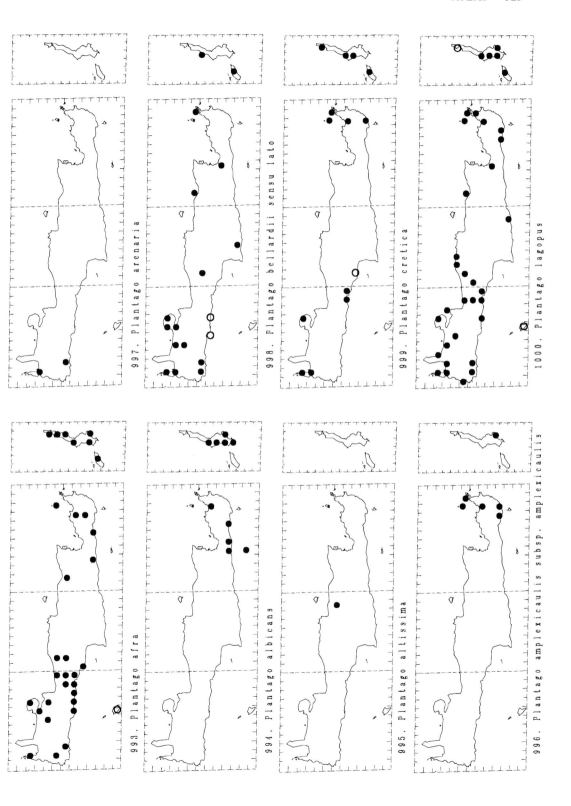

993. Plantago afra

994. Plantago albicans

995. Plantago altissima

996. Plantago amplexicaulis subsp. amplexicaulis

997. Plantago arenaria

998. Plantago bellardii sensu lato

999. Plantago cretica

1000. Plantago lagopus

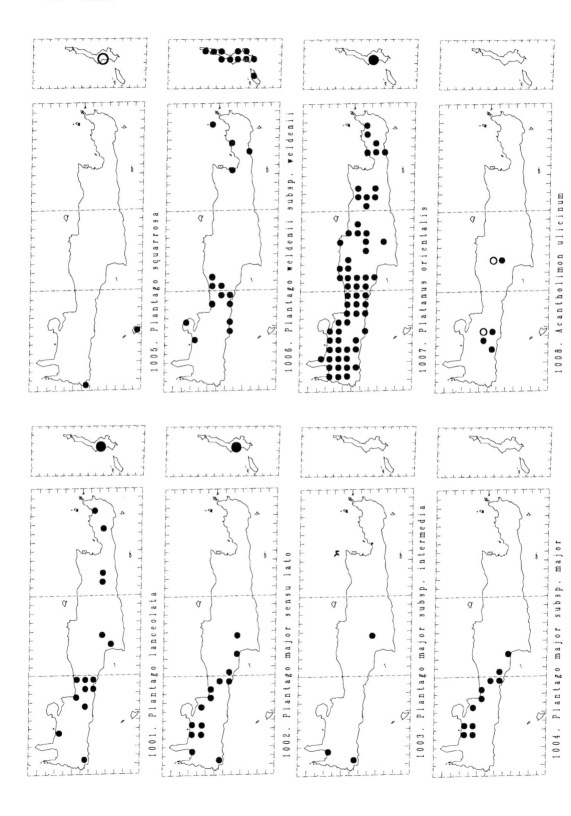

1005. Plantago squarrosa

1006. Plantago weldenii subsp. weldenii

1007. Platanus orientalis

1008. Acantholimon ulicinum

1001. Plantago lanceolata

1002. Plantago major sensu lato

1003. Plantago major subsp. intermedia

1004. Plantago major subsp. major

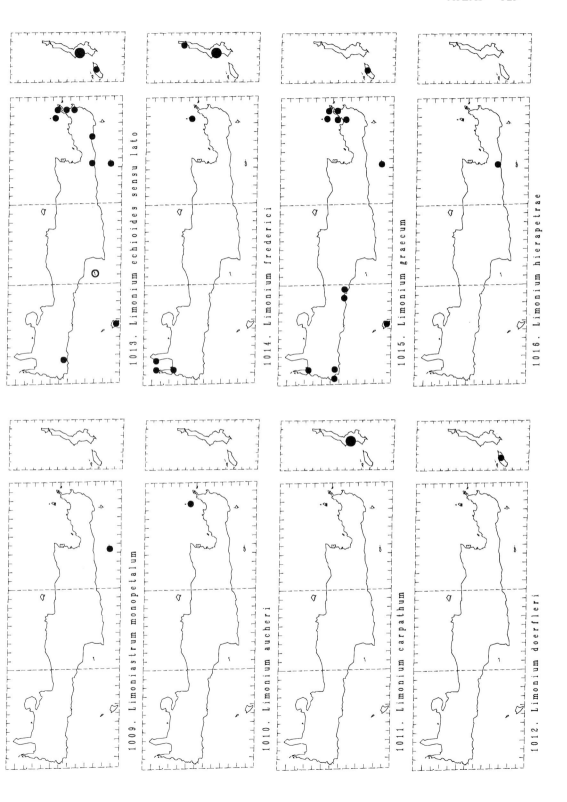

1009. Limoniastrum monopetalum

1010. Limonium aucheri

1011. Limonium carpathum

1012. Limonium doerfleri

1013. Limonium echioides sensu lato

1014. Limonium frederici

1015. Limonium graecum

1016. Limonium hierapetrae

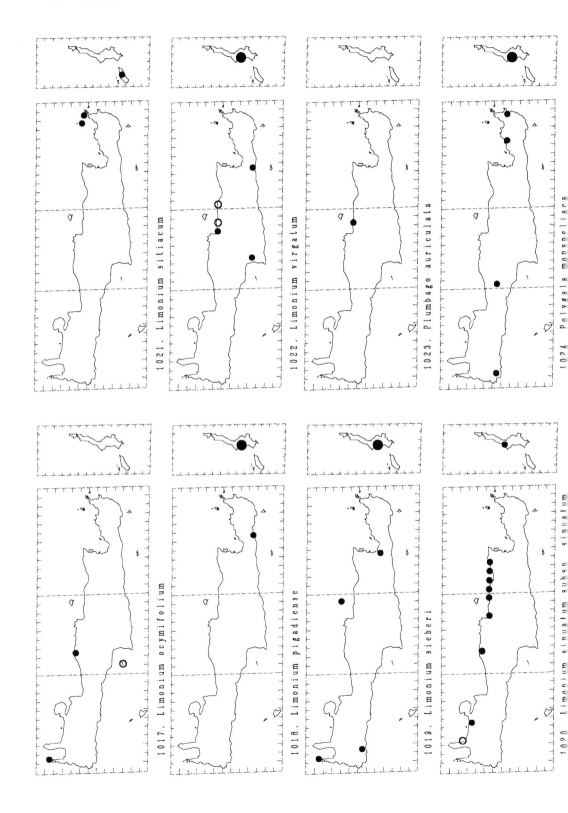

1017. Limonium ocymifolium

1018. Limonium pigadiense

1019. Limonium sieberi

1020. Limonium sinuatum subsp. sinuatum

1021. Limonium sitiacum

1022. Limonium virgatum

1023. Plumbago auriculata

1024. Polygala monspeliaca

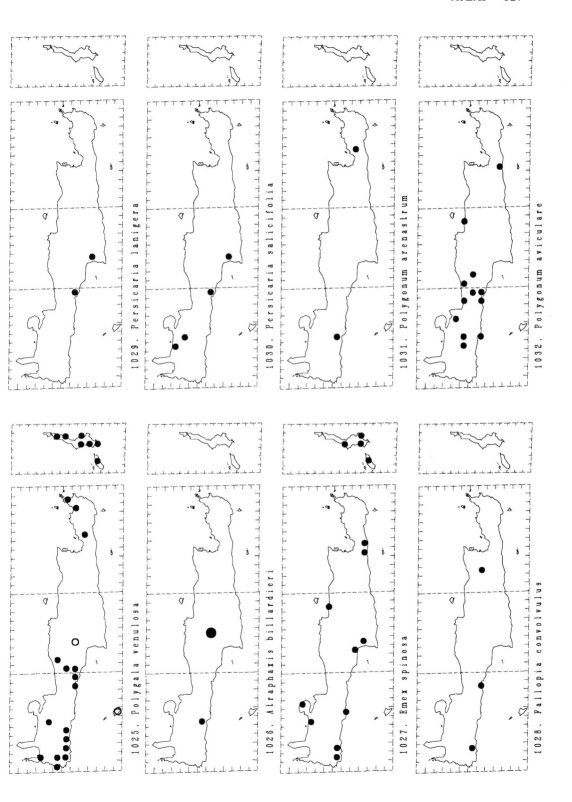

1029 . Persicaria lanigera

1030 . Persicaria salicifolia

1031 . Polygonum arenastrum

1032 . Polygonum aviculare

1025 . Polygala venulosa

1026 . Atraphaxis billardieri

1027 . Emex spinosa

1028 . Fallopia convolvulus

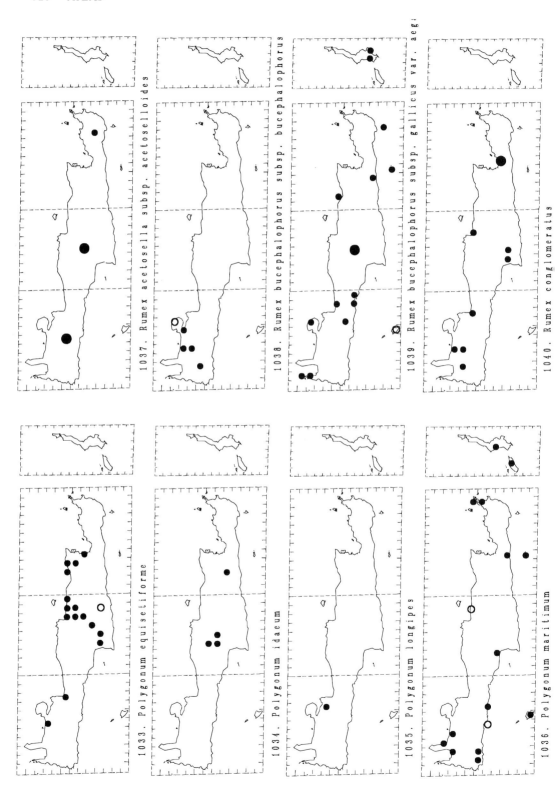

1033. Polygonum equisetiforme

1034. Polygonum idaeum

1035. Polygonum longipes

1036. Polygonum maritimum

1037. Rumex acetosella subsp. acetoselloides

1038. Rumex bucephalophorus subsp. bucephalophorus

1039. Rumex bucephalophorus subsp. gallicus var. aegi

1040. Rumex conglomeratus

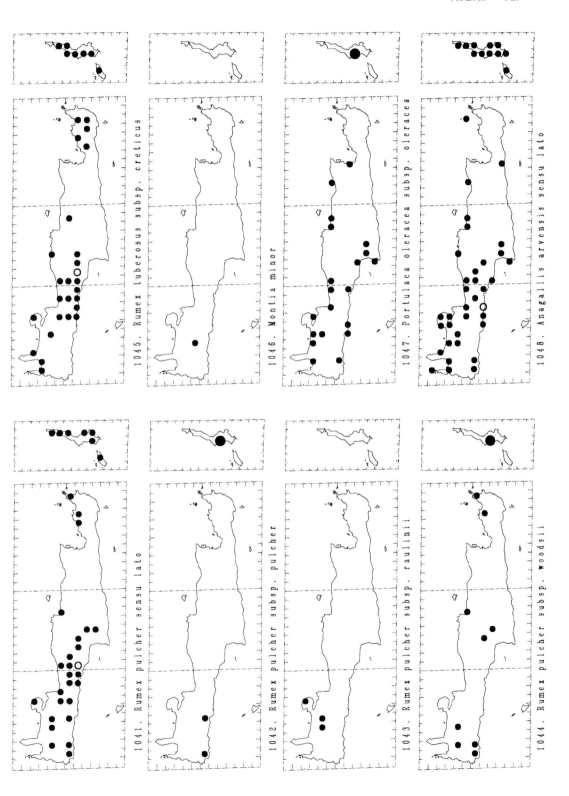

1041. Rumex pulcher sensu lato

1042. Rumex pulcher subsp. pulcher

1043. Rumex pulcher subsp. raulinii

1044. Rumex pulcher subsp. woodsii

1045. Rumex tuberosus subsp. creticus

1046. Montia minor

1047. Portulaca oleracea subsp. oleracea

1048. Anagallis arvensis sensu lato

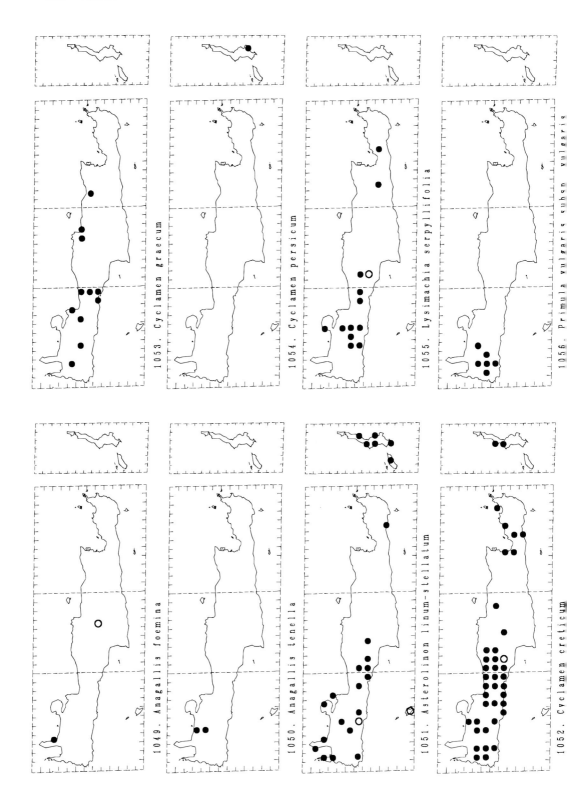

1053. Cyclamen graecum

1054. Cyclamen persicum

1055. Lysimachia serpyllifolia

1056. Primula vulgaris subsp vulgaris

1049. Anagallis foemina

1050. Anagallis tenella

1051. Asterolinon linum-stellatum

1052. Cyclamen creticum

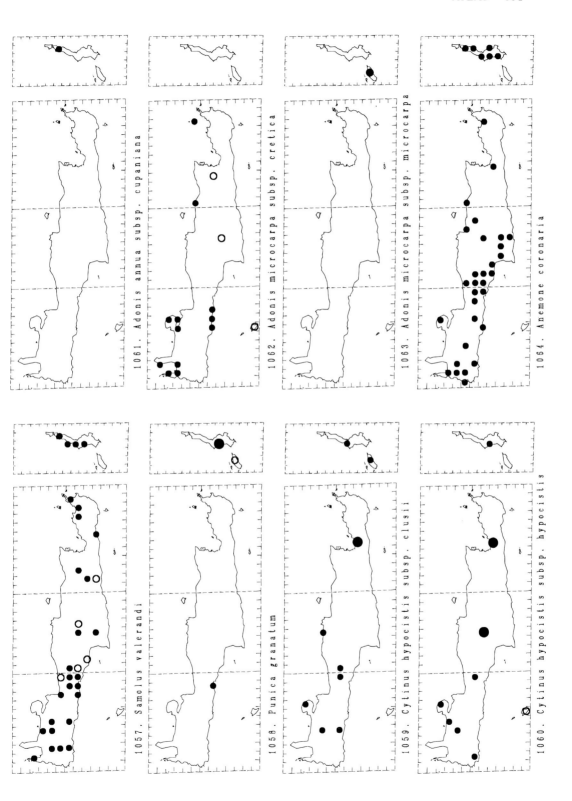

1061. Adonis annua subsp. cupaniana

1062. Adonis microcarpa subsp. cretica

1063. Adonis microcarpa subsp. microcarpa

1064. Anemone coronaria

1057. Samolus valerandi

1058. Punica granatum

1059. Cytinus hypocistis subsp. clusii

1060. Cytinus hypocistis subsp. hypocistis

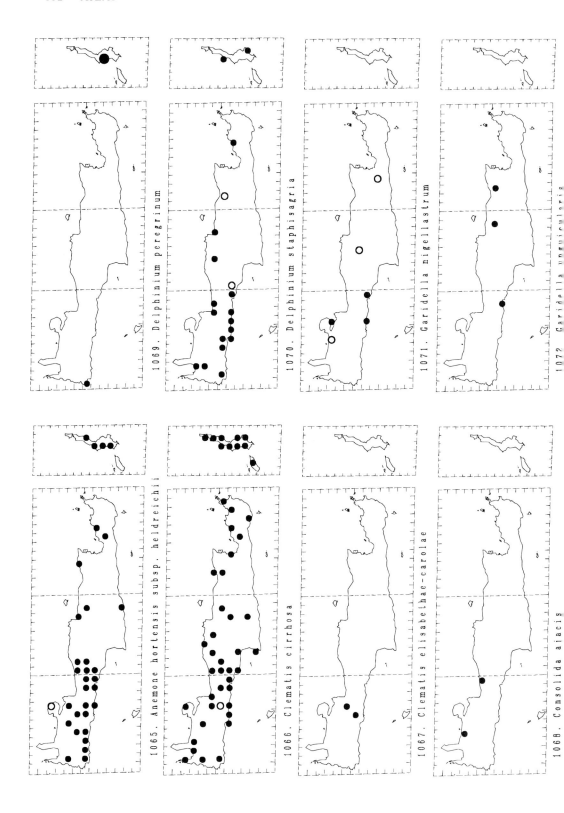

1069. Delphinium peregrinum

1070. Delphinium staphisagria

1071. Garidella nigellastrum

1072. Garidella unguicularis

1065. Anemone hortensis subsp. heldreichii

1066. Clematis cirrhosa

1067. Clematis elisabethae-carolae

1068. Consolida aiacis

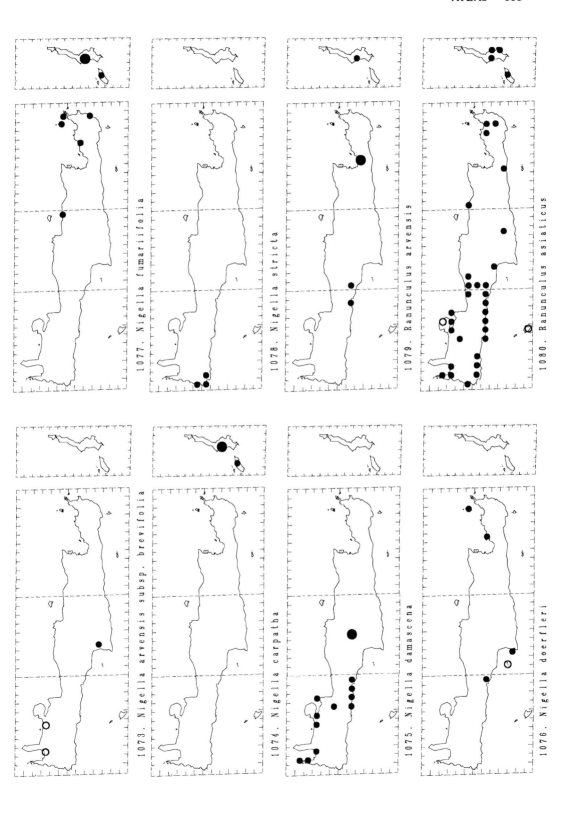

1073. Nigella arvensis subsp. brevifolia

1074. Nigella carpatha

1075. Nigella damascena

1076. Nigella doerfleri

1077. Nigella fumariifolia

1078. Nigella stricta

1079. Ranunculus arvensis

1080. Ranunculus asiaticus

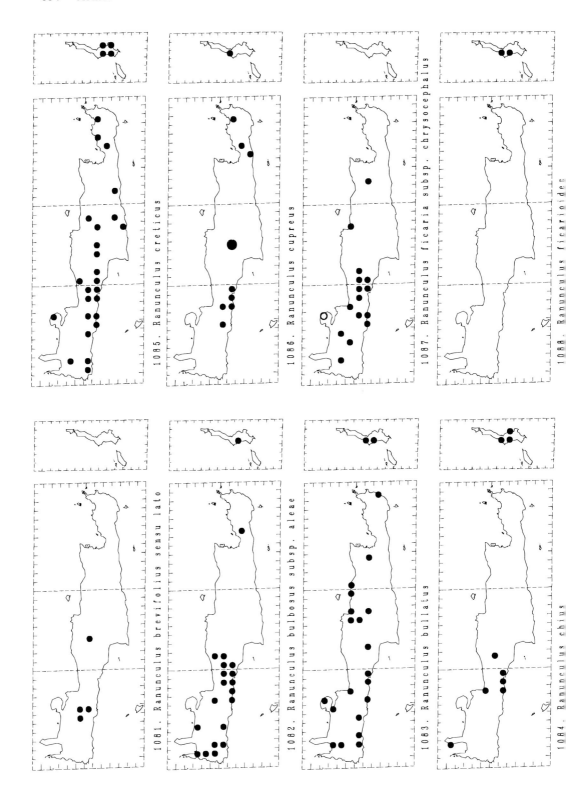

1085. Ranunculus creticus

1086. Ranunculus cupreus

1087. Ranunculus ficaria subsp. chrysocephalus

1088. Ranunculus ficarioides

1081. Ranunculus brevifolius sensu lato

1082. Ranunculus bulbosus subsp. aleae

1083. Ranunculus bullatus

1084. Ranunculus chius

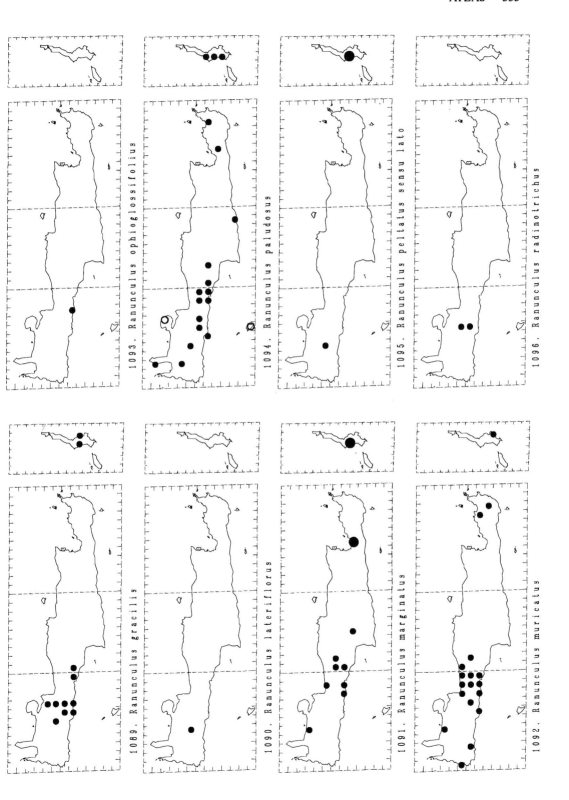

1089. Ranunculus gracilis

1090. Ranunculus lateriflorus

1091. Ranunculus marginatus

1092. Ranunculus muricatus

1093. Ranunculus ophioglossifolius

1094. Ranunculus paludosus

1095. Ranunculus peltatus sensu lato

1096. Ranunculus radinotrichus

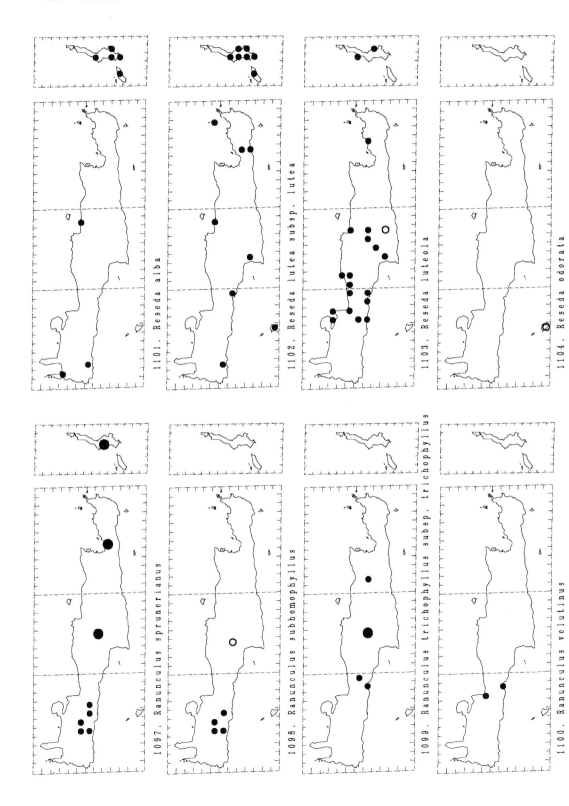

1101. Reseda alba

1102. Reseda lutea subsp. lutea

1103. Reseda luteola

1104. Reseda odorata

1097. Ranunculus sprunerianus

1098. Ranunculus subhomophyllus

1099. Ranunculus trichophyllus subsp. trichophyllus

1100. Ranunculus velutinus

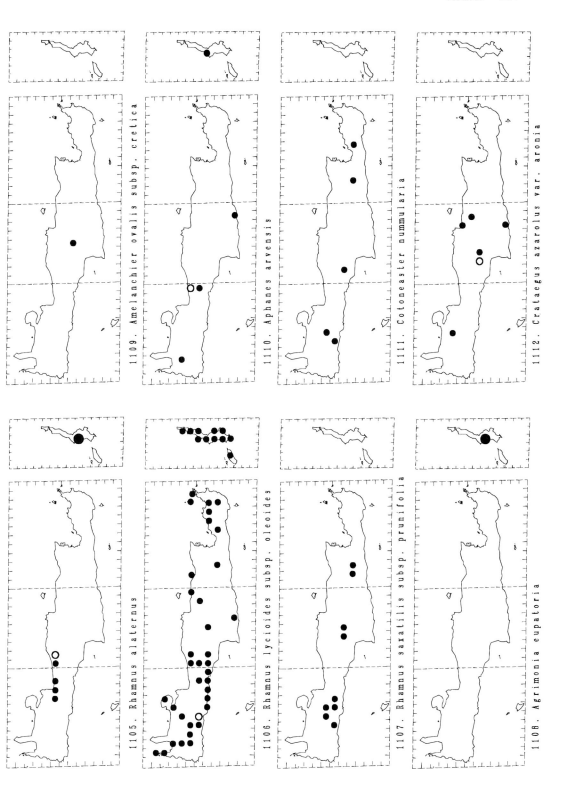

1105. Rhamnus alaternus

1106. Rhamnus lycioides subsp. oleoides

1107. Rhamnus saxatilis subsp. prunifolia

1108. Agrimonia eupatoria

1109. Amelanchier ovalis subsp. cretica

1110. Aphanes arvensis

1111. Cotoneaster nummularia

1112. Crataegus azarolus var. aronia

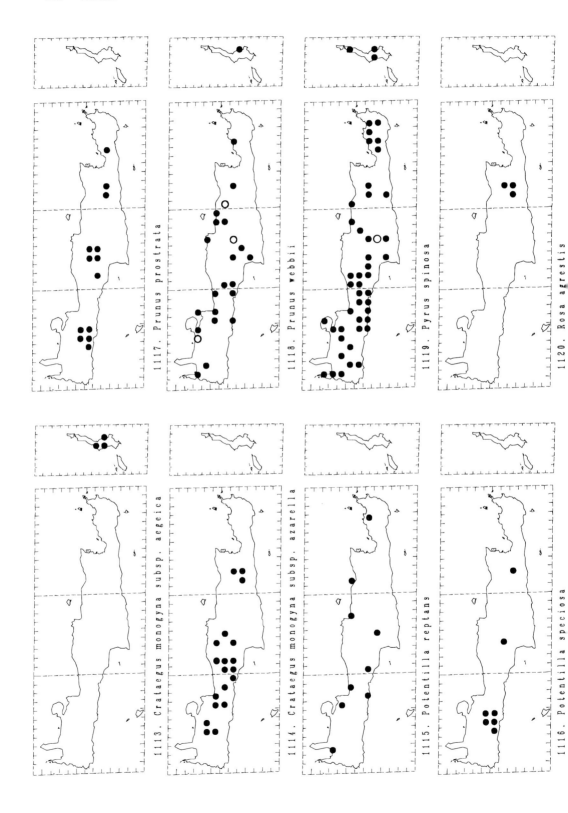

1117. Prunus prostrata

1118. Prunus webbii

1119. Pyrus spinosa

1120. Rosa agrestis

1113. Crataegus monogyna subsp. aegeica

1114. Crataegus monogyna subsp. azarella

1115. Potentilla reptans

1116. Potentilla speciosa

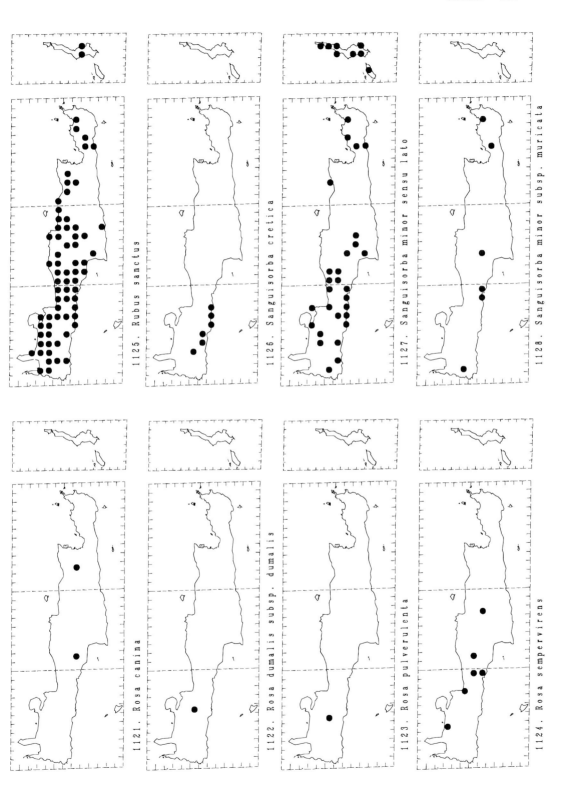

1125. Rubus sanctus

1126. Sanguisorba cretica

1127. Sanguisorba minor sensu lato

1128. Sanguisorba minor subsp. muricata

1121. Rosa canina

1122. Rosa dumalis subsp. dumalis

1123. Rosa pulverulenta

1124. Rosa sempervirens

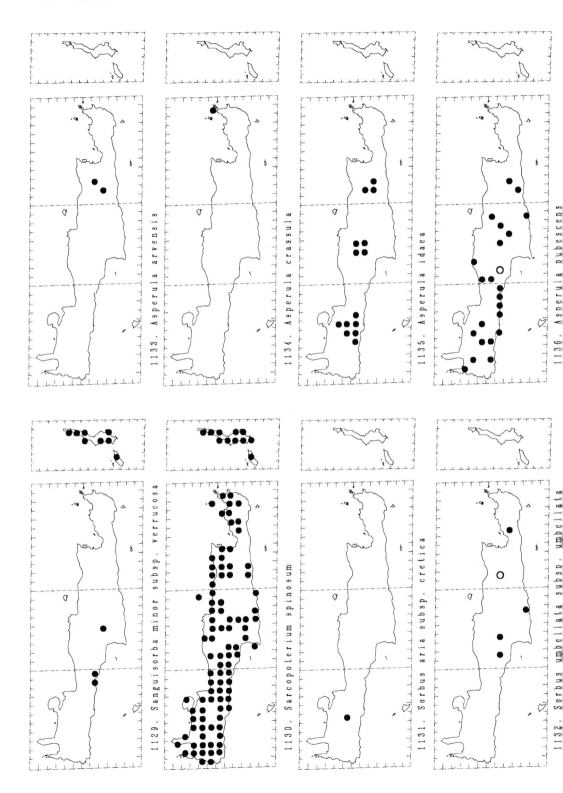

1133. Asperula arvensis

1134. Asperula crassula

1135. Asperula idaea

1136. Asperula pubescens

1129. Sanguisorba minor subsp. verrucosa

1130. Sarcopoterium spinosum

1131. Sorbus aria subsp. cretica

1132. Sorbus umbellata subsp. umbellata

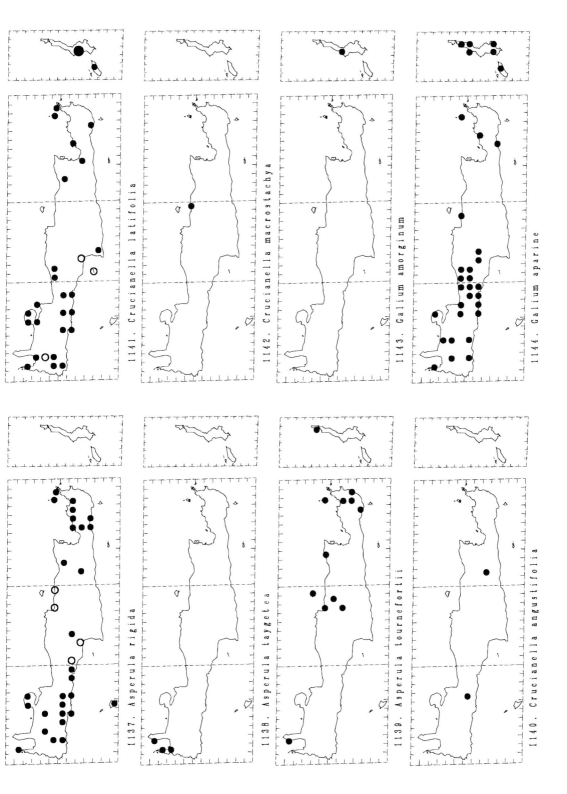

1137. Asperula rigida

1138. Asperula taygetea

1139. Asperula tourneforti

1140. Crucianella angustifolia

1141. Crucianella latifolia

1142. Crucianella macrostachya

1143. Galium amorginum

1144. Galium aparine

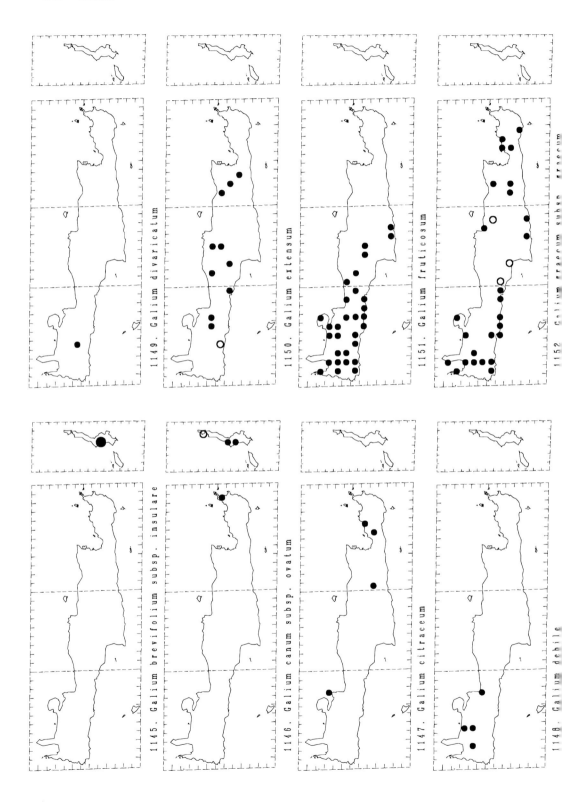

1149. Galium divaricatum

1150. Galium extensum

1151. Galium fruticosum

1152. Galium graecum subsp. graecum

1145. Galium brevifolium subsp. insulare

1146. Galium canum subsp. ovatum

1147. Galium citraceum

1148. Galium debile

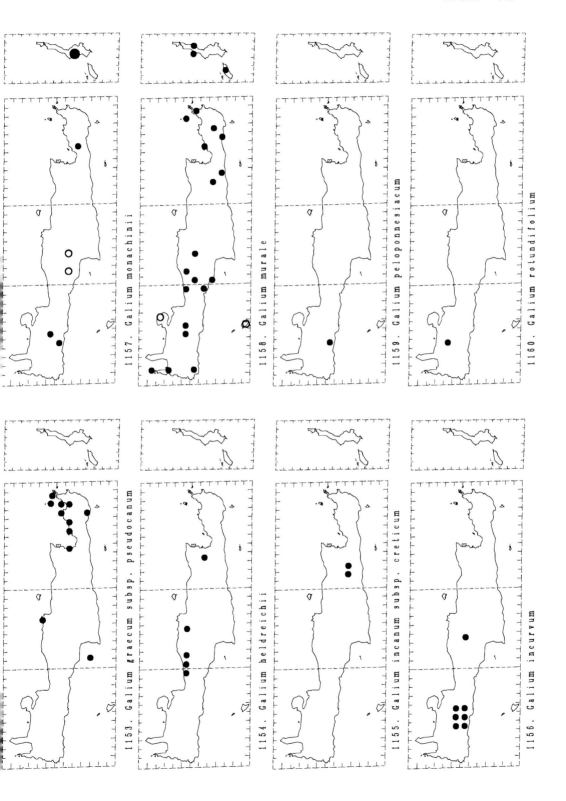

1157. Galium monachinii

1158. Galium murale

1159. Galium peloponnesiacum

1160. Galium rotundifolium

1153. Galium graecum subsp. pseudocanum

1154. Galium heldreichii

1155. Galium incanum subsp. creticum

1156. Galium incurvum

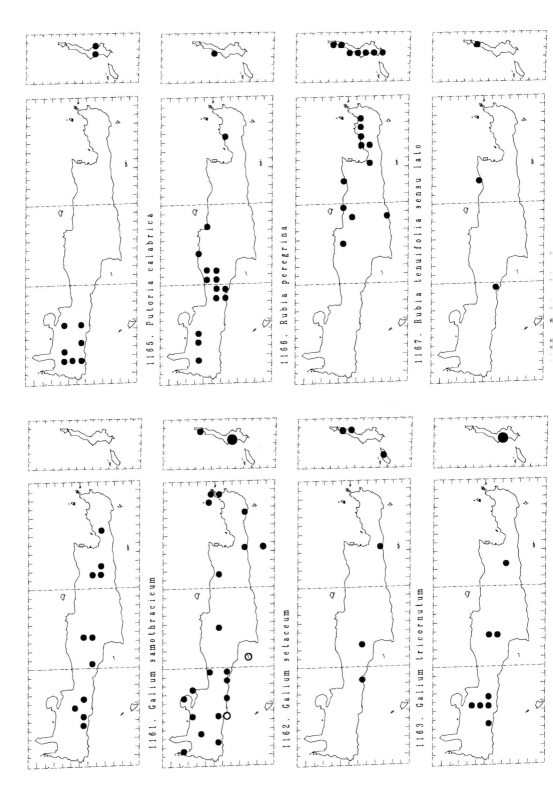

1165. Putoria calabrica

1166. Rubia peregrina

1167. Rubia tenuifolia sensu lato

1161. Galium samothracicum

1162. Galium setaceum

1163. Galium tricornutum

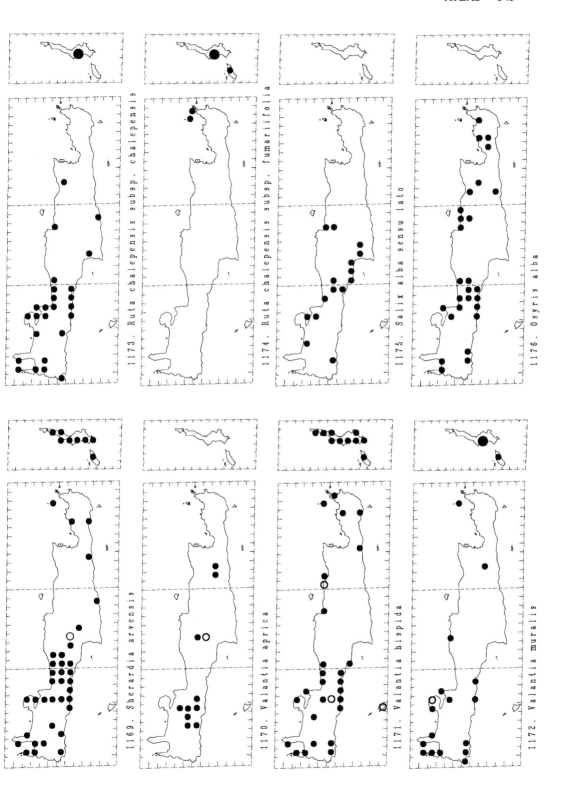

1169. Sherardia arvensis

1170. Valantia aprica

1171. Valantia hispida

1172. Valantia muralis

1173. Ruta chalepensis subsp. chalepensis

1174. Ruta chalepensis subsp. fumariifolia

1175. Salix alba sensu lato

1176. Osyris alba

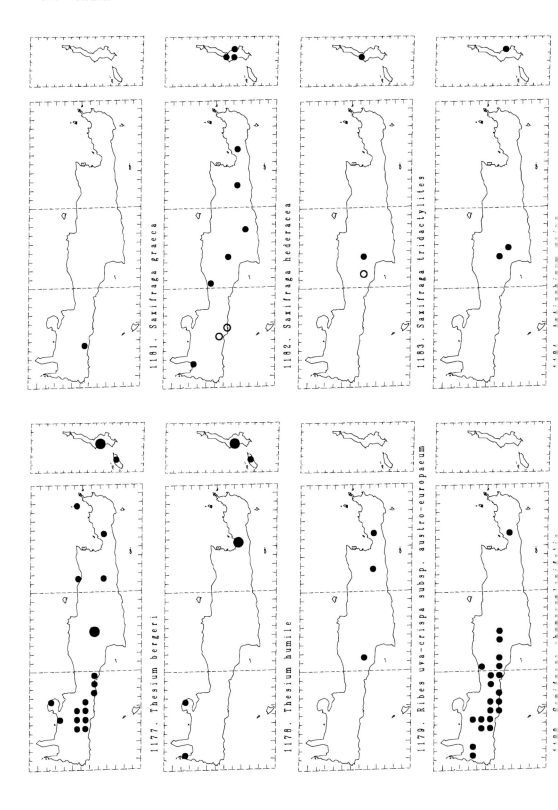

1177. Thesium bergeri

1178. Thesium humile

1179. Ribes uva-crispa subsp. austro-europaeum

1181. Saxifraga graeca

1182. Saxifraga hederacea

1183. Saxifraga tridactylites

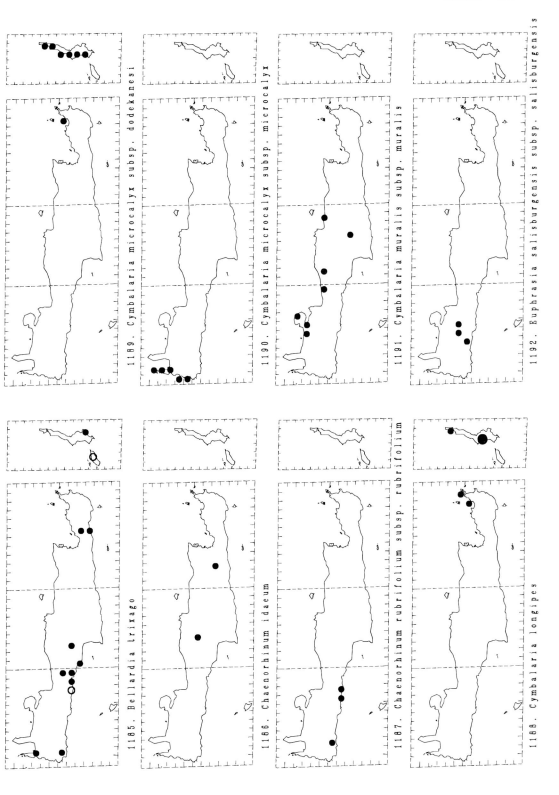

1185. Bellardia trixago

1186. Chaenorhinum idaeum

1187. Chaenorhinum rubrifolium subsp. rubrifolium

1188. Cymbalaria longipes

1189. Cymbalaria microcalyx subsp. dodekanesi

1190. Cymbalaria microcalyx subsp. microcalyx

1191. Cymbalaria muralis subsp. muralis

1192. Euphrasia salisburgensis subsp. salisburgensis

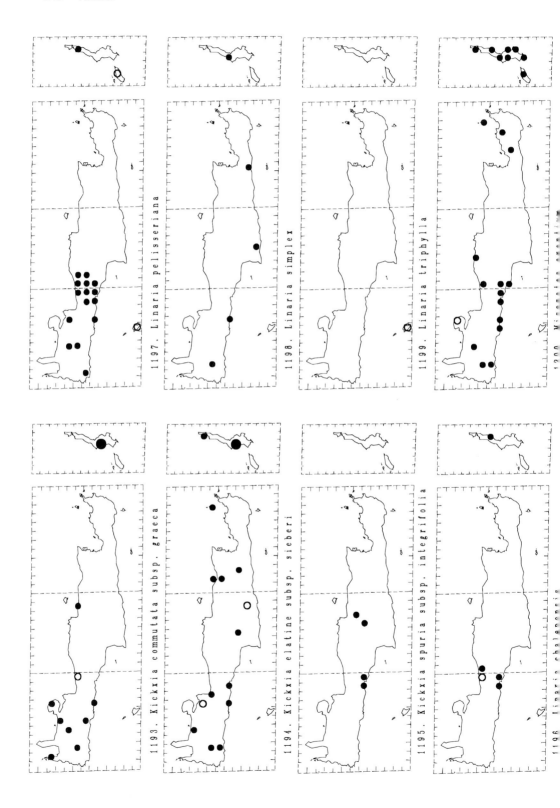

1197. Linaria pelisseriana

1198. Linaria simplex

1199. Linaria triphylla

1200. Misopates orontium

1193. Kickxia commutata subsp. graeca

1194. Kickxia elatine subsp. sieberi

1195. Kickxia spuria subsp. integrifolia

1196. Linaria chalepensis

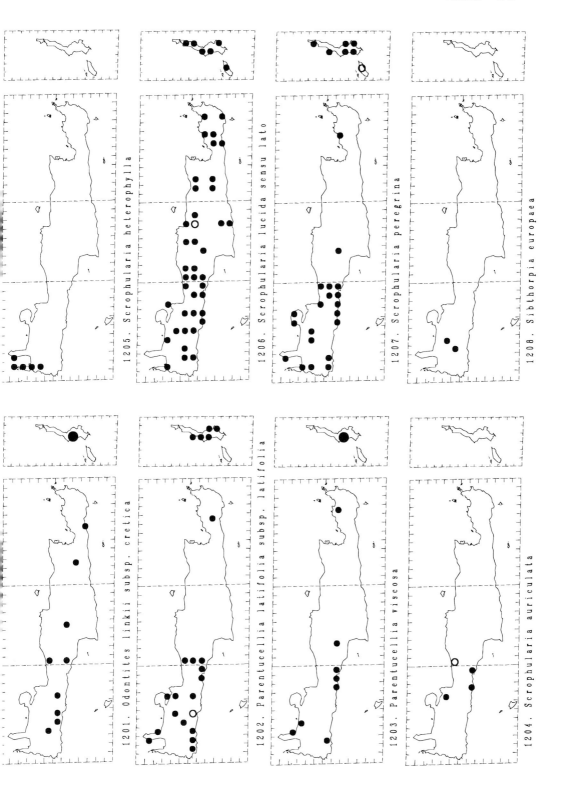

1205. Scrophularia heterophylla

1206. Scrophularia lucida sensu lato

1207. Scrophularia peregrina

1208. Sibthorpia europaea

1201. Odontites linkii subsp. cretica

1202. Parentucellia latifolia subsp. latifolia

1203. Parentucellia viscosa

1204. Scrophularia auriculata

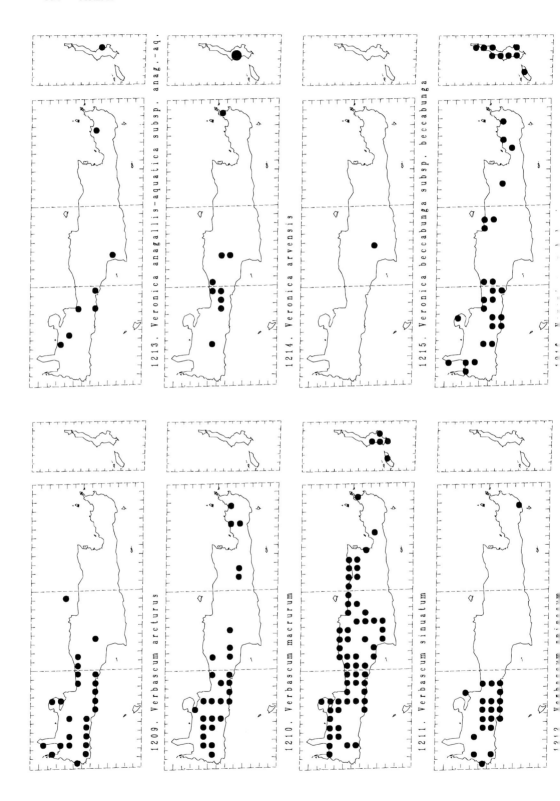

1213. Veronica anagallis-aquatica subsp. anag.-aq.

1214. Veronica arvensis

1215. Veronica beccabunga subsp. beccabunga

1209. Verbascum arcturus

1210. Verbascum macrurum

1211. Verbascum sinuatum

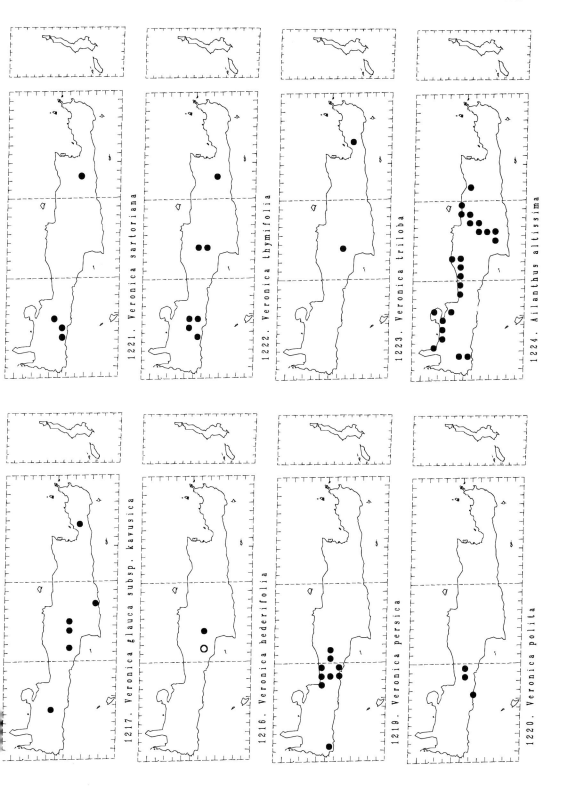

1221. Veronica sartoriana

1222. Veronica thymifolia

1223. Veronica triloba

1224. Ailanthus altissima

1217. Veronica glauca subsp. kavusica

1216. Veronica hederifolia

1219. Veronica persica

1220. Veronica polita

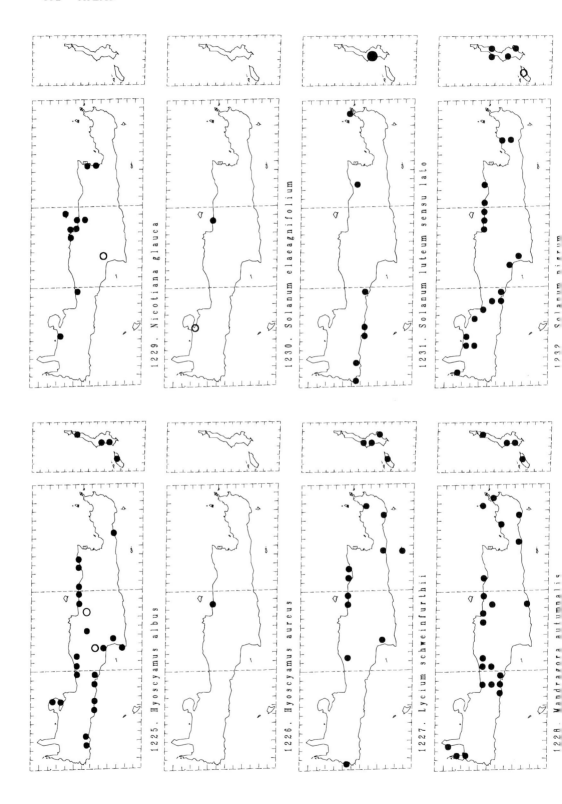

1229. Nicotiana glauca

1230. Solanum elaeagnifolium

1231. Solanum luteum sensu lato

1232. Solanum nigrum

1225. Hyoscyamus albus

1226. Hyoscyamus aureus

1227. Lycium schweinfurthii

1228. Mandragora autumnalis

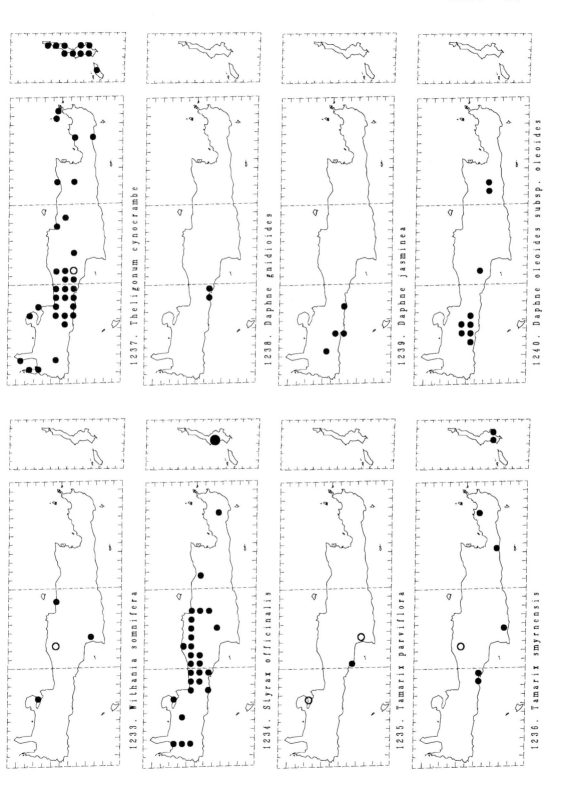

1233. Withania somnifera

1234. Styrax officinalis

1235. Tamarix parviflora

1236. Tamarix smyrnensis

1237. Theligonum cynocrambe

1238. Daphne gnidioides

1239. Daphne jasminea

1240. Daphne oleoides subsp. oleoides

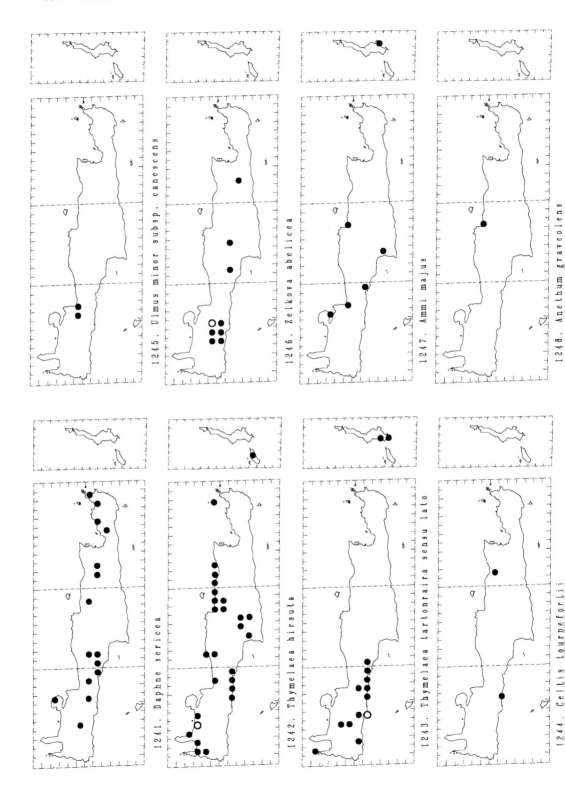

1245. Ulmus minor subsp. canescens

1246. Zelkova abelicea

1247. Ammi majus

1248. Anethum graveolens

1241. Daphne sericea

1242. Thymelaea hirsuta

1243. Thymelaea tartonraira sensu lato

1244. Celtis tournefortii

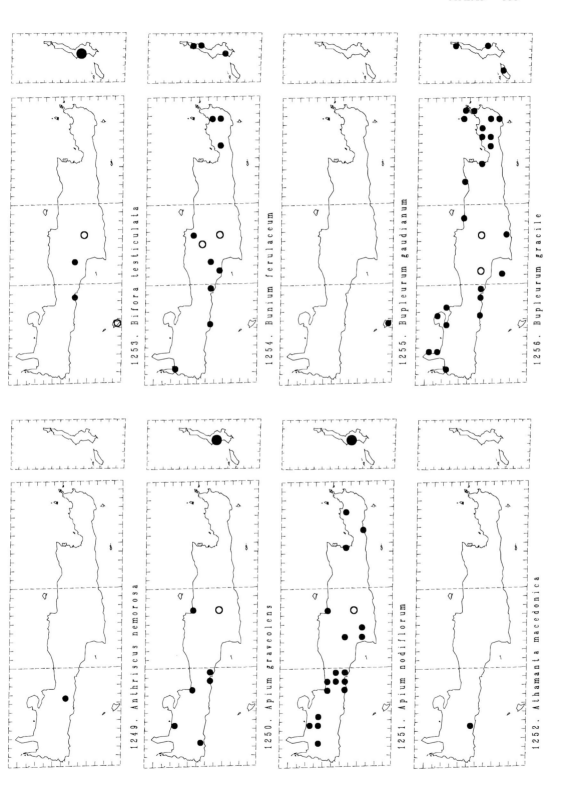

1253. Bifora testiculata

1254. Bunium ferulaceum

1255. Bupleurum gaudianum

1256. Bupleurum gracile

1249. Anthriscus nemorosa

1250. Apium graveolens

1251. Apium nodiflorum

1252. Athamanta macedonica

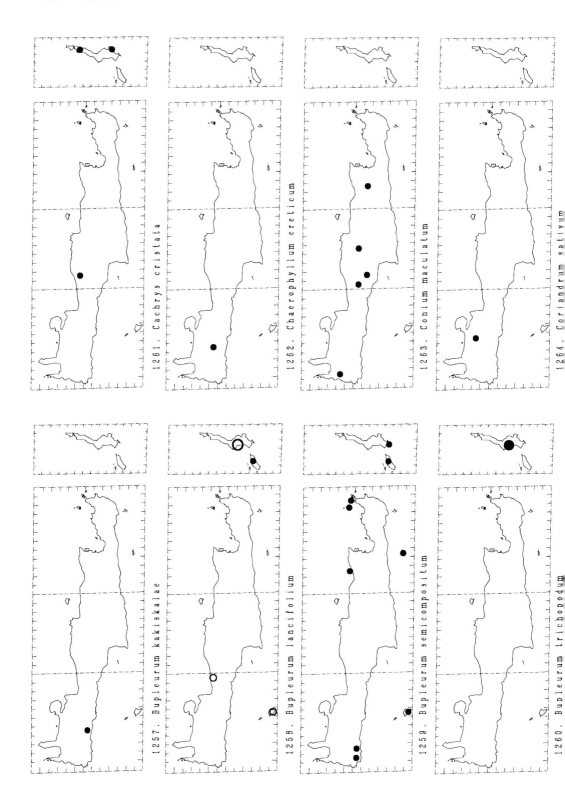

1257. Bupleurum kakiskalae

1258. Bupleurum lancifolium

1259. Bupleurum semicompositum

1260. Bupleurum trichopodum

1261. Cachrys cristata

1262. Chaerophyllum creticum

1263. Conium maculatum

1264. Coriandrum sativum

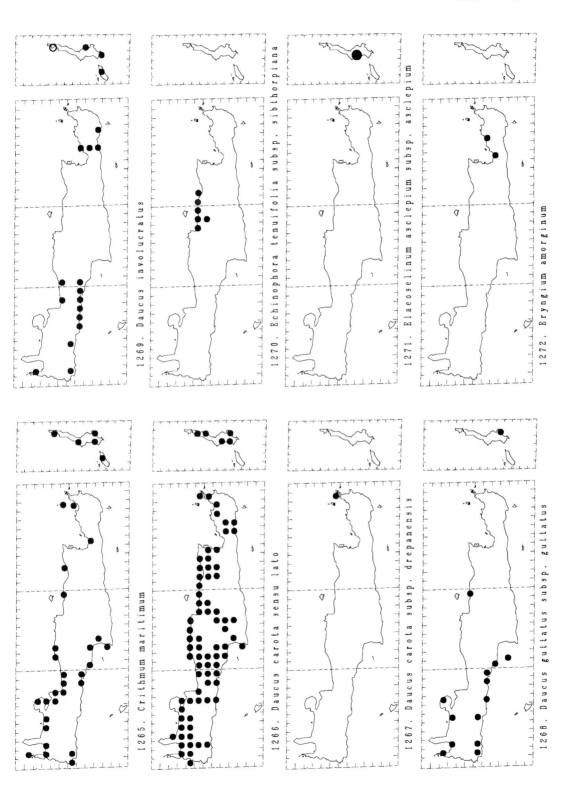

1265. Crithmum maritimum

1266. Daucus carota sensu lato

1267. Daucus carota subsp. drepanensis

1268. Daucus guttatus subsp. guttatus

1269. Daucus involucratus

1270. Echinophora tenuifolia subsp. sibthorpiana

1271. Elaeoselinum asclepium subsp. asclepium

1272. Eryngium amorginum

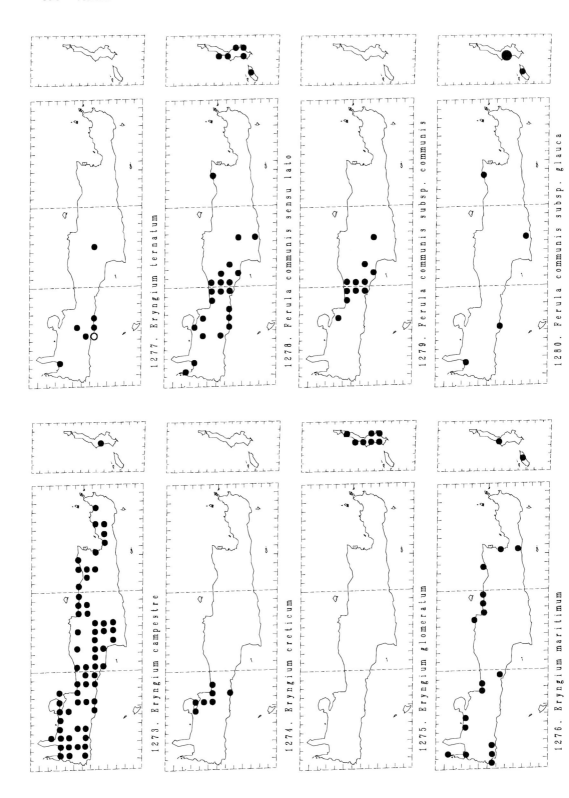

1277. Eryngium ternatum

1278. Ferula communis sensu lato

1279. Ferula communis subsp. communis

1280. Ferula communis subsp. glauca

1273. Eryngium campestre

1274. Eryngium creticum

1275. Eryngium glomeratum

1276. Eryngium maritimum

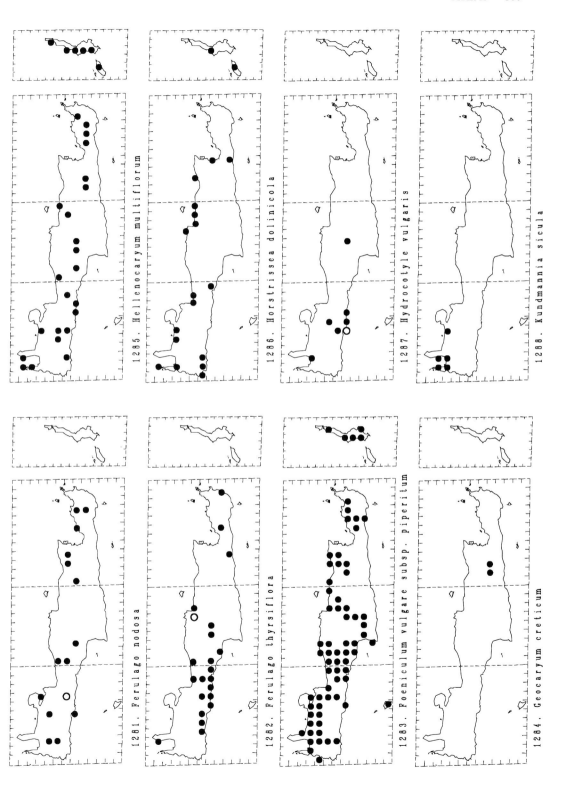

1281. Ferulago nodosa

1282. Ferulago thyrsiflora

1283. Foeniculum vulgare subsp. piperitum

1284. Geocaryum creticum

1285. Hellenocaryum multiflorum

1286. Horstrissea dolinicola

1287. Hydrocotyle vulgaris

1288. Kundmannia sicula

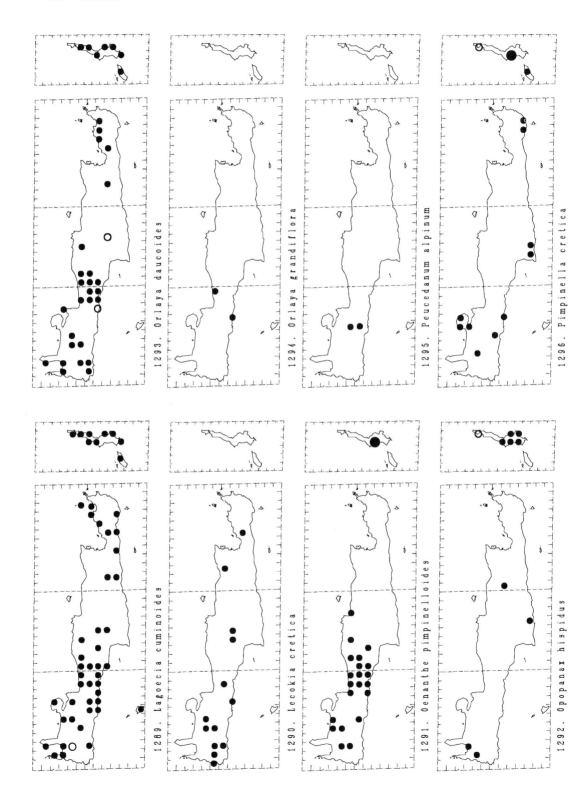

1289. Lagoecia cuminoides

1290. Lecokia cretica

1291. Oenanthe pimpinelloides

1292. Opopanax hispidus

1293. Orlaya daucoides

1294. Orlaya grandiflora

1295. Peucedanum alpinum

1296. Pimpinella cretica

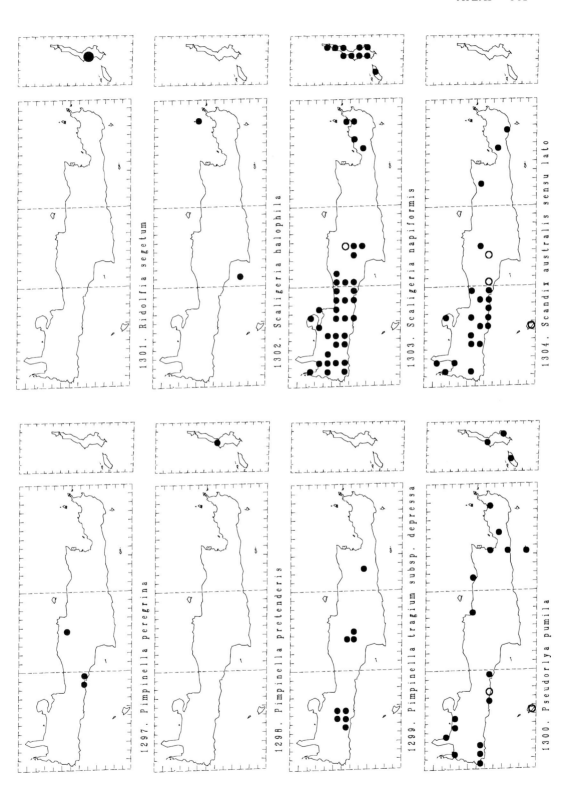

1301. Ridolfia segetum

1302. Scaligeria halophila

1303. Scaligeria napiformis

1304. Scandix australis sensu lato

1297. Pimpinella peregrina

1298. Pimpinella pretenderis

1299. Pimpinella tragium subsp. depressa

1300. Pseudorlya pumila

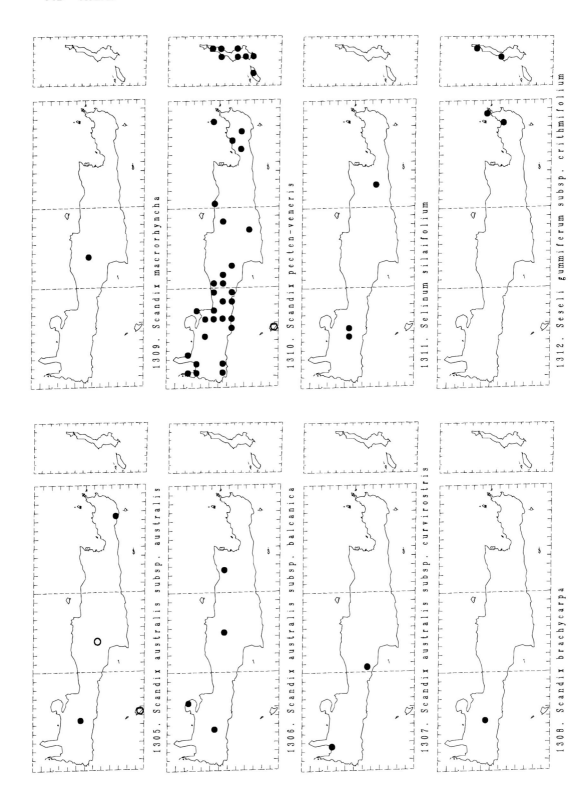

1309. Scandix macrorhyncha

1310. Scandix pecten-veneris

1311. Selinum silaifolium

1312. Seseli gummiferum subsp. crithmifolium

1305. Scandix australis subsp. australis

1306. Scandix australis subsp. balcanica

1307. Scandix australis subsp. curvirostris

1308. Scandix brachycarpa

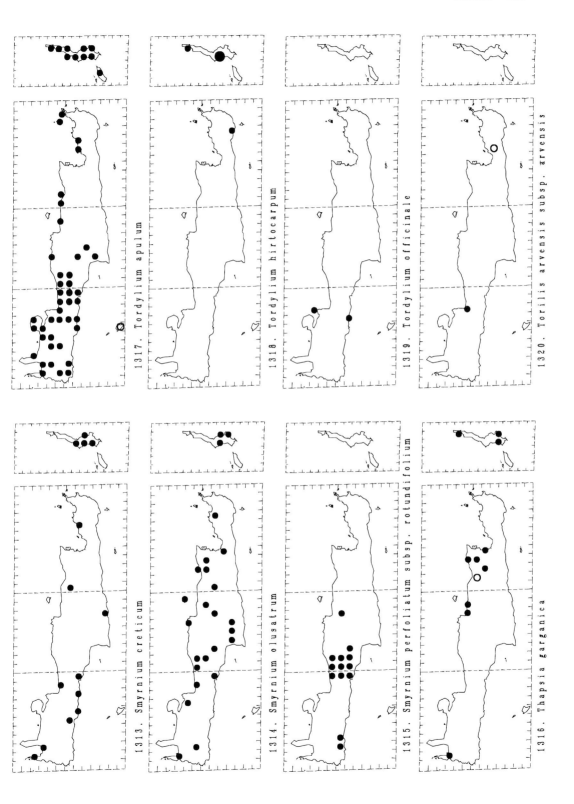

1317. Tordylium apulum

1318. Tordylium hirtocarpum

1319. Tordylium officinale

1320. Torilis arvensis subsp. arvensis

1313. Smyrnium creticum

1314. Smyrnium olusatrum

1315. Smyrnium perfoliatum subsp. rotundifolium

1316. Thapsia garganica

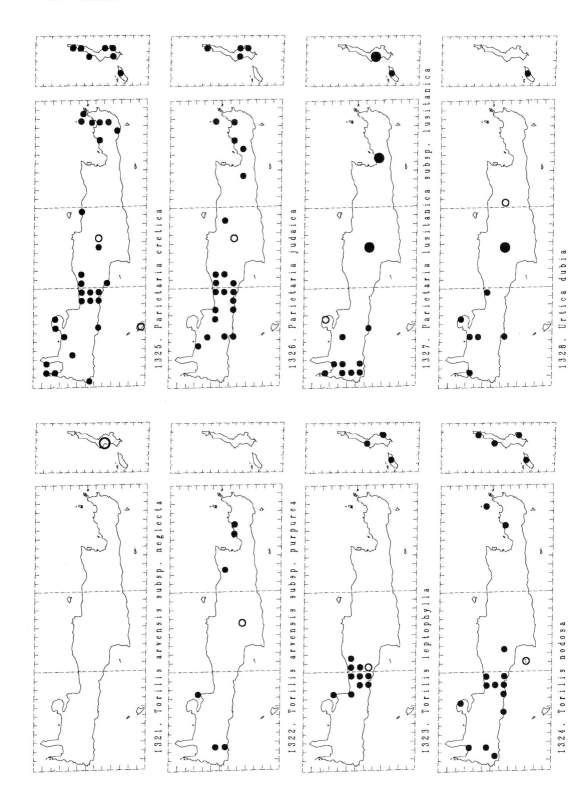

1321. Torilis arvensis subsp. neglecta

1322. Torilis arvensis subsp. purpurea

1323. Torilis leptophylla

1324. Torilis nodosa

1325. Parietaria cretica

1326. Parietaria judaica

1327. Parietaria lusitanica subsp. lusitanica

1328. Urtica dubia

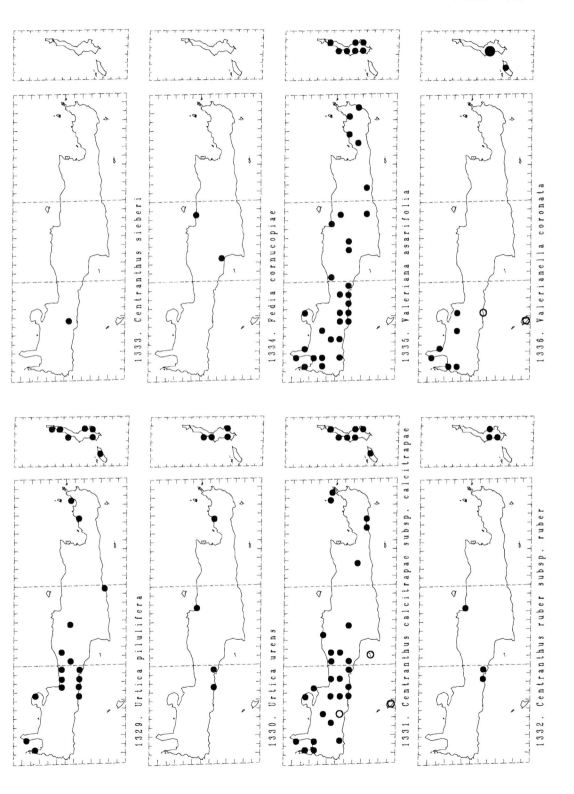

1333. Centranthus sieberi

1334. Fedia cornucopiae

1335. Valeriana asarifolia

1336. Valerianella coronata

1329. Urtica pilulifera

1330. Urtica urens

1331. Centranthus calcitrapae subsp. calcitrapae

1332. Centranthus ruber subsp. ruber

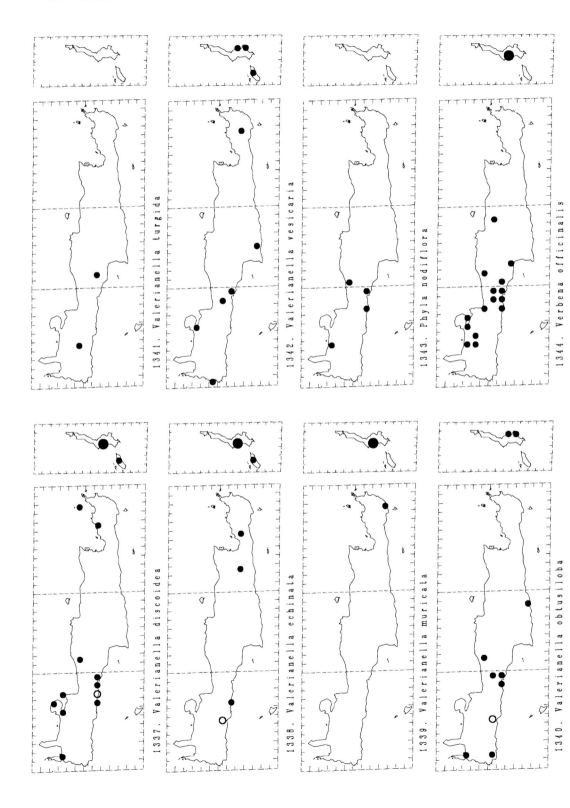

1341. Valerianella turgida

1342. Valerianella vesicaria

1343. Phyla nodiflora

1344. Verbena officinalis

1337. Valerianella discoidea

1338. Valerianella echinata

1339. Valerianella muricata

1340. Valerianella obtusiloba

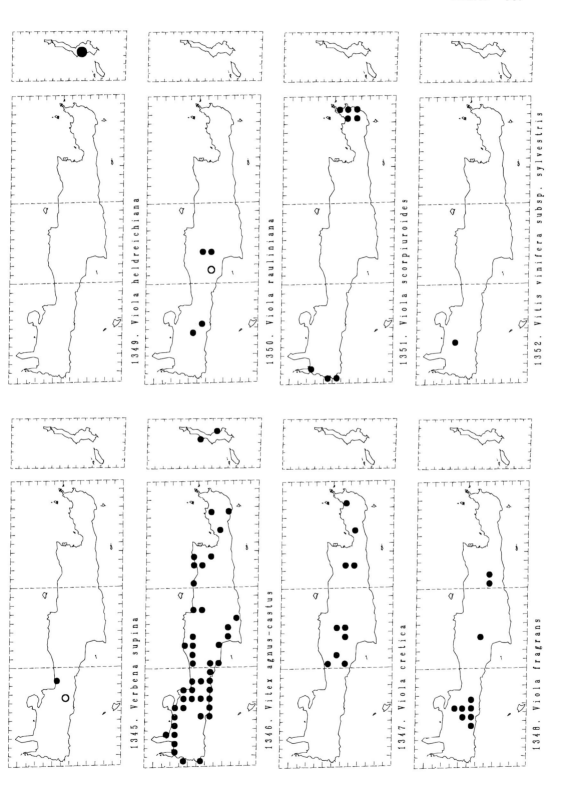

1349. Viola heldreichiana

1350. Viola rauliniana

1351. Viola scorpiuroides

1352. Vitis vinifera subsp. sylvestris

1345. Verbena supina

1346. Vitex agnus-castus

1347. Viola cretica

1348. Viola fragrans

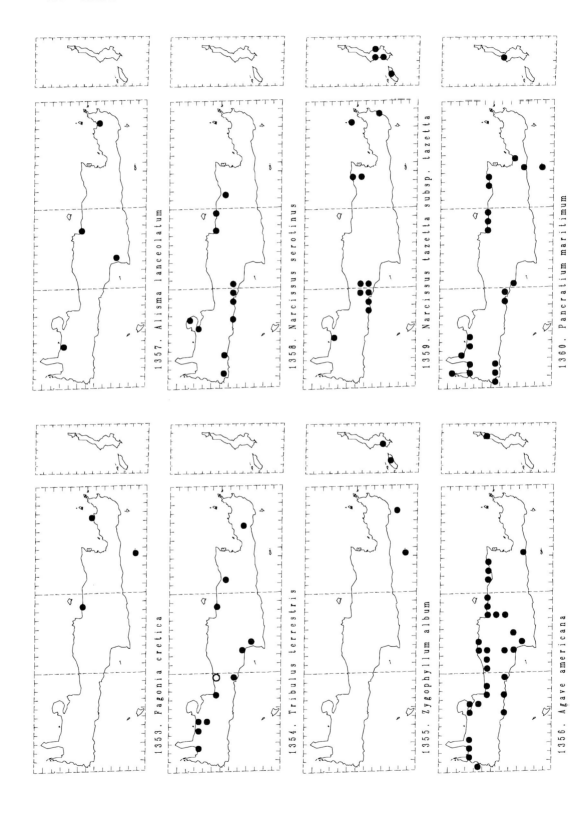

1353. Fagonia cretica

1354. Tribulus terrestris

1355. Zygophyllum album

1356. Agave americana

1357. Alisma lanceolatum

1358. Narcissus serotinus

1359. Narcissus tazetta subsp. tazetta

1360. Pancratium maritimum

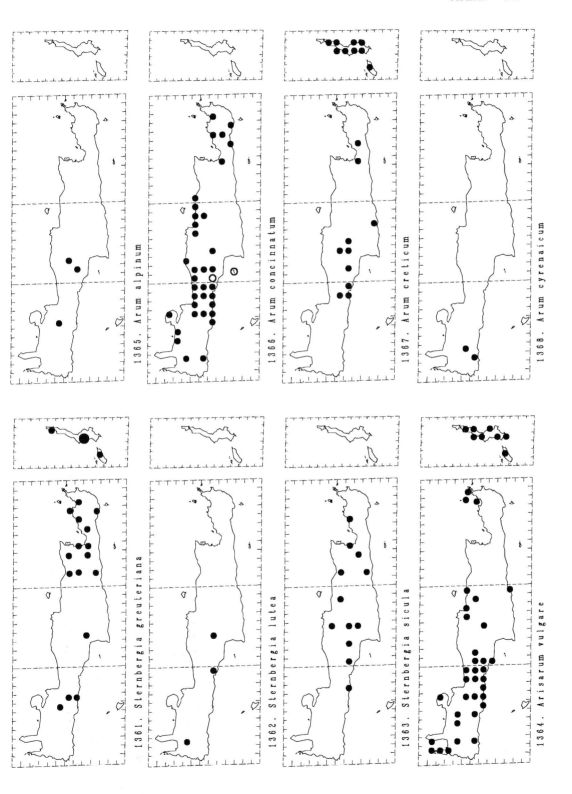

1361. Sternbergia greuteriana

1362. Sternbergia lutea

1363. Sternbergia sicula

1364. Arisarum vulgare

1365. Arum alpinum

1366. Arum concinnatum

1367. Arum creticum

1368. Arum cyrenaicum

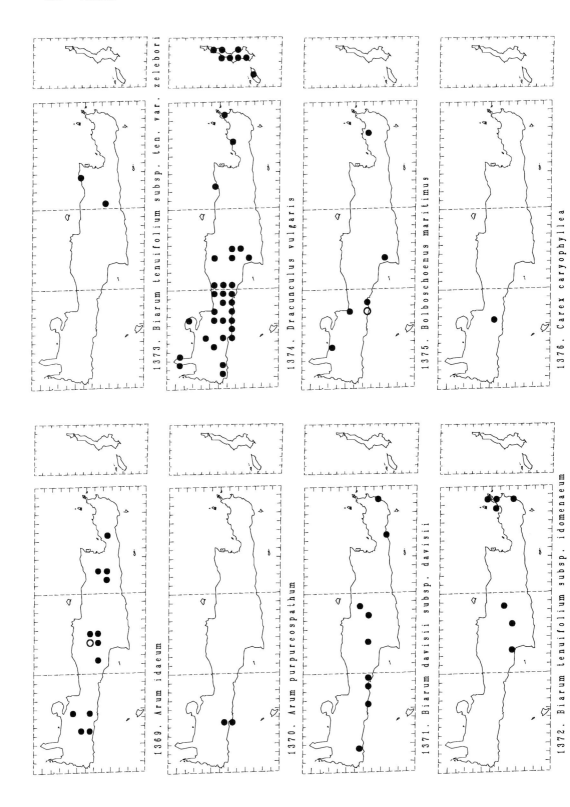

1373. Biarum tenuifolium subsp. ten. var. zelebori

1374. Dracunculus vulgaris

1375. Bolboschoenus maritimus

1376. Carex caryophyllea

1369. Arum idaeum

1370. Arum purpureospathum

1371. Biarum davisii subsp. davisii

1372. Biarum tenuifolium subsp. idomenaeum

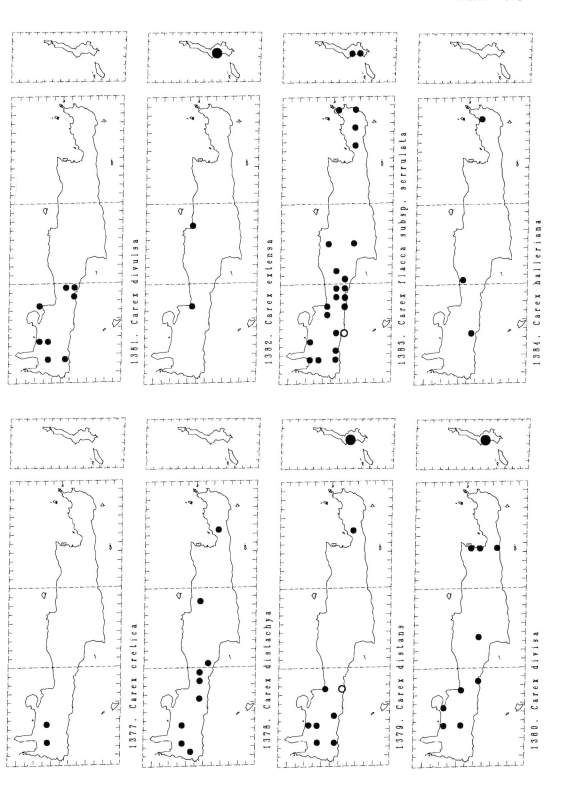

1377. Carex cretica

1378. Carex distachya

1379. Carex distans

1380. Carex divisa

1381. Carex divulsa

1382. Carex extensa

1383. Carex flacca subsp. serrulata

1384. Carex halleriana

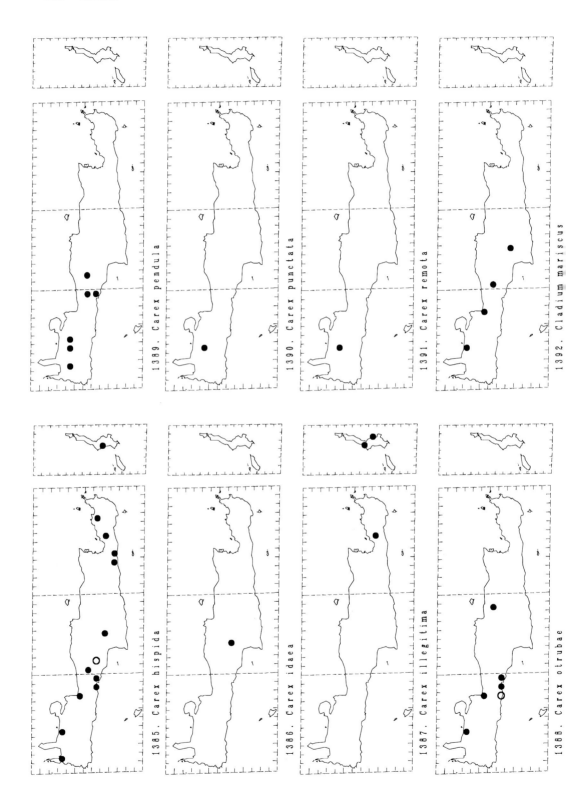

1389. Carex pendula

1390. Carex punctata

1391. Carex remota

1392. Cladium mariscus

1385. Carex hispida

1386. Carex idaea

1387. Carex illegitima

1388. Carex otrubae

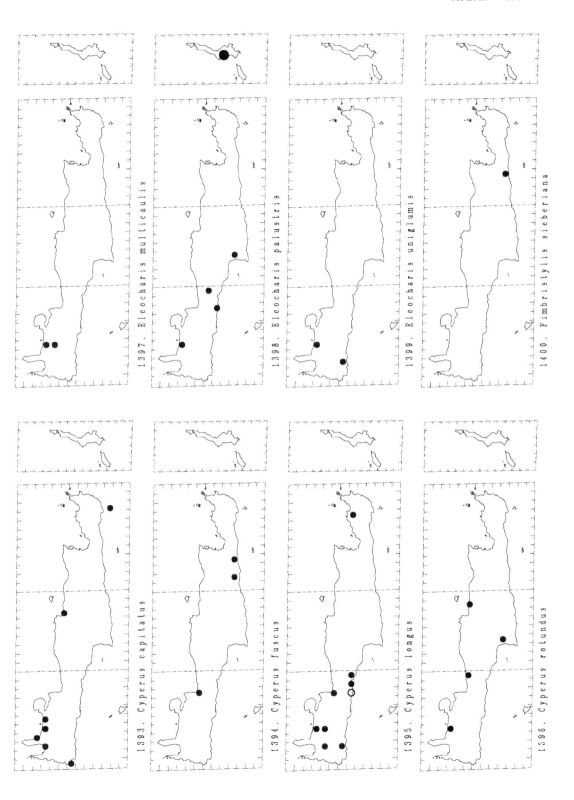

1393. Cyperus capitatus

1394. Cyperus fuscus

1395. Cyperus longus

1396. Cyperus rotundus

1397. Eleocharis multicaulis

1398. Eleocharis palustris

1399. Eleocharis uniglumis

1400. Fimbristylis sieberiana

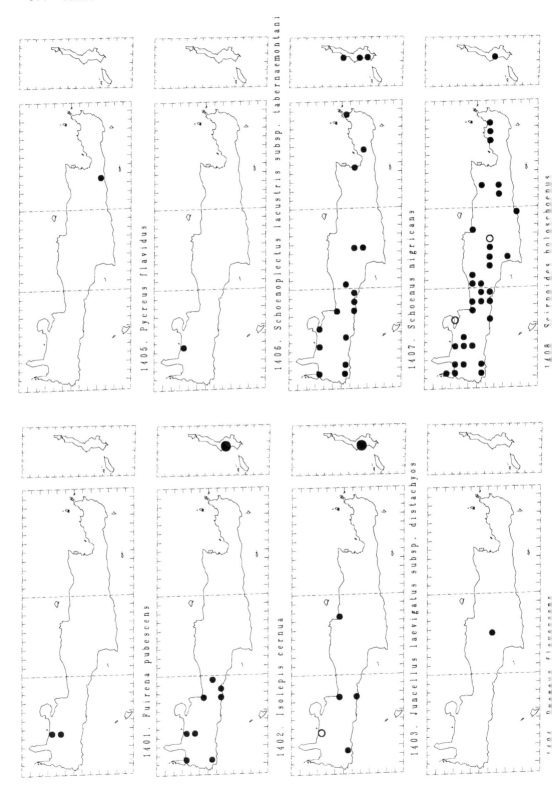

1405. Pycreus flavidus

1406. Schoenoplectus lacustris subsp. tabernaemontani

1407. Schoenus nigricans

1408. Scirpoides holoschoenus

1401. Fuirena pubescens

1402. Isolepis cernua

1403. Juncellus laevigatus subsp. distachyos

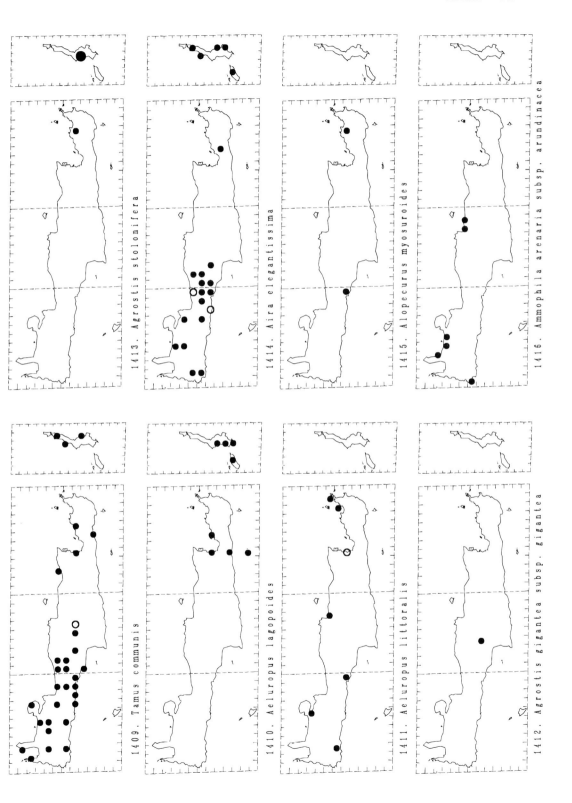

1413. Agrostis stolonifera

1414. Aira elegantissima

1415. Alopecurus myosuroides

1416. Ammophila arenaria subsp. arundinacea

1409. Tamus communis

1410. Aeluropus lagopoides

1411. Aeluropus littoralis

1412. Agrostis gigantea subsp. gigantea

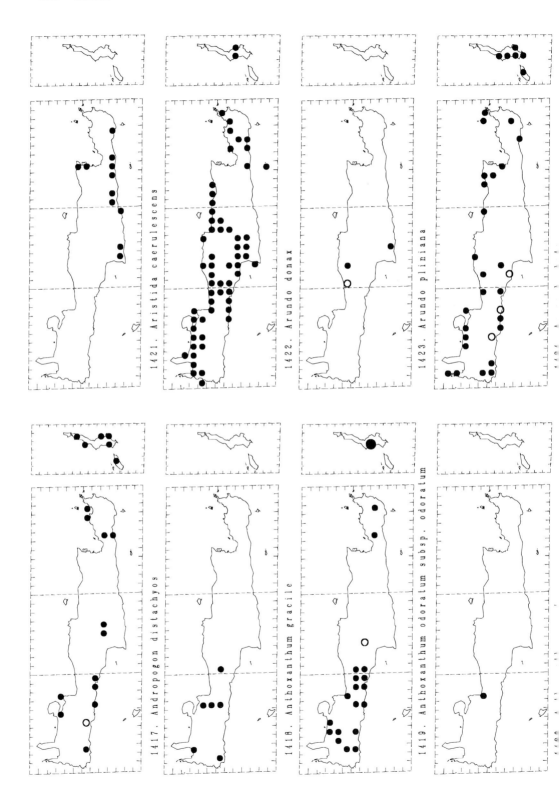

1421. *Aristida caerulescens*

1422. *Arundo donax*

1423. *Arundo pliniana*

1417. *Andropogon distachyos*

1418. *Anthoxanthum gracile*

1419. *Anthoxanthum odoratum subsp. odoratum*

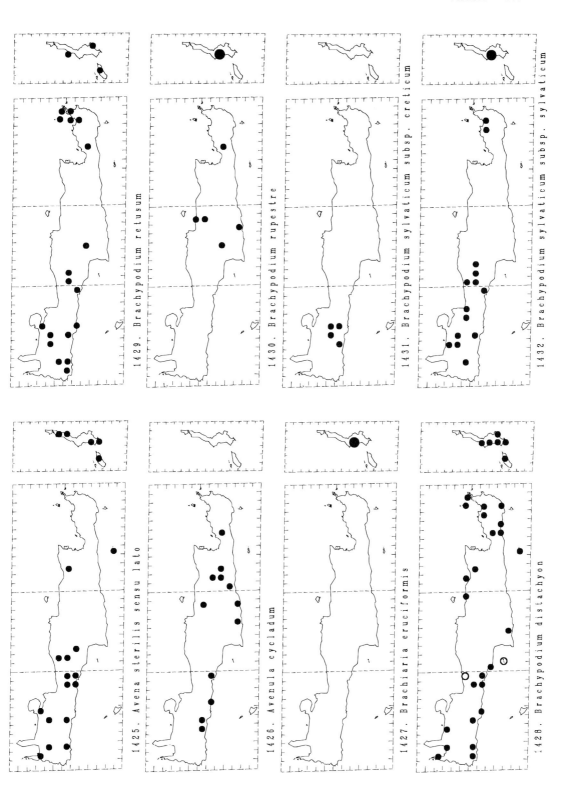

1429. Brachypodium retusum

1430. Brachypodium rupestre

1431. Brachypodium sylvaticum subsp. creticum

1432. Brachypodium sylvaticum subsp. sylvaticum

1425. Avena sterilis sensu lato

1426. Avenula cycladum

1427. Brachiaria eruciformis

1428. Brachypodium distachyon

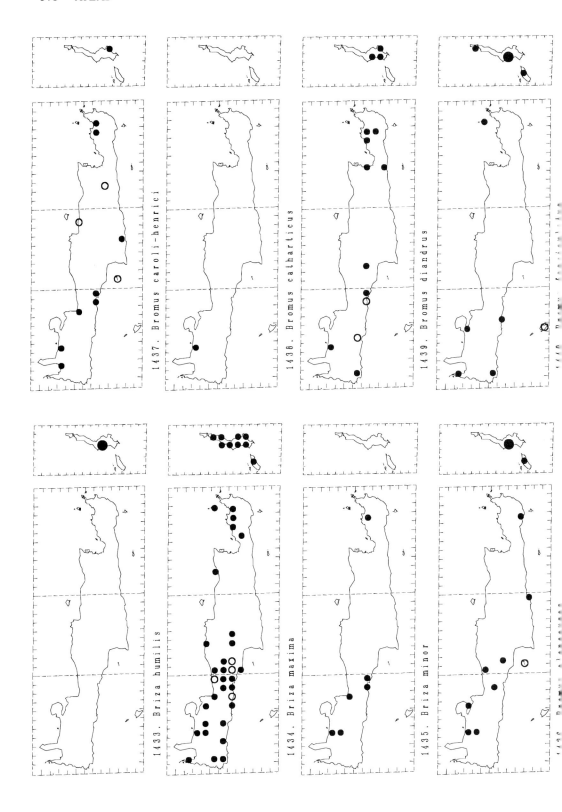

1437 . Bromus caroli-henrici

1438 . Bromus catharticus

1439 . Bromus diandrus

1433 . Briza humilis

1434 . Briza maxima

1435 . Briza minor

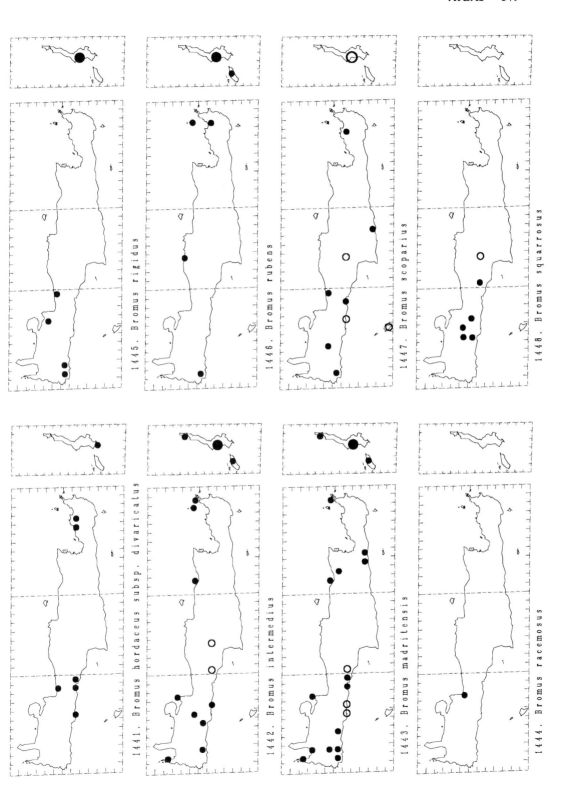

1441. Bromus hordaceus subsp. divaricatus

1442. Bromus intermedius

1443. Bromus madritensis

1444. Bromus racemosus

1445. Bromus rigidus

1446. Bromus rubens

1447. Bromus scoparius

1448. Bromus squarrosus

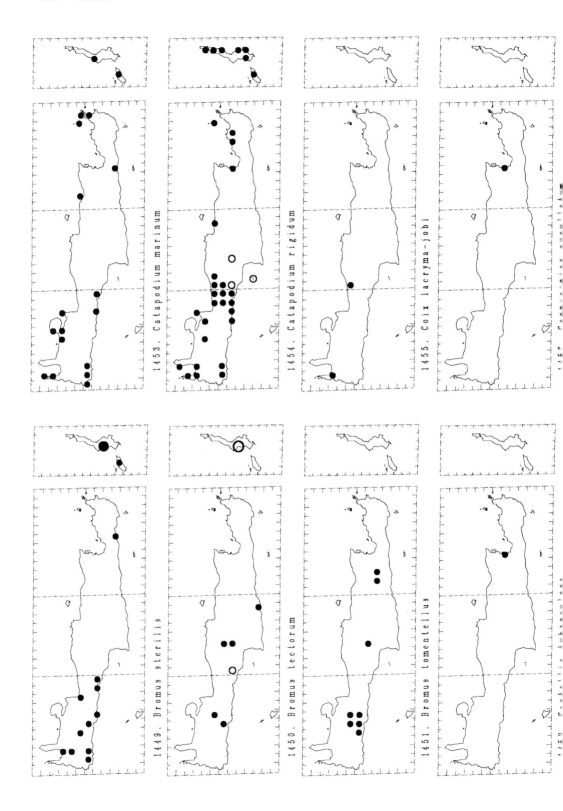

1453. Catapodium marinum

1454. Catapodium rigidum

1455. Coix lacryma-jobi

1449. Bromus sterilis

1450. Bromus tectorum

1451. Bromus tomentellus

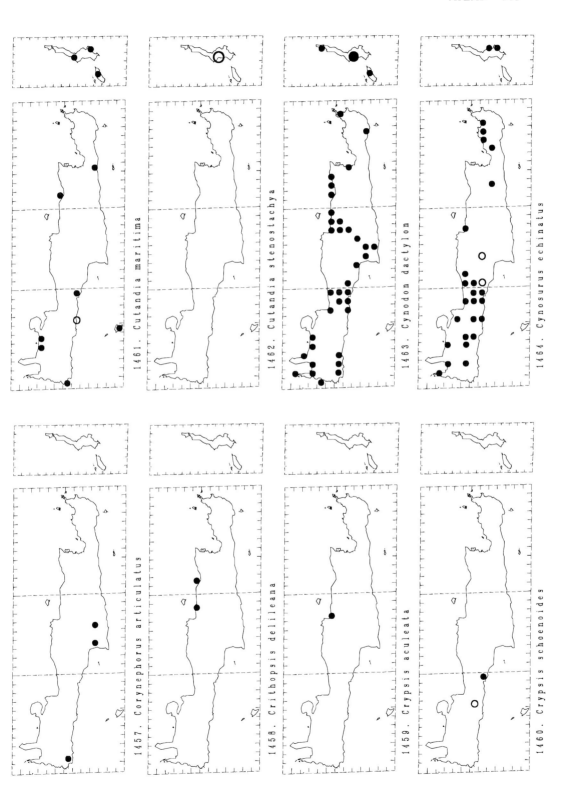

1457. Corynephorus articulatus

1458. Crithopsis delileana

1459. Crypsis aculeata

1460. Crypsis schoenoides

1461. Cutandia maritima

1462. Cutandia stenostachya

1463. Cynodon dactylon

1464. Cynosurus echinatus

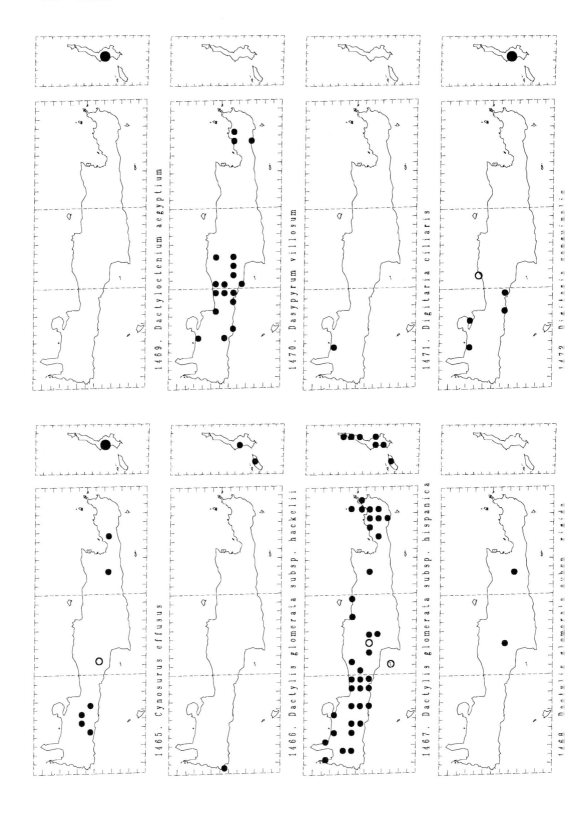

1469. Dactyloctenium aegyptium

1470. Dasypyrum villosum

1471. Digitaria ciliaris

1472. Digitaria sanguinalis

1465. Cynosurus effusus

1466. Dactylis glomerata subsp. hackelii

1467. Dactylis glomerata subsp. hispanica

1468. Dactylis glomerata subsp. rigida

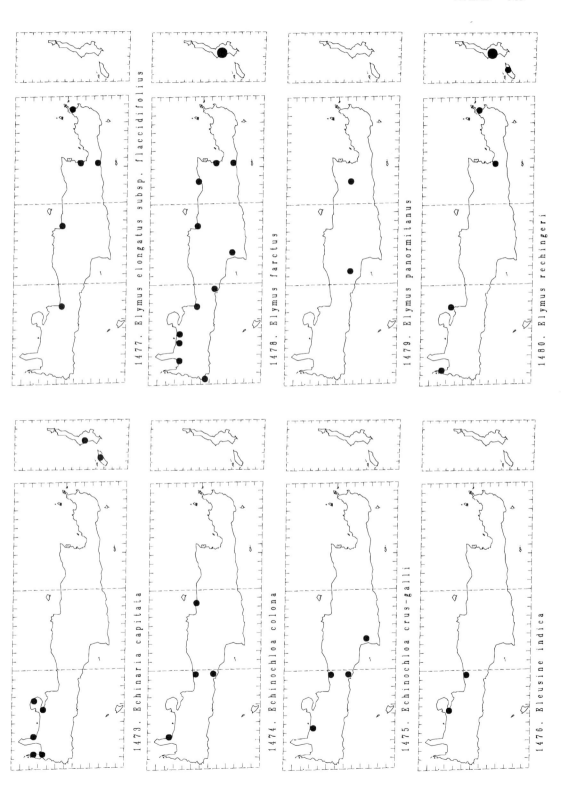

1477. Elymus elongatus subsp. flaccidifolius

1478. Elymus farctus

1479. Elymus panormitanus

1480. Elymus rechingeri

1473. Echinaria capitata

1474. Echinochloa colona

1475. Echinochloa crus-galli

1476. Eleusine indica

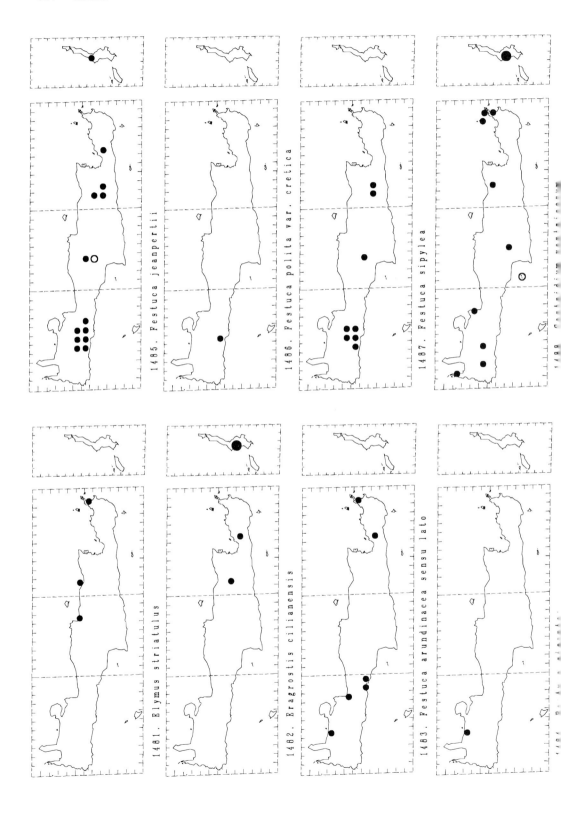

1485. Festuca jeanpertii

1486. Festuca polita var. cretica

1487. Festuca sipylea

1481. Elymus striatulus

1482. Eragrostis cilianensis

1483. Festuca arundinacea sensu lato

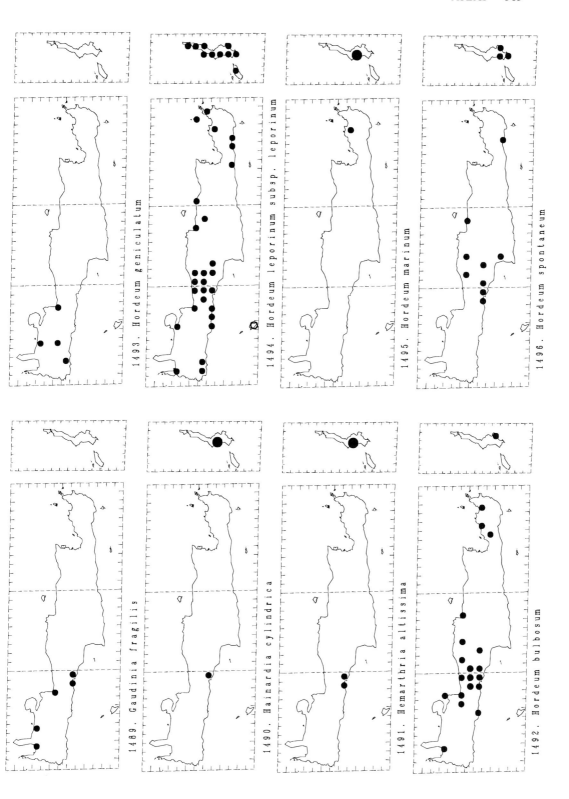

1489. Gaudinia fragilis

1490. Hainardia cylindrica

1491. Hemarthria altissima

1492. Hordeum bulbosum

1493. Hordeum geniculatum

1494. Hordeum leporinum subsp. leporinum

1495. Hordeum marinum

1496. Hordeum spontaneum

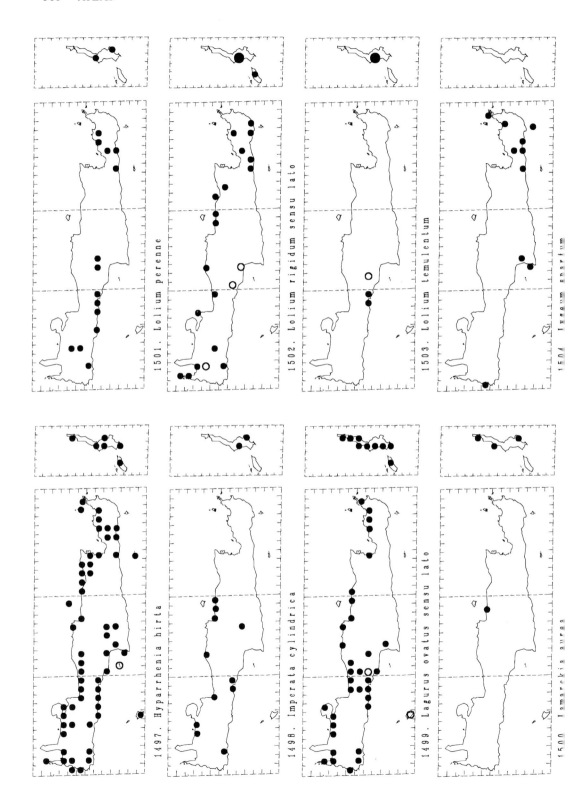

1497. Hyparrhenia hirta

1498. Imperata cylindrica

1499. Lagurus ovatus sensu lato

1500. Lamarckia aurea

1501. Lolium perenne

1502. Lolium rigidum sensu lato

1503. Lolium temulentum

1504. Lygeum spartum

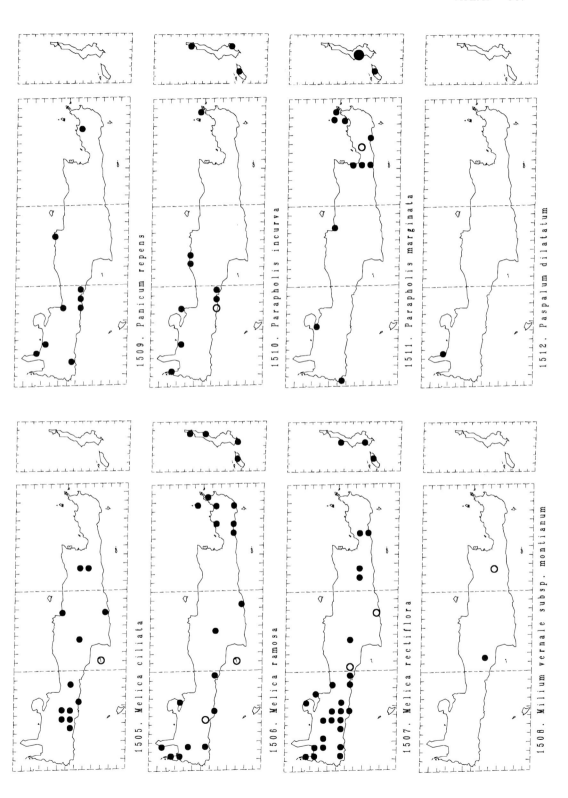

1505. Melica ciliata

1506. Melica ramosa

1507. Melica rectiflora

1508. Milium vernale subsp. montianum

1509. Panicum repens

1510. Parapholis incurva

1511. Parapholis marginata

1512. Paspalum dilatatum

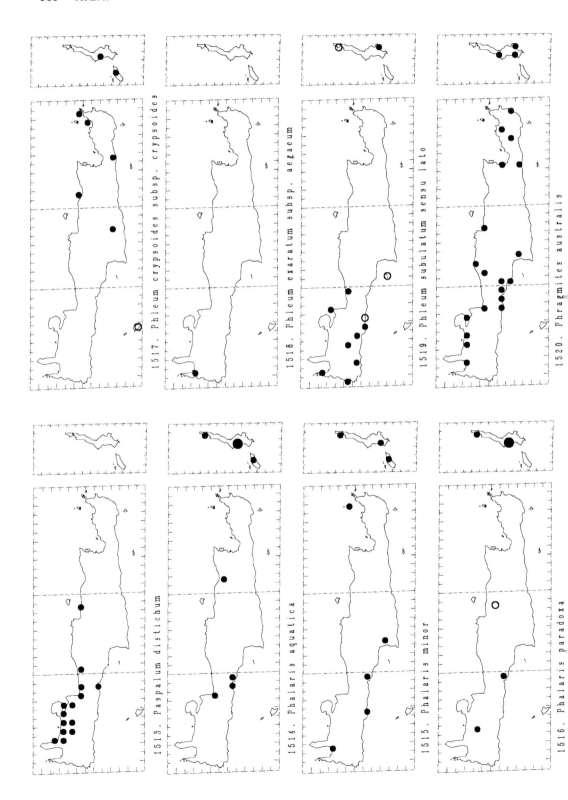

1517. Phleum crypsoides subsp. crypsoides

1518. Phleum exaratum subsp. aegaeum

1519. Phleum subulatum sensu lato

1520. Phragmites australis

1513. Paspalum distichum

1514. Phalaris aquatica

1515. Phalaris minor

1516. Phalaris paradoxa

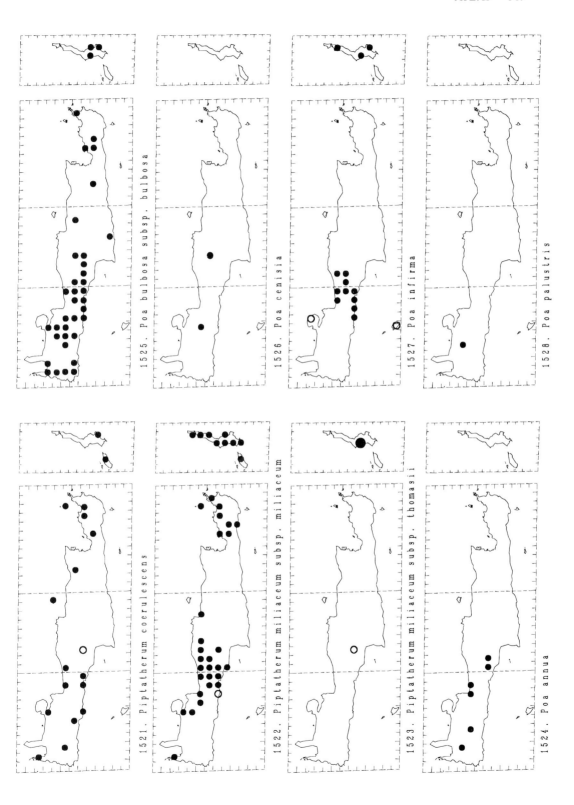

1525. Poa bulbosa subsp. bulbosa

1526. Poa cenisia

1527. Poa infirma

1528. Poa palustris

1521. Piptatherum coerulescens

1522. Piptatherum miliaceum subsp. miliaceum

1523. Piptatherum miliaceum subsp. thomasii

1524. Poa annua

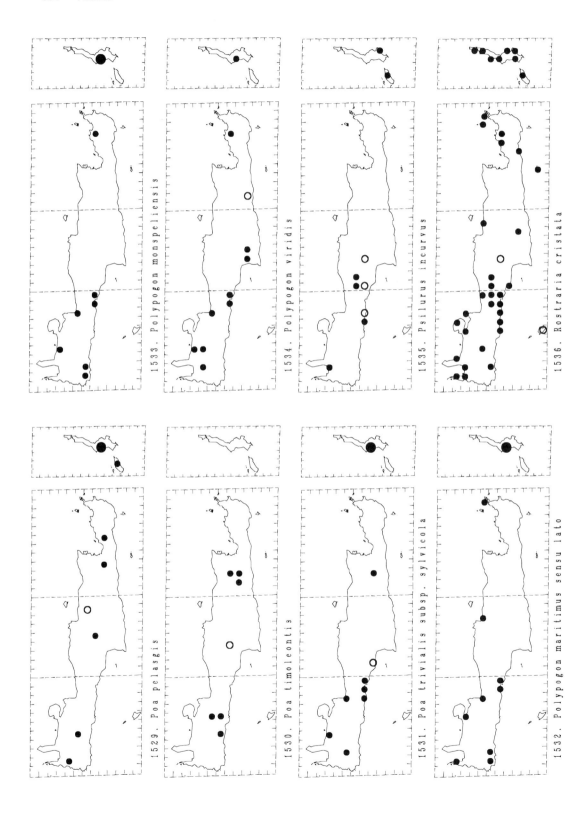

1533. Polypogon monspeliensis

1534. Polypogon viridis

1535. Psilurus incurvus

1536. Rostraria cristata

1529. Poa pelasgis

1530. Poa timoleontis

1531. Poa trivialis subsp. sylvicola

1532. Polypogon maritimus sensu lato

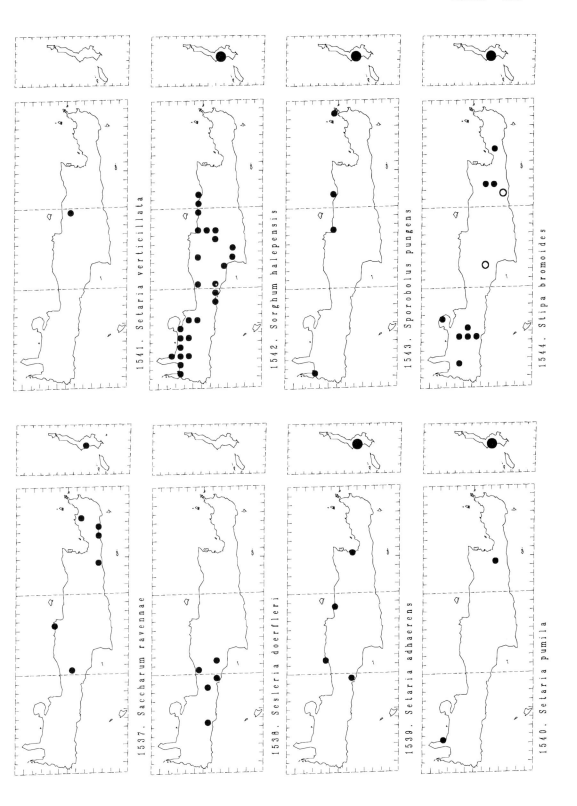

1541. Setaria verticillata

1542. Sorghum halepensis

1543. Sporobolus pungens

1544. Stipa bromoides

1537. Saccharum ravennae

1538. Sesleria doerfleri

1539. Setaria adhaerens

1540. Setaria pumila

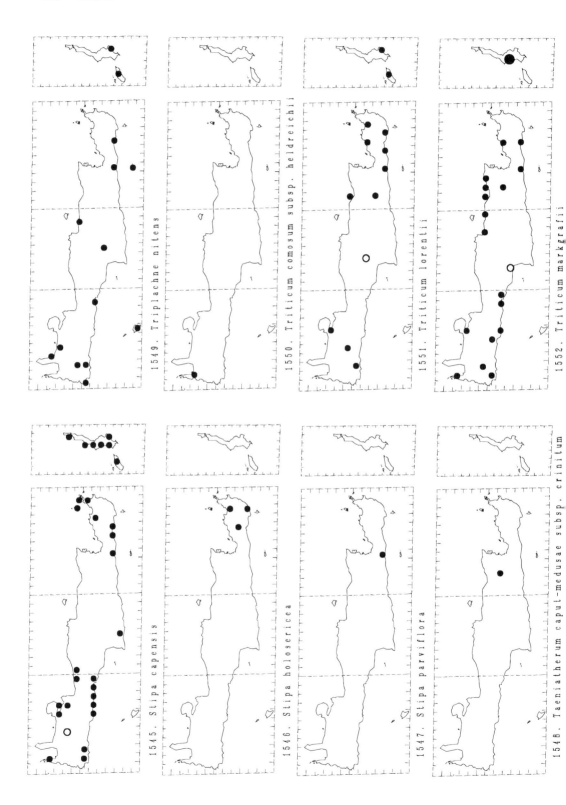

1549. Triplachne nitens

1550. Triticum comosum subsp. heldreichii

1551. Triticum lorentii

1552. Triticum markgrafii

1545. Stipa capensis

1546. Stipa holosericea

1547. Stipa parviflora

1548. Taeniatherum caput-medusae subsp. crinitum

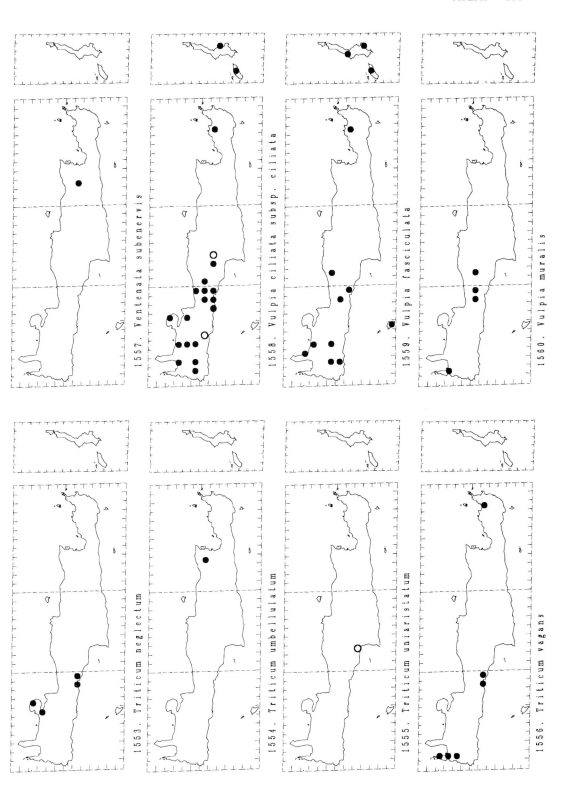

1557. Ventenata subenervis

1558. Vulpia ciliata subsp. ciliata

1559. Vulpia fasciculata

1560. Vulpia muralis

1553. Triticum neglectum

1554. Triticum umbellulatum

1555. Triticum uniaristatum

1556. Triticum vagans

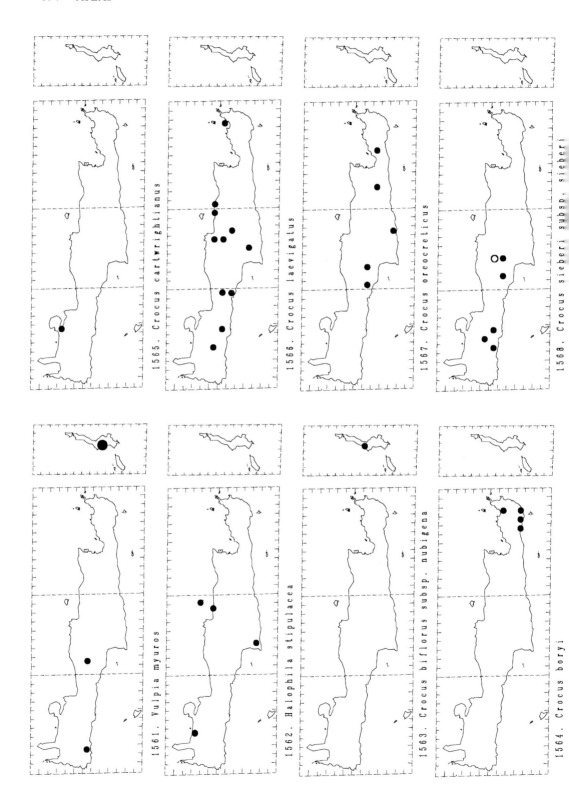

1565. Crocus cartwrightianus

1566. Crocus laevigatus

1567. Crocus oreocreticus

1568. Crocus sieberi subsp. sieberi

1561. Vulpia myuros

1562. Halophila stipulacea

1563. Crocus biflorus subsp. nubigena

1564. Crocus boryi

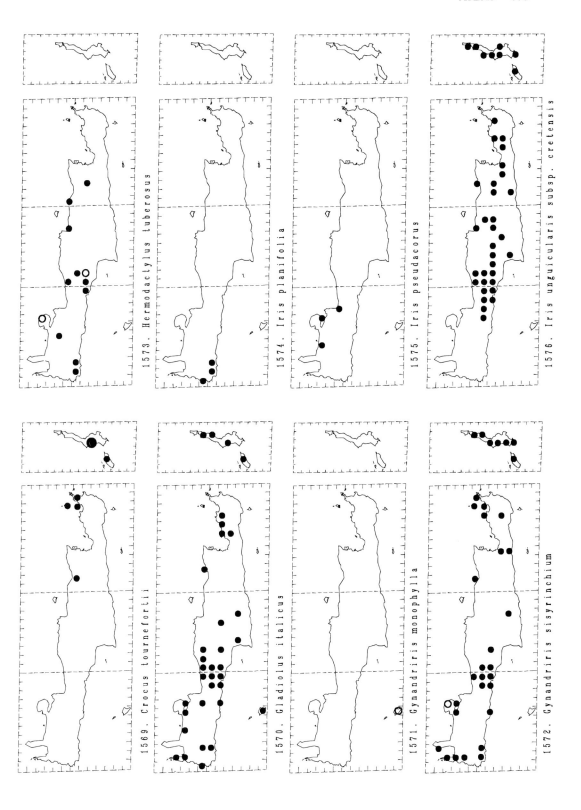

1573. Hermodactylus tuberosus

1574. Iris planifolia

1575. Iris pseudacorus

1576. Iris unguicularis subsp. cretensis

1569. Crocus tournefortii

1570. Gladiolus italicus

1571. Gynandriris monophylla

1572. Gynandriris sisyrinchium

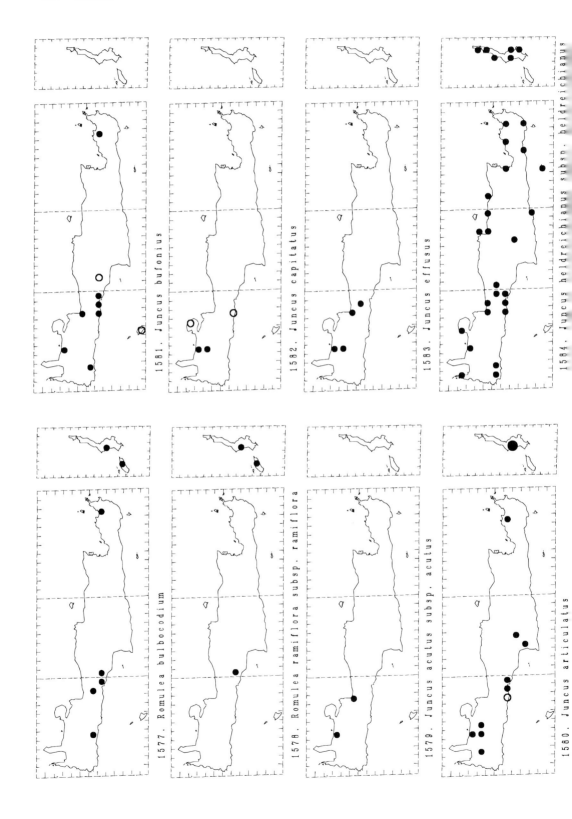

1581. Juncus bufonius

1582. Juncus capitatus

1583. Juncus effusus

1584. Juncus heldreichianus subsp. heldreichianus

1577. Romulea bulbocodium

1578. Romulea ramiflora subsp. ramiflora

1579. Juncus acutus subsp. acutus

1580. Juncus articulatus

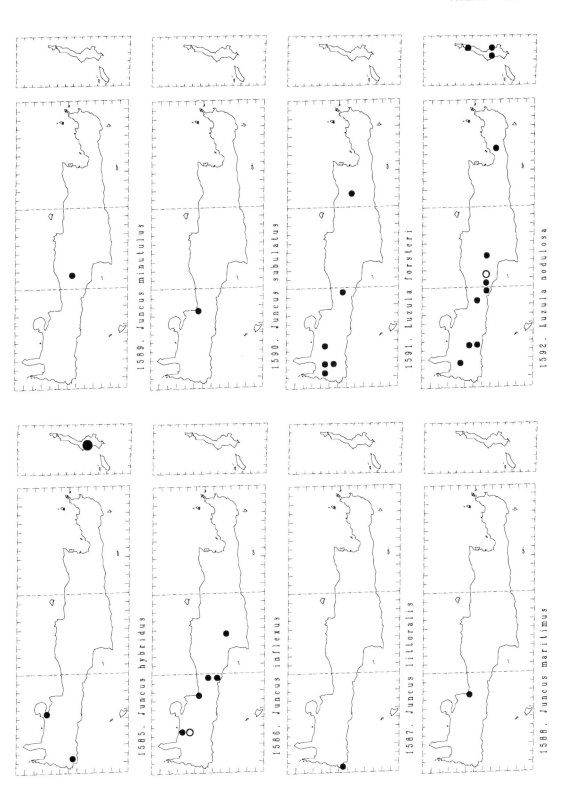

1589. Juncus minutulus

1590. Juncus subulatus

1591. Luzula forsteri

1592. Luzula nodulosa

1585. Juncus hybridus

1586. Juncus inflexus

1587. Juncus littoralis

1588. Juncus maritimus

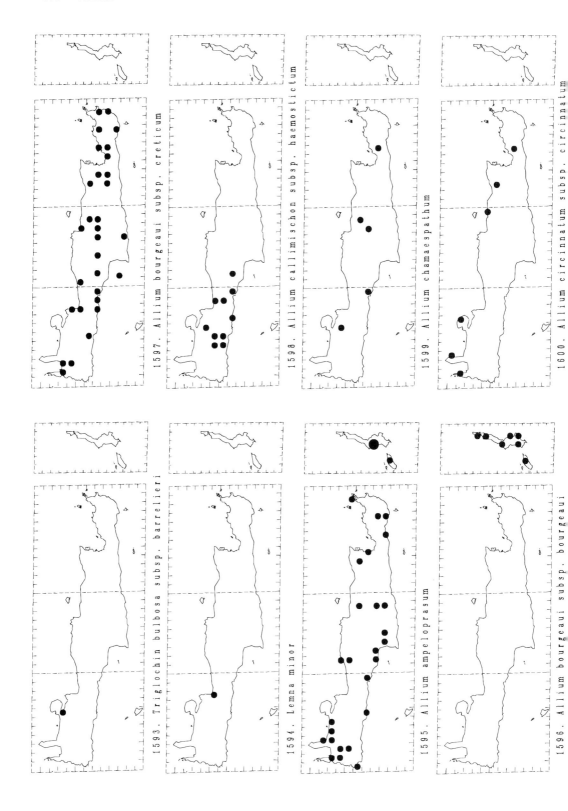

1597. Allium bourgeaui subsp. creticum

1598. Allium callimischon subsp. haemostictum

1599. Allium chamaespathum

1600. Allium circinnatum subsp. circinnatum

1593. Triglochin bulbosa subsp. barrelieri

1594. Lemna minor

1595. Allium ampeloprasum

1596. Allium bourgeaui subsp. bourgeaui

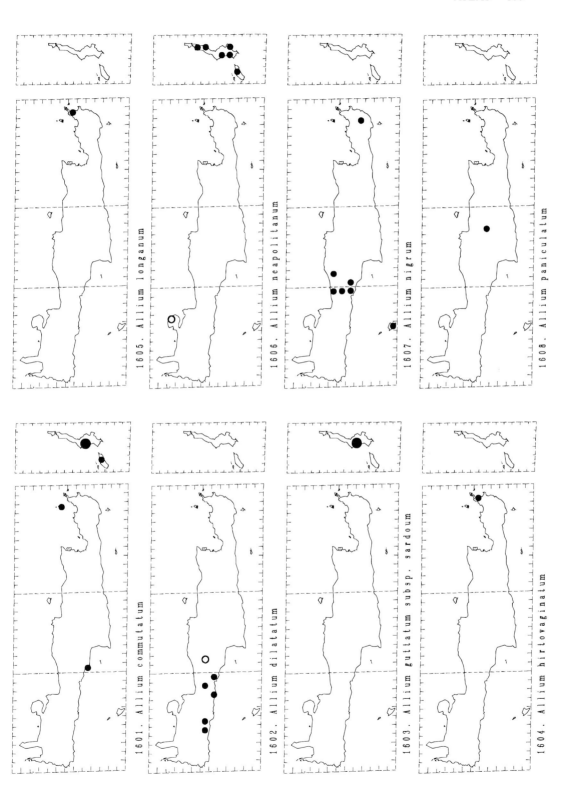

1605. Allium longanum

1606. Allium neapolitanum

1607. Allium nigrum

1608. Allium paniculatum

1601. Allium commutatum

1602. Allium dilatatum

1603. Allium guttatum subsp. sardoum

1604. Allium hirtovaginatum

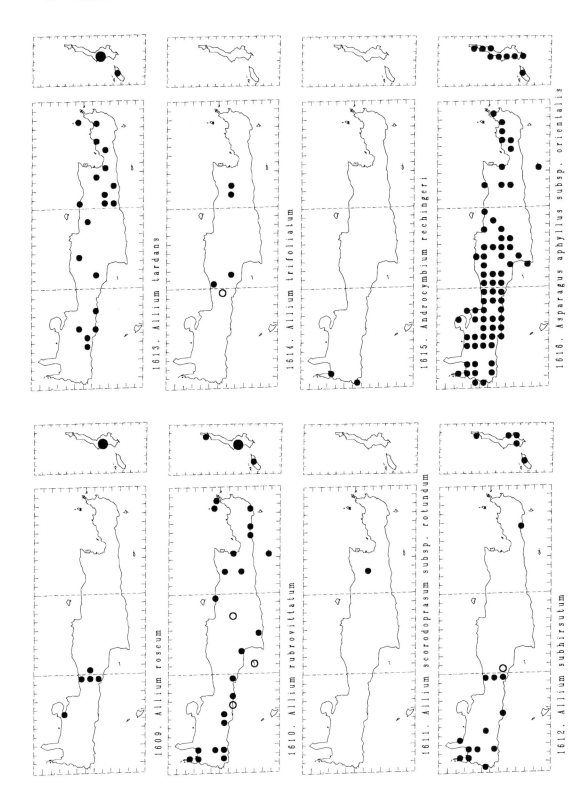

1613. Allium tardans

1614. Allium trifoliatum

1615. Androcymbium rechingeri

1616. Asparagus aphyllus subsp. orientalis

1609. Allium roseum

1610. Allium rubrovittatum

1611. Allium scorodoprasum subsp. rotundum

1612. Allium subhirsutum

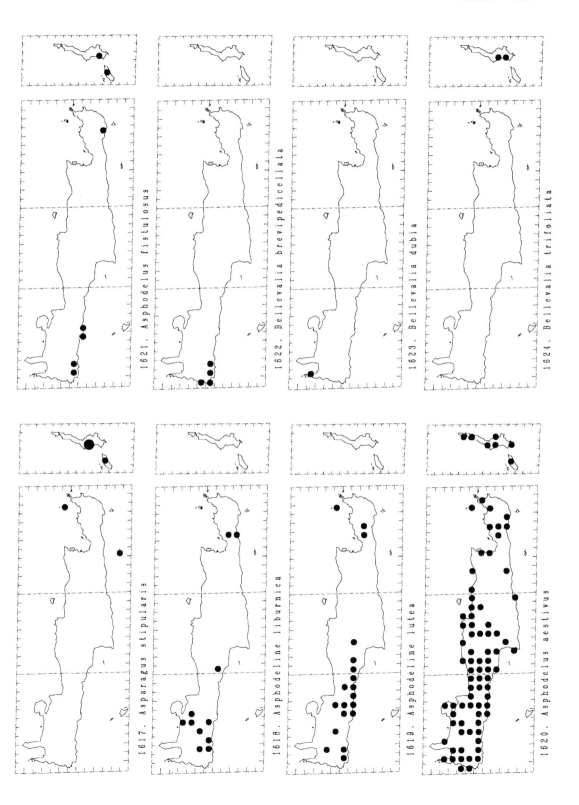

1617. Asparagus stipularis

1618. Asphodeline liburnica

1619. Asphodeline lutea

1620. Asphodelus aestivus

1621. Asphodelus fistulosus

1622. Bellevalia brevipedicellata

1623. Bellevalia dubia

1624. Bellevalia trifoliata

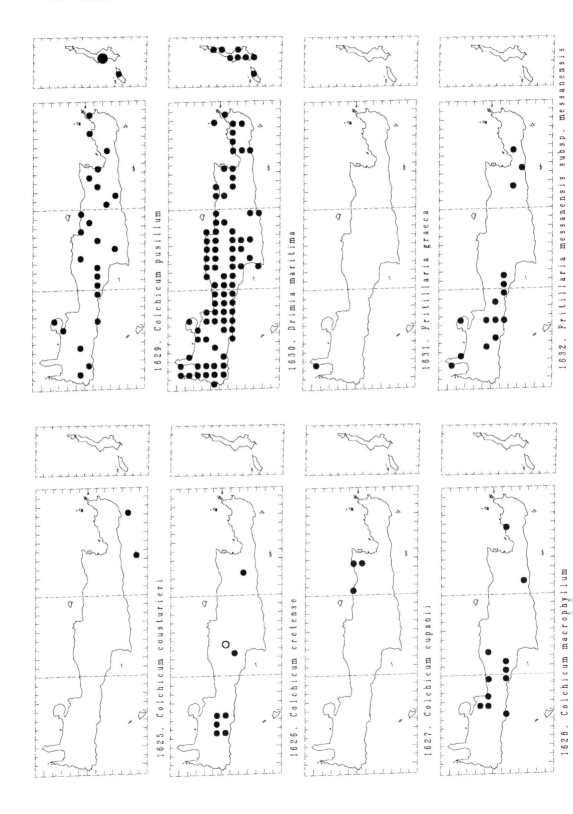

1625. Colchicum cousturieri

1626. Colchicum cretense

1627. Colchicum cupanii

1628. Colchicum macrophyllum

1629. Colchicum pusillum

1630. Drimia maritima

1631. Fritillaria graeca

1632. Fritillaria messanensis subsp. messanensis

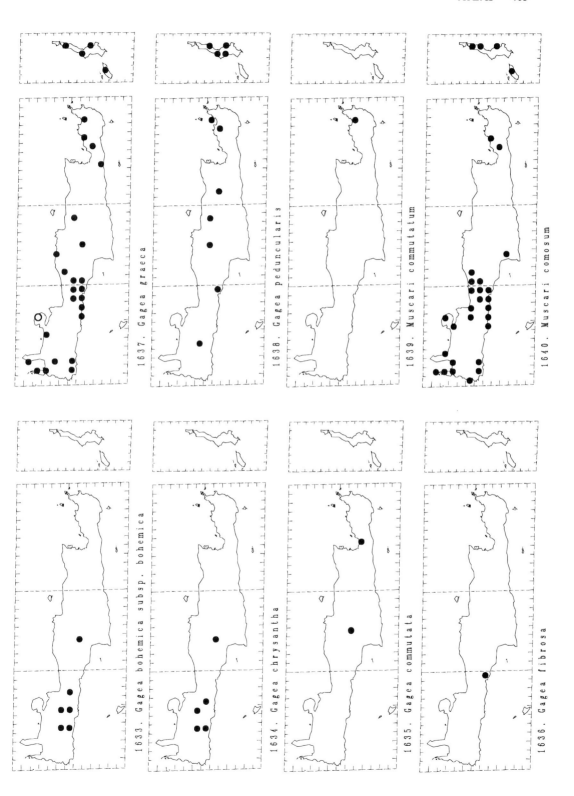

1637. Gagea graeca

1638. Gagea peduncularis

1639. Muscari commutatum

1640. Muscari comosum

1633. Gagea bohemica subsp. bohemica

1634. Gagea chrysantha

1635. Gagea commutata

1636. Gagea fibrosa

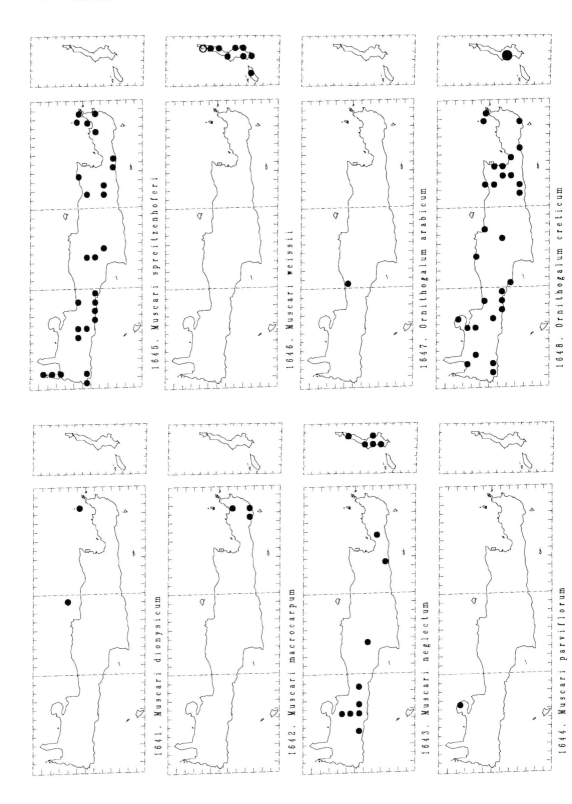

1641. Muscari dionysicum

1642. Muscari macrocarpum

1643. Muscari neglectum

1644. Muscari parviflorum

1645. Muscari spreitzenhoferi

1646. Muscari weissii

1647. Ornithogalum arabicum

1648. Ornithogalum creticum

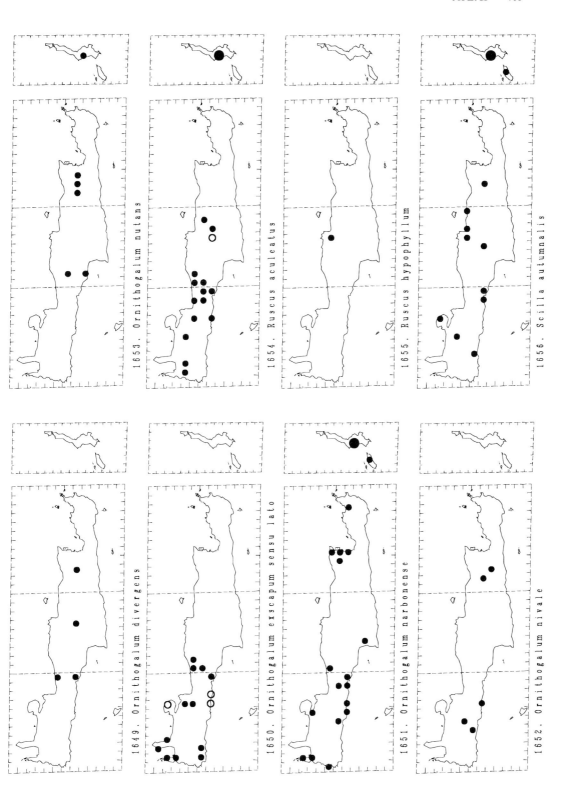

1649. Ornithogalum divergens

1650. Ornithogalum exscapum sensu lato

1651. Ornithogalum narbonense

1652. Ornithogalum nivale

1653. Ornithogalum nutans

1654. Ruscus aculeatus

1655. Ruscus hypophyllum

1656. Scilla autumnalis

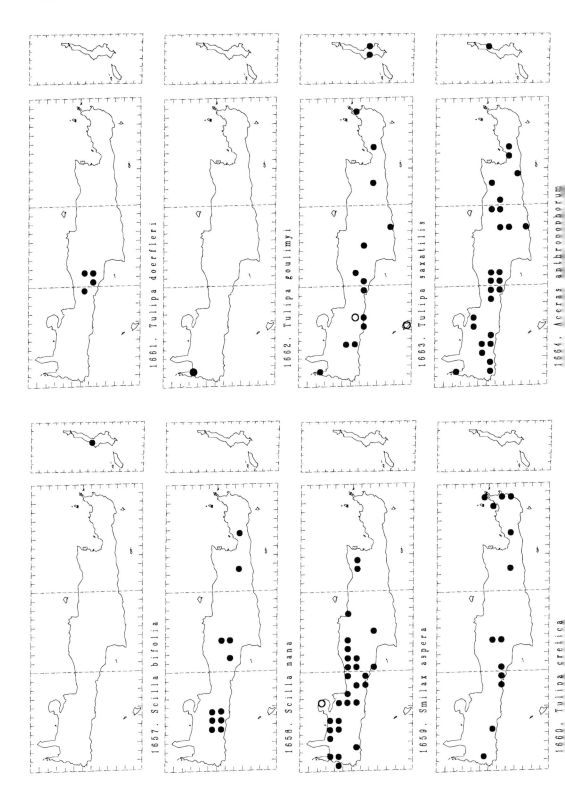

1661. Tulipa doerfleri

1662. Tulipa goulimyi

1663. Tulipa saxatilis

1664. Aceras anthropophorum

1657. Scilla bifolia

1658. Scilla nana

1659. Smilax aspera

1660. Tulipa cretica

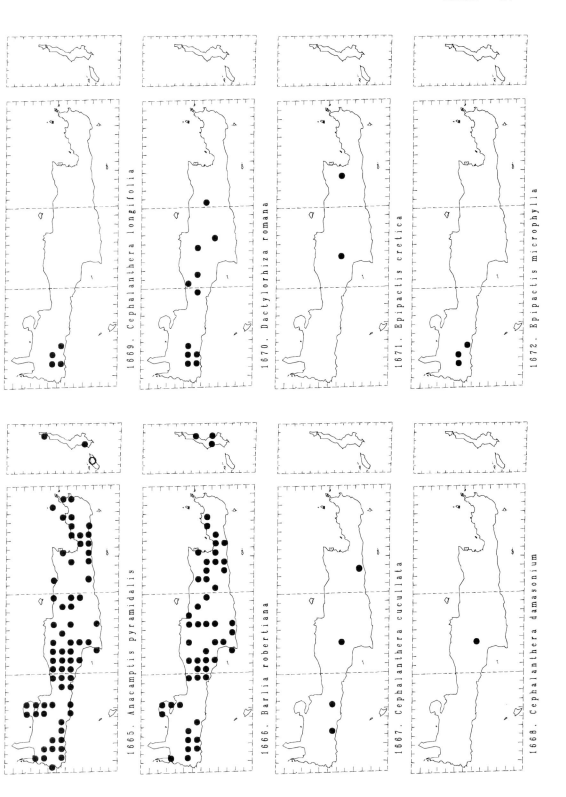

1669. Cephalanthera longifolia

1670. Dactylorhiza romana

1671. Epipactis cretica

1672. Epipactis microphylla

1665. Anacamptis pyramidalis

1666. Barlia robertiana

1667. Cephalanthera cucullata

1668. Cephalanthera damasonium

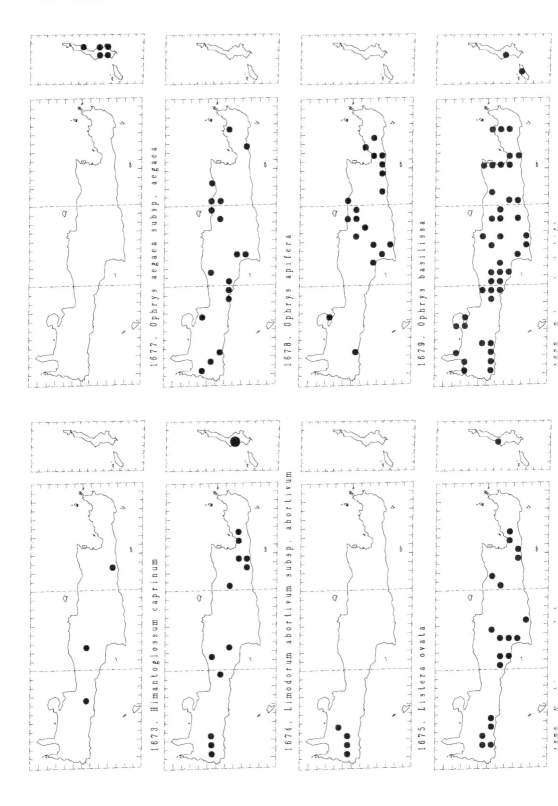

1673. Himantoglossum caprinum

1674. Limodorum abortivum subsp. abortivum

1675. Listera ovata

1677. Ophrys aegaea subsp. aegaea

1678. Ophrys apifera

1679. Ophrys basilissa

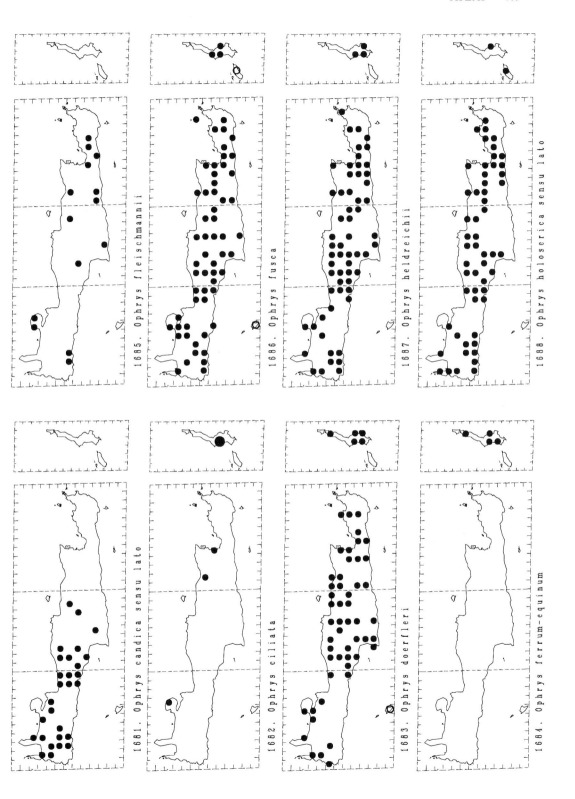

1685. Ophrys fleischmannii

1686. Ophrys fusca

1687. Ophrys heldreichii

1688. Ophrys holoserica sensu lato

1681. Ophrys candica sensu lato

1682. Ophrys ciliata

1683. Ophrys doerfleri

1684. Ophrys ferrum-equinum

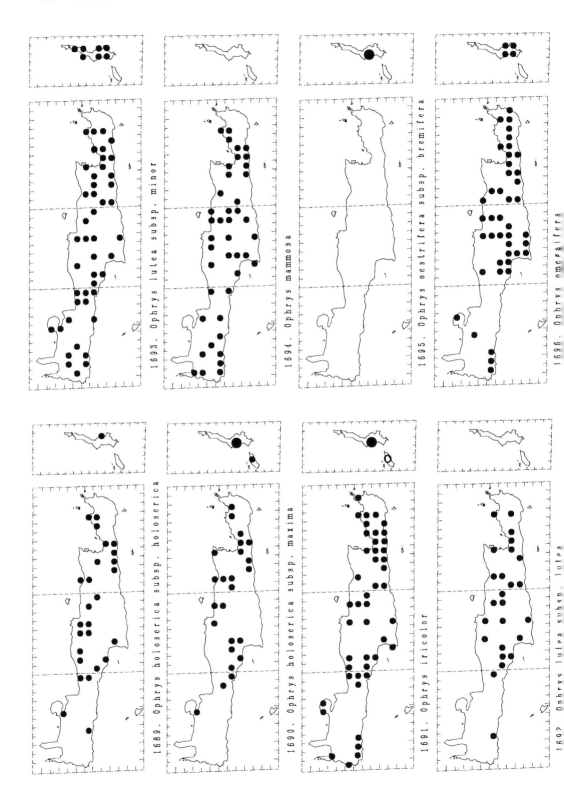

1693. Ophrys lutea subsp. minor

1694. Ophrys mammosa

1695. Ophrys oestrifera subsp. bremifera

1696. Ophrys omegaifera

1689. Ophrys holoserica subsp. holoserica

1690. Ophrys holoserica subsp. maxima

1691. Ophrys iricolor

1692. Ophrys lutea subsp. lutea

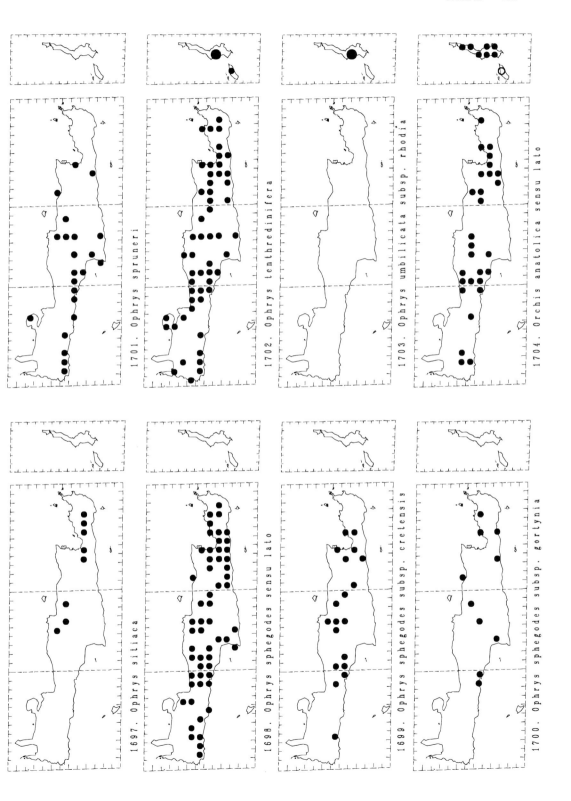

1697. Ophrys sitiaca

1698. Ophrys sphegodes sensu lato

1699. Ophrys sphegodes subsp. cretensis

1700. Ophrys sphegodes subsp. gortynia

1701. Ophrys spruneri

1702. Ophrys tenthredinifera

1703. Ophrys umbilicata subsp. rhodia

1704. Orchis anatolica sensu lato

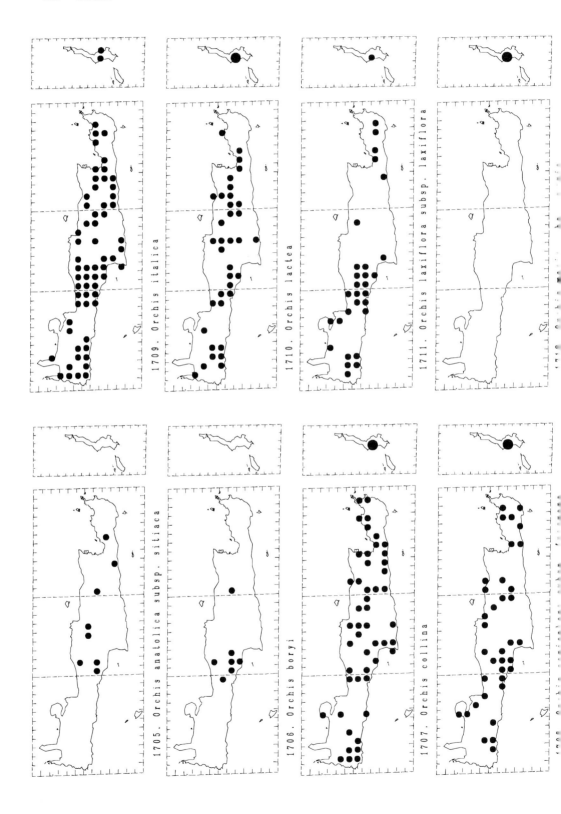

1705. Orchis anatolica subsp. sitiaca

1706. Orchis boryi

1707. Orchis collina

1709. Orchis italica

1710. Orchis lactea

1711. Orchis laxiflora subsp. laxiflora

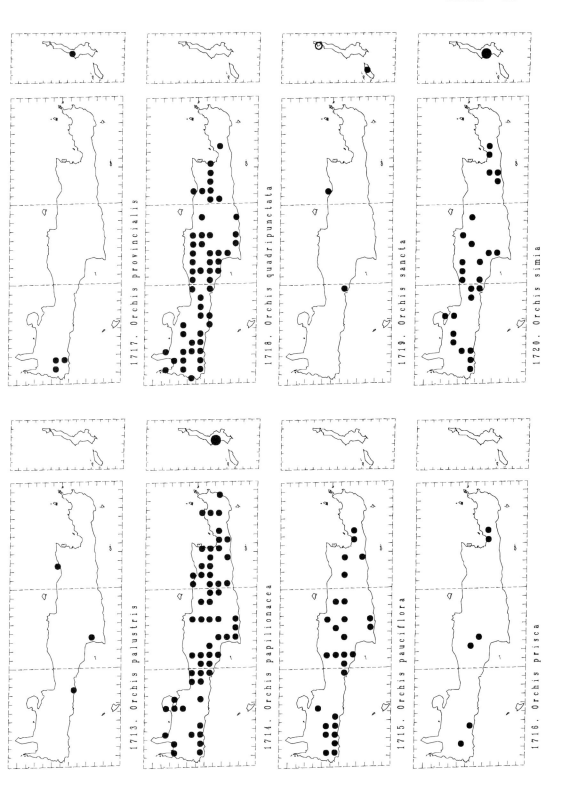

1717. Orchis provincialis

1718. Orchis quadripunctata

1719. Orchis sancta

1720. Orchis simia

1713. Orchis palustris

1714. Orchis papilionacea

1715. Orchis pauciflora

1716. Orchis prisca

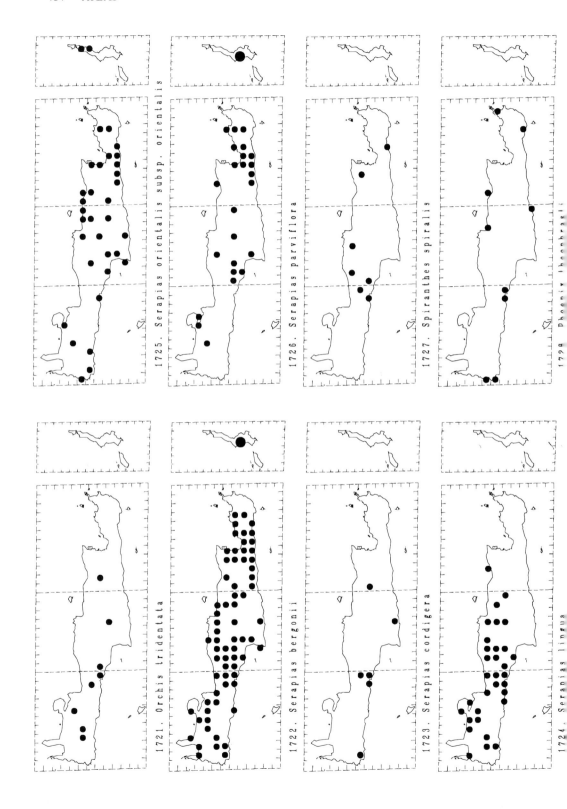

1725. Serapias orientalis subsp. orientalis

1726. Serapias parviflora

1727. Spiranthes spiralis

1728. Phoenix theophrasti

1721. Orchis tridentata

1722. Serapias bergonii

1723. Serapias cordigera

1724. Serapias lingua

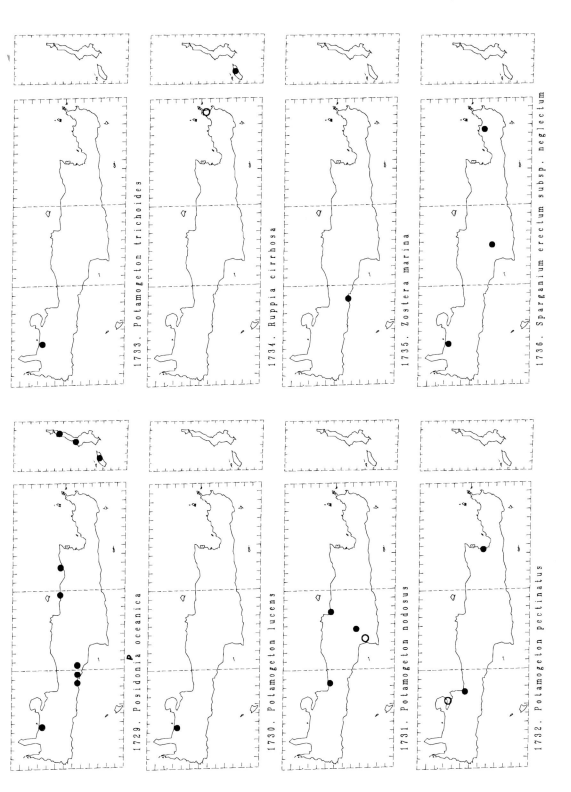

1729. Posidonia oceanica

1730. Potamogeton lucens

1731. Potamogeton nodosus

1732. Potamogeton pectinatus

1733. Potamogeton trichoides

1734. Ruppia cirrhosa

1735. Zostera marina

1736. Sparganium erectum subsp. neglectum

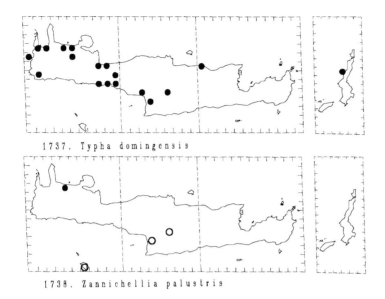

1737. Typha domingensis

1738. Zannichellia palustris

APPENDIX 1

TAXA APPARENTLY NOT RECORDED SINCE 1930

The following taxa appear not to have been recorded from Crete, the Karpathos island group, or the the Cretan area as a whole since 1930, even though they are given as present in these areas in the text. No records have been found in the literature seen (see references: p. 424), except possibly a few which are considered doubtful or are known to be erroneous, and no field observations or collections have been made by the authors. It is tempting to suggest, therefore, that a significant proportion of the taxa on this list may now be very rare or no longer extant in the areas given.

[ ] = introduced
○ = apparently not recorded since 1930
● = post-1930 records known
— = never recorded
? = doubtfully recorded

	From Crete	From the Karpathos island group
[Amaranthus hypochondriacus]	○	—
Lithospermum sibthorpianum	○	●
[Opuntia vulgaris]	○	—
Callitriche pulchra	○	—
Legousia falcata	○	●
L. speculum-veneris	●	○
Viburnum lantana	○	—
Vaccaria hispanica	●	○
Noaea mucronata	○	●
Fumana laevipes	○	●
Helianthemum aegyptiacum	○	○
H. sanguineum	○	—
H. syriacum	○	—
Achillea ligustica	○	—
Ambrosia maritima	○	—
Anthemis altissima	●	○
A. arvensis	●	○
A. melanolepis	○	—

417

	From Crete	From the Karpathos island group
Cardopatium corymbosum	○	—
Carthamus boissieri	○	●
Catananche lutea	○	●
Centaurea hyalolepis	○	—
Chamaemelum mixtum	○	—
Chlamydophora tridentata	○	—
Cnicus benedictus	○	—
Crepis micrantha	○	●
C. sancta	○	—
Cynara cardunculus	○	—
Hypochoeris cretensis	○	—
Pulicaria sicula	○	—
[Tanacetum parthenium]	○	—
[Xanthium saccharatum]	○	—
Xeranthemum inapertum	○	—
Convolvulus libanoticus	○	—
Cuscuta palaestina	○	●
Crassula vaillantii	○	—
Alyssum simplex	●	○
Coronopus squamatus	○	—
Draba heterocoma	—	○
Lepidium spinosum	●	○
Rorippa sylvestris	○	—
Sisymbrium irio	○	—
Chrozophora tinctoria	●	○
Euphorbia platyphyllos	○	—
E. taurinensis	○	—
E. terracina	○	—
E. valerianifolia	○	—
Erodium botrys	○	—
Ajuga iva	○	●
Lamium moschatum	○	●

	From Crete	From the Karpathos island group
Astragalus boeticus	○	●
A. echinatus	○	●
A. epiglottis	—	○
A. idaeus	○	—
A. peregrinus	○	—
Hippocrepis unisiliquosa	—	○
[Lathyrus sativus]	○	—
[Lens culinaris]	○	●
L. nigricans	○	●
Lotus conimbricensis	●	○
Lupinus albus subsp. **graecus**	○	—
L. angustifolius	●	○
Medicago doliata	○	—
Ononis diffusa	○	—
O. serrata	—	○
Ornithopus pinnatus	○	—
Trifolium barbeyi	—	○
T. bocconei	○	●
T. dasyurum	●	○
T. patens	○	—
T. squamosum	○	—
[Trigonella foenum-graecum]	○	—
T. gladiata	○	●
Vicia villosa subsp. **microphylla**	●	○
[Linum usitatissimum]	●	○
Alcea setosa	○	—
Althaea hirsuta	○	—
[Gossypium herbaceum]	○	—
Hibiscus trionum	○	—
Lavatera punctata	○	—
Malva nicaeensis	○	●
Orobanche alba	○	—

	From Crete	From the Karpathos island group
O. cernua	○	●
O. gracilis	○	—
O. grisebachii	○	●
[Papaver somniferum subsp. somniferum]	○	—
Roemeria hybrida	●	○
[Sesamum indicum]	○	—
Plantago squarrosa	●	○
Limonium hyssopifolium	○	●
Rumex pulcher subsp. anodontus	○	—
Reseda odorata	○	—
Rosa heckeliana	○	—
Crucianella imbricata	○	—
Galium incrassatum	○	—
G. verrucosum	○	●
Linaria micrantha	○	—
L. triphylla	○	—
Veronica acinifolia	○	—
V. agrestis	○	—
V. glauca subsp. glauca	○	—
Solanum luteum subsp. alatum	○	—
Bupleurum lancifolium	○	●
Daucus carota subsp. major	○	—
Torilis arvensis subsp. neglecta	?	○
Turgenia latifolia	○	—
Valerianella eriocarpa	○	—
V. hirsutissima	○	—
V. microcarpa	○	●
Viola odorata	○	—
V. reichenbachiana	○	—
Alisma plantago-aquatica	○	—
[Cyperus esculentus]	○	—
Schoenoplectus litoralis	○	●

	From Crete	From the Karpathos island group
Aira cupaniana	○	—
Alopecurus creticus	○	—
A. rendlei	○	—
Antinoria insularis	○	—
Arrhenatherum palaestinum	○	●
Avellinia michelii	○	—
Bromus lanceolatus	○	—
B. scoparius	●	○
B. tectorum	●	○
Cutandia stenostachya	—	○
Holcus lanatus	○	—
Lolium multiflorum	○	—
Phalaris coerulescens	○	●
Piptatherum miliaceum subsp. **thomasii**	○	●
Poa pratensis	○	—
Setaria viridis	○	—
Triticum uniaristatum	○	—
Vulpia ligustica	○	—
Gynandriris monophylla	○	—
Romulea columnae	○	—
Allium neapolitanum	○	●
Ruppia cirrhosa	○	●
R. maritima	○	●
Cymodocea nodosa	○	●

APPENDIX 2

TAXA RECORDED AS NEW TO KARPATHOS IN THIS CHECKLIST

The following taxa were recorded by the first two authors as new to Karpathos in April 1992, during the field trip supported by the Park Fund (Natural History Museum). The names are arranged in the order of this checklist; full details of records (localities, dates, specimens, etc.) will be published in a forthcoming paper (Turland & Chilton, in prep.)

* = new to Karpathos
** = new to the Karpathos island group
*** = new to the Cretan area
**** = new to Europe
[ ] = introduced

**   **Asplenium ruta-muraria** L.
**   **[Vinca major** L.]
**   **Hedera helix** L. (doubtfully native)
**   **[Opuntia ficus-barbarica** A.Berger]
**** **Asyneuma giganteum** (Boiss.) Bornm.
**   **Cerastium brachypetalum** Pers. sensu lato
*   **Sagina apetala** Ard.
*   **Sagina maritima** Don
**   **Beta maritima** L.
**   **Bellis sylvestris** Cirillo
**   **Centaurea calcitrapa** L.
**   **Rhagadiolus edulis** Gaertn. (not separated from *R. stellatus* (L.) Gaertn. in the text, but recorded on distribution map no. 436)
**   **Tyrimnus leucographus** (L.) Cass. (earlier records (Rechinger, 1943a: 655) are referable to *Carduus argentatus* L. (Greuter et al., 1983a: 52))
**   **Crassula alata** (Viv.) A.Berger
**   **Eruca sativa** Mill.
**   **Teesdalia coronopifolia** (J.P.Bergeret) Thell.
**   **Knautia integrifolia** (L.) Bertol.
*   **Euphorbia helioscopia** L.
**   **Erodium moschatum** (L.) L'Hér.
**   **Geranium tuberosum** L.
**   **Hypericum perforatum** L.
**   **Rosmarinus officinalis** L. (probably planted)
**   **Stachys arvensis** (L.) L.
**   **Lathyrus annua** L.
**   **[Vicia faba** L. (only casual)]
**   **Lavatera cretica** L.
**   **Plantago amplexicaulis** Cav.
**   **Ranunculus cupreus** Boiss. & Heldr.

**   **Linaria chalepensis** (L.) Mill.

*   **Scrophularia peregrina** L.

**   **Smyrnium olusatrum** L.

**   **[Agave americana L.]**

**   **Carex illegitima** Ces.

**   **Bromus diandrus** Roth

**   **Bromus hordeaceus** subsp. **divaricatus** (Bonnier & Layens) Kerguélen

**   **Hordeum spontaneum** K.Koch

**   **Imperata cylindrica** (L.) Raeusch.

*   **Lamarckia aurea** (L.) Moench

*   **Romulea ramiflora** Ten.

**   **Bellevalia trifoliata** (Ten.) Kunth (confirms occurrence in the Cretan area)

***   **Scilla bifolia** L.

**   **Typha domingensis** (Pers.) Steud.

REFERENCES

Entries prefixed with an asterisk (*) are sources of literature records used in compiling the distribution maps.

* **Ackermann, M. & Ackermann, M.** 1986. *Ophrys vernixia* Brot. - neu für Kreta. *MittBl. ArbKreis heim. Orch. Baden-Württ.* **18**: 151 - 158.
* **Akeroyd, J. R.** 1987. Two overlooked species of *Polygonum* from SE Europe. *In* A. O. Chater (Ed.), Flora Europaea: Notulae systematicae ad Floram Europaeam spectantes. Series 2. No. 1. *Bot. J. Linn. Soc.* **95**: 251 - 257.
* —— **& Preston, C. D.** 1987. Floristic notes from the Aegean region of Greece. *Willdenowia* **16**: 349 - 372.
* —— **& Walters, S. M.** 1988. Taxonomic notes on *Silene* L. *In* A. O. Chater (Ed.), Flora Europaea: Notulae systematicae ad Floram Europaeam spectantes. Series 2. No. 2. *Bot. J. Linn. Soc.* **97**: 338 - 342.
* **Al-Eisawi, D. & Jury, S. L.** 1988. A taxonomic revision of the genus *Tordylium* L. (Apiaceae). *Bot. J. Linn. Soc.* **97**: 357 - 403.
* **Aldén, B.** 1982. *Andrachne telephioides* subsp. *oreocretensis*, a new subspecies. *Willdenowia* **12**: 211 - 212.
  Alibertis, C. & Alibertis, A. 1988. Rayon d'espoir en ce qui concerne le Céphalanthère de Crète. *Orchidophile* **81**: 68 - 70.
  —— **& ——** 1989*a*. *The Wild Orchids of Crete*. Published by the authors, Iraklio.
  —— **& ——** 1989*b*. La Crète n'a pas fini de livrer ses secrets aux orchidophiles (1 ère partie). *Orchidophile* **86**: 79 - 83.
* —— **& ——** 1989*c*. La Crète n'a pas fini de livrer ses secrets aux orchidophiles (2 ème partie). *Orchidophile* **87**: 108 - 112.
* ——, —— **& Reinhard, H. R.** 1990. Untersuchungen am *Ophrys omegaifera*-Komplex Kretas. *MittBl. ArbKreis heim. Orch. Baden-Württ.* **22**: 181 - 236.
  Andersson, I. A., Carlström, A., Franzén, R., Karlén, T. & Nybom, H. 1983. A revision of the *Aethionema saxatile* complex (Brassicaceae). *Willdenowia* **13**: 3 - 42.
  Anon. 1989. Sheep's-bit? *Q. Bull. alp. Gdn Soc.* **57**: 194 - 195.
* **Barclay, Sir C.** 1968. Searching for the Phoenix in Crete. *Gdnrs' Chron.* ser.3, **164(15)**: 15 - 17.
* —— 1974. A new locality for wild *Phoenix* in Crete. *Annls Mus. Goulandris* **2**: 23 - 29.
  —— 1986. Crete. Checklist of the vascular plants. *Englera* **6**.
* **Baumann, B. & Baumann, H.** 1991. Hybridogene Populationen zwischen *Orchis anatolica* Boiss. und *Orchis quadripunctata* Cyr. ex Ten. in der Ostmediterraneis. *MittBl. ArbKreis heim. Orch. Baden-Württ.* **23**: 203 - 242.
  Baumann, H. & Künkele, S. 1982. *Die wildwachsenden Orchideen Europas*. Kosmos-Naturführer, Stuttgart.
* —— **& ——** 1986. Die Gattung *Ophrys* L. - eine taxonomische Übersicht. *MittBl. ArbKreis heim. Orch. Baden-Württ.* **18**: 305 - 688.
  —— **& ——** 1988. Neue Beiträge zur Taxonomie europäischer und mediterraner Orchideen. *MittBl. ArbKreis heim. Orch. Baden-Württ.* **20**: 610 - 651.
  —— **& ——** 1989. Die Gattung *Serapias* L. - eine taxonomische Übersicht. *MittBl. ArbKreis heim. Orch. Baden-Württ.* **21**: 701 - 946.
* **Bentzer, B.** 1973. Taxonomy, variation and evolution in representatives of *Leopoldia* Parl. (Liliaceae) in the southern and central Aegean. *Bot. Notiser* **126**: 69 - 132.
* **Blaich, G.** 1991. Ergänzungen zur Kenntnis der Orchideenflora Westkretas. *MittBl. ArbKreis heim. Orch. Baden-Württ.* **23**: 467 - 472.

Boratynski, A., Browicz, K. & Zielinski, J. 1983. Contributions to the woody flora of Greece. *Arboretum korn.* **28**: 7 - 68.

* **Bothmer, R. von** 1970. Studies in the Aegean Flora XV. Chromosome numbers in Labiatae. *Bot. Notiser* **123**: 52 - 60.

—— 1972. Four species of *Allium* sect. *Allium* in Greece. *Bot. Notiser* **125**: 62 - 76.

—— 1974. Studies in the Aegean Flora XXI. Biosystematic studies in the *Allium ampeloprasum* complex. *Op. bot. Soc. bot. Lund* **34**.

* —— 1975. The *Allium ampeloprasum* complex on Crete. *Mitt. bot. StSamml. Münch.* **12**: 267 - 288.

* **Boyce, P.** 1987. A new species of *Arum* L. from Crete. *Aroideana* **10(1)**: 6 - 8.

—— 1989 ["1987"]. A new subspecies of *Biarum davisii* Turrill from Turkey. *Aroideana* **10(4)**: 14 - 15.

* —— **& Athanasiou, K.** 1991. A new subspecies of *Biarum tenuifolium* (Araceae) from Crete. *Flora medit.* **1**: 5 - 13.

Briggs, M. 1989. The fifth tulip in Crete. *Q. Bull. alp. Gdn Soc.* **57**: 41 - 46.

* —— 1990. First record of *Tulipa Goulimyi* (Liliaceae) on Crete. *Annls Mus. Goulandris* **8**: 41 - 44.

* **Browicz, K.** 1975. *Vincetoxicum canescens* (Willd.) Decne and *V. tmoleum* Boiss. - systematic problems and geographical distribution. *Fragm. flor. geobot.* **21**: 261 - 271.

* —— 1985. The genus *Lithodora* Griseb. (Boraginaceae) in the eastern Mediterranean region. *Annls Mus. Goulandris* **7**: 39 - 48.

* **Brownsey, P. & Jermy, A. C.** 1973. A fern collecting expedition to Crete. *Brit. Fern Gaz.* **10**: 285 - 302.

Brullo, S. 1988. Miscellaneous notes on the genus *Limonium* (Plumbaginaceae). *Willdenowia* **17**: 11 - 18.

* **Burtt, B. L.** 1951. Two new species of *Colchicum. Kew Bull.* **5**: 431 - 434.

* —— **& Davis, P. H.** 1949. On the flora of the nearer east: XXIII. Miscellaneous new species and records. *Kew Bull.* **4**: 97 - 115.

Buttler, K. P. (& Davies, P., consultant ed.) 1991. *Field guide to orchids of Britain and Europe.* Crowood Press, Swindon.

* **Byatt, J. I.** 1976. The genus *Crataegus* (Rosaceae) in Greece. *Candollea* **31**: 283 - 301.

* **Campbell, N. R.** 1979. The occurrence of *Orchis robusta* (T.Stephenson) Gölz & Reinhard in Crete. *Watsonia* **12**: 253 - 255.

* **Carlström, A.** 1985. Two new species of *Sedum* (Crassulaceae) from S Greece and SW Turkey. *Willdenowia* **15**: 107 - 113.

* —— 1986*a*. A revision of *Arenaria* sect. *Orientales* ser. *Orientales* incl. ser. *Deflexae* (Caryophyllaceae) in the Aegean and SW Turkey. *Willdenowia* **15**: 359 - 374.

* —— 1986*b*. A revision of the *Campanula drabifolia* complex (Campanulaceae). *Willdenowia* **15**: 375 - 387.

—— 1987. *A survey of the flora and phytogeography of Rodhos, Simi, Tilos and the Marmaris peninsula (SE Greece, SW Turkey).* University of Lund.

* **Christodoulakis, D., Georgiadis, T., Economidou, E., Iatrou, G. & Tzanoudakis, D.** 1990. Flora und Vegetation der Dionysaden-Inseln (Südägäis, Griechenland). *Willdenowia* **19**: 425 - 443.

* **Contandriopoulos, J.** 1969. Contribution à l'étude cytotaxonomique des *Alysseae* Adams de Grèce. *Ber. schweiz. bot. Ges.* **79**: 313 - 334.

* —— 1970. Contribution à l'étude cytotaxonomique des Campanulacées du Proche Orient. *Bull. Soc. bot. Fr.* **117**: 55 - 70.

Cook, C. D. K. 1983. Aquatic plants endemic to Europe and the Mediterranean. *Bot. Jb.* **103**: 539 - 582.

Dahl, Å. E. 1989. Taxonomic and morphological studies in *Hypecoum* sect. *Hypecoum* (Papaveraceae). *Pl. Syst. Evol.* **163**: 227 - 280.

* **Dahlgren, G.** 1980. Cytological and morphological investigation of the genus *Erodium* L'Hér. in the Aegean. *Bot. Notiser* **133**: 491 - 514.

Damanakis, M. 1983. *Katologos ton agrostodon tis Elladas.* Kifissia, Athina.

—— 1985. Paratirisis epi tou agrostodous *Coix lacryma-jobi* L. (Poaceae) stin Kriti. *Bot. Chronika* **4**: 12 - 16.

* —— & **Scholz, H.** 1990. Phytogeographical notes on the Poaceae of Greece. *Willdenowia* **19**: 413 - 423.

* **Damboldt, J. & Phitos, D.** 1966. Ein Beitrag zur Zytotaxonomie der Gattung *Silene* L. in Griechenland. *Öst. bot. Z.* **113**: 169 - 175.

—— & —— 1970. Beiträge zur Flora Ionica II. Bemerkungen zu einigen *Silene*-Arten aus Griechenland. *Öst. bot. Z.* **118**: 341 - 352.

* **Davies, P., Davies, J. & Huxley, A.** 1983. *Wild Orchids of Britain and Europe.* Chatto & Windus, London.

* **Davis, A. P. & Jury, S. L.** 1990. A taxonomic review of *Iris* L. series *Unguiculares* (Diels) Lawrence. *Bot. J. Linn. Soc.* **103**: 281 - 300.

* **Davis, P. H.** 1953. Notes on the summer flora of the Aegean. *Notes R. bot. Gdn Edinb.* **21**: 101 - 142.

* —— (Ed.) 1965-1985. *Flora of Turkey and the East Aegean Islands* **1** (1965); **2** (1967); **3** (1970); **4** (1972); **5** (1975); **6** (1978); **7** (1982); **8** (1984); **9** (1985). Edinburgh.

——, **Mill, R. R. & Tan, K.** (Eds.) 1988. *Flora of Turkey and the East Aegean Islands* **10**. Edinburgh.

Egli, B. R. 1989. Ecology of dolines in the mountains of Crete (Greece). *Bielefelder ökolog. Beitr.* **4**: 59 - 63.

—— 1991. The special flora, ecological and edaphic conditions of dolines in the mountains of Crete. *Bot. Chronika* **10**: 325 - 335.

* ——, **Gerstberger, P., Greuter, W. & Risse, H.** 1990. *Horstrissea dolinicola*, a new genus and species of umbels (Umbelliferae, Apiaceae) from Kriti (Greece). *Willdenowia* **19**: 389 - 399.

* **Engstrand, L.** 1970. Studies in the Aegean flora XVIII. Notes and chromosome numbers in Aegean Umbelliferae. *Bot. Notiser* **123**: 384 - 393.

* **Erben, M.** 1985. Cytotaxonomische Untersuchungen an südosteuropäischen *Viola*-Arten der Sektion *Melanium. Mitt. bot. StSamml. Münch.* **21**: 339 - 740.

* **Ettlinger, D. M. T.** 1988. *Notes on orchids seen in Crete - 1978, 1983 & 1988.* Privately published by the author, Cliftonville.

* **Garbari, F., Greuter, W. & Miceli, P.** 1979. The *"Allium cupanii"* group: a preliminary taxonomic, caryological and leaf anatomical study. *Webbia* **34**: 459 - 480.

* **Gjærum, H. B. & Hansen, A.** 1974. *Aster creticus*, a new host record for *Puccinia cnici-oleracei. Annls Mus. Goulandris* **2**: 31 - 34.

* —— & —— 1990. Additions to the rust flora of the Greek Islands. *Annls Mus. Goulandris* **8**: 81 - 96.

* **Goulandris, N. A., Goulimis, C. N. & Stearn, W. T.** 1968. *Wild Flowers of Greece.* Goulandris Botanical Museum, Kifissia.

Goulimis, C. N. 1956. *New additions to the Greek flora.* Athens.

* **Gradstein, S. R. & Kern, J. H.** 1968. A new *Carex* from Crete. *Acta bot. neerl.* **17**: 242 - 247.

—— & **Smittenberg, J. H.** 1968. *Bron- beek- en moeras-vegetaties van west Kreta.* Utrecht (polycop.)

* —— & —— 1977. The hydrophilous vegetation of western Crete. *Vegetatio* **34**: 65 - 86.

* **Greuter, W.** 1965. Beiträge zur Flora der Südägäis 1-7. *Candollea* **20**: 167 - 218.

* —— 1967a. Beiträge zur Flora der Südägäis 8-9. *Bauhinia* **3**: 243 - 254.

* —— 1967b. Contributiones floristicae austro-aegaeae 10-12. *Candollea* **22**: 233 - 253.

* —— 1968a. Contributio floristica austro-aegaea 13. *Candollea* **23**: 143 - 150.

* —— 1968b. Le dattier de Théophraste, spécialité crétoise. *Mus. Geneve* **81**: 14 - 16.

* —— 1969a. Contributio floristica austro-aegaea 14. *Candollea* **24**: 45 - 49.

* —— 1969b. Contributio floristica austro-aegaea 15. *Candollea* **25**: 189 - 192.

* —— 1971a. *Bromus caroli-henrici*, eine verkannte ostmediterrane Graminee. *Annln naturh. Mus. Wien* **75**: 83 - 89.

—— 1971b. Betrachtungen zur Pflanzengeographie der Südägäis. *Op. bot. Soc. bot. Lund* **30**: 49 - 64.

* —— 1972a. L'écueil à *Silene holzmannii*, en Crète, et son peuplement végétal. *Saussurea* **3**: 157 - 166.

—— 1972b. The relict element of the flora of Crete and its evolutionary significance. *In* D. H. Valentine (Ed.), *Taxonomy, phytogeography and evolution*: 161 - 177. London & New York.

* —— 1973a. Additions to the flora of Crete, 1938-1972. *Annls Mus. Goulandris* **1**: 15 - 83.

* —— 1973b. Monographie der Gattung *Ptilostemon* (Compositae). *Boissiera* **22**.

* —— 1974. Floristic report on the Cretan area. *Mems Soc. broteriana* **24**: 131 - 171.

—— 1975a. *First OPTIMA Meeting in Crete - September 1975. Guide to the excursions.* Genève.

—— 1975b. Historical phytogeography of the southern half of the Aegean area. *In* D. Jordanov et al., Problems of Balkan flora and vegetation. *Proceedings of the first international symposium on Balkan flora and vegetation, Varna, June 7-14, 1973*: 17 - 21. Sofija.

—— 1976. The flora of Psara (E. Aegean Islands, Greece) - an annotated catalogue. *Candollea* **31**: 191 - 242.

* —— (Ed.) 1980-1981. Med-Checklist Notulae, 1-3. *Willdenowia* **10**: 13 - 21, 227 - 232 (1980); **11**: 23 - 43 (1981).

* —— 1984. Les *Arum* de la Crète. *Bot. helv.* **94**: 15 - 22.

——, **Burdet, H. & Long, G.** (Eds.) 1984; 1986; 1989. *Med-Checklist. A critical inventory of vascular plants of the circum-mediterranean countries* **1** (1984a); **3** (1986); **4** (1989). Genève.

* —— **& Grau, J.** 1970. Zum Vorkommen von drei Unterarten der *Myosotis refracta* Boiss. auf Kreta. *Candollea* **25**: 7 - 10.

* ——, **Matthäs, U. & Risse, H.** 1982. Notes on Cardaegean plants. 3. *Medicago strasseri*, a new leguminous shrub from Kriti. *Willdenowia* **12**: 201 - 206.

* ——, —— & —— 1984a. Additions to the flora of Crete, 1973-1983 - I. *Willdenowia* **14**: 27 - 36.

* ——, —— & —— 1984b. Additions to the flora of Crete, 1973-1983 (1984) - II. *Willdenowia* **14**: 269 - 297.

* ——, —— & —— 1985. Additions to the flora of Crete, 1973-1983 (1984) - III. *Willdenowia* **15**: 23 - 60.

* ——, **Pleger, R. & Raus, T.** 1983a. The vascular flora of the Karpathos island group (Dodecanesos, Greece). A preliminary checklist. *Willdenowia* **13**: 43 - 78.

* ——, ——, ——, **Zimmer, B. & Greuter J. J.** 1983b. *Asplenium bourgaei* a new addition to the flora of Europe. *Fern Gaz.* **12**: 271 - 274.

* —— **& Raus, T.** (Eds.) 1981-1989. Med-Checklist Notulae, 4, 6-15. *Willdenowia* **11**: 271 - 280 (1981); **12**: 183 - 199 (1982); **13**: 79 - 99, 277 - 288 (1983); **14**: 37 - 54, 299 - 308 (1984); **15**: 61 - 84 (1985), 413 - 432 (1986); **16**: 103 - 116 (1986), 439 - 452 (1987); **19**: 27 - 48 (1989).

—— **& Rechinger, K. H.** 1967. Flora der Insel Kythera, gleichzeitig Beginn einer nomenklatorischen Überprüfung der griechischen Gefässpflanzenarten. *Boissiera* **13**.

* —— & Strid, A. 1981. Notes on Cardaegean plants 2. A new species of *Ranunculus* sect. *Ranunculus* from the mountains of W Kriti. *Willdenowia* **11**: 267 - 269.

* **Gustafsson, M.** 1970. Studies in the Aegean Flora XVII. Variation and distribution of *Atriplex recurva* D'Urv. (Chenopodiaceae). *Bot. Notiser* **123**: 371 - 383.

* **Gustavsson, L.-Å.** 1977. *Drabopsis verna* C.Koch (Brassicaceae), new to Europe. *Bot. Notiser* **130**: 213 - 214.

* **Hagemann, I.** 1987. On subspecific taxa of *Hypericum empetrifolium* (Hypericaceae) from Crete. *Pl. Syst. Evol.* **155**: 165 - 187.

   Halx, G. 1972. Über einige Bastarde von *Ophrys cretica* (Vierh.) Nelson. *Hoppea* **30**: 97 - 110.

* **Hautzinger, L.** 1976. Kurze Mitteilung. *Orchis prisca* (Orchidaceae), eine neue Art aus Kreta. *Pl. Syst. Evol.* **124**: 311 - 313.

* **Heneen, W. K. & Runemark, H.** 1962. Chromosomal polymorphism and morphological diversity in *Elymus rechingeri*. *Hereditas* **48**: 545 - 564.

* —— & —— 1972. Chromosomal polymorphism in isolated populations of *Elymus (Agropyron)* in the Aegean I. *Elymus striatulus* sp. nov. *Bot. Notiser* **125**: 419 - 429.

* **Henke, E.** 1986. Exkursionen in die Orchideenflora Kretas. *Ber. ArbKreis heim. Orch.* **3**: 13 - 38.

* **Heyn, C. C.** 1966. A study of the *Lotus peregrinus* group. *Israel J. Bot.* **15**: 37 - 47.

   Higton, R. N. & Akeroyd, J. R. 1991. Variation in *Capparis spinosa* L. in Europe. *In* M. E. Newton (Ed.), Flora Europaea: Notulae systematicae ad Floram Europaeam spectantes. Series 2. No. 4. *Bot. J. Linn. Soc.* **106**: 104 - 112.

* **Hiller, W. & Kalteisen, M.** 1988. Die Orchideen der Insel Karpathos. *MittBl. ArbKreis heim. Orch. Baden-Württ.* **20**: 443 - 518.

* **Hölzinger, C. & Hölzinger, J.** 1986. Beiträge zur Orchideenflora von Kreta. *MittBl. ArbKreis heim. Orch. Baden-Württ.* **18**: 137 - 150.

* **Höner, D.** 1986. *Hippocrepis cyclocarpa* (Leguminosae) new to Europe. *Willdenowia* **16**: 57 - 60.

* —— & Greuter, W. 1988. Plant population dynamics and species turnover on small islands near Karpathos (South Aegean, Greece). *Vegetatio* **77**: 129 - 137.

   Huber-Morath, A. 1971. Novitae florae anatolicae IX. *Bauhinia* **4**: 197 - 222.

* **Jalas, J. & Suominen, J.** (Eds.) 1972-1991. Atlas Florae Europaeae **1** (1972); **2** (1973); **3** (1976); **4** (1979); **5** (1980); **6** (1983); **7** (1986); **8** (1989); **9** (1991). Helsinki.

   Jury, S. L. 1987. A new species of the genus *Torilis* Adanson (Apiaceae). *Bot. J. Linn. Soc.* **95**: 293 - 299.

* **Kadereit, J. W.** 1988. A revision of *Papaver* L. section *Rhoeadum* Spach. *Notes R. bot. Gdn Edinb.* **45**: 225 - 286.

   Kalopissis, Y. T. 1984. *Episkopisi ton Orheoidon tis Kritis.* Mousio Kritikis Ethnologias, Vori.

   —— 1988. *The orchids of Greece - inventory and review.* Mousio Kritikis Ethnologias, Vori.

* —— & Robatsch, K. 1980. *Epipactis cretica* Kalopissis & Robatsch, spec. nov., ein neuer kretischer Endemit. *Orchidee* **31**: 141 - 143.

* **Kalteisen, M. & Reinhard, H. R.** 1987. Zwei neue *Ophrys*-taxa (Orchidaceae) aus dem Ägäischen Archipel. *MittBl. ArbKreis heim. Orch. Baden-Württ.* **19**: 895 - 938.

* **Kamari, G. & Artelari, R.** 1990. Karyosystematic study of the genus *Sternbergia* (Amaryllidaceae) in Greece. 1. South Aegean Islands. *Willdenowia* **19**: 367 - 388.

* —— & Matthäs, U. 1986. Cytotaxonomic contributions on the flora of Crete III. *Willdenowia* **15**: 515 - 520.

   Kellenberger, W. 1978. *Orchis anatolica* x *O. patens* ssp. *nitidifolia*. *Orchidee* **29**: 112.

   Klein, E. 1978a. Zwei neue *Ophrys*-Hybriden von der Insel Kreta. *Hoppea* **36**: 467 - 471.

—— 1978b. Eine neue Hybride mit einen Mitglied der *Ophrys*-Subsektion *Aegaeae: Ophrys cretica* (Vierh.) Nelson x *O. bombyliflora* Link. *Orchidee* **29**: 215 - 217.

* **Krendl, F.** 1987 ["1986-7"]. Die Arten der *Galium mollugo*-Gruppe in Griechenland. *Bot. Chronika* **6-7**: 5 - 168.

* **Kreutz, K.** 1990. Beitrag zur Orchideenflora Kretas. *MittBl. ArbKreis heim. Orch. Baden-Württ.* **22**: 358 - 384.

Künkele, S. 1979. Historischer Überblick zur Erforschung der Orchideen Kretas. *MittBl. ArbKreis heim. Orch. Baden-Württ.* **11**: 283 - 309.

* **Kypriotakis, Z. & Kalopissis, Y. T.** 1988. Neue Standorte der *Cephalanthera cucullata* Boiss. et Heldr. *MittBl. ArbKreis heim. Orch. Baden-Württ.* **20**: 69 - 73.

Lassen, P. 1989. A new delimitation of the genera *Coronilla, Hippocrepis* and *Securigera* (Fabaceae). *Willdenowia* **19**: 49 - 62.

Lesins, K. A. & Lesins, I. 1979. *Genus Medicago (Leguminosae). A taxogenetic study.* Den Haag.

Lidén, M. 1986. Synopsis of *Fumarioideae* (Papaveraceae) with a monograph of the tribe *Fumariae. Op. bot. Soc. bot. Lund* **88**: 1 - 133.

—— 1988. Tuberous *Corydalis* in the Mediterranean checklist area. *Notes R. bot. Gdn Edinb.* **45**: 349 - 363.

* **Lovis, J. D. & Reichstein, T.** 1985. *Asplenium trichomanes* subsp. *pachyrachis* (Aspleniaceae, Pteridophyta), and a note on the typification of *A. trichomanes. Willdenowia* **15**: 187 - 201.

* **Markgraf-Dannenberg, I.** 1976. Die Gattung *Festuca* in Griechenland. *Veröff. geobot. Inst. Zürich* **56**: 92 - 182.

Mathew, B. 1982. *The crocus. A revision of the genus Crocus (Iridaceae).* B. T. Batsford Ltd., London.

Meikle, R. D. 1957. Notes on the flora of Cyprus 1. *Kew Bull.* **12**: 545 - 549.

—— 1977-1985. *Flora of Cyprus.* 1 (1977); 2 (1985). Kew.

—— 1979. Some notes on *Laurentia* Adanson (Campanulaceae). *Kew Bull.* **34**: 373 - 375.

* **Melzheimer, V.** 1978. Bemerkungen zur cytologie einiger arten der Gattung *Silene* (Caryophyllaceae) als Zentralgriechenland und Kreta. *Pl. Syst Evol.* **130**: 203 - 207.

* —— 1981. *Silene multicaulis* Guss. subsp. *cretica* Melzh., subspec. nov., von der Insel Kreta (Griechenland). *Phyton, Horn* **21**: 131 - 136.

* **Merxmüller, H. & Podlech, D.** 1976. *Fimbristylis ferruginea* in Kreta. *Mitt. bot. StSamml. Münch.* **12**: 683 - 684.

* **Meyer, K. K.** 1986. Eine neue *Noccaea*-Art (Cruciferae) von Kreta. *Willdenowia* **15**: 389 - 391.

* **Miege, J. & Greuter, W.** 1973. Nombres chromosomiques de quelques plantes récoltées en Crète. *Annls Mus. Goulandris* **1**: 105 - 111.

* **Montmollin, B. de** 1982. Etude cytotaxonomique de la flore endémique de la Crète I. Note préliminaire. *Bull. Soc. neuchâtel. Sci. nat.* **105**: 65 - 77.

Murbeck, S. 1936. Nachträge zur Monographie der Gattung *Verbascum. Acta Univ. lund.* ser.2, **32(1)**.

* **Nardi, E.** 1991. The genus *Aristolochia* L. (Aristolochiaceae) in Greece. *Webbia* **45**: 31 - 69.

* —— **& Nardi, C. N.** 1987. Taxonomic and chorological notes on the genus *Aristolochia* L. (Aristolochiaceae) from the central and eastern Mediterranean area. *Bot. helv.* **97**: 155 - 165.

Nelson, E. 1962. *Gestaltwandel und Artbildung erörtert am Beispiel der Orchidaceen Europas und der Mittelmeerländer insbesondere der Gattung Ophrys. Mit einer Monographie und Ikonographie der Gattung Ophrys.* Chernex-Montreux.

* **Nordenstam, B.** 1960. Studies in the Aegean flora II. The genus *Lyrolepis. Bot. Notiser* **113**: 451 - 457.

* —— 1971. Cytogeography of the genus *Hedypnois* (Compositae). *Bot. Notiser* **124**: 483 - 489.

Paulus, H. F. 1988. Beobachtungen und Experimente zur Pseudokopulation auf *Ophrys*-Arten (Orchidaceae) Kretas (II) - mit einer Beschreibung von *Ophrys sitiaca* H.F.Paulus & C. + A.Alibertis, nov. spec. aus dem *Ophrys-fusca-omegaifera*-Formenkreis. *MittBl. ArbKreis heim. Orch. Baden-Württ.* **20**: 817 - 882.

* **Pawłowski, B.** 1971. De genere *Procopiana* Guşuleac. *Fragm. flor. geobot.* **17**: 39 - 58.

* **Persson, J.** 1971. Sudies in the Aegean flora XIX. Notes on *Alyssum* and some other genera of Cruciferae. *Bot. Notiser* **124**: 399 - 418.

* **Phitos, D.** 1970. Die Gattung *Aubrieta* in Griechenland. *Candollea* **25**: 69 - 87.

* —— 1981. The genus *Bolanthus* (Caryophyllaceae) in Greece. *Bot. Chronika* **1**: 35 - 45.

* —— 1982. *Silene greuteri* (Caryophyllaceae), species nova. *Bot. Chronika* **2**: 53 - 54.

* —— & **Kamari, G.** 1974. Zytotaxonomische Beiträge zur Flora von Kreta I. *Bot. Notiser* **127**: 302 - 308.

—— & —— 1988. Contribution to the cytotaxonomy of the genus *Campanula* (Campanulaceae) in Greece. *Willdenowia* **17**: 103 - 105.

* **Polatschek, A.** 1973. Die Vertreter der Gattung *Erysimum* auf Kreta. *Annls Mus. Goulandris* **1**: 113 - 126.

Press, J. R. 1988. Intraspecific variation in *Rumex bucephalophorus* L. *In* A. O. Chater (Ed.), Flora Europaea: Notulae systematicae ad Floram Europaeam spectantes. Series 2. No. 2. *Bot. J. Linn. Soc.* **97**: 344 - 355.

Raamsdonk, L. van 1984. *Biosystematic studies on the umbellatum-angustifolium complex in the genus Ornithogalum L.* Thesis, s.l. (Utrecht).

Rackham, O. 1990*a*. Ancient Landscapes. *In* O. Murray & S. Price (Eds.), *The Greek City. From Homer to Alexander*: 85 - 111. Clarendon Press, Oxford.

—— 1990*b*. The greening of Myrtos. *In* S. Bottema, G. Entjes-Nieborg & W. van Zeist (Eds.), Man's role in the shaping of the eastern Mediterranean landscape. *Proceedings of the Inqua/Bai Symposium on the impact of ancient man on the landscape of the eastern Mediterranean region and the near east, Groningen, Netherlands, March 6-9, 1989*: 341 - 348. A. A. Balkema, Rotterdam.

—— 1990*c*. Vegetation history of Crete. *In* A. T. Grove, J. A. Moody & O. Rackham (Eds.), *Petromarula 1. Stability and change in the Cretan landscape*: 29 - 39. Published by O. Rackham & A. T. Grove, Corpus Christi College, Cambridge.

* **Raus, T.** 1983. Ein für Europa neuer Krokus. *Bot. Chronika* **3**: 12 - 14.

* —— 1990 ["1989"]. Die Flora von Armathia und der Kleininseln um Kasos (Dodekanes, Griechenland). *Bot. Chronika* **9**: 19 - 39.

* —— 1991. Asia or Europe ? - The phytogeographical position of the Karpathos archipelago (SE Aegean, Greece). *In* T. Engel, W. Frey & H. Kürschner (Eds.), Contributiones selectae ad floram et vegetationem orientis. *Proceedings of the Third Plant Life of Southwest Asia Symposium Berlin 1990*: 301 - 310. Berlin, Stuttgart: J. Cramer.

* **Rechinger, K. H.** 1936. Einige neue Pflanzen aus der Südöstlichen Ägäis. *Annln naturh. Mus. Wien* **47**: 147 - 152.

* —— 1938. Plantae novae aegaeae. *Reprium Spec. nov. Regni veg.* **43**: 144 - 151.

* —— 1939. Plantae novae aegaeae II. *Reprium Spec. nov. Regni veg.* **47**: 49 - 51.

* —— 1943*a*. Flora aegaea. *Denkschr. Akad. Wiss. Wien* **105(1)**.

* —— 1943*b*. Neue Beiträge zur Flora von Kreta. *Denkschr. Akad. Wiss. Wien* **105(2,1)**.

* —— 1949. Florae aegaeae supplementum. *Phyton, Horn* **1**: 194 - 228.

* —— 1951. Phytogeographia aegaea. *Denkschr. Akad. Wiss. Wien* **105(2,2)**.

* —— 1962. Zur Kenntnis orientalischer Labiaten. *Kulturpflanze Beih.* **3**: 47 - 73.

* —— 1965. Zwei neue Arten aus der griechischen Flora. *Öst. bot. Z.* **112**: 186 - 187.

* —— 1974. *Aetheorhiza bulbosa* (L.) Cass. und ihre geographischen Rassen. *Phyton, Horn* **16**: 211 - 220.

* **Reichstein, T., Lovis, J. D., Greuter, W. & Zaffran, J.** 1973. Die Asplenien der Insel Kreta. *Annls Mus. Goulandris* **1**: 133 - 163.

* **Robatsch, K.** 1978. *Cephalanthera damasonium* - Neufund für Kreta. *Orchidee* **29**: 110 - 111.

* **Robson, N. K. B.** 1985. Studies in the genus *Hypericum* (Guttiferae) 3. Sections 1. *Campylosporus* to 6a. *Umbraculoides. Bull. Br. Mus. nat. Hist. (Bot.)* **12**: 163 - 325.

Rückbrodt, U. & Rückbrodt, D. 1987. *Himantoglossum affine* (Boiss.) Schltr. auf Kreta. *Ber. ArbKreis heim. Orch.* **4**: 314 - 321.

* **Runemark, H.** 1967*a*. Studies in the Aegean flora X. Cytologic and morphologic notes on *Plantago. Bot. Notiser* **120**: 9 - 16.

* —— 1967*b*. Studies in the Aegean flora XI. *Procopiana* (Boraginaceae) included into *Symphytum. Bot. Notiser* **120**: 84 - 94.

* —— 1967*c*. Studies in the Aegean flora XII. Cytologic and morphologic investigations in *Centaurea. Bot. Notiser* **120**: 161 - 176, 486.

* —— 1968. Studies in the Aegean flora XIII. *Tordylium* L. (Umbelliferae). *Bot. Notiser* **121**: 233 - 258.

* —— 1980. Studies in the Aegean flora XXIII. The *Dianthus fruticosus* complex (Caryophyllaceae). *Bot. Notiser* **133**: 475 - 490.

* —— 1984. A new annual *Bupleurum* from Kriti. *Willdenowia* **14**: 309 - 311.

* —— **& Greuter, W.** 1981. Notes on Cardaegean plants 1. The *Sedum litoreum* group. *Willdenowia* **11**: 13 - 21.

* ——, **Snogerup, S. & Nordenstam, B.** 1960. Studies in the Aegean flora I. Floristic notes. *Bot. Notiser* **113**: 421 - 450.

Schäfer, H. I. 1973. Zur Taxonomie der *Vicia narbonensis*-Gruppe. *Kulturpflanze* **21**: 211 - 273.

* **Schippmann, U.** 1991. Revision der europäischen Arten der Gattung *Brachypodium* Palisot de Beauvois (Poaceae). *Boissiera* **45**.

* **Schneider, G.** 1987. Neufund von *Orchis sancta* L. auf Kreta. *MittBl. ArbKreis heim. Orch. Baden-Württ.* **19** : 95 - 96.

* —— 1989. Ein Fund von *Orchis sancta* L. x *Orchis coriophora* L. auf Kreta. *MittBl. ArbKreis heim. Orch. Baden-Württ.* **21**: 126 - 132.

* **Scholz, H.** 1985. *Poa*-Studien 4. Über *Poa hackelii* und *P. pelasgis* sp. nova (Gramineae). *Willdenowia* **15**: 91 - 97.

* —— 1990. Neue und wenig bekannte mediterrane Gramineen-Taxa. *Willdenowia* **19**: 405 - 412.

* **Segelberg, I.** 1966. *Erodium hirtum* (Forssk.) Willd. in Crete. *Bot. Notiser* **119**: 373 - 375.

Sell, P. D. 1991. A new subspecies of *Ranunculus ficaria* L. *In* M. E. Newton (Ed.), Flora Europaea: Notulae systematicae ad Floram Europaeam spectantes. Series 2. No. 4. *Bot. J. Linn. Soc.* **106**: 117 - 118.

Small, E., Lassen, P. & Brookes, B. S. 1987. An expanded circumscription of *Medicago* (Leguminosae, *Trifoliae*) based on explosive flower tripping. *Willdenowia* **16**: 415 - 437.

* **Snogerup, B.** 1980. The genus *Reichardia* (Asteraceae) in the Aegean area. *Bot. Notiser* **133**: 515 - 520.

* **Snogerup, S.** 1962. Studies in the Aegean flora IV. *Bupleurum flavum* Forsk. and related species. *Bot. Notiser* **115**: 357 - 375.

* —— 1967. Studies in the Aegean flora VIII. *Erysimum* sect. *Cheiranthus* A. Taxonomy. *Op. bot. Soc. bot Lund* **13**.

—— 1971. Evolutionary and plant-geographical aspects of chasmophytic communities. *In* P. H. Davis et al. (Eds.), *Plant life in South-West Asia*: 157 - 170. Aberdeen.

* ——, **Gustafsson, M. & Bothmer, R. von** 1990. *Brassica* sect. *Brassica* (Brassicaceae) 1. Taxonomy and variation. *Willdenowia* **19**: 271 - 365.

Sonderhousen, O. 1977. The fourth tulip from Crete. *Q. Bull. alp. Gdn Soc.* **45**: 143 - 148.

* **Speta, F.** 1976. Über *Chionodoxa* Boiss., Ihre Gliederung und Zugehörigkeit zu *Scilla* L. *Naturk. Jb. Stadt Linz* **21**: 9 - 79.

* **Stearn, W. T.** 1977. *Allium longanum*, a species new to the south-eastern Aegean region. *Annls Mus. Goulandris* **3**: 39 - 44.

* **Stork, A. L.** 1972. Studies in the Aegean flora XX. Biosystematics of the *Malcolmia maritima* complex. *Op. bot. Soc. bot. Lund* **33**.

* **Strasser, W.** 1988. *West-Kreta. Botanische Studien 1987.* Privately published by the author, Steffisburg.

* —— 1989. *West-Kreta. Botanische Exkursionen der zürcherischen botanischen Gesellschaft 26.3-6.4.1989.* Privately published by the author, Steffisburg.

* **Strid, A.** 1965*a*. Studies in the Aegean flora VI. Notes on some genera of Labiatae. *Bot. Notiser* **118**: 104 - 122.

—— 1965*b*. Studies in the Aegean flora VII. Chromosome morphology in the *Nigella arvensis* complex. *Bot. Notiser* **118**: 139 - 165.

* —— 1969. *Garidella unguicularis* Lam. (Ranunculaceae) - new for Europe. *Bot. Notiser* **122**: 330 - 332.

* —— 1970. Studies in the Aegean flora XVI. Biosystematics of the *Nigella arvensis* complex. With special reference to the problem of non-adaptive radiation. *Op. bot. Soc. bot. Lund* **28**.

* —— (Ed.) 1986. *Mountain Flora of Greece* 1. Cambridge.

* ——, **Bentzer, B., Bothmer, R. von, Engstrand, L. & Gustafsson, M.** 1989. *Euphorbia sultan-hassei* (Euphorbiaceae), a new species from SW Crete. *Willdenowia* **19**: 63 - 67.

* —— **& Tan, K.** (Eds.) 1991. *Mountain Flora of Greece* 2. Edinburgh.

* **Teschner, W.** 1975*a*. Bemerkungen zu einigen Orchideenvorkommen auf Kreta. *Orchidee* **26**: 169 - 170.

* —— 1975*b*. Eine hybridogene *Orchis*-Sippe auf Kreta? *Orchidee* **26**: 217 - 221.

* **Turland, N. J.** 1988. Mountains and gorges in western Crete. *Q. Bull. alp. Gdn Soc.* **56**: 46 - 57.

* —— 1991. A close look at a Cretan *Daphne. Kew Mag.* **8**: 37 - 45.

* —— 1992*a*. Floristic notes from Crete. *Bot. J. Linn. Soc.* **108**: 345 - 357.

* —— 1992*b*. Studies on the Cretan flora 1. Floristic notes. *Bull. Br. Mus. nat. Hist. (Bot.)* **22**: 159 - 164.

* —— 1992*c*. Studies on the Cretan flora 2. The *Dianthus juniperinus* complex (Caryophyllaceae). *Bull. Br. Mus. nat. Hist. (Bot.)* **22**: 165 - 169.

* —— **& Chilton, L.** In prep. Studies on the Cretan flora 3. Additions to the flora of Karpathos. *Bull. Br. Mus. nat. Hist. (Bot.)*

* **Turrill, W. B.** 1938. *Biarum davisii. Grdnrs' Chron.* ser.3, **104**: 437.

* —— 1941. On the flora of the nearer east XXII. New records and new species from Greece and the Greek islands. *Kew Bull.* **1940**: 262 - 266.

* —— 1957. *Serratula* in Crete. *Kew Bull.* **12**: 391 - 392.

Tutin, T. G. et al. (Eds.) 1964-1980. *Flora Europaea* 1 (1964); 2 (1968); 3 (1972); 4 (1976); 5 (1980). Cambridge.

* **Tzanoudakis, D.** 1983. Karyotypes of ten taxa of *Allium* section *Scorodon* from Greece. *Caryologia* **36**: 259 - 284.

* —— 1985. Chromosome studies in some species of *Allium* sect. *Allium* in Greece. *Annls Mus. Goulandris* **7**: 233 - 247.

* —— **& Iatrou, G.** 1982. A cytogeographical study of *Allium circinnatum* Sieber. *Bot. Chronika* **2**: 152 - 158.

* **Vamvoukakis, J. A.** 1988. *Phoenix theophrasti* on Crete. *Principes* **32**: 82 - 83.

* **Vöth, W.** 1981. Fundorte griechischer Orchideen. *MittBl. ArbKreis heim. Orch. Baden-Württ.* **13**: 1 - 89.

* **Wagenitz, G.** 1970. Die Gattung *Filago* L. s.l. (Compositae-*Inulae*) in der Ägäis. *Willdenowia* 6: 115 - 138.

* **Wellinghausen N. & Koch, H.** 1989. Orchideensuche auf Kreta. *Ber. ArbKreis heim. Orch.* 6: 85 - 100.

* **Yannitsaros, A.** 1977. The genus *Paspalum* in Kriti. *Biologia gallo-hellen.* 7: 87 - 92.

—— 1979. *Tagetes minuta* L. in Greece. *Candollea* 34: 99 - 107.

* —— 1986. New data on the naturalization and distribution of *Coronopus didymus* (Cruciferae) in Greece. *Willdenowia* 16: 61 - 64.

* —— **& Economidou, E.** 1974. Studies on the adventive flora of Greece I. General remarks on some recently introduced taxa. *Candollea* 29: 111 - 119.

* **Zaffran, J.** 1966. Une Campanule nouvelle de la flore crétoise: *Campanula aizoides* Zaffran. *Bull. Soc. bot. Fr.* 113: 69 - 73.

* —— 1967. Découverte du genre *Melitella* Somm. en Crète. *C. r. hebd. Séanc. Acad. Sci., Paris* ser.D (Sci. Nat.), 264: 805 - 808.

* —— 1970. Les Ptéridophytes de l'île de Crète. *Israel J. Bot.* 19: 236 - 244.

—— 1976. *Contributions à la flore et à la végétation de la Crète 1. Floristique.* Université de Provence.

* —— 1990. *Contributions à la flore et à la végétation de la Crète.* Université de Provence.

* **Zahariadi, C. A.** 1977a. Cinq espèces nouvelles du genre *Ornithogalum* (Liliaceae) trouvées en Grèce. *Annls Mus. Goulandris* 3: 51 - 75.

* —— 1977b. Quelques taxons rares ou nouvellement découverts de la flore de la Grèce (II partie). *Annls Mus. Goulandris* 3: 77 - 104.

* ——, **Stamatiadou, E. & Dima, A.** 1982. Geographical distribution of species of *Ornithogalum* (Liliacae) in Greece, including two new taxa. *Annls Mus. Goulandris* 5: 131 - 162.

* **Zeltner, L.** 1978. Notes de cytotaxonomie sur les genres *Blackstonia* Huds. et *Centaurium* Hill en Crète. *Bull. Soc. neuchâtel Sci. nat.* 101: 107 - 117.

INDEX TO GENERA

This index refers to the main text of the checklist only (pp. 30-195). All generic names are included, with synonyms shown in italic type.

A

Abutilon Mill. 118
Acacia Mill. 102
Acantholimon Boiss. 125
Acanthus L. 35
Acer L. 35
Aceras R.Br. 186
Achillea L. 57
Acinos Mill. 99
Adiantum L. 30
Adonis L. 130
Aegilops L. 176, 177
Aeluropus Trin. 163
Aeonium Webb & Berthel.
 76
Aetheorhiza Cass. 57
Aethionema R.Br. 78
Agave L. 157
Agrimonia L. 134
Agrostemma L. 44
Agrostis L. 163
Ailanthus Desf. 145
Ainsworthia Boiss. 154
Aira L. 163
Aizoon L. 35
Ajuga L. 95
Alcea L. 118
Alisma L. 158
Alkanna Tausch 38
Alliaria Scop. 78
Allium L. 180
Aloë L. 181
Alopecurus L. 163
Althaea L. 118
Alyssoides Mill. 84
Alyssum L. 78
Amaranthus L. 35
Ambrosia L. 57
Amelanchier Medik. 135
Ammi L. 148
Ammophila Host 163
Anacamptis (L.) Rich. 186
Anagallis L. 129

Anagyris L. 102
Anchusa L. 38
Andrachne L. 88
Androcymbium Willd. 182
Andropogon L. 163
Anemone L. 130
Anethum L. 148
Anogramma Link 32
Anthemis L. 57
Anthoxanthum L. 163
Anthriscus Pers. 148
Anthyllis L. 102
Antinoria Parl. 164
Antirrhinum L. 141
Aphanes L. 135
Apium L. 148
Aptenia N.E.Br. 35
Arabidopsis (DC.) Heynh.
 79
Arabis L. 79
Arbutus L. 88
Arctium L. 58
Arctotheca Wendl. 58
Arenaria L. 44
Arisarum Mill. 158
Aristida L. 164
Aristolochia L. 37
Arrhenatherum P.Beauv.
 164
Artemisia L. 58
Arthrocnemum Moq. 53
Arum L. 158
Arundo L. 164
Asclepias L. 37
Asparagus L. 182
Asperugo L. 39
Asperula L. 137
Asphodeline Rchb. 182
Asphodelus L. 182
Asplenium L. 30
Aster L. 58
Asteriscus Tourn. ex Mill.
 59
Asterolinon Hoffmanns. &
 Link 129

Astracantha Podlech 103
Astragalus L. 103
Asyneuma Griseb. &
 Schenk 42
Athamanta L. 148
Athyrium Roth 32
Atractylis L. 59
Atraphaxis L. 127
Atriplex L. 53
Aubrieta Adans. 79
Aurinia Desv. 79
Avellinia Parl. 164
Avena L. 164
Avenula (Dumort.)
 Dumort. 164

B

Ballota L. 95
Barlia Parl. 187
Bassia All. 54
Bellardia All. 141
Bellevalia Lapeyr. 182
Bellis L. 59
Bellium L. 59
Berberis L. 38
Beta L. 54
Biarum Schott 159
Bifora Hoffm. 148
Bilderdykia Dumort. 127
Biropteris Kümmerle 32
Biscutella L. 79
Biserrula L. 103
Bituminaria Fabr. 104
Blackstonia Huds. 91
Blechnum L. 32
Bolanthus (Ser.) Rchb. 45
Bolboschoenus Asch. ex
 Palla 159
Bombycilaena (DC.)
 Smoljan. 59
Bonannia Guss. 148
Borago L. 39
Botrychium Sw. 33